Handbook of Drainage and Construction Products

ERRATA

Page

30 Second paragraph, 4th line. Add comma after "rarely."

36 Show angle △ in drawing above R_1.
Stop arrow R_1 at inside of corrugation.

50 Fig. 41. Add "per Foot of Seam" to abscissa "Load in Thousand Pounds."

78 Fig. 61. Add fraction line between T and 2. Remove minus sign in front of 1⅛″ Rad.
Table 8-7. Add asterisk (*) after word "Gyration" in 7th column.

113 Seventh line in example, change 9-11 to 9-10.

116 First line in footnote under Table 9-14 should read: Range of ratio of rise over span is from 0.2 to 0.5.

202
203
204
205 } Upper left hand caption should be changed to "Once in 2 Years."

206 14th line. Strike out "100."

234 Last footnote under table, add comma after "provided."

247 Under "Skew Angles," eliminate the sentence in the parentheses.

281 Tenth line, second word should be "pervious."

283 Fig. 190. Under 2-pc. Elbow, change to "x=5° to 90°." Under 3-pc. Elbow, change to "x=30° to 90°."

401 Table 48-2. Headings in 5th and 6th columns should be R_1 and R_2.

430 Second line under item 7, change 51-3 to 51-5.

444 End of second complete sentence, add, "A table of strut sizes and spacing is available from the pipe manufacturer."

571 Index, Liner Plate. Add "section modulus, 402."

575 After Sharp, add: , H. O.,
After Shaw, add comma.

Note: We recommend that these corrections be made directly on the pages shown.

HANDBOOK OF DRAINAGE AND CONSTRUCTION PRODUCTS

PRICE $5.00

ARMCO
DRAINAGE & METAL PRODUCTS
OF CANADA LTD.

Head Office and Plant
GUELPH, ONTARIO

1955

Branch Offices and Plants in the Following Cities:

BISHOPS FALLS, NEWFOUNDLAND
SACKVILLE, NEW BRUNSWICK
STE. FOY (QUEBEC), P.Q.
MONTREAL, QUEBEC
TORONTO, ONTARIO
WINNIPEG, MANITOBA
REGINA, SASKATCHEWAN
EDMONTON, ALBERTA
CALGARY, ALBERTA
VANCOUVER, BRITISH COLUMBIA

For the convenience of the reader,
only the initial letters in such marks are
capitalized throughout this handbook.

Printed in U.S.A. by The Lakeside Press,
R. R. Donnelley & Sons Company
Chicago, Illinois

PREFACE

SINCE THE FIRST EDITION of this drainage handbook appeared nearly a quarter century ago, under the title of *Handbook of Culvert and Drainage Practice*, tremendous changes have taken place in engineering construction—in materials, products and methods.

What is written today by engineers is more of a backsight or a bench mark from which to measure future progress. Armco engineers throughout the world have contributed of their experience and know-how to make this the only book of its kind. As before, it was prepared for engineers in private practice and public service as well as for students in municipal, highway, railway and other branches of engineering.

The following table of contents quickly reveals the wide scope of this handbook. Most of the chapters are briefly summarized to enable the user to conserve his time in searching for information. The Index has been carefully planned for the same purpose. All illustrations are referrred to in the text, thereby helping to clarify many points.

Acknowledgment is made to the various engineering societies and journals, text-book writers, engineering college experiment stations and to others for source material. Thanks is extended to the various engineering authorities who gave of their time to review the texts and who offered valuable suggestions.

Special acknowledgment is made to the Armco Drainage Engineers who wrote the chapters on which they were best versed, including G. E. Shafer, J. M. Robertson, W. T. Adams, H. L. White, M. H. Bailey, R. L. Mueller, W. J. Kropf and W. B. Roof. All of the Armco Drainage Division Engineers aided by their review of the copy, but special help was given by J. E. Kunkler, R. N. Tracy (deceased), K. E. Seppa and T. A. Bither.

Your help in suggesting changes or improvements for future editions will be greatly appreciated.

W. H. SPINDLER, *Editor*
MARKET DEVELOPMENT DIVISION
ARMCO STEEL CORPORATION

CONTENTS

PAGE

INTRODUCTION **1**

SECTION I—STRENGTH RESEARCH

CHAPTER 1. DEAD LOADS **5**
2. SURFACE LOADS **22**
3. TRANSVERSE EARTH PRESSURES **30**
4. INTERNAL PRESSURES **32**
5. CORRUGATED STEEL AND IRON SHEETS AND PLATES **35**
6. RIVETED AND BOLTED SEAMS **47**
7. PIPE, ARCHES AND PIPE-ARCHES **55**
Part I. *Laboratory Deflection Tests* **55**
II. *Beam Tests* **60**
III. *Column Tests* **62**

SECTION II—STRENGTH DESIGN

FOREWORD **65**
CHAPTER 8. DESIGN OF CORRUGATED METAL STRUCTURES **66**
Part I. *Design of Multi-Plate Pipe* **81**
II. *Design of Multi-Plate Pipe-Arches* **83**
III. *Design of Multi-Plate Arches* **87**
9. HIGHWAY LOADINGS AND GAGES **105**
10. SEWER LOADINGS AND GAGES **118**
11. RAILWAY LOADINGS AND GAGE TABLES **124**
12. DESIGN FOR LEVEE LOADINGS **133**
13. DESIGN FOR AIRPORT LOADINGS **134**
14. TUNNEL LINER PLATE GAGES **140**
15. MISCELLANEOUS LOADINGS **144**

SECTION III—DURABILITY STUDIES

CHAPTER 16. METHODS OF DETERMINING DURABILITY **147**
17. HIGHWAY CULVERT INSPECTIONS **154**
18. RAILWAY CULVERT INSPECTIONS **159**
19. SEWER INSPECTIONS **162**

PAGE

SECTION IV—DURABILITY DESIGN

CHAPTER 20. SOIL AND WATER CONDITIONS
Part I. *Practical Durability* **165**
II. *Service Conditions* **167**
III. *Sewer Service Conditions* **170**
21. DURABILITY OF METALS AND COATINGS
Part I. *Corrugated Metal Structures* **172**
II. *Miscellaneous Products and Service Conditions* ... **176**

SECTION V—ECONOMIC FACTORS

CHAPTER 22. INSTALLATION COSTS **179**

SECTION VI—DESIGN PRINCIPLES AND PRACTICES

CHAPTER 23. HYDROLOGY **195**
24. DESIGN OF OPEN CHANNELS **206**
25. THEORY OF CRITICAL FLOW **212**
26. DESIGN OF CULVERTS OR CROSS DRAINS FOR SIZE AND SHAPE **224**
27. CULVERT LOCATION AND LENGTH **241**
28. HIGHWAY SURFACE DRAINAGE **250**
29. RAILWAY SURFACE DRAINAGE **254**
30. CULVERTS UNDER LEVEES AND DIKES **256**
31. END FINISH OF CULVERTS **258**
32. DESIGN OF SEWERS FOR SIZE **265**
33. HYDRAULICS OF SEWERS **269**
34. SEWER APPURTENANCES **281**
35. PART CIRCLE CULVERTS **291**

SECTION VII—SUBSURFACE DRAINAGE

CHAPTER 36. SOIL STUDIES
Part I. *Soils* **295**
II. *Soil Moisture* **307**
37. DESIGN OF SUBDRAINS **311**
38. HIGHWAY SUBDRAINAGE **317**
39. RAILWAY SUBDRAINAGE **323**
40. MUNICIPAL SUBDRAINAGE **329**
41. AGRICULTURAL SUBDRAINAGE **333**

PAGE

SECTION VIII—SPECIAL DRAINAGE PROBLEMS

CHAPTER 42. DRAINAGE OF BRIDGES AND GRADE SEPARATIONS 341
43. AIRPORT DRAINAGE 344
44. LANDSLIDES 355
45. SOIL CONSERVATION
Part I. *Roadway Erosion Prevention* 359
II. *Soil-Saving Dams* 367
46. FLOOD CONTROL AND LAND RECLAMATION 371

SECTION IX—MISCELLANEOUS PROBLEMS

CHAPTER 47. EARTH CONTROL
Part I. *Retaining Walls* 379
II. *Sheeting* 389
48. TUNNELS, UNDERPASSES, CONDUITS 397
49. GUARDRAIL AND BRIDGE RAIL 407
50. VENTILATION 415
51. STORAGE BINS 420

SECTION X—INSTALLATION INSTRUCTIONS

CHAPTER 52. CORRUGATED METAL DRAINAGE STRUCTURES 433
Part I. *Preparation of Base* 434
II. *Assembly of Structures* 438
III. *Strutting* 443
IV. *Backfilling* 446
53. PERFORATED PIPE SUBDRAINS 452
54. JACKING 455
55. BORING 461
56. TUNNELING 462
57. LINING 465
58. BRIDGE FILLING 468
59. BIN WALLS 470
60. SHEETING 473
61. BEAM TYPE GUARDRAIL 477
62. METAL BRIDGE PLANK 480
63. ARMCO GATES 483
64. FLAP GATE DRAINAGE STRUCTURES THROUGH LEVEES AND DIKES 486

SECTION XI—TABLES

Part I. *Conversion Tables* 491
II. *General Tables* 498

APPENDIX 513

INDEX 563

Fig. 1. Large underground conduits can now be designed with confidence.

INTRODUCTION

Development of Modern Construction

ONE OF THE most significant changes in the construction field during the past half century has been the swing from heavy, massive materials to lighter weight but stronger flexible materials. Fifty to 100 years ago the engineer and builder had but little choice. To cite a few examples:

Timber: Large timbers were plentiful and skilled labor was available for converting them into covered bridges, high trestles, buildings, foundation grillages and many other structures.

Stone: Pipe culverts were practically unknown. Not only culverts but many large bridges were built of stone because of its availability and because labor was plentiful and cheap. Tunnels, too, were lined with stone. Nowadays stone is used more for adornment than as the basic structure.

Brick: Sewers and culverts of brick, as in the case of stone, have largely passed out of the picture in favor of materials more quickly placed and better adapted to present service conditions.

Cast Iron: Once used extensively for culverts under railroads, cast iron pipe for this purpose has been supplanted almost entirely by lighter-weight, stronger materials.

Twentieth Century Problems

The turn of the century brought new problems to the engineer and builder—new and improved means of transportation. The slow "horseless carriage" has changed to streamlined, high speed automobiles, trucks and buses. Railroads have become a roller-bearing, streamlined, high speed means of transporting people and goods.

From a fragile "kite" first flown by the Wright Brothers at Kitty Hawk, N. C., in 1903, the airplane has become a flying behemoth—ranging up to 200 tons for the latest bomber. We have indeed become nations on wheels and wings.

Time is money. As distances have shrunk and the volume of traffic stepped up, the time element in construction has become a more important and costly consideration. Interruptions to heavy traffic and delays to costly fleets of construction equipment are sufficient causes to influence the choice of construction methods and materials.

Mechanization of construction processes has changed the picture, too. Old arts and skills have been lost. Builders of covered bridges and stone arches would now be hard to find or to train.

Fig. 2. Steel means economical construction of many kinds. *Upper left:* Geo. Washington suspension bridge. *Upper right:* Oil fractionating unit of Humble Oil & Refining Co. *Center:* Diesel-electric locomotive, Southern Ry. (3 photos courtesy Stand. Oil Co. of N. J.) *Bottom left:* Bin-type steel retaining wall. *Bottom right:* Multi-Plate pipes.

New Materials and Processes

With the new problems fortunately have come new materials and methods of using them. Research, both fundamental and commercial, has kept in step with the needs. Fig. 3.

Metallurgists, chemists, physicists and research engineers have contributed by developing many new grades and alloys of steel—to say nothing of rubber, petroleum products, cements, plastics, electronics and a host of other items. In this handbook we are concerned mostly about new steels, new protective coatings, new products and new methods of installation as they apply to engineering construction.

Research has played an important part in the growth of Armco Steel Corporation, largest manufacturer of specialty sheet steels, and also of its subsidiaries, Armco Drainage & Metal Products, Inc. and The Armco International Corporation. In this field, Armco has found its greatest opportunity to be of service to mankind.

Better controlled manufacturing conditions, more prefabrication, and less on-the-job labor has had a tremendous effect on speeding up engineering construction and reducing costs. Fig. 2.

Future Developments

Without attempting to prophesy the future, certain things are evident to the discerning builder. Nothing is static. Nothing is permanent in the sense that changing conditions will not make it obsolete or outmoded. This ever-changing scene makes it desirable to look for *adaptability* even more so than for permanence.

This "atomic age" calls for continuous progress. If the past is any indication, man's resourcefulness combined with God's providence will find and develop new materials, new processes to meet the builder's needs.

Fig. 3. Planned research in laboratory and field leads to development of better materials and construction methods. Armco's main research laboratories.

SECTION ONE

STRENGTH RESEARCH

CHAPTER ONE

Dead Loads

EXTERNAL LOADS AND EARTH PRESSURES ON UNDERGROUND CONDUITS

Summary

Each year millions of feet of conduits are placed underground for culverts, sewers, water mains, gas lines and other purposes.* However, only during the past four decades has the subject of soil mechanics progressed toward analyzing the loads reaching these conduits.

Extensive loading research has been carried on by engineering organizations and individuals. This has been supplemented by planned studies of the performance of many hundreds of culverts and sewers under the widest variety of actual service conditions—in Nature's laboratory.

Not all elements of loading research and design have been mastered, but much progress has been made toward a rational method of design. This progress is summarized in a paper entitled "Underground Conduits—An Appraisal of Modern Research," in Appendix A,[1] this handbook.

Early Load Theories and Practices

History records the use of underground conduits for the past 3,000 years. Some have lasted for centuries. Evidently these conduits were built as a result of experience, observation or by guess, rather than on the basis of rational design. No doubt there were many failures due to poor construction or to the disregard of simple engineering principles. On the other hand, many were built wastefully strong for similar reasons.

Before an engineer can design an underground conduit properly, he must consider the conditions surrounding its use:

1. The character, direction and magnitude of the loads;
2. The physical properties of the material from which the conduit is to be constructed;

---

*Conduits also include tubes for receiving electric wires or cables; "utilidors"; underpasses or tunnels for pedestrians, livestock, conveyors, materials or utility lines.

[1]References to literature are given at end of chapter, page 21.

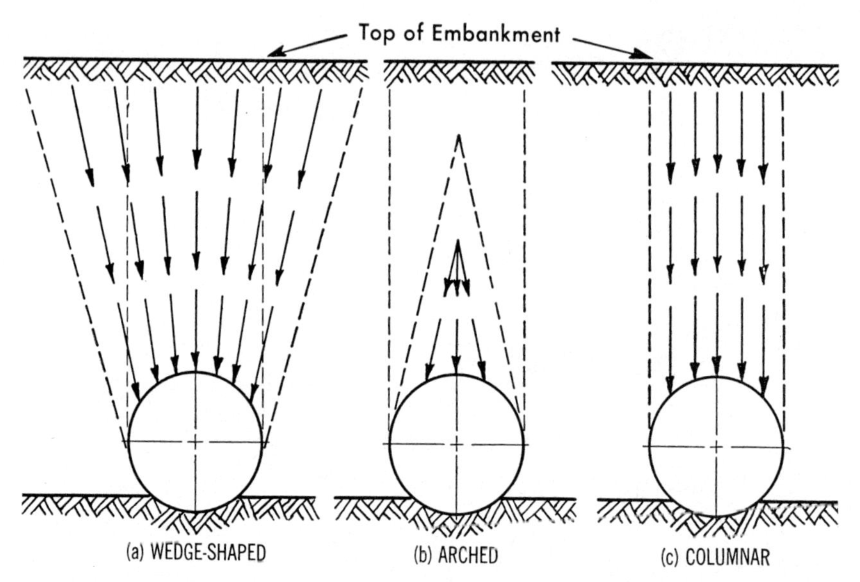

Fig. 4. Three theories of loads on underground conduits—wedge-shaped, arched, vertical.

3. The behavior of the material under the loads to which it is to be subjected; and
4. The size of opening required.

The first three items are necessary from a strength standpoint; the last requirement is to assure the conduit having adequate capacity. It is always advisable, however, to be guided by a study of existing installations. This study applies particularly to the behavior of the existing structures in regard to their ability to carry the superimposed loads without failure, the ability of the soil to carry the structure without excessive settlement, as well as the determination of the correct size of opening to accommodate the material to be carried through it.

Until Dean Anson Marston, in 1913, published the results of his work on conduit loadings,[2] there were only vague ideas of the loads acting on buried structures. One theory was that the load was equal to the weight of the earth directly over the structure, and that it varied only with the height. Some contended that arch action caused the load to be less. Others believed the load, for various reasons, was greater. These three theories are roughly illustrated in Fig. 4.

None of these theories was completely correct because they failed to recognize modifying factors such as installation conditions. Now it can be demonstrated by rational principles of mechanics that the load on a conduit is greatly influenced by:

1. Settlement of the soil directly over the conduit in relation to
2. Settlement of the soil at the sides of the conduit.

These settlements are in turn influenced by settlement of the original ground line under and adjacent to the conduit, the width of trench, the type of bedding, compaction of the fill, deflection of the conduit, and other factors. See description on following pages and in Appendix A.

Research Progress

Extensive loading research at Iowa State College, the University of North Carolina, and by the American Railway Engineering Association, included the weighing of loads over conduits, measuring the pressures, and determining relative settlements. This research led to:

1. Classifying conduits as to degree of flexibility.
2. Differentiation between conduits installed in a trench or under an embankment ("ditch" or trench conduits and "projecting" conduits).
3. Recognition of importance of bedding conditions, along with relative settlement of soil above, alongside, and under a conduit.

Iowa State College, 1908–1952

Most notable of all load research has been that of the Iowa Engineering Experiment Station of Iowa State College, Ames, Iowa. Begun in 1908 by Anson Marston, Dean of the Engineering Division, the research has been carried on almost continuously since then. W. J. Schlick participated in the work in the late 1910's and early 1920's, and M. G. Spangler beginning in 1926 has aided greatly in this research and in publishing its results. Much of the work has been in cooperation with the United States Bureau of Public Roads.

Cracking and failures of many drain tile and sewer pipe in Iowa led to this research. Apparatus was developed for actually weighing the load over pipe *in ditches* (trenches), resulting in the discovery that "the side pressure of filling materials against the sides of the ditch develops frictional resistance which helps to carry part of the weight."[2]

Next, Marston weighed the loads under a 20-ft *embankment* of top soil (1919–1920) and under a 16-ft sand and gravel embankment (1922). The maximum load was 1.92 times the weight of the fill material directly over the rigid pipe.

This research led to the discovery and publication by Dean Marston in 1922[3] of what is widely known as Marston's Theory of Loads on Underground Conduits. Although some factors still are not fully understood, this theory helps make it possible to estimate more rationally the loads on buried structures. Marston also developed methods of determining the strength of underground conduits, and methods of installing conduits to increase their load-carrying capacity. See Appendix A.

Kinds of Conduits

Conduits are of many shapes and materials, but one major distinction—degree of *flexibility*—is important in classifying from a load standpoint:[4]

1. *Rigid conduits,* such as concrete, cast iron or clay, fail by rupture of the pipe walls. Their principal load supporting ability lies in the inherent strength or stiffness of the pipe.
2. *Flexible conduits,* such as corrugated metal pipes and thin-walled steel pipe fail by deflection. Flexible pipe relies only partly on its inherent strength to resist external loads. In deflecting under load, the horizontal diameter increases, compresses the soil at the sides and thereby builds up "passive resistance" which in turn helps support the vertically-applied load.

On the basis of construction conditions under which they are installed, conduits are divided into three main classes: (1) *trench conduits,* (2) *projecting conduits,* and

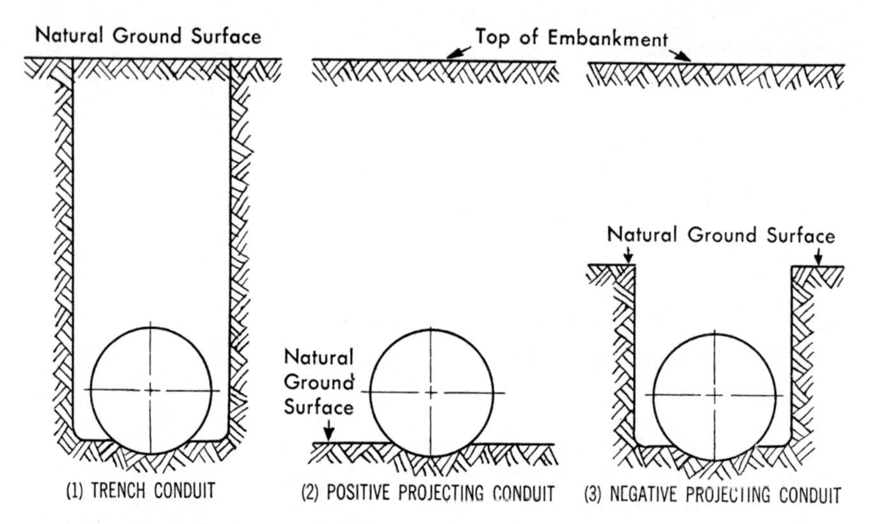

Fig. 5. Conduits are classified according to three construction conditions.

(3) *negative projecting conduits,* a variation of (2). See Fig. 5.

1. *Trench conduits* are structures installed and completely buried in narrow trenches in relatively passive or undisturbed soil. Examples are sewers, drains and water mains.
2. *Projecting conduits* are structures installed in shallow bedding with the top of the conduit projecting above the surface of the natural ground, and then covered with an embankment. Railway and highway culverts are good examples. Conduits installed in ditches wider than two or three times their maximum horizontal breadth may also be treated as projecting conduits.
3. *Negative projecting conduits.*[5] Highway or railway culverts are sometimes placed in a shallow ditch at one side of the existing water course, with the top of the conduit below the natural ground surface and then covered with an embankment above this ground level.

Bedding conditions affect settlement and thereby affect the supporting strength of conduits. These bedding conditions, illustrated for trench conduits in Fig. 6, are: (a) impermissible, (b) ordinary, (c) first class and (d) concrete cradle, used only for rigid conduits.

Field Measurement of Settlement

Two series of field measurements of settlement ratios were made by M. G. Spangler on twenty-four culverts in Iowa. The culverts included rigid and flexible prefabricated pipe and monolithic box and arch culverts. Height of fill over these various size culverts ranged from 8 to 61 ft.

Quoting Spangler's report,[6] "In the present state of knowledge it is difficult to predict the values of the settlement ratio, which has such an important effect on the relationship between load and height of fill. Nevertheless it is present and effective in every culvert installation and scientific progress demands that it be recognized and studied. This same comment applies to the projection ratio, except that the latter factor is more easily determined for a specific pipe installation."

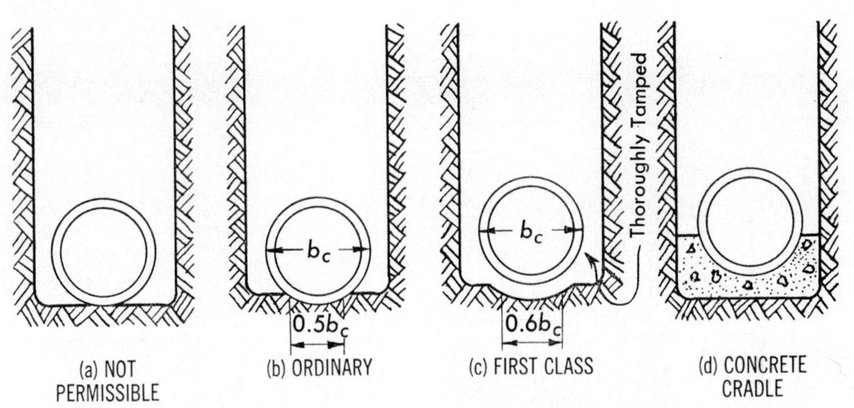

Fig. 6. Typical bedding specifications for trench conduits.

Check on Box Culvert

Pressure cell readings made by Wilson V. Binger of the U. S. Corps of Engineers, on a concrete box culvert 9 ft wide by 10 ft 10 in. high under 50 ft of clay fill on a relocation of the Panama Railroad, gave results comparable to those computed by Marston's theory for "incomplete projection condition."[7] See Fig. 7.

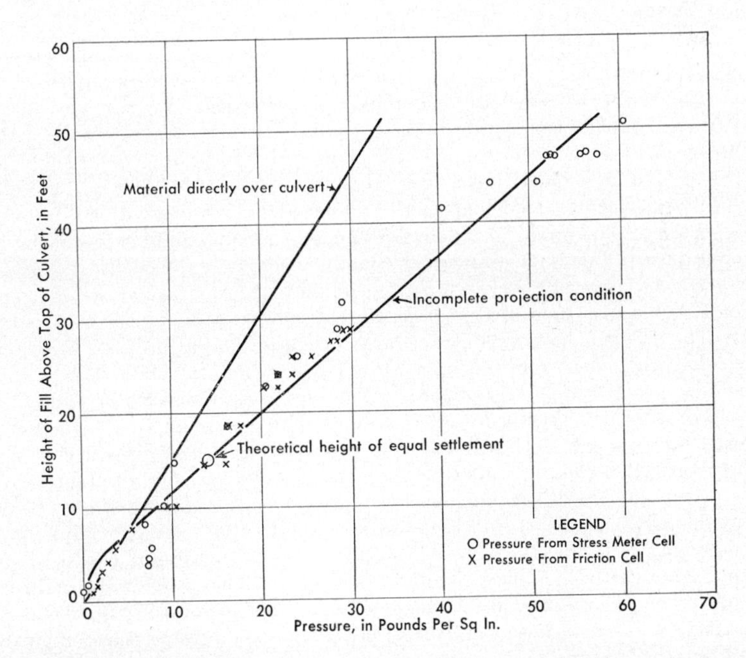

Fig. 7. Pressures versus heights of cover over culvert on Panama Railroad verifies the Marston theory of loads on underground conduits.

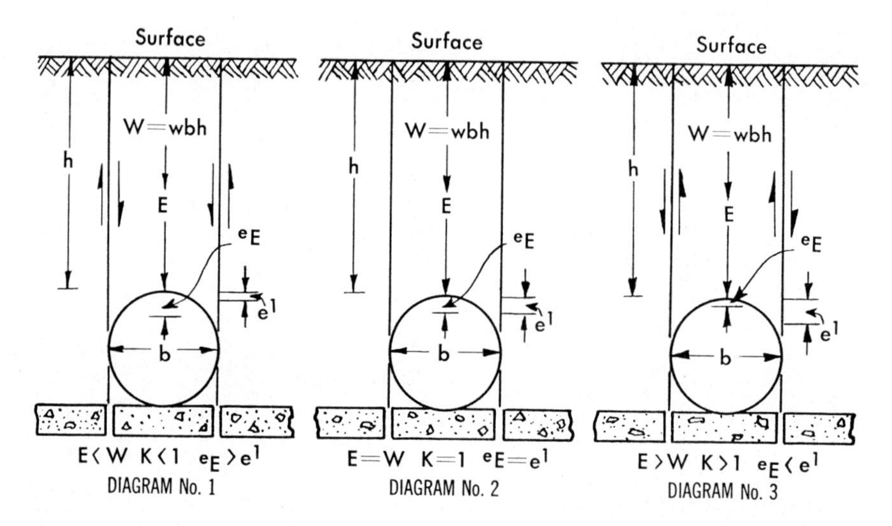

Fig. 8. Action of earth pressures on culvert pipe according to Dr. Wm. Cain of University of North Carolina. (After Public Roads.)

Special Cases

There are cases where the classifications "trench conduits" and "projecting conduits" do not apply. These may occur where either the terrain at the site or the designer will produce conditions other than those defined.

(a) In *wide ditches,* the load on a rigid conduit increases in accordance with the trench-conduit theory until it equals the load predicted by the projecting conduit theory. (b) For *rock foundations,* it is possible to reduce the vertical load on the conduit by excavating a trench in the rock material and refilling with a compressible soil. (c) *Rock fills* are found to act similar to earth embankments in producing loads on conduits. (d) Loads on projecting conduits may be reduced by the *imperfect trench method of construction* in which the soil on both sides and above the conduit for some distance is thoroughly compacted by rolling, tamping, or other suitable means. Then a ditch or trench is excavated over the conduit in this compacted fill and refilled with loose compressible material after which the embankment is completed in a normal manner. (e) *Negative projecting conduit*[5] is a term applying when a highway or railway culvert is installed in a trench dug through an old embankment or at one side of a channel and then covered over with a fill of considerable height. The load on such a conduit will be between that on a trench conduit and the weight of the prism of earth directly above the conduit.

Spangler advances the theory that loads on negative projecting conduits provide a sound approach to the study of loads on this class of structures and leads to proper design and construction of conduits that can safely withstand the loads produced by high fills. This theory may also be used to estimate loads on conduits installed by the *imperfect trench method,* described above. Spangler states that "there is no factual basis at the present time upon which design values of the settlement ratio can be recommended. Further extensive studies are needed."

Time Effect on Loads

Three test culverts at Iowa Engineering Experiment Station were placed under a 15-ft embankment late in the fall of 1927. Load observations have been made ever since. Maximum load was reached in April of the following year, dropping about 10 per cent below the maximum in the following October. Since then the load has fluctuated between these limits—high in spring, low in fall.

"The loads on conduits measured soon after the completion of the fill over them should be increased 20 to 25 per cent to allow safely for the *ultimate* loads . . . Field observations of cracked conduits show that such cracks often develop months or even years after construction."[4]

University of North Carolina Tests

Twelve important load experiments were made at the University of North Carolina at Chapel Hill from 1924 to 1927, in two series. These consisted of placing pipe of varying degrees of flexibility directly on weighing apparatus, without any bedding, and then covering with fills of sand and of clay from 11 to 20 ft high.

The final report[8] on these tests was made by G. M. Braune and H. F. Janda, with appendices by William Cain. These North Carolina culvert tests conform closely to results calculated by Marston's theory. According to Professor Cain, "The simple laws of mechanics and certain experiments indicate that the vertical earth pressure, E, on pipe culvert varies according to the relative deflections of the top of the pipe and the adjacent soil (soil settlement). In diagram No. 1 (Fig. 8) the top of the pipe deflects much more than the adjacent soil (settles) and there will be a tendency for a prism directly over the pipe to move downward, relative to the earth alongside it, and through friction and cohesion it transfers part of its weight to the soil adjacent to the pipe. Therefore, the earth pressure, E, is less than W, the weight of the material directly over the pipe. In the case illustrated by diagram No. 2 the

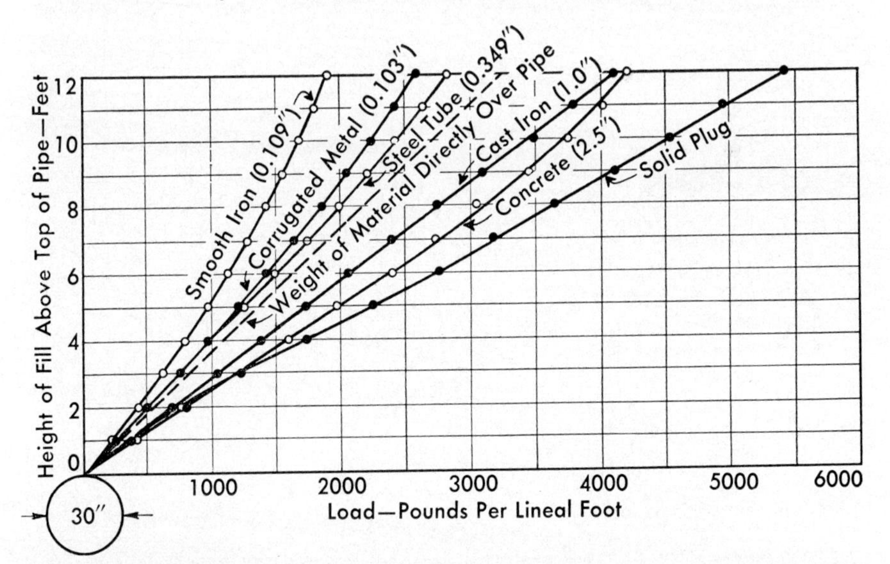

Fig. 9. Vertical loads transmitted to 30-in. pipe, 100 per cent projection condition, under sand fill at North Carolina. Numbers in parentheses indicate thickness of pipe. (After Public Roads.)

deflections of the top of the pipe and the soil adjacent are assumed to be the same and there will be equal settlement of both the prism of earth and the adjacent soil, no relative motion ensuing. Consequently there will be no friction exerted along the sides of the prism and the earth pressure E will then be equal to W. The other case, illustrated by diagram No. 3, is just the converse to that of the first diagram. The earth outside the prism over the pipe is moving downward, relatively to the prism itself, this being due to the rigidity of the pipe. Thus, through the medium of friction and cohesion, part of the weight of the outside material is transferred to the prism over the pipe and E becomes much greater than the weight of the prism W."

Although these experiments led to no new concept, they did advance the idea that the load on a pipe varies with the rigidity of the pipe, being less than the weight of the prism of earth W for flexible pipe, and greater for rigid pipe. Results of some of the North Carolina tests are shown in Fig. 9.

American Railway Engineering Association Tests

Field tests by the roadway committee of the American Railway Engineering Association (1923–1926) were an important contribution to the subject of culvert loading. The final tests were under a 35-ft embankment on the Edgewood cut-off of the Illinois Central Railroad near Farina, Illinois. Layout of the test is shown in Fig. 10.

At the conclusion of the test, this summary was published:[9]

1. The intensity of vertical pressure measured by the top cells on the corrugated culverts is about one-third of the measured vertical pressure on the rigid type of culvert under the same condition of loading.

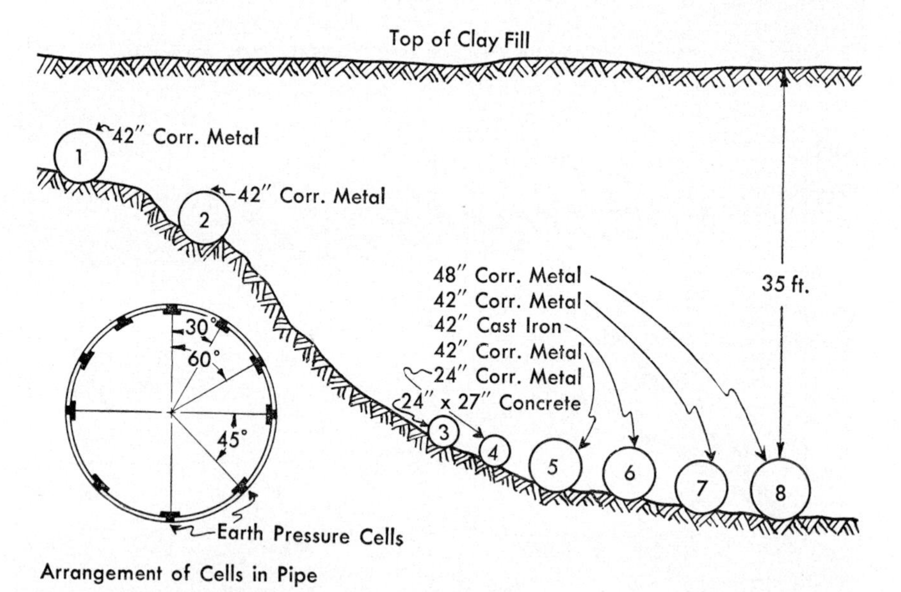

Fig. 10. American Railway Engineering Association's tests on culvert pipe were made under actual field conditions under the Illinois Central Railroad at Farina, Ill. Readings were taken on earth pressure cells as the fill height increased.

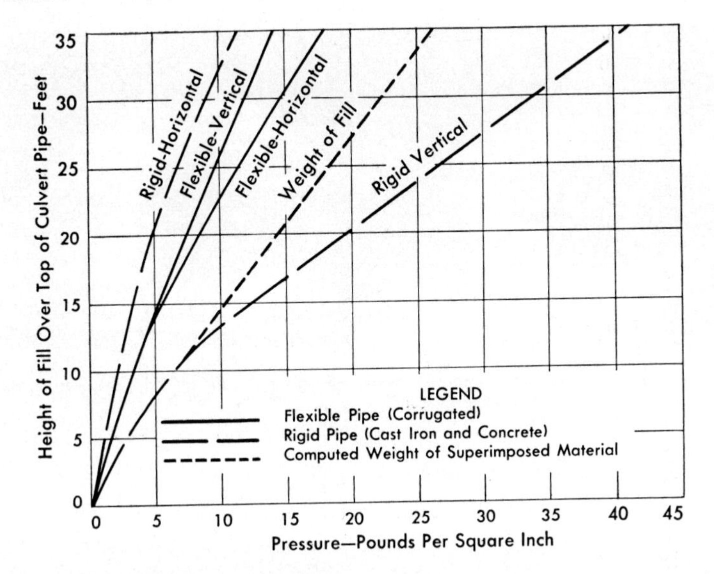

Fig. 11. Results of the A.R.E.A. Tests at Farina, Ill. show that flexible pipe needs to support less load than the weight of fill, and rigid pipe more.

2. The intensity of vertical pressure measured by the top cells of the corrugated culverts is about 54 per cent of the weight of the unit columns of the material above the cells.
3. The intensity of vertical pressure measured by the top cells of the rigid culverts is about 158 per cent of the weight of the unit columns of the material above the cells.
4. The intensity of pressure at the horizontal axis of the corrugated culvert is equal to or greater than the intensity of pressure at the vertical axis.
5. The intensity of pressure at the horizontal axis of the rigid culvert is about one-third of the intensity of pressure at the vertical axis. See Figs. 11 and 12.

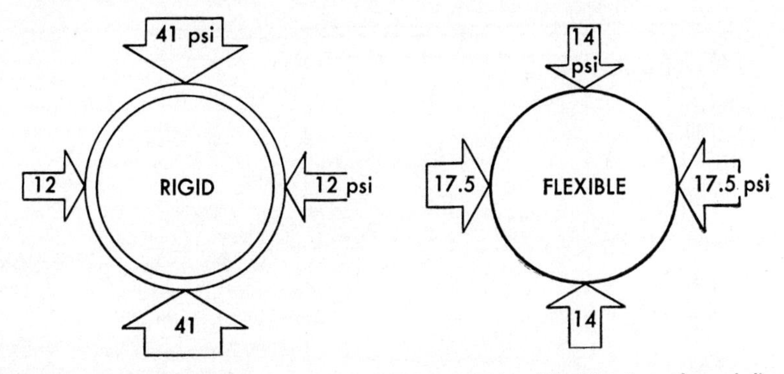

Fig. 12. Comparative vertical and horizontal pressures on rigid and flexible pipes of equal diameter in A.R.E.A. tests at Farina, Ill.

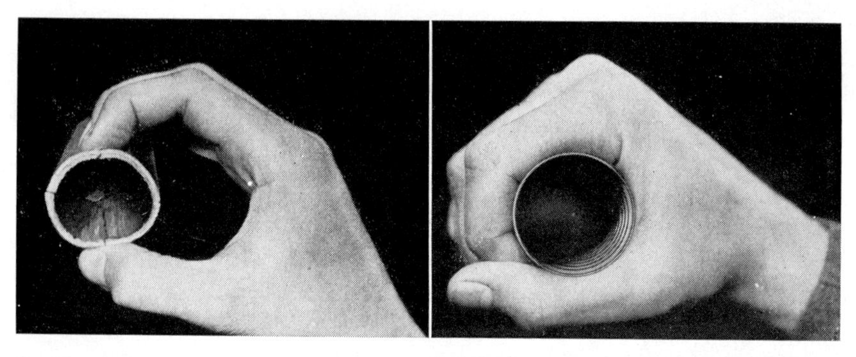

Fig. 13. Method of demonstrating concentrated and uniformly distributed pressures on rigid and flexible pipes, as typical of Farina test results.

Peck Study of Railroad Culverts

Installation of large-diameter, flexible metal culverts was made on the Denver & Rio Grande Western Railroad in Colorado, Utah and New Mexico in 1926–1939. About thirty such culverts ranging in diameter from 7½ to 15 ft were placed under fills varying from 2 to 50 ft. Deflection measurements and frequent observations were made by O. K. Peck and R. B. Peck[10] on a number of these structures. Detailed studies were made of two.

Fig. 14 shows a longitudinal section through a fill over Coal Creek, 23 miles west of Denver, Colo., in which is buried a Multi-Plate* pipe culvert 15 ft in diameter. The backfill material, 41.5 ft over the pipe, Structure A, was granular. The pipe was "strutted" but when the struts were removed after about 90 days, the vertical diameter shortened rapidly for a few weeks. Practically no shortening could be observed after 200 days.

Structure B, a 10-ft diameter pipe, installed under the most adverse conditions of any of the thirty culverts, reached equilibrium after 3 years. Behavior of the other culverts is shown in Table 1-1.

*The words "Multi-Plate" and "structural plate" are used interchangeably in this handbook. Multi-Plate is a trade name of Armco Steel Corporation.

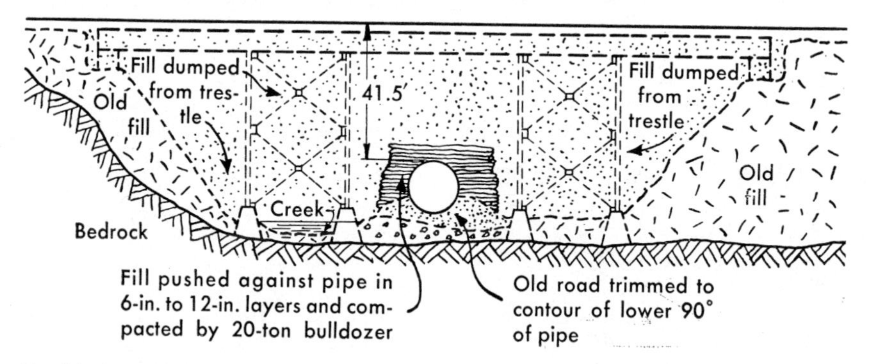

Fig. 14. Longitudinal section through a fill in which is buried a 15-ft. diameter corrugated metal culvert. (After Peck.)

TABLE 1-1 OBSERVED DEFLECTION OF FLEXIBLE CULVERTS AT CENTER OF FILL (D&RGW RR)

Diameter in Feet	*Metal Thickness in Inches*	*Overburden in Feet*	*Years Since Erection*	*Percentage by Which Vertical Diam. Is Less Than That of True Circle*
7.5	0.1875	2	3	−2.5
7.5	0.1875	4	3	2.7
7.5	0.2188	9	3	1.4
8.75	0.2188	4	3	1.7
8.75	0.2188	5	4	1.7
8.75	0.2188	9	3	4.7
8.75	0.2188	12	3	0.0
8.75	0.2188	13	3	3.2
8.75	0.2188	15	3	1.9
10.0	0.2188	3	2	1.3
10.0	0.2188	3	6	4.3
10.0	0.2188	6	3	0.3
10.0*	0.1875	13	5	7.1
10.0	0.2813	19	2	2.8
10.0	0.2813	19	2	1.8
10.0	0.2500	46	3	2.3
10.0	0.2813	50	4	5.1
15.0†	0.2813	37	2	0.1

NOTE: Total vertical diameter change approximately 3 per cent plus value given in table.
*Structure B.
†Structure A.

One conclusion from these observations was that "theoretical analyses based on the results of soil tests are not warranted in the design of flexible metal culverts . . . Field supervision of backfilling operations is, on the other hand, of outstanding importance."

Dead Load Tests on Riveted Pipe-Arches

The first change from the shape of a round pipe to that of a "pipe-arch" was made in 1937. The purpose was to reduce headroom required. Later research showed certain hydraulic advantages.

Tests were made at Topeka, Kansas,[11] to determine the most favorable shape (ratio of span to rise) as well as the load-carrying capacity. Included were three sizes placed on a sand bed, but with no surrounding fill.

In every instance, failure was caused by crushing of the arch from the top and corresponding spreading at the sides. At no time did the bottom deform upward.

Tests were next made under field installation conditions with results as illustrated in Table 1-2, and in Fig. 15.

TABLE 1-2 DEAD-LOAD TEST ON PIPE-ARCH

Weight Applied to a Plate 25½ in. x 50 in. (8.85 sq ft)

Span = 42 in. Length = 12 ft
Rise = 27 in. Gage = No. 12

Total Load in Pounds	*Pounds per Square Foot*	*Vertical Deflection in Inches*	*Horizontal Deflection in Inches*	*Bottom Deflection in Inches*
9,937	1,122	¼	⅛	0
15,621	1,770	½	¼	0
19,563	2,210	¾	⅜	0
23,428	2,650	1⅛	½	0
24,784	2,800	1½	⅝	⅛ up
26,818	3,030	1⅝	¾	⅛ up
27,123	3,070	1¾	¾	¼ up
27,428	3,150	2	⅞	¼ up
31,000	3,500	2¼	⅞	¼ up
34,615	3,930	Total failure by top crushing		

Fig. 15. Dead-load test on riveted pipe-arch at Topeka, Kans. Ultimate load was 34,615 lb applied over area of 8.85 sq ft. Span, 42 in.; rise, 27 in.; length, 12 ft; 12 gage.

Fig. 16. Engineers inspecting corrugated metal culvert in eastern Canada.

Field Measurements on Existing Structures

The value of laboratory tests is usually increased when supplemented by studies of structures in actual service. Although the conditions surrounding these structures cannot always be determined, because of lack of records or the cost of determining them, these installations are a helpful guide.

For example, by measuring the vertical diameter it is possible to determine the deflection that has taken place on a culvert of known gage under a known fill height. Provided the pipe was not strutted during installation and provided the foundation soil and backfill were normal, it is possible to determine whether a safe gage was chosen. The larger the number of structures under various conditions, the more accurate are the conclusions that can be drawn. If a few failures can be included, the conclusions will be sounder.

Engineers from state highway departments, the Highway Research Board, railroads, engineering college experiment stations, and city engineering departments have examined thousands of flexible metal culverts and sewers along with conduits of other types of materials. The results have generally not been published but have been used as a guide in establishing suitable gages of metal.

The earliest of these "look under your roads" investigations date back to the early 1920's. Others include the AREA test at Farina,[9] and the Peck study of culverts under the D. & R. G. W. Railroad in Colorado, Utah and New Mexico.[12] Most recent is a survey of 200 corrugated metal structures, standard riveted and structural plate, by a number of the railroads in 1950–1951. Page 161.

Armco engineers have made deflection measurements on many actual installations of corrugated metal pipe and arches. (See chapter on Durability.) Among these was a series of culverts installed in 1928 under a new line on the Union Pacific Railroad in Wyoming. Diameters ranged from 24 to 60 in. Some pipes were strutted; others were not. Deflections were measured over a period of nine years.

TABLE 1-3 DEFLECTION OF MULTI-PLATE PIPE CULVERTS ON NATION-WIDE INSPECTION 1943–1944

Diameter of Pipe in Inches	*Quantity*	*Cover Over Pipe in Feet*	*Deflection in Per Cent*	*Average in Per Cent*
60 to 180	238	1.5 to 84.5	2.32	
60 to 105	128	Under 20 ft	1.69	2.41
60 to 105	37	20 ft and over	4.87	
120 to 180	53	Under 20 ft	1.99	2.14
120 to 180	20	20 ft and over	2.52	

In 1943–1944, Armco engineers investigated 355 Multi-Plate pipe in diameters of 60 to 180 in. all over the United States. Heights of cover ranged from 1.5 to 84.5 ft. Deflections averaged 2.32 per cent for all structures with a maximum of 10.5 per cent for a 120-in. pipe under 11 ft of cover, and 9.05 per cent for a 105-in. pipe under 30 ft of cover. Averages are given in Table 1-3.[13]

This same investigation included 479 Multi-Plate arch structures with spans from 5 to 27 ft.[14]

The remarkable fact is that of the thousands of corrugated metal structures investigated, the percentage in trouble was negligible, indicating that the design criteria used were on the safe side.

Studies of Flexible Metal Culverts Under High Fills

The effect of careful installation of corrugated metal structures is revealed by several jobs of large diameter pipe under extremely high fills. By paying special attention to foundation conditions and backfill operations, the full strength possibilities of the pipe can be achieved. (Not a corollary to these jobs, but obviously for normal installations, satisfactory results can be obtained with only ordinary precautions.)

1. *Cullman, Alabama.* Load research was carried on in 1952 jointly by the Alabama State Highway Department and Armco.[15] At Cullman, Ala., three 84-in. Multi-Plate pipes were installed under 138 ft of fill. Fig. 17. Careful bedding was done and the pipe installed by the "imperfect trench method" as developed by M. G. Spangler of Iowa State College. The fill over the pipe was placed in uniform layers. Of the initial camber of 6 in. in the pipe, about 3 in. remained on completion of the fill.

Strain gages (SR-4) were attached to one line of pipe. To measure the load on the timber struts, a calibrated load cell was placed between the strut and the compression cap—at a point under the center line of the road and under the midpoint of the lower embankment slope. Settlement and deflection readings were made as the building of the fill progressed and after completion.

2. *Western North Carolina.* Similar research procedures under the direction of the North Carolina State Highway Department, with M. G. Spangler as consultant, were followed in a project on U. S. Route 70 in western North Carolina where six miles of new road was built through mountainous country. Here a single line of 66-in. diameter Multi-Plate pipe was installed under a fill of 165 ft on center line. The major portion of the fill was made by the end dumping method from one side,

Fig. 18, a practice not recommended by the pipe manufacturers, particularly for cohesive soils.[16]

3. *Montana.* Under a relocation of U. S. Route 10 in western Montana, twin lines of elliptical Multi-Plate pipe, 102-in. vertical diam. by 90-in. horizontal, were placed under about 105 ft of fill. See Fig. 1. The pipes, which serve as equalizers for a reservoir, were placed on 50 ft of rock fill. This foundation fill settled 12 in. due to the weight of the 100-ft fill plus partial inundation. Approximately 9 in. of the original 24 in. of camber remained in the pipe.

Timber struts were used to hold the elliptical shape (elongation about 8 per cent) during placing of the fill. Compression caps used between the struts and the top sills were calibrated so that the amount of load could be estimated as the fill height increased. Deflection measurements were made during and after installation, but without strain gage readings. Of the 8 per cent elongation of the vertical diameter of the pipe, approximately 5 per cent remained when the struts were removed.

General conclusions drawn from these three high fill installations are:

1. The vertical load on the pipe (as shown by strain gage readings on the Alabama job) agrees substantially with the weight of the column of fill immediately above the pipe. (This is the weight used by Armco to design the strength of the longitudinal seams of flexible culverts under high fills.)
2. Data taken on strut cells and pipe-wall strain gages at successive fill heights show that each increment of fill resulted in an increment of load in almost direct proportion.

Fig. 17. Three 7-ft diameter metal culverts under partly completed 138 ft of cover at Cullman, Alabama. Pressure readings were taken.

Fig. 18. A 66-in. Multi-Plate culvert being installed prior to placing 165 ft of fill above it, on U.S. 70 in western North Carolina.

3. Analysis of the observed loads on the pipe shows that the methods used to construct a fill can affect the amount of load transmitted to the structure. In constructing high fills, it appears desirable to place the material in horizontal layers. The fill material should be compacted uniformly to avoid "hard spots" and to transmit the load to the original ground and to the structure in a uniform manner.
4. Part of the elongation of the vertical diameter of the pipes still remained after completion of the fill and removal of the struts. This indicates that granular backfill can be so compacted that little or no change in pipe diameter will occur.
5. These jobs indicate that by paying special attention to foundation and backfill conditions, selection of pipe gage, spacing of struts, and amount of elongation, that a satisfactory installation will result even under extreme conditions.

REFERENCES

1. "Underground Conduits—An Appraisal of Modern Research," by M. G. Spangler, Paper No. 2337, ASCE Transactions, Vol. 113, pp. 316–374. June 1947 Proceedings of ASCE. Reprinted as "Appendix A," this handbook.
2. "The Theory of Loads on Pipes in Ditches and Tests of Cement and Clay Drain Tile and Sewer Pipe," by Anson Marston and A. O. Anderson, Bulletin No. 31, Iowa Eng. Experiment Station, Ames, Iowa, Feb. 1913.
3. "Second Progress Report to the Joint Concrete Culvert Pipe Committee," by Anson Marston, Iowa Eng. Experiment Station, April 7, 1922 (mimeographed).
4. "The Theory of External Loads on Closed Conduits in the Light of the Latest Experiments," by Anson Marston, Bulletin No. 96, Iowa Eng. Experiment Station, Ames, Iowa, 1930, pp. 5–8.
5. "A Theory of Loads on Negative Projecting Conduits," by M. G. Spangler, Proceedings, Vol. 30, Highway Research Board, Washington, D. C., 1951, p. 153.
6. "Field Measurement of the Settlement Ratios of Various Highway Culverts," by M. G. Spangler, Bulletin No. 170, Iowa Eng. Experiment Station, 1950, pp. 10–31.
7. A discussion of M. G. Spangler's paper No. 2337 on "Underground Conduits—An Appraisal of Modern Research," ASCE Transactions, Vol. 113, p. 346, 1948. W. V. Binger, Chief, Soils and Geology Branch, Missouri River Div., Corps of Engineers, Omaha, Nebr.
8. "Earth Pressure Experiments on Culvert Pipe," by G. M. Braune, William Cain and H. F. Janda, *Public Roads*, Nov. 1929, p. 157.
9. "Culvert Load Determination," American Railway Eng. Assn. Bull. 284, Vol. 27, 1926.
10. "Contributions to Proc. of the 2nd International Conference on Soil Mechanics and Foundation Engineering," by O. K. Peck and R. B. Peck, Univ. of Illinois Bulletin, Vol. 46, No. 53, March 1949, pp. 16–21.
11. "Armco Arch Strength Tests," Report by The Road Supply and Metal Co., Topeka, Kansas, 1937.
12. "Cutting Culvert Costs Under High Fills," *Engineering News-Record*, Nov. 7, 1940.
13. "Summary of Inspection of Armco Multi-Plate Pipe and Arches," Report by Armco Drainage & Metal Products, Inc., 1943–1944.
14. "Probable Life of Corrugated Culverts," by G. E. Shafer and W. J. Kropf, *Engineering News-Record*, Oct. 18, 1945.
15. "Question?—Road or Bridge Across Gorge," by J. F. Tribble, Ass't Constr. Engr., Alabama Highway Dept., in *Roads and Streets*, June 1952.
16. "Spectacular Mountain Road Job Being Graded Without Rolling," *Roads and Streets*, July 1952.

CHAPTER TWO

Surface Loads

Summary

A modest amount of research has been done to measure the surface and impact loads on underground conduits. The greatest effect is measured under shallow covers but is dissipated or spread rapidly as the depth of cover increases to 4 ft or more. The impact factor varies from 1.0 when the surface load is static, to possible values of 3.0 or 4.0 for highway traffic on a rough roadway. The impact factor for landing airplanes has been found to vary from less than 1.0 to as much as 3.5. Deflection of corrugated metal conduits under live load and impact has been measured in various tests. The deflection of corrugated metal structures under traffic loads is of approximately the same magnitude as that of the adjacent soil and well within the elastic limit of both. There is no hard spot—no damage to road surface. Surface loads are taken into account in design tables.

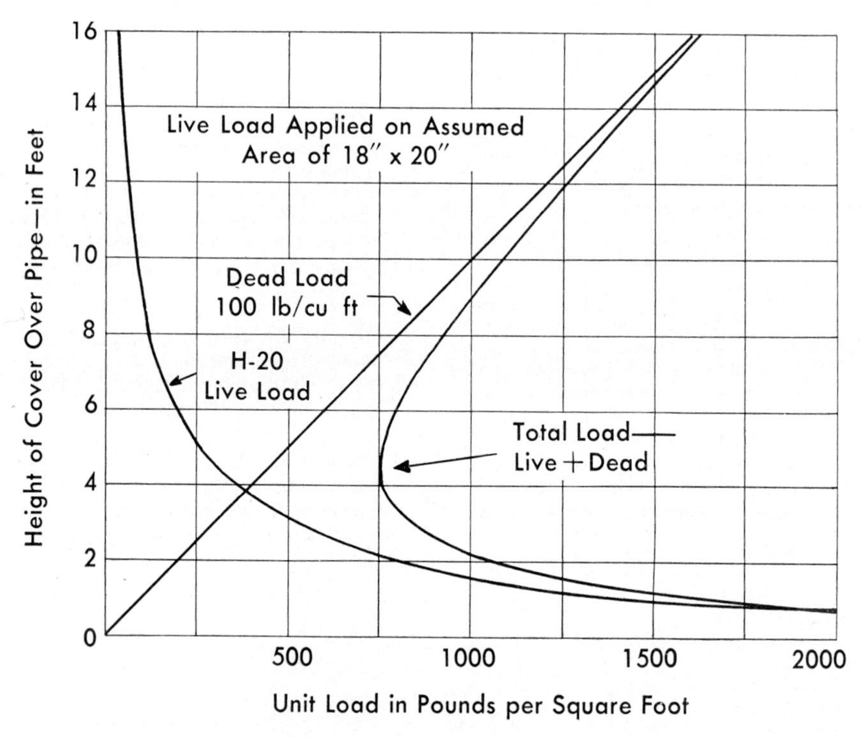

Fig. 19. Separate and combined live load (H-20) and dead load, showing that minimum combined effect is at about 4 ft. Load is applied through flexible pavement 1 ft thick.

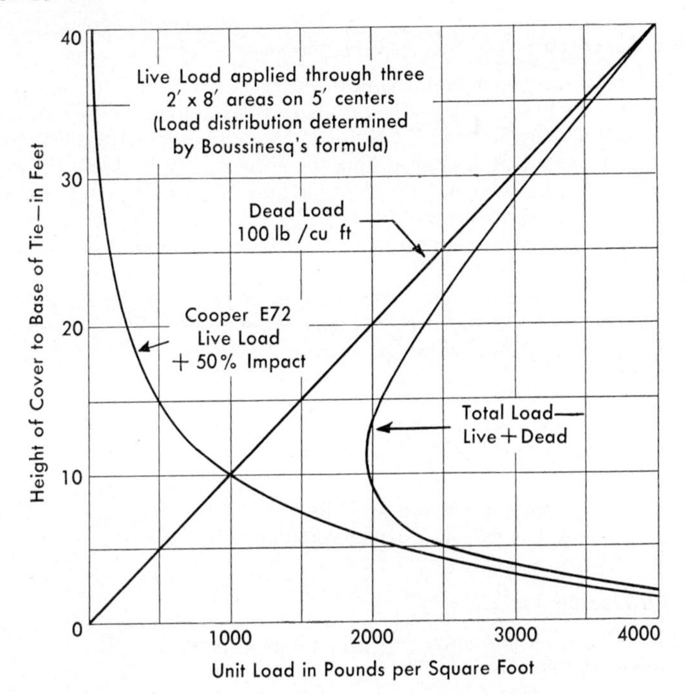

Fig. 20. Railroad surface loading, Cooper E72. Minimum effect of combined live load and dead load is at 11 ft. Load is applied through three 2 ft by 8 ft areas on 5-ft centers.

Nature of Surface Loads

Underground conduits frequently are subjected to loads other than the weight of the filling material above them. Such loads may consist of heavy grading equipment before the conduit is fully protected by fill material, or may consist of highway, railway, airplane or other traffic. These superimposed "live loads" may be in motion or not. If the load moves, it may produce an impact or shock reaction; in case of a rough surface or obstruction, it may produce a drop reaction or hammering effect. Moving and standing loads may also produce vibration. When the motors of a standing airplane are accelerated ("revved up"), for example, the vibration is quite severe.

The effect of live loads on underground conduits is modified by various factors other than (1) the weight of the loads. These include (2) speed of the vehicle, (3) shock absorbance by the tires or springing arrangement of the vehicle, (4) uplift of airplane wings, (5) the kind and thickness of the surface, sub-base or track, (6) roughness of roadway surface, (7) area over which the load is applied, and (8) kind, condition and depth of embankment surrounding the conduit.

Surface loads are of greatest importance when a conduit is placed under a relatively shallow covering of earth.[1] The effect decreases as the depth increases whereas the fill load increases with depth.

In the case of highways, the minimum combined surface and fill load occurs at about 4 ft, and for railways at about 11 ft. See Figs. 19 and 20. Impact is a major factor at shallower depths.

Highway Research

Extensive tests on the effect of highway surface loads on underground conduits were made at Iowa State College, the results of which appear in the various bulletins of the Engineering Experiment Station.[2] A mathematical theory was established and formulas set up for calculating the effect of live load and impact.

Highway authorities believe that unless conduits are near the road or street surface, live loads and impact are not likely to be important. However, very heavy loads such as are sometimes moved over the roads under special permit, may create a critical loading.

This is especially true of rigid conduits where a single application of a load in excess of that for which it was designed may cause failure. Flexible conduits, designed with a larger factor of safety, usually are elastic enough to regain their original shape.

Effect of Speed

The stress and deflection of a pavement decreases as the speed of a vehicle passing over it increases. This varies with kinds of loading and condition of support, but averages 20 per cent less at speeds of 40 mph than at creep speeds. From this it may be inferred that impact on underground conduits is less at high speeds than at slow speeds.[3]

Railroad Research

The railroad associations have made investigations of the effect of impact on track, roadbed and structures.[4] That work is still underway and includes the de-

Fig. 21. One of the heaviest wheel loads on record, 346 tons, or 21 tons per wheel is produced by this thermos or ladle car carrying molten pig iron. It is passing over a 72-in. corrugated metal culvert installed in 1927. View at right shows present excellent structural condition.

velopment of more reliable instruments for measuring impact. One interesting fact is that the use of diesel electric locomotives spreads the loads over a larger area and also avoids the blows produced by the drivers and counterweights on the wheels of steam locomotives.

Live Load Tests on Helical Corrugated Lock-Seam Pipe

Field tests were made on 6-in. 18-gage, 8-in. 18-gage and 8-in. 16-gage Hel-Cor lock seam pipe in shallow trenches. After being subjected to a truck rear axle load of 15,810 lb (equivalent to H-10 loading), the pipe showed no measurable deflection.

Live Load Test on Standard Corrugated Pipe

Construction of a special railroad line to the open hearth furnaces of Armco Steel Corporation at Middletown, Ohio, in 1927, involved the installation of a 72-in. 8-gage corrugated metal culvert under 3½ ft of cover (base of rail to top of pipe). Fig. 21. This railroad carries molten pig iron in a special insulated car with one of the heaviest wheel loads on record. Loaded, the car weighs 346 tons, concentrated on sixteen wheels.

The pipe was strutted less than normal and the backfill tamped only fairly well. Consequently the pipe deflected a little more than normal, or an average of about 6 per cent below a true circle. Additional measured deflection over the past twenty years has been about ¼ in. and has been at a decreasing rate. Since 1940 there has been no measurable change, indicating that equilibrium has been reached.

Live Load Tests on Pipe-Arches

A series of field tests was made[5] to determine the strength of the pipe-arch as compared with full-round corrugated metal pipe under live load, and to determine the proper gage to use. The investigation included four pipe and six pipe-arches each 16 ft long as shown in the accompanying Fig. 22 and Table 2-1.

Fig. 22. General view of live load tests on corrugated metal pipe and pipe-arches.

TABLE 2-1 LIVE LOAD TESTS ON PIPE AND PIPE-ARCHES
Sizes of Structures

Specimen No.	*Pipe or Pipe-Arch*	*Rise and Span in Inches*	*Diameter in Inches*	*Gage*	*Cover in Inches*
1	Pipe-Arch	31x17		14	6
2	Pipe-Arch	31x17		14	12
3	Pipe-Arch	31x17		12	12
4	Pipe		24	14	12
5	Pipe		24	12	12
6	Pipe-Arch	31x17		14	24
7	Pipe-Arch	61x34		12	12
8	Pipe-Arch	61x34		10	12
9	Pipe		48	12	12
10	Pipe		48	10	12

The structures were carefully bedded and the backfill of moist clay and loam was well tamped.

The load on a truck tractor which made trips back and forth over the structure was increased until it reached 27,390 lb. Deflections measured after each trip showed a maximum of .36 in. on a pipe-arch with 61-in. span and 34-in. rise. The maximum load was equivalent to an earth fill 27 ft high.

It was found that a pipe-arch of a given span is equally as strong as a pipe of the same diameter and gage.

Live Load and Impact on Multi-Plate Pipe-Arch

Because of the successful use of riveted pipe-arches up to 72-in. span, the same general cross section was adapted to field assembled Multi-Plate structures.

Tests were made in 1945[6] on a Multi-Plate pipe-arch with a span of 93 in., a rise of 64 in., in 10-gage steel with a corrugation 6 in. by 1¾ in. Cover was 30 in. of earth. A highway truck with successive axle loads of 10,000 lb, 18,300 lb and 29,940 lb was run over the culvert repeatedly.

Maximum deflection readings were ½ in. under the 29,940 lb live load before the side support was built up and the structure reached a point of "maximum deflection." This minor deflection showed the structure to be amply strong in this gage and shape. Succeeding equivalent loads produced even less deflection.

Strain gage readings taken at various points around the inside and outside of the structure showed no points of excessive strain. The maximum readings in tension and compression were roughly equal. This led to the conclusion that for strength the plates may be the same gage around the entire periphery.

Live Load Tests on Multi-Plate Arches

Arch structures are generally used under shallow cover and therefore are subject to live load and impact rather than to dead loads.

One test was made on an arch of 20-ft span, 7-ft rise, 10 ft long, No. 3 gage plates on concrete footings, with an earth backfill and cover of 2 ft. The arch was first subjected to a repeated live load consisting of a truck loaded with steel ingots. Under a rear axle load of 57,560 lb, the maximum deflection was 0.65 in. See

Fig. 23. Live load test on Multi-Plate arch at Middletown, Ohio. Span 20 ft; rise 7 ft; length 10 ft; No. 3 gage. Gross load, 33.7 tons; rear axle load, 28.8 tons.

Fig. 23. This arch was designed for an H-10 loading, but actually carried 3.6 times this load without failure. This same arch was then subjected to a dead load of 345 tons—equivalent to a factor of safety of 3.7 for a 10-ft fill.

Another live load test was made in May, 1936 by the Minnesota State Highway Dept. on a Multi-Plate arch of 24-ft span, 8½-ft rise. Radial readings were taken on four sectors—two at a distance of 8 ft left and right of the center line of the road and two at 17 ft from the center line. Readings were made when the endwalls were in place (1) with no backfill, (2) with the backfill in place, and (3) with a 52-ton shovel over the arch. The maximum radial movement at the crown due to this live load was only 3/16 in.

Vicksburg Load Tests

Surface load tests were made on reinforced concrete and corrugated metal pipe by the U. S. Waterways Experiment Station of the Corps of Engineers, Vicksburg, Miss.[7] The purpose was to determine the stress distribution on drain pipe due to stationary surface loads. The pipe consisted of 12 to 48-in. standard strength reinforced concrete culvert pipe and standard corrugated metal pipe.

Based on an allowable crack of 0.01 in., a table was developed of *minimum* allowable cover requirements for concrete pipe. A comparable table for corrugated metal pipe was based on an allowable deflection of 2.5 per cent of pipe diameter for dense backfill and 5.0 per cent for medium dense backfill. Parts of these two tables are combined in Table 2-2 to show the comparative loads to produce allowable cracks or deflection under equal depths of cover.

Another way of stating the results is that the reinforced concrete pipe requires a greater depth of protective cover than corrugated metal pipe to withstand an equal surface load.

TABLE 2-2 COMPARISON OF LOADS TO PRODUCE 0.01-in. CRACK IN REINFORCED CONCRETE PIPE AND 2½–5% DEFLECTION IN C.M.P.

Based on Field Tests by U.S. Waterways Experimental Station

Field Test No.	*Pipe Diam. in In.*	*Gage of Corr. Metal Pipe*	*Surface Load on Pipe†*		*Depth of Cover in Test in Feet*
			at 0.01-in. Crack Based on ASTM	*at Allowable Deflection*	
			Reinf. Concr. in Pounds	*Corr. Metal in Pounds*	
40	12	16		66,000	1
26	12		47,000		2
39	12	16		110,000	2
42	18		56,000		2
34	18	16		102,000	2
46	18		48,000		3
35	18	16		142,000	3
28	24		57,700		2
31	24	14		114,000	2
29	24		92,300		3
30	24	14		180,000	3
57	36		24,200		2
65*	36	12		58,000	2
56	36		51,400		3
64*	36	12		88,000	3
58	36		53,000		4
70*	36	12		122,000	4
60	48		39,400		2
63*	48	12		50,000	2
59	48		66,100		3
62*	48	12		66,000	3
61	48		70,800		4
69*	48	12		108,000	4

*Medium dense backfill, pipe deflection 5%—comparable to 2½% deflection in dense backfill.

†Equivalent plane weight = twice these values, divided by 1.5 which is the factor to provide for effect of impact, variation in backfill density, etc.

REFERENCES

1. "Underground Conduits—An Appraisal of Modern Research," ASCE Paper No. 2337, Tr. Vol. 113, 1948, p. 332 (see Appendix A, this handbook).

2. "Experimental Determinations of Static and Impact Loads Transmitted to Culverts," by M. G. Spangler, Clyde Mason, and Robley Winfrey, Bulletin No. 79, Iowa Eng. Experiment Station, Ames, Iowa, 1926.

3. "Road Test One-MD," Highway Research Bd. Special Report 4, 1952, p. 142.

4. "Soils Engineering in Railway Construction and Maintenance," by Rockwell Smith, Assn. of Amer. Railroads, in Highway Research Board Proceedings, Vol. 30, 1950, pp. 420–434.

5. "Live Load Tests on Armco Arches," Armco Drainage Products Assn., Aug. 1938.

6. "Live Load and Impact Tests on Corrugated Metal Structures," Armco Drainage & Metal Products, Inc., Middletown, Ohio, July 1945.

7. "Investigation of Stress Distribution on Drain Pipe Due to Surface Load," Prelim. Report, U. S. Waterways Experiment Station, Vicksburg, Miss., April 15, 1942.

CHAPTER THREE

Transverse Earth Pressures

Summary

Transverse earth pressures caused by the subsidence of soils and aggravated by moisture and frost action have been measured with values up to one-tenth of the maximum vertical load. Such pressures should definitely be provided for in the design of underground conduits.

Transverse Movement of Soil

Design engineers recognize that conduits under embankments are subject to *transverse* pressures—pressures at right angles to the roadway or in the general direction of the conduit center line (longitudinal axis). These transverse pressures while affecting corrugated pipe only rarely are evidenced by the disjointing of short sectional pipe, the overturning of headwalls and in pulling apart of rigid monolithic structures which have cracked under load. Although more marked under high embankments, this tendency to disjoint is also present under embankments of 10 ft or less.

Tests by F. N. Menefee* show that the maximum horizontal stress may be taken as one-tenth of the maximum vertical stress.[1]

Transverse pressures are presumably caused by the action of gravity or superimposed weight, and are manifested by the tendency of soil to move downward and outward, seeking equilibrium at its angle of repose. Where ground moisture abounds, the extreme but common result is a landslide.

Embankments placed on unstable soils or improperly made with large voids—as with large frozen chunks—may continue to settle for many years before reaching stability or equilibrium. This is likely to cause active or uneven pressures against side walls of conduits, resulting in what may be termed "shifting soils."

Although few authorities have published anything about these stresses, Terzaghi and Peck[2] recognize them: "If a culvert is located on a nonrigid base, it is acted upon not only by earth pressure but also by bending in a vertical plane through its longitudinal axis on account of the trough-shaped settlement of the base of the fill. It is also subjected to *axial tension* because of the shearing stresses that increase the width of the base of the fill. The failure of culverts by axial tension is not uncommon."

Lateral Flow

"Saturated soils with decreased internal friction and cohesion, plastic soils such as clays, and sands and silts with rounded grains, wet or dry, are subject to *lateral flow* under pressure. These conditions may result in slump of roadbed fill, settlement of the ballast section . . . or subsidence of fill by squeezing outward and upward such materials in the original ground."[3]

Various railroads recognize these transverse pressures. On steep slopes and under high fills they sometimes specify that cables and hooks be attached at the

---

*Professor of engineering mechanics, Univ. of Mich.

Fig. 24. Cables and hooks used to prevent disjointing of short sectional pipe due to transverse forces.

one-third points on rigid sectional pipe before backfilling. Fig. 24. On flexible corrugated metal pipe, they may specify the use of wider coupling bands or field bolted connections.

Pressure of expansion caused by change in water content of soils (for example, bulking of sand) may be considerable. However, no quantitative measurements have been made, so far as is known.

Pressures Due to Frost Action

Freezing water increases approximately 8½ per cent in volume, the resulting expansive force being 30,000 lb (15 tons) per sq in.[4] The trouble is augmented in fine-grained soils by the building up of ice layers which are fed from below by capillary moisture. Heaving is the result. When thawing occurs, stability of the soil is destroyed (see Chapter 36, Soil Studies).

REFERENCES

1. Transactions, ASCE, 1922, discussion of Paper No. 1506 by Geo. Paaswell.
2. "Soil Mechanics in Engineering Practice," by Karl Terzaghi and Ralph B. Peck, John Wiley & Sons, N. Y., 1948, p. 540.
3. Proceedings, AREA, Vol. 39, 1938, Roadway Committee, p. 321.
4. "Civil Engineer's Pocket-Book," by J. C. Trautwine.

CHAPTER FOUR

Internal Pressures

Summary

Limited laboratory tests have been made on internal pressures for watertightness of corrugated metal structures with various kinds of seams and couplings. For conduits requiring watertightness, such as tunnels, sewers and siphons, practical results can be achieved by special fabrication such as close-riveting and soldering or dipping in asphalt, by welding, by the use of mastics and by joining sections with special couplings.

Only brief reference is made here to internal pressures exerted by liquids flowing through conduits. Complete data will be found in the many excellent published textbooks.

Internal pressures are created either by differences in elevation in various parts of the conduit (known as *head*) or by pumping. These unit pressures are usually much higher than external pressures due to earth backfill and superimposed loads and impact. For example, the allowable internal working pressures on water supply and transmission lines or penstocks range up to 1000 lb per sq in. (diameters 4 to 36 in.). The design pressures are usually not less than 100 lb per sq in.[1] This is in contrast to external pressures of 10 to 50 lb per sq in. due to earth loadings.

Fig. 25. Watertight siphon built of Multi-Plate pipe at Plum Creek, Nebr. Size 13 ft 9 in. diameter, 290 ft long. All seams were welded.

Fig. 26. Watertight coupling band under test on 24-in. diameter bituminous coated pipe. No leaks at 60 lb per sq in. pressure. These tests were made under ideal conditions and gave results higher than would be obtained in ordinary practice.

Watertightness of Corrugated Metal Pipe and Couplings

Ordinary culvert pipe on moderate slopes, unless flowing full, need not be watertight. Culverts under levees do require practical watertightness from the inside, as do culverts through storage reservoir dams or under irrigation canals. On enclosed irrigation systems where the pipe is under internal pressure, watertightness is essential. Sewers (especially aerial sewers) should be practically watertight to prevent escape of sewage and to prevent infiltration of ground water. Subdrainage pipe, on the other hand, is deliberately perforated to freely admit ground water.

Hydrostatic tests have been made on corrugated metal pipe and couplings to determine their watertightness under different heads. One simple test consisted of 24-in. riveted corrugated metal pipe 29 ft long with the bottom end sealed, set vertically and filled with water. The only joint was a 12-in. wide coupling band, 2 ft from the bottom, made tight with ½-in. rods and cast shoes (lugs). The pipe was dipped in hot asphalt before assembly to help seal the seams. It was watertight for the six months that it remained under test.

Bituminous coated galvanized corrugated metal pipe may be made watertight when proper conditions of manufacture or field installation are observed. Close riveting, soldering, or welding of the seams are means of assuring absolute watertightness. Practical watertightness is obtained with the normal bituminous coating. Particular care must be taken in tightening the coupling bands firmly.

Test on Couplings

An 8-ft length of 24-in. diameter 14-gage asphalt-coated corrugated metal pipe with close-riveted circumferential seams was bulkheaded at each end. A coupling band 24 in. wide was substituted for the usual riveted circumferential seam. Six

TABLE 4-1 LEAKAGE TESTS ON ASPHALT-COATED CORRUGATED METAL PIPE AND COUPLING
24-in. Diam. Corrugated Metal Pipe

Pressure in Pounds per Square Inch	*Duration of Tests*		*Leaks*
	Hours and Minutes		
20	20	0	None
30	1	30	None
40		30	None
50		50	None
60	2	30	Negligible

These tests were made under ideal conditions and gave results higher than would be obtained in ordinary practice.

½-in. rods and cast shoes were used to draw this coupling tight (see Fig. 26). No leaks developed until the pressure reached 60 psi. The results are shown in Table 4-1.

Test on Hel-Cor Pipe

A 50-ft length of nominal 12-in. diameter 18-gage lock-seam Hel-Cor pipe was taken from regular production and subjected to an internal pressure test using water.[2] Steel closure plates with openings for water entry and air exit were welded to the ends of the pipe. The pipe was filled with water under pressure until all air was expelled from the pipe.

Yielding of the corrugations occurred at 90 psi gage pressure. This pressure corresponds to a "hoop stress" of 11,880 psi in the pipe barrel. At this point the depth of corrugation began to change noticeably. Bursting by unlocking of the seam occurred at 145 psi gage pressure.

Tests with Other Materials

Brief references are made to tests on pressures from air, gas, grain, minerals, etc., under various other chapters of this handbook.

REFERENCES

1. "Design Standards for Steel Water Pipe," by R. E. Barnard, Journal of AWWA, Vol. 40, No. 1, Jan., 1948, p. 34.
2. "Report of Hydrostatic Pressure Test on Armco Hel-Cor Pile Shell," by R. E. Barnard, Armco Drainage & Metal Products, Inc., Middletown, Ohio, Jan. 29, 1946.

CHAPTER FIVE

Corrugated Steel and Iron Sheets and Plates

Summary

Numerous physical tests have been made on metal sheets and plates, with various types of corrugated sections, such as are used in constructing culverts and bridges in the shape of pipe, arches and pipe-arches. Most recent of these was a series of tests by the Bridge Committee of the American Association of State Highway Officials at Michigan State College. These latter tests dealt with such factors as the effect of depth of corrugation, gage, and radius of plate curvature on plate performance, joint efficiency and bolt stresses. Other tests on corrugated metal sections have been for beam and column strength.

Types of Corrugations

It has long been recognized that corrugating a flat sheet of any flexible, non-shattering material adds greatly to its beam strength and column strength parallel to the corrugations. This is simply illustrated in Fig. 27.

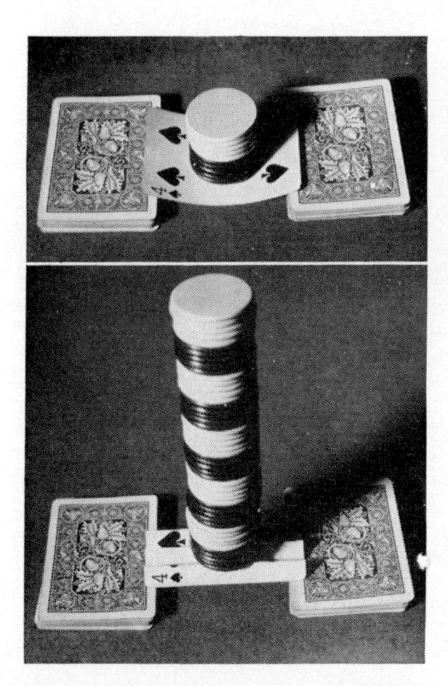

Fig. 27. Simple demonstration of how corrugations increase the supporting strength of a playing card.

Fig. 28. Helical type of corrugation with a continuous lock seam. Other types of corrugations are usually circumferential.

TABLE 5-1 DIMENSIONS AND PHYSICAL PROPERTIES OF STANDARD CORRUGATED SHEETS (Revised 1939)

Corrugation—½ inch x 2⅔ inches

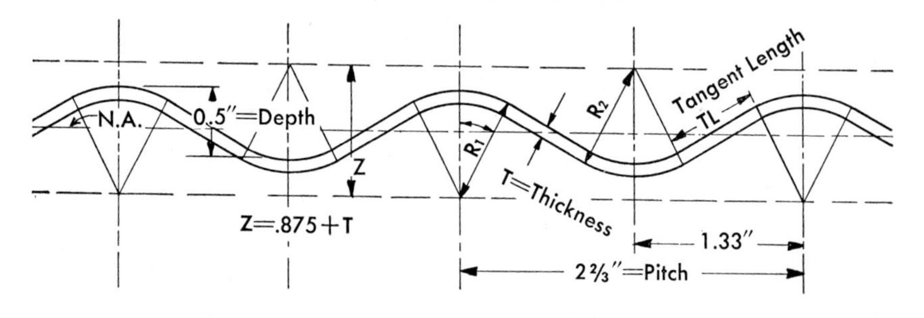

Gage	*Thickness T in Inches*	*Tangent Length in Inches*	*Angle △ in Degrees and Min*	*Moment of Inertia* I Inches⁴*	*Section Modulus* S Inches³*	*Radius of Gyration r Inches*
16	.0598	.77	26°–46′	.00200	.00711	.1775
14	.0747	.76	26°–52′	.00250	.00872	.1758
12	.1046	.74	27°–08′	.00350	.01153	.1758
10	.1345	.72	27°–23′	.00450	.01407	.1760
8	.1644	.70	27°–34′	.00550	.01650	.1760

*Per inch of horizontal projection about neutral axis.

There are many kinds of corrugations. One most commonly used for iron and steel sheets for more than half a century has an actual pitch of 2⅔-in.† from center to center of corrugation and a depth of ½ in. (see Table 5-1). The curved elements are connected by means of short tangents. This corrugation is widely used for culverts, in No. 8 through No. 16 gage and for roofing, siding, grain bins and other purposes, in gages up to No. 28.

Multi-Plate Corrugations

In 1931, Armco[1] introduced a larger corrugation for Multi-Plate—heavy structural plate structures—for large pipe and arches that are field assembled. This corrugation had a pitch of 6 in. and depth of 1½ in. For extreme loading conditions, Armco in 1939 came out with a "super Multi-Plate" corrugation (6 in. by 2 in.). These two corrugations were superseded in 1945 by an intermediate corrugation, 6 in. by 1¾ in. However, based on the Michigan tests on various size corrugations described on page 38, the 6-in. by 2-in. corrugation was adopted in 1951 and is now the standard of the American Association of State Highway Officials.[2]

†Sometimes erroneously called the 2½-in. corrugation.

Hel-Cor Corrugations

Most corrugations are parallel to the length of a sheet and usually circumferential or at right angles to the axis of a pipe or cylinder. One exception is in Armco Hel-Cor Pipe where the continuous lock seam and corrugations run helically (or spirally) around the pipe (see Fig. 28).

For diameters of pipe from 6 in. to 10 in., the pitch and depth are 1½ in. and ¼ in. respectively. For larger diameters, the pitch and depth are 2 in. and ½ in. respectively.

Other types and dimensions of corrugations are used for guard rail, sheet piling (or sheeting), tunnel liner plates, steel bridge plank and other purposes. These are illustrated in Fig. 29.

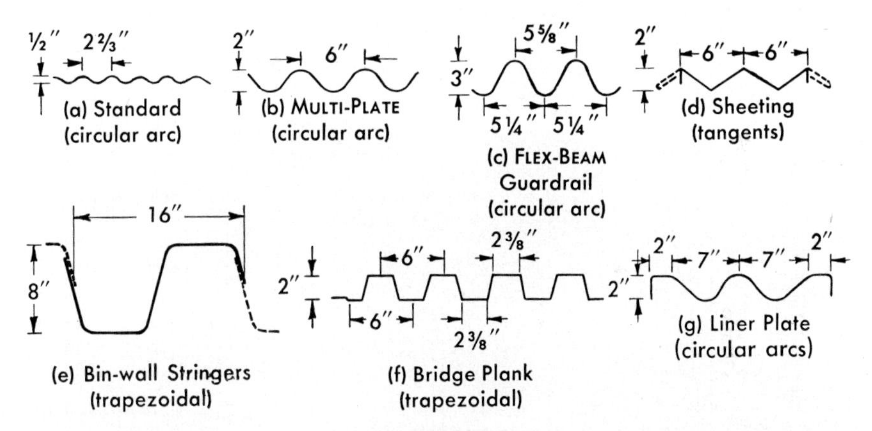

Fig. 29. Various types of corrugations commonly used for steel sheets and plates, and fabricated products.

TABLE 5-2 SECTION MODULI OF CORRUGATED STEEL PRODUCTS
Values in Inches Cubed Per Inch of Width

Product	*Gage*								
	16	*14*	*12*	*10*	*8*	*7*	*5*	*3*	*1*
Stand. Corr. ½″ x 2⅔″	.0071	.0087	.0115	.0141	.0165				
Multi-Plate 2″ x 6″			.0574	.0732	.0888	.0989	.1147	.1303	.1458
Liner Plate		.0341	.0478	.0608	.0736	.0797	.0918	.1035	
Sheeting—Flange Type			.0517	.0658	.0796	.0860	.0988	.1104	
Sheeting—Interlocking			.0545	.0702	.0857	.0929			
Flex-Beam Guardrail			.1054	.1262					
Bridge Plank			.098	.124		.162			
Flat Plate	.0006	.0009	.0018	.0030	.0045	.0054	.0073	.0095	.0121

Beam Tests on Curved Corrugated Plates

A series of tests was made at the University of Illinois' materials testing laboratory in 1936 under the direction of Professor Jamison Vawter,[3] to determine what effect corrugating and curving of ingot iron plates had upon their yield stress and apparent ultimate stress in bending; also to determine the effect of the thickness of the metal and radius of curvature on bending stresses.

Curved plates of three different radii and four different gages were tested. The corrugations had a pitch of 6 in. and a depth of 1½ in. The two sets of curves in Fig. 30, below, show the load-deflection for the No. 1 and 7-gage plates. The stress at the yield point (of the corrugated plate), or apparent elastic limit, as obtained from the curves, averages 46,300 lb per sq in., or 70½ per cent of the apparent modulus of rupture.

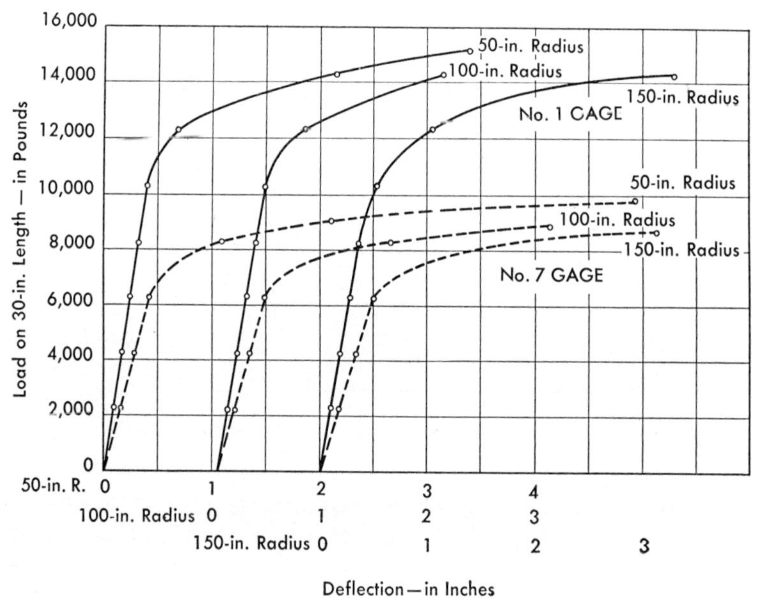

Fig. 30. Load-deflection curves for No. 1 and No. 7 gage Multi-Plate, by Vawter at University of Illinois.

A.A.S.H.O. Tests at East Lansing, Mich.

An investigation was carried on in 1950 at Michigan State College for the Bridge Committee of the American Association of State Highway Officials, in cooperation with the Bureau of Public Roads, Michigan State Highway Department, Armco Drainage & Metal Products, Inc., United Steel Fabricators, Inc. and Republic Steel Corporation.[2] Answers were sought to three questions:

1. Are cross-sectional area and section modulus sufficient information upon which to compute the strength of corrugated metal plates under axial and bending loads respectively?
2. Can the empirical formulas used for design of the old style 1½-in. corrugation be used for the design of 1¾-in. and 2-in. corrugation depths?

3. Do the methods of jointing the plates fully develop the strength of the metal in bending and thrust?

Part of the study was on the influence of the size and shape of corrugation on the plate deflections due to loads; also on the effect of metal thickness upon plate deflections. The five types of corrugations studied were:

	Shape	*Depth*	*Pitch*	*See Fig.*
Type A	Circular Arc and Tangent	1¾ in.	6 in.	31A
Type OA	Circular Arc and Tangent	1½	6	31B
Type R	Circular Arc and Tangent	2	6	31C
Type OR	Circular Arc and Tangent	1½	6	31D
Type U	Box Type (trapezoidal)	2	6	31E

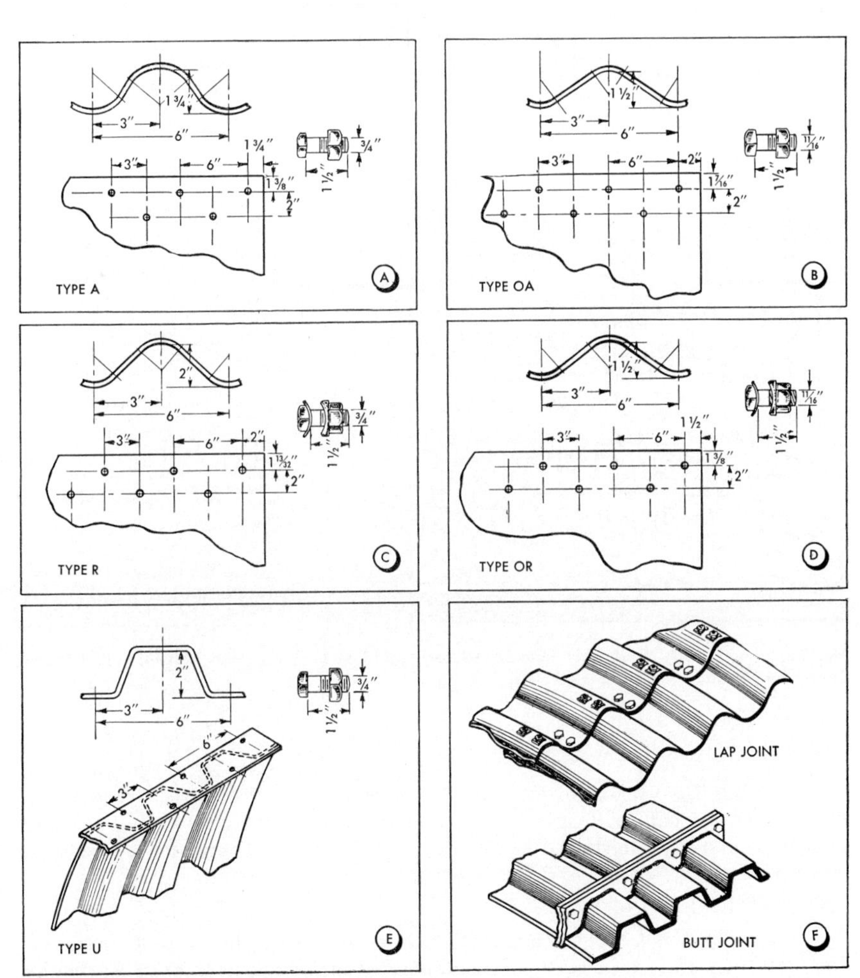

Fig. 31. Details of corrugations, plates, bolts and joints tested by the Michigan State Highway Dept. for the American Assn. of State Highway Officials.

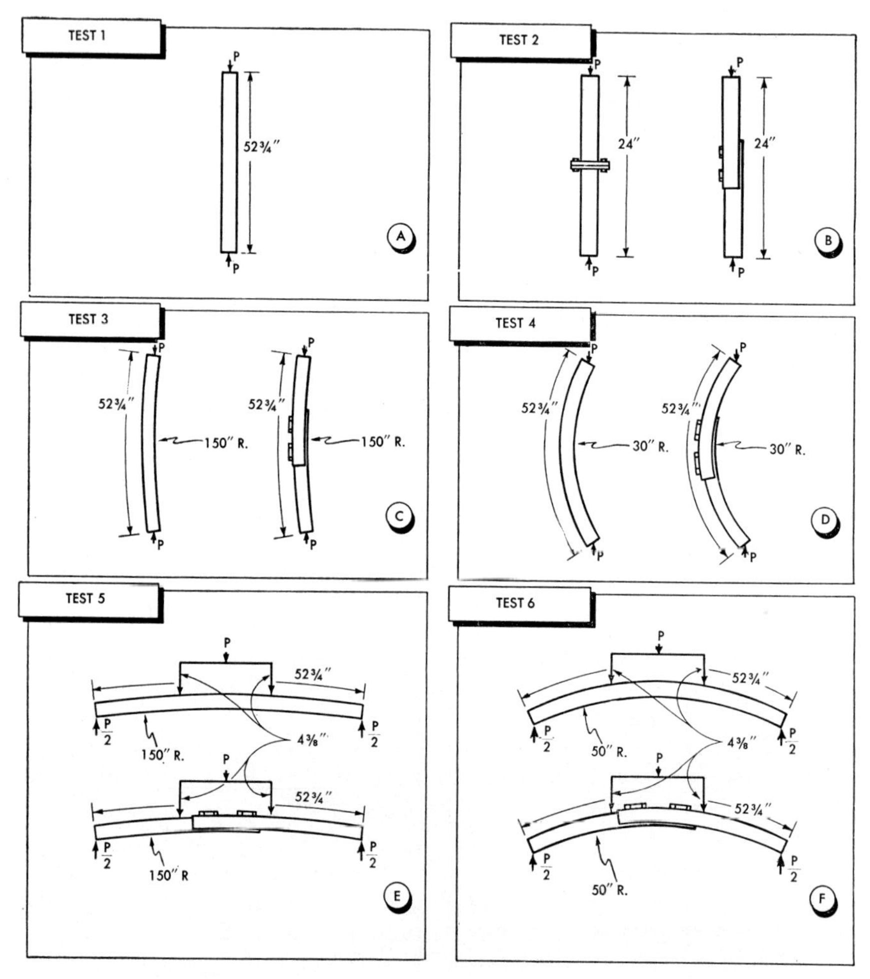

Fig. 32. The six tests on straight and curved corrugated sections with and without bolted seams. Tested by Michigan State Highway Dept.

The six fundamental tests are illustrated in Fig. 32.

1. *Straight Column Tests—Effect of Corrugation.* The effect of the style of corrugation on over-all load-carrying capacity, when the plates are acting as intermediate columns, is illustrated in Fig. 33. In all styles of corrugation tested there was a progressive spreading and consequent reduction of depth in the cross section of the plates at the center.

Thickness of Metal. As the metal thickness is increased, the over-all strength of the plates as columns increases. This illustrates the principle that as the section area increases, assuming constant radius of gyration, the load carrying capacity of the plates is also increased.

2. *Column Tests—Effectiveness of Seams.* In Test 2 the joints were subjected to vertical thrust and the criterion for evaluation was plate slippage. A typical failure is shown in Fig. 34.

3. *Curved Column Tests.* Tests 3 and 4 were made on plain and bolted specimens, both formed to 150-in. and 30-in. radii. In the bolted specimens of Test 4 on 6-in. pitch, 2-in. deep corrugations, the arc and tangent type corrugation was slightly superior to the trapezoidal type.

4. *Curved Beams.* Specimens in the Beam Tests 5 and 6 were the same as in Column Tests 3 and 4. These beam tests were for the purpose of measuring (1) resistance to load, (2) the rate of vertical and horizontal deformation of the plate, (3) the characteristics of the failed section and (4) the effectiveness of the joint while the plate was acting as a beam.

Results showed that there is a relationship between published section modulus

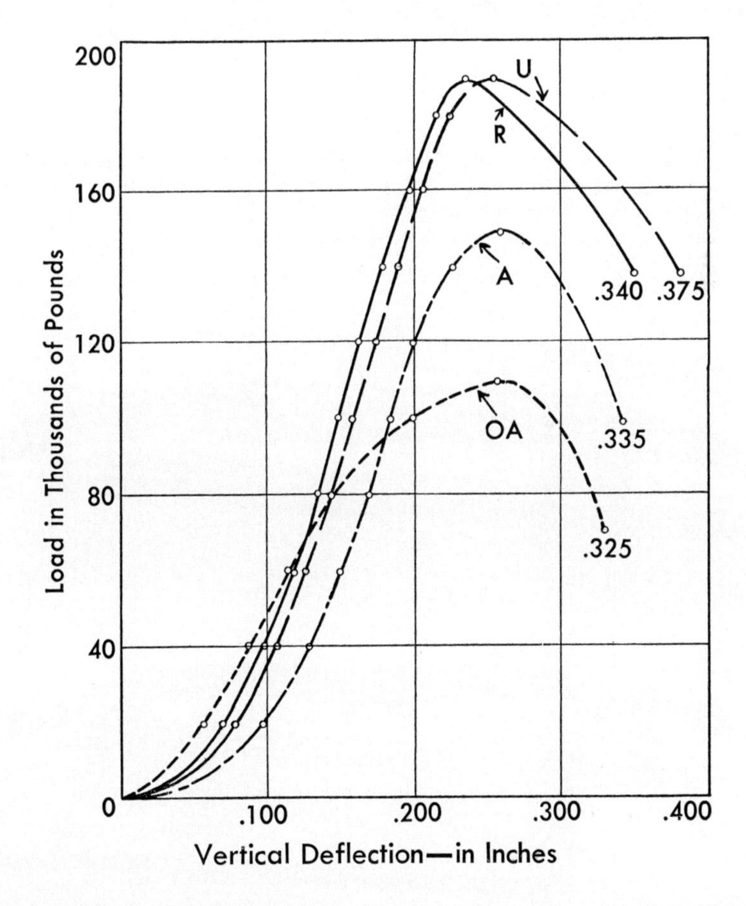

Fig. 33. Influence of corrugation on deflection of 7-gage plain columns in Test 1 by Mich. State Highway Dept. Depth of corrugations: OA = 1½ in., A = 1¾ in., R and U = 2 in.

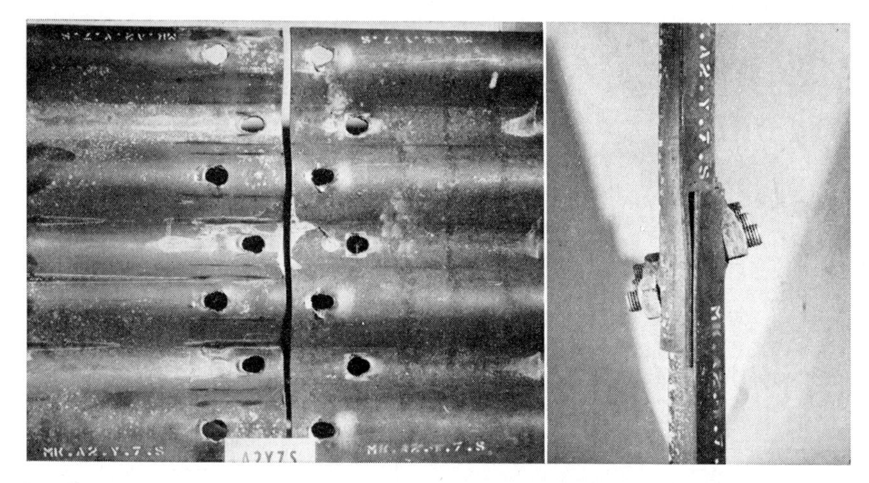

Fig. 34. Typical failure at seams of Type A corrugation.—Photos courtesy Mich. State Highway Dept. and Mich. State College.

and the load carrying capacity of the various corrugations. As the section modulus increases by changing the depth of the section (corrugation), the load carrying capacity increases at an even greater rate.

Typical failures of Corrugation Type A are shown in Fig. 35.

Conclusions. The principles in use by manufacturers for the design of the

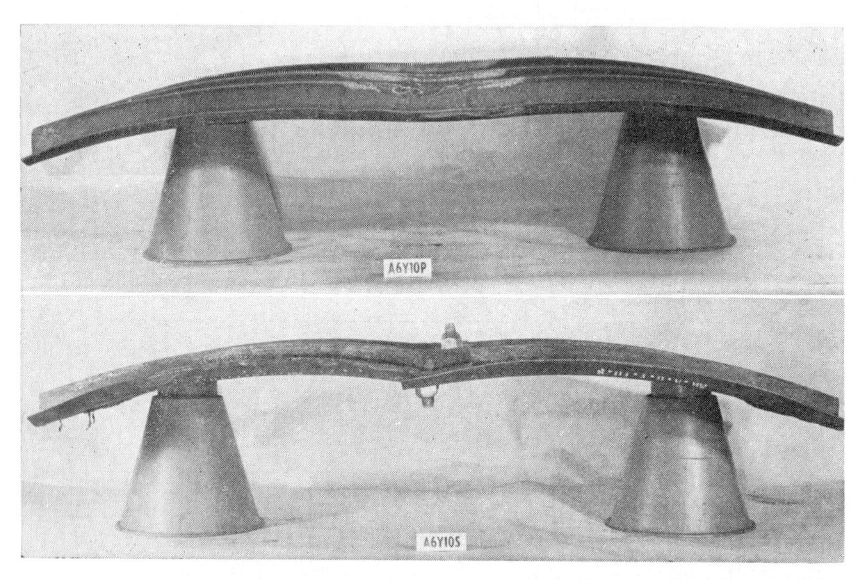

Fig. 35. Typical failures of plain and bolted corrugated plates, Type A, in Test 6.—Photos courtesy Mich. State Highway Dept. and Mich. State College.

Multi-Plate type structures are substantiated by the Michigan State College tests.[2] Two of the conclusions are very pertinent to the design of structures and because of their importance are quoted below verbatim:

Conclusion 1: "When using 1¾ and 2-in. circular arc type and 2-in. box type corrugations in the design of culverts, experience with the old type 1½-in. depth material may be used by assuming that corrugations having the same section modulus will give the same strength against bending."

Conclusion 6: "Plate curvature had little effect on magnitude of extreme fiber stress."

Impact Tests on Guardrail

The first field impact tests on guardrail were made by the Missouri State Highway Department in 1934. Tests included sections of corrugated steel plate guardrail known as Sheffield (now Armco) Flex-Beam Guardrail. Heavy passenger automobiles (4800 to 5100 lb) were aimed and sent by gravity down an inclined track to strike this and other kinds of guardrail or fence at an angle of about 20 degrees and at a speed of 32 to 35 miles an hour.

No strain gage readings were made, the results being interpreted broadly in determining which types of rail or fence served their purpose satisfactorily. "Under the conditions of these tests, the single element steel plate rails which were sufficiently strong to withstand the impact force applied were the most satisfactory. These rails prevented the cars from leaving the roadway, deflected them into a path parallel to the rail for a sufficient interval to give the driver some chance to regain control of the car, and decelerated the cars gradually enough that there was small probability of serious injury to the occupants. Furthermore, they did least damage to the car and seemed to be in more serviceable condition after one impact."[5]

Fig. 36. Racing car striking Flex-Beam guardrail is better than a simulated test. Flying "doughnut" is the left front tire.

Deflection Tests on Flex-Beam Corrugated Sections

Flex-Beam sections were tested in the Armco Research Laboratories by applying the load at the center and recording the deflection for each increment of load.[4] The results are shown in Fig. 37 and Table 5-3 for standard (12-gage) and heavy-duty (10-gage) sections.

Similar tests were made on Flex-Beam Guardrail sections by the California State Highway Commission with the results also shown in Fig. 37. The supports were 12 ft apart and the concentrated load applied at the center. Deflection read-

TABLE 5-3 LOAD, DEFLECTION AND PERMANENT SET ON FLEX-BEAM GUARDRAIL

Standard (12 Gage)			*Heavy Duty (10 Gage)*		
Load in Pounds	*Deflection in Inches*	*Set in Inches*	*Load in Pounds*	*Deflection in Inches*	*Set in Inches*
0	0	0	0	0	0
400	0.43		400	0.32	
0		0	0		0
800	0.87		800	0.65	
0		0.03	0		0.02
1200	1.34		1200	1.03	
0		0.06	0		0.04
1600	1.87		1600	1.40	
0		0.15	0		0.06
2000	2.50		2000	1.81	
0		0.30	0		0.12
2200	2.91		2400	2.27	
0		0.46	0		0.20
2400	3.46		2600	2.53	
0		0.73	0		0.25
2600	4.43		2800	2.80	
0		1.34	0		0.32
2700	Max.		3000	3.11	
0		2.32	0		0.42
			3200	3.53	
			0		0.60
			3400	4.07	
			0		0.88
			3600	5.31	
			0		1.77
			3655	Max.	
			0		2.37

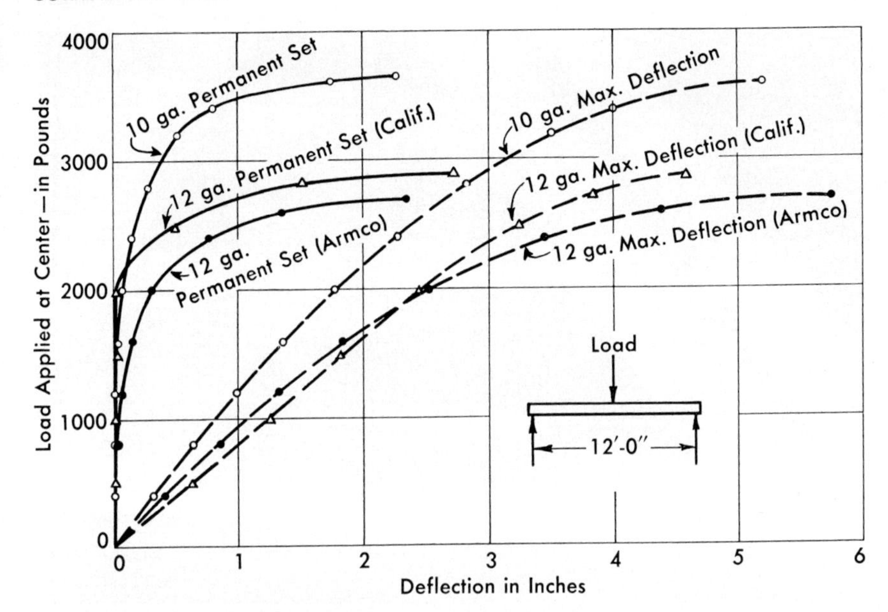

Fig. 37. Curves showing maximum and permanent deflection on 10 and 12 gage Flex-Beam guardrail by California Division of Highways and by Armco.

ings were taken at each 100 lb additional load. At each 500 lb the load was released and the permanent set was read. The first permanent set, 1⁄64-in. was at 1500 lb. At the maximum pressure of 2940 lb the permanent set was 2¾ in.

Other states have made deflection tests on beam type guardrails, with comparable results.

Steel Bridge Plank

Bridge flooring of corrugated steel has been in use in Ohio and other mid-western states since 1948. The first known installation consisted of Armco Flex-Beam Guardrail plates fillet welded at the sides and to the steel stringers, replacing a wood floor on a highway bridge. Asphalt was applied to fill the corrugations and give a smooth roadway surface.

Laboratory tests on two types of corrugated steel bridge flooring were made in 1951 at Wooster and Middletown, Ohio, jointly by United Steel Fabricators, Inc. and Armco Drainage & Metal Products, Inc.[6] The testing apparatus shown in Fig. 38 consisted of an A-frame with a yoke carrying an axle and single and dual wheels for applying highway loadings to corrugated steel bridge plank or flooring. This flooring was supported on steel stringers on 24, 36, 42 and 48-in. centers, and by steel floor beams on 12-ft centers. The tires rested on sand box surface 3 in. over the corrugations—and in supplementary tests, on an asphalt pavement. (Incidentally, a hot-mix bituminous pavement properly applied to a primed surface will not creep or crawl.)

Increasing loads to 36,000 lb were applied by a 60-ton hydraulic jack. Supplementary ultimate load tests were made with 12-in. I-beams cut 19 in. long in substitution for the rubber-tired wheels. These ultimate loading tests indicated safety

Fig. 38. Wheel load test on corrugated bridge plank section.

factors of 3 or 4, using conventional design stresses for two types of corrugations, considering various materials, gages and spans.

REFERENCES

1. Armco Drainage & Metal Products, Inc.
2. "Load Deflection Tests on Corrugated Metal Sections," Michigan State College Engineering Experiment Station Bulletin 109, E. Lansing, Mich. Summer, 1951, 62 pp.
3. Not published.
4. "Flex-Beam Guardrail and Bridge Rail," Manual, P.O. 5749, AD&MP, Inc., 1949, pp. 11–13.
5. "Tests of Various Highway Guardrails," Missouri Report 34-2, 1934.
6. "Bridge Deck, Flex-Beam Type—Loading Under Truck Tires," by H. L. White and D. S. Wolford, Armco Research Laboratories, March 13, 1952.

CHAPTER SIX

Riveted and Bolted Seams

Summary

Rivets and bolts are commonly used for shop and field assembly of corrugated metal pipe, arches and other structures. Riveted seams are highly efficient.

Acceptance of high-strength bolts as commonly used for the seams and joints of structural plate pipes during the past fifteen years, has in recent years spread to structural engineering in general.

Bolts of high tensile steel for field assembly of large plate structures easily withstand a recommended torque of 100 to 200 ft -lb. Impact wrenches are less suitable for liner plate than for Multi-Plate because of the likelihood of overstressing the smaller diameter bolts.

Bolted lap joints in the Michigan Tests were found to be 97 per cent as efficient

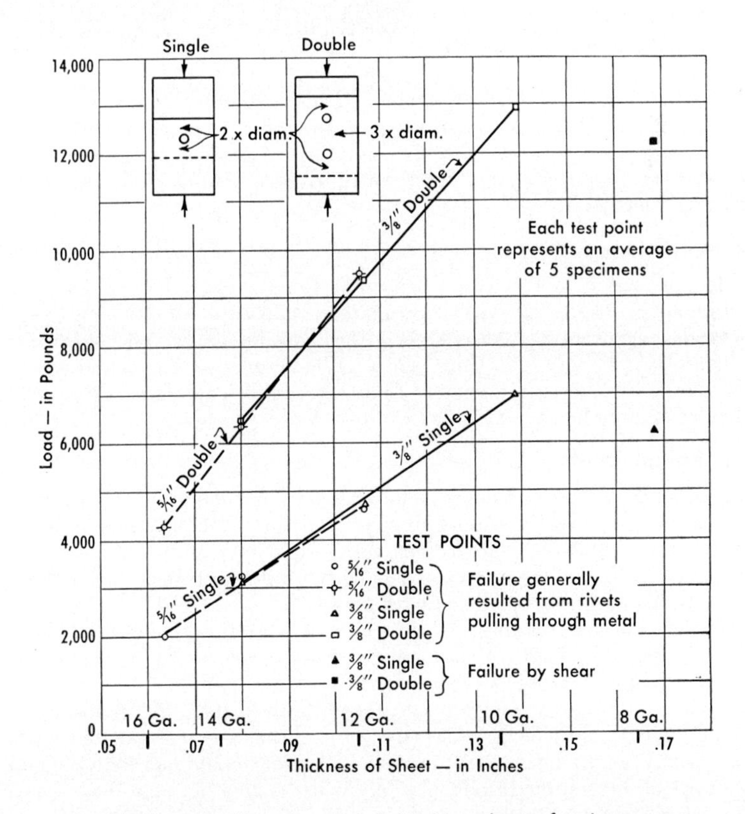

Fig. 39. Strength of ingot iron rivets in ingot iron sheets of various gages.

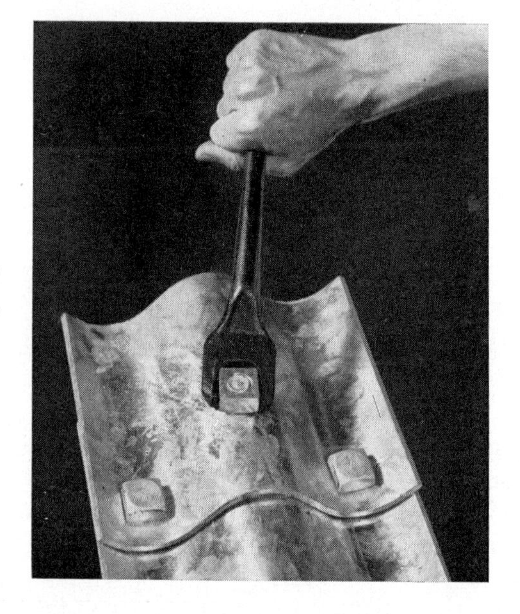

Fig. 40. Bolted joints have been quite successful in developing the full load transfer across joints in large culverts and tunnels.

as the plates of seamless sections. When standard steel bolts were used, the bolts were the limiting factor in the strength of the joint, whereas when heat treated bolts were used, the plates were the limiting factor. Seams with six and eight bolts per foot were found to have significantly greater load-carrying capacity than seams with four bolts.

Riveted Joints

Tests were made by Armco to determine the strength of riveted longitudinal seams in corrugated metal pipe. Corrugated iron sheets, 4 in. by 5 in., of 16, 14, 12, 10 and 8 gage were riveted together with single and double (one and two) rivets, and then tested to failure, in single shear. The double rows of 5⁄16 and 3⁄8-in. ingot iron rivets were placed 2 diameters from the edge of the sheet. Results of the seventy tests are shown in Fig. 39.

Use of Bolted Joints

The use of high tensile strength bolts for seams and joints in Multi-Plate structures has been eminently successful over a period of more than fifteen years. Fig. 40. These bolts have also been used satisfactorily in tunnel liner plate construction. Such bolts permit developing the full load transfer across the joints which is particularly important under high fills.

As evidence of the soundness of this practice, structural engineers have turned to the use of high-strength bolts in place of hot-driven rivets of carbon steel for fabricating permanent steel structures.[1]

"A bolted joint, like a riveted joint, resists the shear to which it is subjected by the friction between the connected parts, but, in the case of the bolted joints, this friction is due to the tension in the bolts." Wilson points out that the clamping force of a 1-in. high-strength bolt is about twice as great as that of a 1-in. carbon-steel rivet.

Bolt Tests for Torque Strength

Bolts used in Multi-Plate structures are ¾-in. in diameter and made of high tensile steel meeting a specification calling for 110,000 to 120,000 lb per sq in., minimum.*

When nuts are tightened on bolts, the bolt is subject to torque and tension. Overtightening either twists the bolt in two or strips the threads. In Michigan Test[2] No. 5, sets of corrugated plates were fastened together with ¾-in. bolts from various manufacturers. These were tightened with a torque wrench until failure occurred. The high tensile bolts withstood about 700 ft-lb torque. Torque used in the main series of tests was 200 ft-lb or well within the working limits of the bolt strength. Torque ordinarily recommended for bolted installations is 100 to 200 ft-lb.

Tests on Tightening Bolts With Impact Wrenches

A study was made to determine the amount of torque that can be applied to bolted joints with a pneumatic impact wrench without damaging the bolts, and how long to hold the wrench to the bolts.[3] These tests were made on ⅝-in. black and galvanized bolts (ASTM: A307) such as are used for the lighter gage tunnel liner plates (14 through 7 gage), and on ¾-in. galvanized high tensile Multi-Plate bolts (ASTM: A325). The position of the bolts and nuts was varied from crest to valley of corrugation and in the flanges.

As a result of the tests, the desirable minimum and maximum torque for the ⅝-in. bolt (ASTM: A307) was established at 50 and 100 ft-lb respectively. For the ¾-in. Multi-Plate bolts, a maximum of 300 ft-lb of torque was found as allowable. The hold-on period varies from 2 to 5 seconds. However, impact wrenches are not altogether suitable for liner plate installations because the flanges interfere with operation of the wrench on more than half of the bolts, and also because of the likelihood of overstressing the smaller diameter bolts. On the other hand, impact wrenches are suitable for Multi-Plate.

Bolted Longitudinal Multi-Plate Seams or Joints

Longitudinal joints of Multi-Plate structures are bolted together as shown in Fig. 1, page 5 and Fig. 2, page 8 of the Michigan Tests. See pages 39 and 40. The plates are lapped and the bolts are staggered in two rows with one bolt in each valley and each crest, or four bolts per foot of seam. (For extreme loading conditions, six or eight bolts per foot of seam are used to develop the full strength of the plates.) The seams in these tests were all tightened to a measured bolt torque of 200 ft-lb per bolt.

In Tests 2 through 6, the "efficiency" of the lap joints was measured in comparison with the seamless sections. It was found that for ultimate loads the joints were 97 per cent as efficient as the plates.

Additional Armco Tests[4] were made to determine the shear strength of Multi-Plate seams using compression loading on the plates. In these tests six bolts were used per foot of seam in comparison with earlier tests using four and eight bolts per foot of seam. Short plates of 1, 3, 5, 7 and 10 gage from two different Armco plants were used for the tests. Standard ¾-in. machine bolts and ¾-in. high tensile bolts (ASTM: A325) were used.

---

*High strength bolts meet ASTM Specification A325-49T and, if galvanized, meet ASTM Specification A153-49.

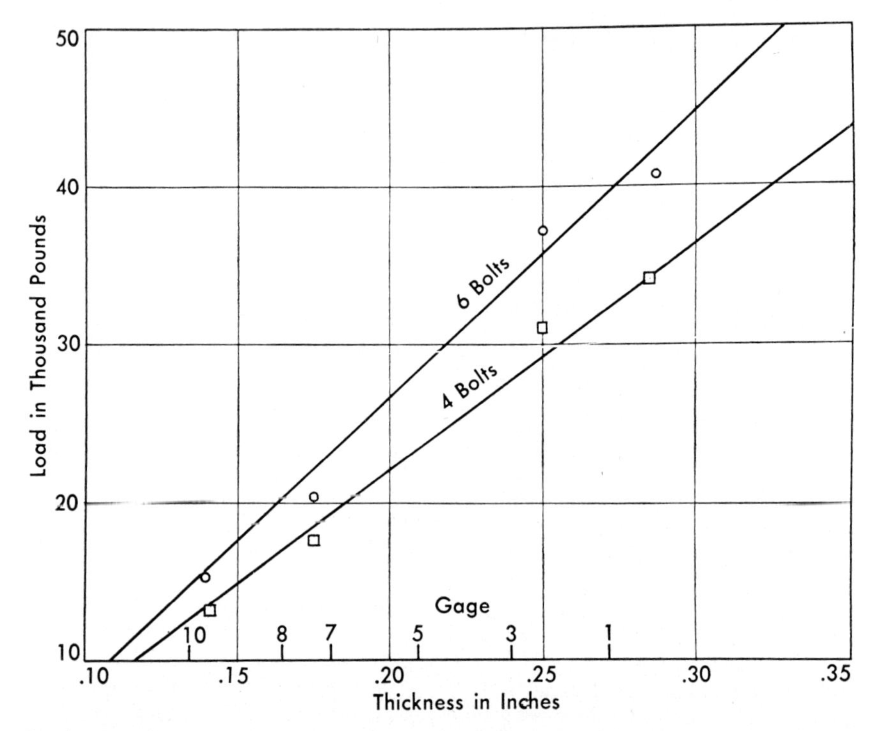

Fig. 41. Load-carrying capacity of Multi-Plate 4 and 6-bolt seams with safety factor of 4, using high tensile bolts.

Results with the heat treated bolts in Middletown plates are shown in Fig. 41. For the gages tested, the results indicated that in the tests with standard machine bolts, the bolts are the limiting factor in the strength of the joint, whereas in the tests made using high tensile bolts the plates are the limiting factor.

The load-carrying capacity of seams with six and eight high tensile bolts per foot was approximately equal, but had a significantly greater load-carrying capacity than seams with four bolts per foot.

Although laboratory test results give the same total load carrying capacity for seams of six and eight bolts per foot, the use of eight bolts per foot of seam is believed to give a somewhat better safety factor under field conditions.

In general there are three types of bolted joint failure associated with these tests:

1. Bolt shear-tension failure—in which the bolt fails due to a combination of shear and tensile forces. See Fig. 42.
2. Plate bearing failure—in which yielding failure occurs near the bolt holes, depending on the properties of the material.
3. Column failure of the plates.

In these tests the strength of the four-bolt joint was limited by either shear-tension bolt failure or local yielding at the bolt holes.

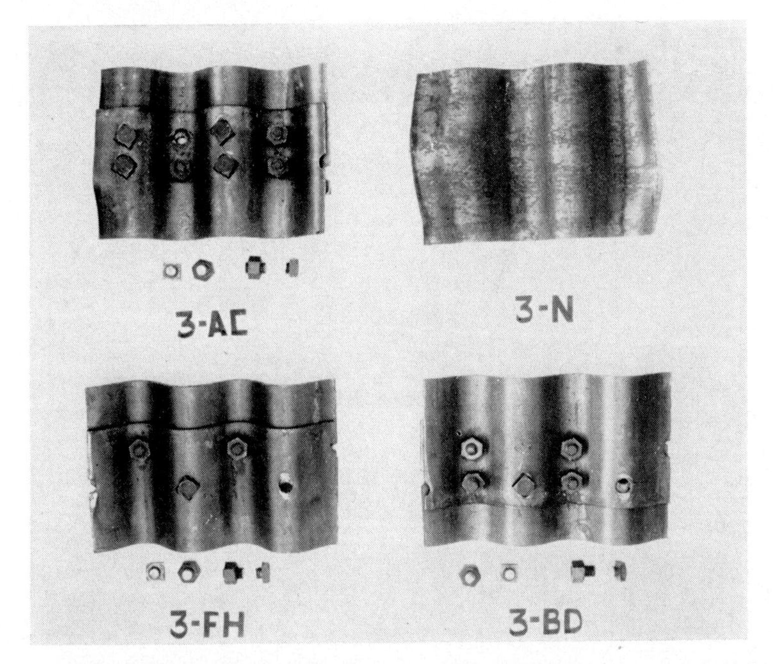

Fig. 42. Tests on joints with no bolts (3-N), four bolts (3-FH), six bolts (3-BD) and eight bolts (3-AC) per foot of seam. Typical shear-tension failure.

Tests on Liner Plate Joints

Tests were made by Prof. W. S. Housel at the University of Michigan,[5] to determine the joint strength of Armco tunnel liner plates. The joints were of standard offset construction with five ⅝-in. diam. mild steel bolts (ASTM: A307). Test results are shown in the lower portion of Fig. 43.

Shear tests were made by Armco on the heavier gages of Armco liner plate, 7, 5 and 3 gage, to determine the strength of the joints with ⅝-in. diameter high tensile bolts (ASTM: A325).[6] The joints for the 3 and 5-gage plates failed by shearing the bolts (see upper portion of Fig. 43). The 7-gage plates failed in bearing before the bolts failed, at the same load as in the test by Housel.

Tests on Offset vs No Offset Joint on Liner Plate

The longitudinal (short) seams on Armco liner plates are fabricated with an offset as shown in cross section, Fig. 45. Comparative compression tests on short lengths were made[7] on lap joints with and without an offset, of 12, 7 and 3-gage plates, with ⅝-in. bolts. Results are shown in Fig. 44. Joint strength increases from 25 per cent for 12 gage to approximately 85 per cent for 3 gage, due to offsetting.

Tension and Compression Tests on Liner Plate Joints for Bins

Tests were made on tunnel liner plates to determine joint strength in tension and in compression transversely to the corrugations.[8] These tests aided in the design of liner plate structures used as *storage bins* (for aggregates, coal, grain).

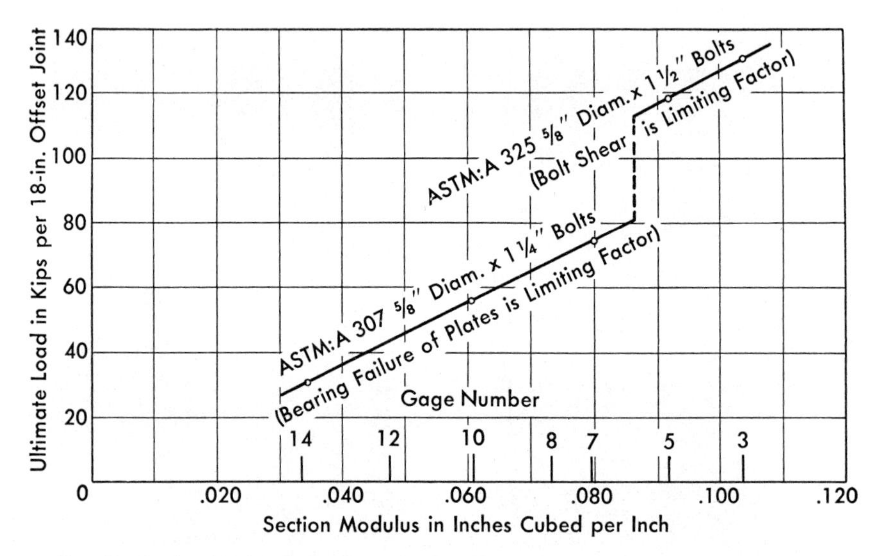

Fig. 43. Results of test on liner plate with offset joint, using ordinary and high tensile bolts.

Arrangement of the plates in the tension test is shown in Fig. 46, using first two plates and then adding side plates. Gages tested were 12, 7 and 3. Bolts used in most of the tests were 5/8-in. diam. tightened with a torque wrench to between 90 and 100 ft-lb.

With the use of side plates (six bolts in addition to the five in the lap joint) the increase in load was about 85 per cent for 12 gage plates, 65 per cent for 7 gage and 45 per cent for 3 gage.

Second part of the tests consisted of loading the plates in compression transversely

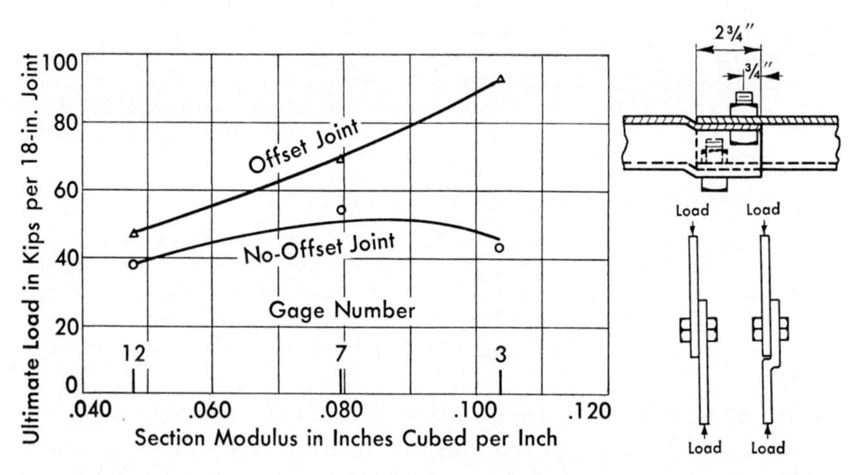

Fig. 44. Test showing comparison of liner plate joint with and without offset, using mild steel bolts. Detail at right bottom shows these joints.

Fig. 45. Detail of liner plate offset joint, at top.

to the corrugations as shown in Fig. 1 (of report). Results of both series of tests are shown in Table 6-1. An increase in plate thickness from 12 to 7 gage (60 per cent increase) gave an increase of about 50 per cent in the load carried by the straight joint, but further increase in gage resulted in a different type of failure and very little more joint strength.

The maximum loads obtained on the compression tests transverse to the corrugations were somewhat erratic due to difficulty of obtaining axial loading. The strength of the section in this direction is materially affected by an increase in gage.

Fig. 46. Tension test on liner plate joint with bolted longitudinal seams.

TABLE 6-1 RESULTS OF TRANSVERSE-COMPRESSION AND TENSION TESTS ON TUNNEL LINER PLATE JOINTS

Gage	*Maximum Load, in Pounds per Joint*			*Type of Failure*
	Transverse Compression Tests	*Tension Tests*		
		Straight Joint	*Reinforced Joint*	
12	4,140 4,075	27,700	52,000	Pulled out square holes in plate
12	4,040 3,905	30,350	55,400	Pulled out square holes in plate
7	8,250 8,850	44,750	74,000	Pulled out square holes in plate
7	8,300 8,500	43,900	72,400	Pulled out square holes in plate
3	23,000 23,150	47,000	64,000*	Sheared bolts
3	22,000 19,750	44,600	69,600*	Sheared bolts
3		76,200		(High tensile bolts used)

*Lap-joint bolts sheared first. Next, with sidebolts only, bolts sheared at 53,200 lb and 54,800 lb respectively.

Mild steel bolts except on last test.

Tension Tests on Flex-Beam Joints

All splices of Flex-Beam Guardrail are made with seven heat treated high tensile bolts of ⅝-in. diameter. Tension tests on a number of joints were made with the results as given in Table 6-2.[9]

TABLE 6-2 TENSION TESTS ON FLEX-BEAM JOINTS

Test No.	*Gage*	*Load in Pounds*	*Average Load in Pounds*
1	12	59,700	
2	12	72,400	
3	12	73,800	
4	12	63,300	63,310
5	12	60,200	
6	12	60,000	
7	12	53,800	
8	10	99,200	
9	10	88,700	
10	10	78,600	88,980
11	10	86,300	
12	10	89,300	
13	10	91,800	

Nestable Pipe Seams

Compression tests on the notched seams of nestable corrugated pipe give an efficiency of 91.5 per cent as compared with the riveted seams of corrugated metal pipe. Tests were on 10 gage to 16 gage pipe in diameters up to 30 in.

REFERENCES

1. "High-Strength Bolts as a Means of Fabricating Steel Structures," by W. M. Wilson, Univ. of Illinois, 1950 Proceedings of Highway Research Board, Wash., D. C., p. 136.
2. "Load Deflection Tests on Corrugated Metal Sections," Mich. State College Engineering Experiment Station Bulletin 109, E. Lansing, Mich., 1951.
3. "Bolt Tests—Manually Tightened vs Tightened with Pneumatic Impact Wrenches." Report by Armco Drainage & Metal Products, Inc., Middletown, Ohio, May 23, 1949.
4. "Testing of Multi-Plate Seam Strength." Report by Armco Research Laboratories, Middletown, Ohio, Nov. 19, 1951.
5. "Tests to Determine Modulus of Rupture and Joint Strength of Armco Tunnel Liner," by Prof. W. S. Housel, Univ. of Michigan, Sept. 23, 1941.
6. "Shear Tests on Armco Liner Plate Joints." Report by Armco Research Laboratories, Middletown, Ohio, June 28, 1950.
7. "Liner Plate Longitudinal Joint Test to Show Value of Offset." Report by Armco Research Laboratories, June, 1949.
8. "Joint Tests on Liner Plate." Report by Armco Research Laboratories, Middletown, Ohio, S.I. 50-16, Mar. 6, 1950.
9. "Flex-Beam Guardrail, Bridge Rail." Manual P. O. 5749, AD&MP, Inc., Middletown, Ohio, 1949. 16 pp.

CHAPTER SEVEN

Pipe, Arches and Pipe-Arches

Summary

The best strength test of a structure is under the actual conditions in which it is to serve. However, field and laboratory testing and analyses are helpful in developing a rational design procedure and in avoiding wasteful overdesign.

Chapters 1 to 4 have dealt with field loading of conduits and measurements of pressures, strains, deflections and bending moments. Chapters 5 and 6 have dealt with laboratory tests on the component parts of fabricated metal structures such as sheets, plates, corrugations, rivets, bolts, seams, etc.

The purpose of this chapter is to describe laboratory tests for determining the physical properties of metal structures, the typical pathway to failure, and methods for arriving at a rational design formula.

A flexible metal structure owes only a small portion of its resistance to failure to its own inherent strength, but as an underground conduit it owes much of its strength to the lateral pressure of the earth. It is possible to analyze the structure itself, which follows the thin-ring elastic theory. However, earth pressures are so variable under conditions of conduit flexure that rational design formulas still contain doubtful elements.

PART ONE

LABORATORY DEFLECTION TESTS

Flexible Pipe Under Load

How is a comparatively thin-walled metal conduit, such as a culvert, able to stand up under tremendously high fills without failing, when by comparison a rigid conduit of brittle material needs to have a very thick wall? The answer is that a flexible structure is able to give or deflect under the load and thereby relieve itself of a large part of that load, whereas a rigid structure is subject to a greater load. This was described in Marston's Theory of Loads in Chapter 1.

A flexible metal conduit therefore reacts differently under load than does a rigid conduit. It relies only partly on its "inherent" strength or stiffness to resist external loads. In deflecting under load, it "bulges" at the sides, compresses the soil, and thereby builds up passive resistance. This in turn helps support the vertically-applied load.

Spangler says[1] "Since so much of the total supporting strength (of a flexible pipe) depends upon the sidefill material, any attempt to analyze the structural behavior of this type of culvert pipe under a fill must consider the earth at the sides to be an integral part of the structure."

It is necessary to test a pipe to failure in order to properly analyze it. A flexible pipe, if sufficiently loaded with earth, usually proceeds to failure not by shearing of the rivets or bolts in the longitudinal seams or by tearing of the metal at the seams, but by deflecting until it collapses. The stages of deflection of a flexible pipe are shown in the accompanying drawing, Fig. 47. "The whole action is one of deflection change unaccompanied by rupture or buckling of the metal ring, although the material in certain parts of the ring may be stressed well beyond its

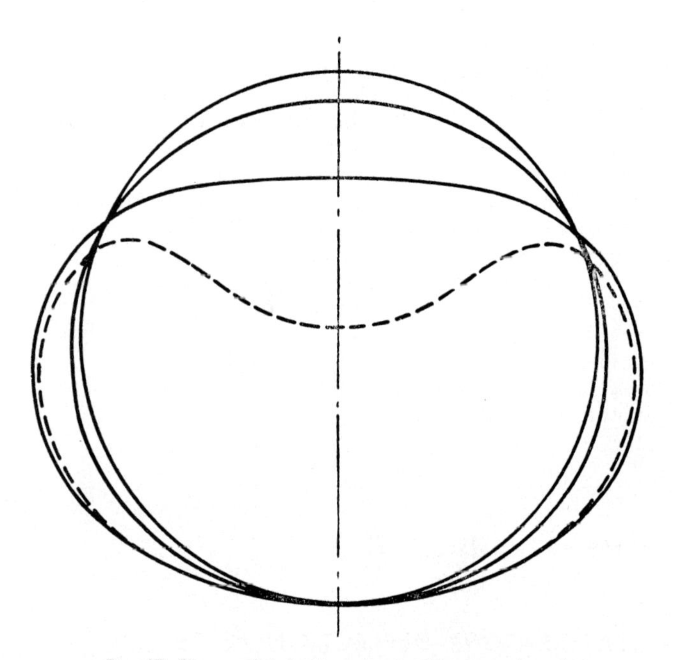

Fig. 47. Stages of deflection of a flexible pipe. (Iowa)

elastic limit. Therefore, any attempt to rationalize the structural design of flexible-pipe culverts should be directed toward the development of a method for predetermining the deflection of the pipe under specified conditions of installation."

Spangler Tests at Iowa State College

Spangler made extensive tests on the structural performance of flexible pipes under earth embankments and in the laboratory toward developing a rational theory of design.[1] This project was made in cooperation with the U. S. Bureau of Public Roads.

One phase of the experimental work included a series of laboratory load tests on nine rings of standard riveted corrugated pipe and one bolted Multi-Plate pipe ring. Specimens included:

One 24-in. 14 gage (1 riveted seam)
Two 36-in. 16 gage (1 riveted seam)

Two 42-in. 14 gage (1 riveted seam)
Two 48-in. 14 gage (2 riveted seams)
Two 60-in. 12 gage (2 riveted seams)
One 120-in. 1 gage (8 bolted seams)

Tests consisted of measuring the deflection and the strain (at top inside or bottom inside) under two-edge and three-edge loads. These tests helped establish the validity of the "thin-ring elastic theory of flexure,"[2] even where the deflection and change in radius is relatively large. Quoting Spangler, "Therefore, if the loads and pressures acting on a flexible pipe are known (or can be assumed confidently), the deflection of the pipe can be determined by this theory within the elastic limit of the material."[1]

However, one important point recognized by G. E. Shafer[3] and his Armco associates is that "flexible pipes do not fail as soon as the metal is stressed beyond the elastic limit, but continue to function structurally until the deflection results in a change in shape to the extent of reversing the curvature in the top or bottom of the structure. If one agrees . . . that structural failure of corrugated metal structures is due to excessive deflection, the problem then is to determine a method of predicting deflection."

Tests have been made by Armco on Multi-Plate pipe with the diameter restrained at approximately the quarter points by means of adjustable steel rods. The purpose is to simulate the restraints afforded by shop struts and other field conditions under load. Results to date have shown little correlation to field measurements.

Bending Moment Within Elastic Range

Early tests were made on concrete and cast iron pipe by Prof. A. N. Talbot at the University of Illinois in 1908. The report on the test[4] includes a complete mathematical analysis of these rigid pipes under different loading conditions.

This mathematical analysis developed the rational equations for bending moment, fiber stress and deflection for a concentrated vertical load, uniform vertical load, and a uniform vertical and horizontal load. Fig. 48 shows these three types of loading as Case (a), (b) and (c) respectively.

Bending moment alone is given here for the reason that it is the direct cause of failure in the rigid type culvert. The equation for bending moments and numerical examples for each of the three cases are given as follows:

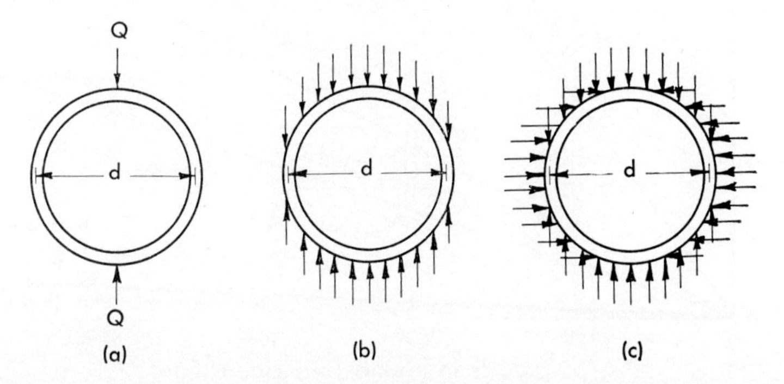

Fig. 48. Three types of loading: (a) concentrated vertical, (b) distributed vertical and (c) distributed horizontal and vertical load.

For a concentrated vertical load, Case (a), the maximum bending moment, at the crown, is

$$M = .159Qd$$

where Q is the total concentrated load per unit length of pipe in pounds, and d the neutral diameter of the pipe in inches. For a numerical example, assume a load of 2000 lb per ft of length concentrated at the crown of a 42-in. neutral diameter pipe. The bending moment at the crown is 13,356 in.-lb.

For a uniformly distributed vertical load, Case (b), the maximum bending moment, at the crown, is

$$M = \tfrac{1}{16}Wd$$

where W is the total load per unit length of pipe in pounds. Assuming the same load and pipe as in the example under Case (a), the bending moment in this case is 5,250 in.-lb.

For a uniformly distributed vertical and horizontal load, Case (c), the bending moment is

$$M = \tfrac{1}{16}(1-q)Wd$$

where q is the ratio of the horizontal to the vertical intensity of pressure. Assuming a q of .37, the maximum bending moment for the same pipe and load as above is at the crown and is equal to 3,308 in.-lb.

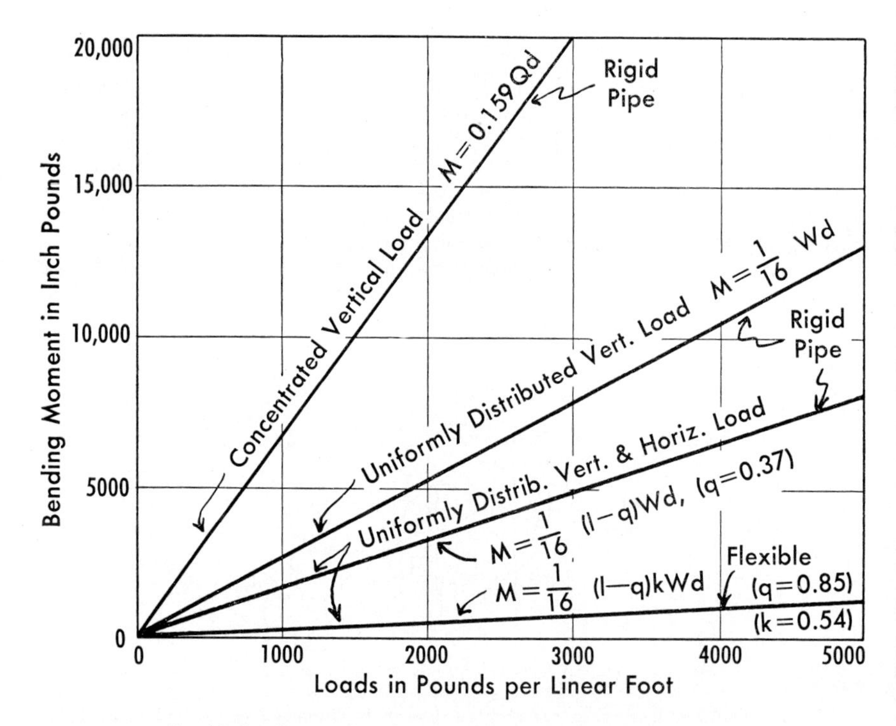

Fig. 49. Bending moments for various loads on 42-in. diameter pipe.

It is seen that the above bending moments, 13,356, 5,250 and 3,308 in.-lb, respectively, have decreased in amount as the load on the pipe has become more evenly distributed around the periphery of the pipe. The bending moment continues to decrease with greater distribution until the equivalent of hydrostatic pressure is established. In this case the pressure at any point on the periphery of the pipe is equal to that at any other point, and the bending moment is zero.

The upper three curves in Fig. 49 show graphically the amount of the bending moments for different loads according to the three formulas above. The fourth curve relates to the tests of the American Railway Engineering Association described on page 12.

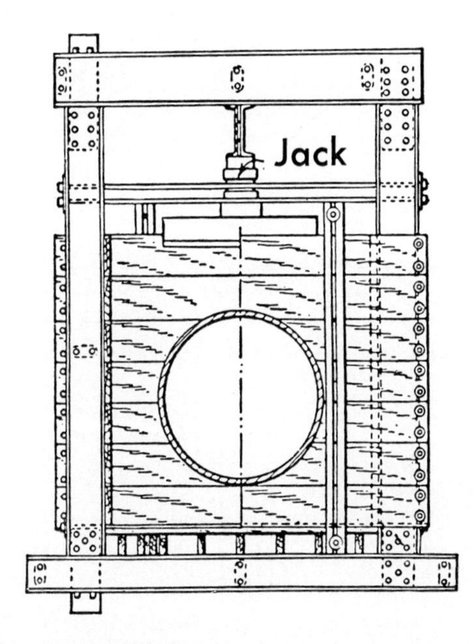

Fig. 50. Sandbox used in testing strength of corrugated metal pipe, 1909. (Talbot)

Crushing Test on Pipe by Talbot

In 1909, Talbot conducted a sandbox test to determine the crushing strength of a 36-in. diameter standard corrugated metal pipe, 8 ft long (see Fig. 50). The total load carried was 184,000 lb or 92 tons. Despite this tremendous load, the report reads, "The pipe was still in good condition, and there was no fracture in the metal."

Crushing Test by Fowler

Seven years later, in 1916, another important investigation on corrugated pipe was made by George L. Fowler, consulting engineer in New York City. One purpose was to establish the collapsing pressure of corrugated metal pipe under external hydrostatic loading; another purpose was to find, if possible, the crushing strength of the pipe in a sandbox test.

Briefly, the results showed that the corrugated metal pipe was capable of withstanding enormous pressures approximately three to fifty times the measured in-

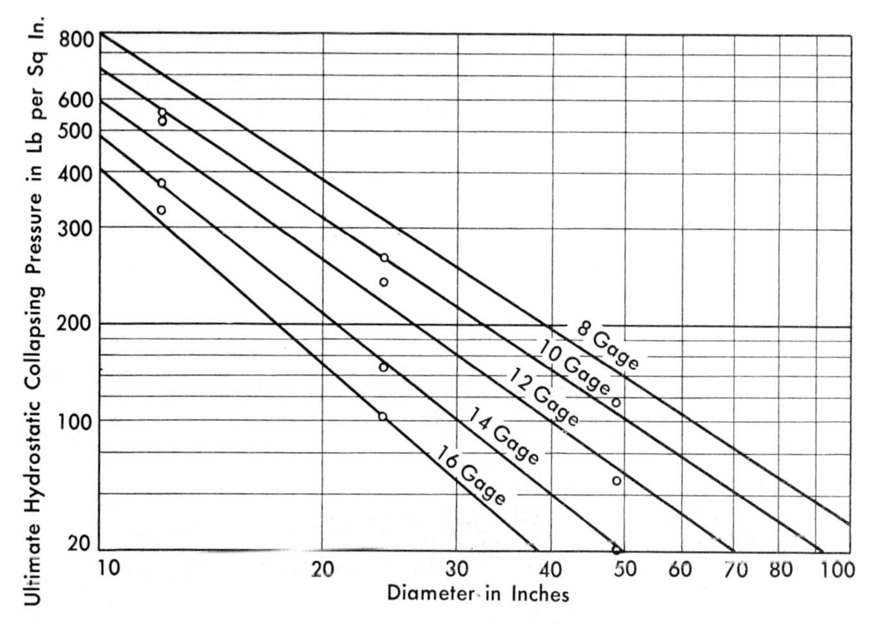

Fig. 51. External hydrostatic collapsing strength of corrugated metal pipe based on Fowler tests. Based on 12, 24 and 48-in. diameters.

tensities of pressures on the corrugated pipe beneath the 35-ft railroad fill in the AREA strength tests. See Fig. 51.

These test specimens differed from an actual culvert installation in that they were only 8 ft long and the ends were confined. Also, the ultimate collapsing strength was the consideration.

PART TWO

BEAM TESTS

Riveted Corrugated Pipe

In designing pipe lines to be supported on piers, saddles or other supports, it is necessary to know the weight of the material to be carried as well as the gage and weight of the pipe; also the permissible deflection. Beam tests on corrugated metal pipe were made at Ohio State University. Results are interpreted and given in the chapter on Design, page 144.

Helical Corrugated Pipe

Tests were made by Armco[5] on 10-ft lengths of 6 and 8-in. diameter helical corrugated pipe; also on 8-in. standard riveted corrugated pipe for comparison purposes. In the tests the supports were 114 in. apart with the load at the one-third points (see Fig. 52).

The loads carried by the pipe with deflection ranging from 1½ to 3 in. are shown in Table 7-1.

The beam strength of helical pipe of equal size and gage is greater than that of standard corrugated metal pipe because of the shallower corrugations and because of the diagonal direction of the corrugations in the helical pipe.

Fig. 52. Method of testing helically corrugated metal pipe as a beam with third-point loading.

TABLE 7-1 BEAM LOADING ON CORRUGATED METAL PIPE

Kind of Corrugation	*Diam. in Inches*	*Ga.*	*Total Load on 10 Ft of Pipe—in Lb*					
			Sag or Deflection in Inches					
			½	*1*	*1½*	*2*	*2½*	*3*
Helical.....	6	18	394	662	892	1060	1158	1278
Helical.....	6	16	472	876	1236	1514	1720	1876
Helical.....	8	18	460	806	1090	1310	1454	1562
Helical.....	8	16	860	1560	1970	2240	2410	2510
Standard...	8	16	496	846	1220	1446	1626	1766

PART THREE

COLUMN TESTS

TESTS were conducted on riveted corrugated pipe at the University of North Carolina in 1927 and the following was determined:

1. Proper size and spacing of circumferential rivets in corrugated metal pipe used as columns.
2. Supporting strength of corrugated pipe for bridge piers and caissons and for columns in general construction.
3. Maximum pressure that can safely be exerted on the end of corrugated pipe in jacking it through an embankment without buckling the corrugations.

Further tests were made at the University of Illinois in 1936. The results of these and the earlier tests are shown in Fig. 53.

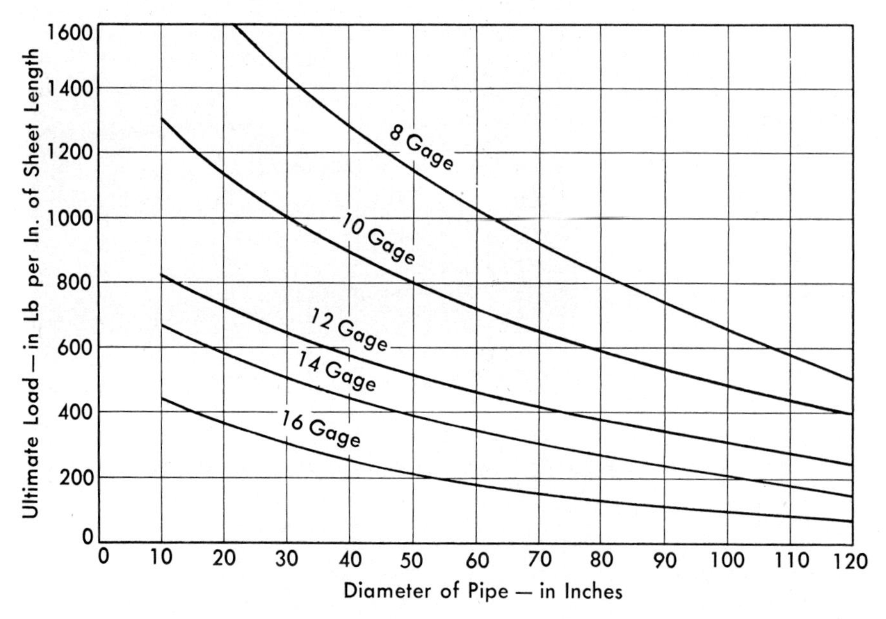

Fig. 53. Column strength of standard corrugated metal pipe—ultimate unit compressive strength of short columns as determined at University of Illinois.

TABLE 7-2 END COMPRESSION TEST ON CORRUGATED METAL PIPE

Kind of Corrugation	*Diam. in Inches*	*Gage*	*Average Max. Load in Lb*
Helical.	6	18	9,325
Helical.	6	16	10,312
Helical.	8	18	9,133
Helical.	8	16	14,875
Standard.	8	16	10,690

Helical Corrugated Pipe

End compression tests were made on 10-ft lengths of 6 and 8-in. helical lock-seam corrugated metal pipe. The results, including 8-in. standard riveted corrugated pipe, are shown in Table 7-2. The diagonal corrugations give greater strength than do the circumferential corrugations.[5]

REFERENCES

1. "The Structural Design of Flexible Pipe Culverts," by M. G. Spangler, Iowa State College, Bulletin 153, 1941, p. 9.
2. "Stresses and Deflections in Circular Rings Under Various Conditions of Loading," by Claude W. L. Filkins and Edwin J. Fort, Trans. Assn. of Civil Engineers of Cornell Univ. 4: 99–112, June 1896.
3. Chief Engineer, Armco Drainage & Metal Products, Inc., in his discussion of "Underground Conduits—an Appraisal of Modern Research," by M. G. Spangler. Trans. ASCE, Vol. 113, 1948, p. 355.
4. University of Illinois, Engineering Experiment Station Bulletin No. 22.
5. "Tests on the Physical Properties of Helical Corrugated Metal Pipe," Report by Armco Culvert Mfrs. Assn., May 1935.

Fig. 53A. An early high fill job. Seventy-two in. Multi-Plate under 74 feet of fill on the Miami-Superior Highway, Arizona.

SECTION TWO

STRENGTH DESIGN

Foreword

EVEN THE simple culvert becomes important when considered in the over-all picture. Around half a billion dollars is spent annually for small drainage structures. Furthermore, these are for the purpose of protecting many billions of dollars worth of engineering construction. Hence the need for engineers to determine when and where drainage structures are required, and to select or design them adequately but not wastefully.

An engineer is defined as "one who understands the forces and materials of nature and applies them for the benefit of mankind with greater economy than a layman."

In building a structure, the following engineering operations are involved:

1. Survey of the conditions.
2. Selection of appropriate engineering principles.
3. Design or selection of the structure, including plans and specifications.
4. Construction or installation.

Each of these steps is subject to a degree of error. Greater accuracy can come only as better information is made available to the engineer.

The engineer evaluates facts and theories and he knows that mathematical formulas and charts are no safe substitute for common sense, experience and understanding.

This section of the handbook deals with design principles and practices as applied to fabricated steel products for drainage and other engineering construction. The discussions and methods given for design are not the only ones, nor are they considered the final word. They are based on many years of engineering experience and are known to be practical. In many instances, the current practices of other engineering groups are cited, so that the engineer can evaluate and use his own judgment as to what best fits the problem at hand.

CHAPTER EIGHT

Design of Corrugated Metal Structures

Summary

A corrugated metal conduit has considerable inherent strength, but by deflecting under a fill load, it obtains a remarkable increase in strength from side support of the surrounding material. Failure occurs through change of shape and buckling under excessive deflection. Deflection for various diameters of pipe under various fill heights can be controlled by change of gage (wall thickness) and by methods of installation discussed later.

The design of flexible conduits for strength is not an exact procedure. Research has not revealed enough facts to permit rational or analytical design. Instead, an empirical formula, based on the observation and measurement of thousands of structures in service, has been used to determine safe and economical gages for pipes (and pipe-arches) under highways, railways, streets, airports, levees and other loadings. Convenient gage tables for various types of loadings have been computed and have been adopted by leading engineering organizations.

Three supplementary means of increasing the strength of pipe have been devised—the elliptical shape, shop strutting and field strutting.

Strong circumferential and longitudinal joints or seams and couplings are of primary importance, particularly under high fills, and for live loads under shallow

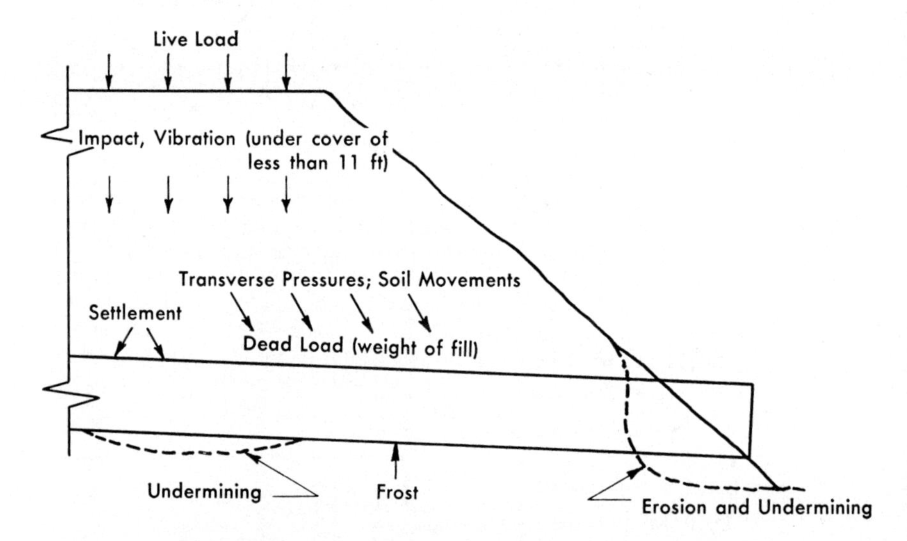

Fig. 54. Principal physical forces acting on underground conduits.

TABLE 8-1 FACTORS IN STRENGTH DESIGN OF UNDERGROUND CONDUITS

Primary Factors	*Related Factors*
LOADS	
1. Surface load—static or moving; weight, impact, vibration	Produced by construction equipment, normal traffic; illegally heavy loads
2. Dead load—weight of fill	Effect of surface load plus dead load is least under highway cover of 4 ft—
3. Transverse pressures and soil movements	—under railroad cover of 11 ft; wet soils; rough surfaces
4. Frost action; ice	Distribution of surface load depends on depth of pavement, track or other base
BACKFILL MATERIAL	
1. Kind of soil—	—internal friction, cohesion, drainability, volume change
2. Moisture content—	—during backfill and later
3. How backfill is placed	End dumped, scrapers, in layers, depth of layers
4. Compaction methods	None, hand, grading equipment, mechanical tampers, or rollers
INSTALLATION CONDITION and METHOD	
1. Trench	
2. Projection (positive or negative)	
3. Tunneling, jacking, threading	
CONDUIT	
1. Flexible or rigid material	Uniformity; inspection methods; control in manufacture
2. Size and gage (wall thickness)	Passive or active resistance. Tensile and compressive strength
3. Joints, couplings, seams	Riveted, bolted, cemented
4. Shape	Circular, elliptical, pipe-arch, other
5. Strutting	Shop or field elongation of vertical diameter Percentage of diameter Compression cap, soft or hard Relief of struts during settlement of fill
FOUNDATION	
1. Supporting strength of native soil	Replaced or aided by granular material, planks, brush mats, saddles, piling
2. Bedding methods	Impermissible, ordinary, first class, concrete saddle
	Settlement under or alongside conduit
	Undermining at end or due to open joints or cracks in conduits

Fig. 55. Battery of five 16-ft diameter pipes. Corrugated metal with bolted seams and known as Multi-Plate, has extended the range of pipe sizes to 15 ft and larger, and arches up to 30 ft.

cover, and on unstable subgrades. Methods of fabricating corrugated metal structures and coupling devices as covered by standard specifications provide a conservative factor of safety for the seams and joints.

Strength Design Considerations

Structural strength of a culvert or conduit is the primary requirement. Without it, other considerations such as material durability, economy and capacity are of little avail.

For calculating strength on an analytical basis, the engineer should know (1) the kind, magnitude and direction of all of the loads and forces on the conduit, (2) the conditions under which the conduit is to serve, (3) the physical properties of the material from which the conduit is made, and (4) the behavior of the material and structure under all of these loads and conditions. Much has been learned about these factors as described in the preceding chapters. However, there are still many indeterminate factors. Fig. 54 and Table 8-1.

The competent designer realizes that design is less a matter of mathematics than it is of selection, engineering judgment and experience. He also knows that unless he can carefully control the method of installation by reasonable enforcement of specifications, he must make greater allowance in his design factor of safety.

Two Kinds—Rigid and Flexible Conduits

Conduits are of many shapes and materials, but they are usually classified as to degree of rigidity or flexibility (see Chapt. 1, Dead Load Research).

Rigid conduits include plain or reinforced concrete masonry or pipes, burnt clay or cast iron—all of which are essentially brittle. (For design data, see the specifications published by the various cement, concrete pipe and vitrified clay pipe manufacturers.)

Flexible conduits include those made of corrugated steel sheets and plates, which are essentially ductile. The present chapter deals with the design of this latter type of structure.

Background of Corrugated Metal Structures

Because of their ability to resist impact, vibration and unforeseen loads, and because of positive joint strength, corrugated metal structures have been found dependable for difficult as well as normal service conditions.

Corrugated metal pipe was first developed and used as culverts in 1896. As confidence was gained in the use of this light-weight, thin-walled pipe, the diameters were increased to 72 and 84 in. Fill heights were increased to 100 ft or more. Users include highway departments, railroads, sewer departments, levee engineers and many others.

A further development in 1931 was the introduction of structural plate (Multi-Plate) pipe with larger corrugations and diameters up to 15 ft and arches up to 30 ft (see Fig. 55).

Investigations of thousands of corrugated metal pipe have definitely established their remarkable structural strength (see page 149). Evidently the gages, couplings and fabrication details recommended by the manufacturers have been safe and efficient. The insignificantly few failures that have occurred have generally been traceable to abuse during construction or failure to follow the manufacturer's simple installation instructions, and seldom because of faulty material or design of the structure.

Fig. 56. Beam strength of 72-in. diameter corrugated metal pipe is demonstrated by this cover for belt conveyor at a mine tipple in Pennsylvania.

Theory and Design Practice

Research during the past forty years by Iowa State College and others has led to a better understanding of corrugated metal structures, including: (1) the principles of flexibility and deflection, and (2) the knowledge that supporting strength depends largely on kind of sidefill material and proper installation methods (see "Importance of Backfill" in chapter on Installation Instructions).

Although M. G. Spangler has developed a *rational* method of designing corrugated metal pipe,[1] it contains some factors[2] difficult to evaluate which have delayed its general use.

G. E. Shafer* and his associates developed an *empirical* formula for determining deflection based on the following hypothesis.[2] A corrugated metal pipe has considerable inherent strength by virtue of the shape of its corrugations and the gage or thickness of the metal. Such pipe can change shape under load without fracture because the corrugated metal is elastic and ductile. Fig. 56.

As the vertical diameter of a pipe shortens under load, the horizontal diameter increases. This outward movement of the sides of an underground pipe develops passive earth pressure. These side forces add to the inherent strength, greatly increasing resistance to vertically-applied loads.

Increased vertical load is generally accompanied by increased side support. The amount of deflection will depend upon the load, the inherent strength of the pipe and the type and compaction of the fill around the pipe.

Since corrugated pipe deflects more or less in proportion to load, the deflection varying from zero to a maximum of 20 per cent of the diameter at failure, it is a simple matter to determine the deflection and safety factor against collapse of any installed pipe by measuring its deflection with an ordinary rule. This has made it possible to derive a "law of deflection" for corrugated pipe based on measurements of the deflection of pipes in thousands of installations. For ordinary soil and installation conditions, the "law of deflection" can be expressed as:

$$y_c = k\frac{H^m D^n}{t^s}$$

where y_c = deflection of pipe in inches
H = height of fill above pipe in feet
D = nominal diameter of pipe in inches
t = thickness of metal in inches
k = a constant
$m, n, s,$ = exponential factors

In order to determine the value of the exponents and the constant k, measurements were made on various diameters of corrugated pipe under different heights of fill. The strength tests described in Chapter 1 were also used in determining the values of the exponents and constant.

Most of the gage-versus-fill-height tables in common use today are based on experience with this empirical formula first developed in 1926. They are computed on the basis of an expected deflection of 5 per cent, or a factor of safety of 4.

How Strength is Specified

The strength of corrugated metal structures is ordinarily established by a *fabrication* specification and a *design* specification. The latter specification includes:

---

*Chief engineer, Armco Drainage & Metal Products, Inc.

1. Size of corrugation (pitch—center to center—and depth)
2. Shape (full circle or pipe-arch)
3. Width of lap
4. Rivets, bolts or other connections
5. Couplings (kind and size)
6. Strutting (if required)
7. Foundation or bedding preparation
8. Backfill, how to be made

The *design* specification requires a certain commercial gage (thickness) of metal for various heights of cover and type of loading.

Specifications in Common Use

Corrugated metal structures are accepted as a standard for practically all types of engineering construction. Specifications have been prepared in collaboration with metal pipe manufacturers and have been adopted by engineering authorities generally. A list of those in common use is found in Table 8-2.

TABLE 8-2 SPECIFICATIONS FOR CORRUGATED METAL DRAINAGE STRUCTURES (1954)

	Culverts, Sewers, Underpasses			
Market	*Galvanized Corrugated Metal Pipe*	*Bituminous Protected Corrugated Metal Pipe*	*Structural Plate Pipes, Arches and Pipe-Arches*	*Under-drains*
State Highways Bureau of Public Roads Counties† Municipalities	AASHO* M-36-47	‡	AASHO Standard Specifications for Highway Bridges —1953 edition Div. IV Sec. 19	AASHO M-136-47
National Forests and Parks	FP-41 Item 253	FP-41 Items 254–255	AASHO Standard Specifications for Highway Bridges —1953 edition Div. IV Sec. 19	FP-41 Item 320 –2.1 (e)
Federal agencies, including U.S. Corps of Engineers	QQ-C-806a		QQ-C-806a	QQ-C-806a
Railways	AREA 1-4-6	AREA 1-4-13	AREA 1-4-25	AREA 1-4-11
Civil Aeronautics Admin.	AASHO M-36-47	CAA Manual D-703-23		AASHO M-136-47

*All states have, in addition, their own specifications (similar to M-36) which cover corrugated metal products.
†Counties in many instances follow the specifications of the state in which they are located.
‡The published specifications of most states include bituminous protected pipe. Majority use industry recommendation, which is same as AREA specification.

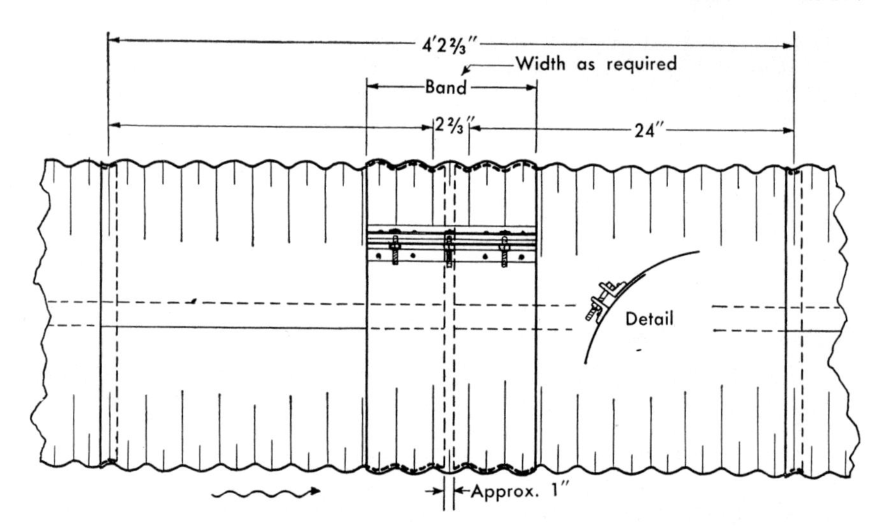

Fig. 57. Side view of riveted pipe and standard connecting band or coupling. For severe conditions a watertight connection may be advisable. See Fig. 59.

1. Fabrication Details of Corrugated Metal Pipe—Riveted, Full-Round Construction

Shop Practice: Standard corrugated sheets (corrugation 2⅔-in. pitch x ½-in. depth) 25½ in. wide and of various lengths are curved or formed into a circle. These are riveted along the longitudinal seam to form a pipe. Additional circular sections are lapped over the preceding section and riveted circumferentially and longitudinally, thereby increasing the length by 24 in. for each section.

The nominal diameter is the unobstructed inside diameter measured from inside crest of corrugation.

For details, including the ¾-in. lip at each end, see Fig. 57.

The sheet dimensions, widths of lap and weights of galvanized corrugated metal pipe are given in Table 8-3.

Rivets and Riveting: The rivets are 5/16-in. diameter for 16 and 14-gage sheets and ⅜-in. diameter for 12, 10 and 8-gage. The lengths vary with the gage and number of thicknesses of metal.

All rivets are driven cold with the center not less than twice the diameter from the edge of the sheet. The longitudinal seams of all pipe 42 in. or more in diameter have two rows of rivets. Circumferential seams have a maximum rivet spacing of 6 in.

Field Joints or Couplings: There are several ways of joining corrugated metal pipe in the field. The method depends on the type of installation and the extent of watertightness required.

1. *Coupling Band.* Unless otherwise specified, field joints are made with outside collars or bands, usually lighter than the gage used for the pipe, except when the pipe is No. 16 gage. The bands are 3, 5 or 9 corrugations wide and have galvanized steel angles riveted near the ends. By means of bolts through the angles, the bands are drawn tight (see Fig. 57).

TABLE 8-3 DIMENSIONS AND WEIGHTS OF GALVANIZED CORRUGATED METAL PIPE
(A. R. E. A. Specifications—1953)

Nominal Diam. in Inches	*Length of Sheet Before Forming Inches*	*Minimum Width of Lap in Inches*	*Computed Weight per Linear Foot of Finished Pipe Exclusive of End Finish (Based on 20-Ft Length of Pipe) in Pounds*				
			Galvanized Sheet Gage Number				
			16	*14*	*12*	*10*	*8*
8	28½	1½	7.3	....	....	....	....
10	35	1½	9.0	....	....	....	....
12	41	1½	10.5	13.1	....	....	....
15	50½	1½	12.9	16.1	....	....	....
18	60	1½	15.3	19.1	26.4	....	....
21	69½	1½	17.7	22.1	30.6	....	....
24	80	2	20.4	25.2	34.7	44.2	....
30	98	2	....	30.9	43.0	54.8	....
36	117	2	....	37.1	51.0	65.4	79.4
42*	137	3	....	43.6	59.5	76.8	93.2
48*	156	3	....	....	68.0	87.4	106.1
54	1– 80 1– 98	3	....	....	77.8	99.4	120.7
60	2– 98	3	....	....	....	108.9	133.5
66	1– 98 1–117	3	....	....	....	120.6	146.4
72	2–117	3	....	....	....	130.4	159.3
78	1–117 1–137	3	....	....	....	142.4	172.8
84	2–137	3	....	....	....	....	185.2

*Two sheets may be used by allowing sufficient total sheet lengths to provide for an additional longitudinal lap.

Fig. 58. Two-piece coupling bands provide positive connections for unusual conditions or where the regular band is difficult to install. The bottom half is shop-riveted to the pipe.

TABLE 8-4 DETAILS OF STANDARD ARMCO CORRUGATED METAL PIPE

Gage, Diameter, Weight and End Area

Gage	*Diam. in* *In.*	*Plain Galvanized* *Lb/Ft*	*Asbestos-Bonded Full-Coated* *Lb/Ft*	*Asbestos-Bonded Full-Coated and Paved* *Lb/Ft*	*Plain Galvanized Full-Coated and Paved* *Lb/Ft*	*Plain Galvanized Full-Coated* *Lb/Ft*	*End Area* *Sq Ft*
	8	7	10	11	11	9	0.35
	10	9	12	14	13	11	0.55
	12	10	14	17	16	13	0.79
16	15	13	17	20	19	16	1.23
	18	15	20	24	23	19	1.77
	21	18	23	28	27	22	2.41
	24	20	27	32	31	25	3.14
	8	9	11	13	12	11	0.35
	10	11	14	16	15	13	0.55
	12	13	16	19	18	15	0.79
	15	16	20	23	22	19	1.23
	18	19	24	28	27	23	1.77
14	21	22	27	32	31	26	2.41
	24	25	31	37	36	30	3.14
	30	31	38	45	43	37	4.91
	36	37	46	54	52	44	7.07
	42	44	54	63	61	52	9.62
	48	50	61	72	69	59	12.6
	8	12	15	16	16	14	0.35
	10	15	18	20	20	18	0.55
	12	18	21	24	23	20	0.79
	15	22	26	29	29	25	1.23
	18	26	31	35	34	30	1.77
	21	31	36	40	39	35	2.41
12	24	35	41	47	45	40	3.14
	30	43	50	57	55	49	4.91
	36	51	60	68	66	58	7.07
	42	60	71	80	78	69	9.62
	48	68	80	91	88	78	12.6
	54	78	92	104	101	89	15.9
	60	86	101	114	111	98	19.6
	66	95	111	126	122	107	23.8
	18	33	38	42	41	37	1.77
	21	39	44	49	48	43	2.41
	24	44	51	56	55	50	3.14
	30	55	62	69	67	61	4.91
	36	65	74	82	80	72	7.07
10	42	77	87	96	94	85	9.62
	48	87	99	110	107	97	12.6
	54	100	113	125	122	110	15.9
	60	110	124	138	135	121	19.6
	66	121	137	151	148	133	23.8
	72	130	149	165	161	145	28.3

TABLE 8-4—(cont'd.) DETAILS OF STANDARD ARMCO CORRUGATED METAL PIPE
Gage, Diameter, Weight and End Area

Gage	*Diam. in*	*Plain Galvanized*	*Asbestos-Bonded Full-Coated*	*Asbestos-Bonded Full-Coated and Paved*	*Plain Galvanized Full-Coated and Paved*	*Plain Galvanized Full-Coated*	*End Area*
	In.	*Lb/Ft*	*Lb/Ft*	*Lb/Ft*	*Lb/Ft*	*Lb/Ft*	*Sq Ft*
	24	54	60	66	65	59	3.14
	30	66	74	80	78	72	4.91
	36	79	88	96	94	86	7.07
	42	93	104	113	110	101	9.62
	48	106	118	128	126	115	12.6
8	54	121	134	146	144	132	15.9
	60	134	148	161	158	145	19.6
	66	146	163	177	174	159	23.8
	72	159	177	193	189	173	28.3
	84	186	207	225	221	203	38.5
	96	212	236	256	251	231	50.3

Note: Weights shown are averaged; not to be used in specifications.

2. *Two-Piece Coupling Band.* On pipe larger than 60 in., or when a band is to be installed under difficult conditions such as under water, a two-piece band is available. Such a band is usually bolted together at opposite sides of the pipe, rather than at the top and bottom.

3. *Modified Two-Piece Band.* Particularly for sewer pipe and for difficult locations, the lower half of the two-piece coupling can be shop riveted to the pipe. The upper half can either be loose or can be shop riveted to the adjacent section of pipe (see Fig. 58).

4. *Watertight Coupling.* This type of coupling is used on aerial sewers, levee culverts and elsewhere. It consists of a corrugated collar drawn tight by means of threaded rods and silo-type lugs. To permit the band to fit snugly into the corrugations of the pipe, the rivets in the longitudinal seam are omitted and the seams welded (see Fig. 59).

Other types of bands are sometimes employed to obtain watertightness at the pipe joint.

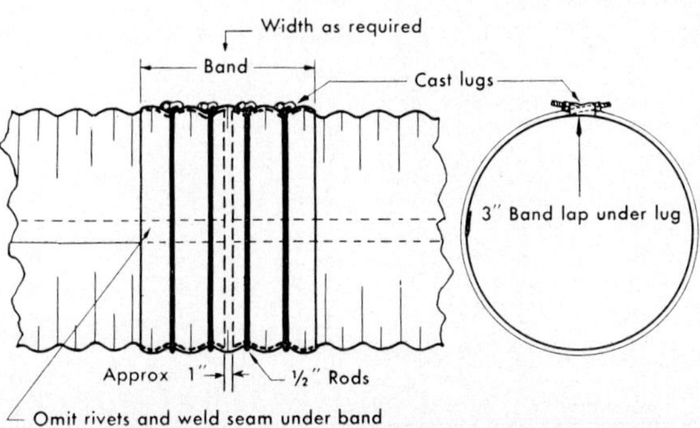

Fig. 59. Details of special watertight joint with rods and lugs.

5 and 6. *Internal Expanding and Internal Contracting Bands.* Internal bands are used on "threading" and other jobs where there is insufficient working space around the outside of the pipe.

7. *Field Riveted or Bolted Joints.* On jacking jobs and some threading jobs, the pipe is specially fabricated and match punched for field riveting or bolting of pipe lengths.

End Finish: The ends of corrugated metal pipe, where exposed, should be protected from damage by impact of vehicles or equipment. Prefabricated metal "end sections" for diameters up to 48 in. provide such protection as well as give a finished appearance (see page 264).

2. Fabrication Details of Corrugated Pipe-Arch

The fabrication of standard riveted pipe-arches is similar in most respects to that of full-round pipe. The difference is in the supplementary operation of forming an arch from the pipe by means of a heavy press after the pipe (and connecting band) is fabricated.

Pipe ranging from 15 to 60 in. in diameter is used in forming arches with a span-rise of 18 x 11 in. to 72 x 44 in. See Fig. 60 for nomenclature, and Table 8-5 for details.

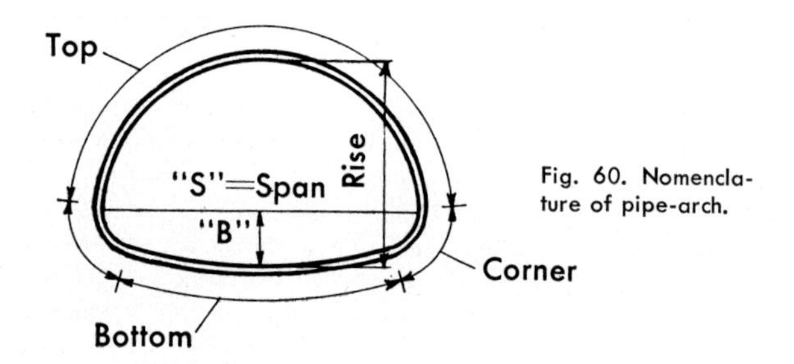

Fig. 60. Nomenclature of pipe-arch.

TABLE 8-5 DETAILS OF CORRUGATED METAL PIPE-ARCHES

Diam. of Pipe of Equal Periphery in Inches	*Span* in Inches*	*Rise* in Inches*	*"B"* in Inches*	*Area in Sq Ft*
15	18	11	4½	1.1
18	22	13	4¾	1.6
21	25	16	5¼	2.2
24	29	18	5½	2.8
30	36	22	6¼	4.4
36	43	27	7	6.4
42	50	31	8	8.7
48	58	36	9¼	11.4
54	65	40	10½	14.3
60	72	44	11¾	17.6

*Manufacturing tolerance = plus or minus one inch.

TABLE 8-6 DETAILS OF STANDARD ARMCO CORRUGATED METAL *PIPE-ARCHES*
Size, Gage, Weight and End Area

Size		*Gage*	*Plain Galvanized*	*Asbestos-Bonded Full-Coated*	*Asbestos-Bonded Full-Coated and Paved*	*Plain Galv. Full-Coated and Paved*	*Plain Galvanized Full Coated*	*End Area*
Span in In.	*Rise in In.*		*Lb/Ft*	*Lb/Ft*	*Lb/Ft*	*Lb/Ft*	*Lb/Ft*	*Sq Ft*
18	11	16	13	17	23	22	16	1.1
		14	16	20	26	25	19	
22	13	16	15	20	27	26	19	1.6
		14	19	24	31	30	23	
		12	26	31	38	37	30	
25	16	16	18	23	31	30	22	2.2
		14	22	27	35	34	26	
		12	31	36	44	43	35	
29	18	14	25	31	40	39	30	2.8
		12	35	41	50	49	40	
36	22	14	31	38	50	48	37	4.4
		12	43	50	62	60	49	
		10	55	62	74	72	61	
43	27	14	37	46	60	58	44	6.4
		12	51	60	74	72	58	
		10	65	74	88	86	72	
50	31	12	60	71	86	84	69	8.7
		10	77	87	103	101	85	
		8	93	104	120	117	101	
58	36	12	68	80	98	96	78	11.4
		10	87	99	117	115	97	
		8	106	118	136	133	115	
65	40	10	100	113	134	131	110	14.3
		8	121	134	155	152	132	
72	44	10	110	124	147	144	121	17.6
		8	134	148	171	168	145	

NOTE: Weights shown are averaged; not to be used in specifications.

3. Fabrication Details of Multi-Plate Structures

Description of Plates: Multi-Plate pipe, arches and pipe-arches are made of metal sections (structural plates) with corrugations of 6-in. pitch and 2-in. depth running at right angles to the length of the section. Fig. 61. The sections vary in thickness up to approximately 9/32 in. or No. 1 gage (see table of gages, Table 8-7).

Standard sections are fabricated in four widths, 9 pi (approx. 29 in.), 15 pi (approx. 48 in.), 18 pi (approx. 58 in.) and 21 pi in. (approx. 67 in.). Table 8-8. The sections are in 6 and 8-ft nominal lengths and punched along each edge and end as shown in Fig. 62.

The actual length of square-end structures is about 4 in. longer than the nominal length because of a 2-in. lip beyond each end corrugation for lapping purposes. Beveled and skewed structures do not have this extra length as the one corrugation lap is removed in forming the special ends.

Plates are furnished flat or are curved to any radius of 30 in. or larger.

Additional physical properties and design data are given in Table 8-7.

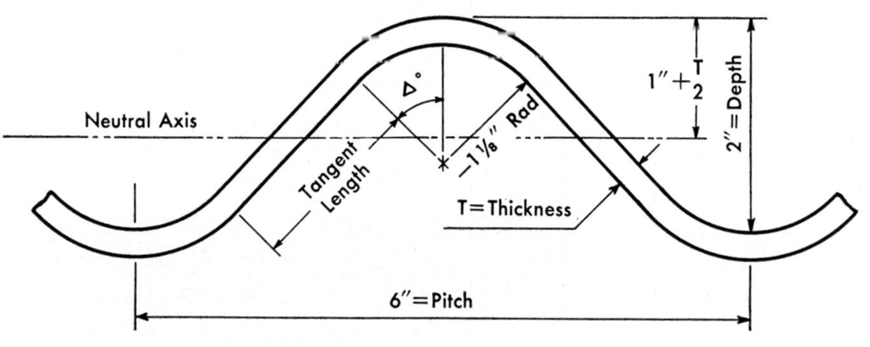

Fig. 61. Details of Multi-Plate corrugation.

TABLE 8-7 PHYSICAL PROPERTIES OF ARMCO MULTI-PLATE

Gage	*Thickness T in Inches*	*Tangent Length in Inches*	*Angle △ in Degrees & Min.*	*Moment of Inertia* in I-Inches⁴*	*Section Modulus* in S-Inches³*	*Radius of Gyration in R-Inches*	*Area of Section* in Inches²*
12	.1046	1.8925	44° 28′	.0604	.0574	.682	.1297
10	.1345	1.8606	44° 44′	.0781	.0732	.684	.1669
8	.1644	1.8283	45° 00′	.0961	.0888	.686	.2041
7	.1838	1.8069	45° 11′	.1080	.0989	.688	.2283
5	.2145	1.7727	45° 29′	.1270	.1147	.690	.2666
3	.2451	1.7377	45° 47′	.1463	.1303	.693	.3048
1	.2758	1.7019	46° 05′	.1659	.1458	.695	.3432

*Per inch of horizontal projection.

TABLE 8-8 DETAILS OF UNCURVED MULTI-PLATE SECTIONS

Net Width in Inches			*Over-all Width in Inches*	*Spaces at 9.6 Inches*	*No. of Circum. Bolt Holes*
Nominal	*Detail*				
9 Pi	28.8	28 13/16	33 9/16	3	4
15 Pi	48.0	48	52 3/4	5	6
18 Pi	57.6	57 5/8	62 3/8	6	7
21 Pi	67.2	67 3/16	71 15/16	7	8

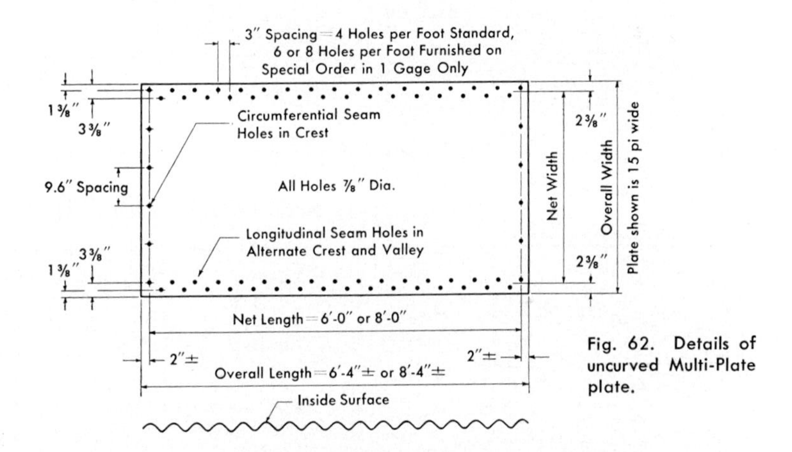

Fig. 62. Details of uncurved Multi-Plate plate.

TABLE 8-9 WEIGHT OF ARMCO MULTI-PLATE SECTIONS

Width in Inches	*Length in Feet*	*Approximate Weight of Individual Plates without Bolts*—in Pounds*							*No. Bolts per Plate†*	
		12 Gage	*10 Gage*	*8 Gage*	*7 Gage*	*5 Gage*	*3 Gage*	*1 Gage*	*Short*	*Long*
21 Pi	8	278	354	431	469	546	622	699	34	4
21 Pi	6	210	268	326	355	413	472	530	26	4
18 Pi	8	241	307	373	406	473	540	605	33	4
18 Pi	6	182	233	283	308	358	409	459	25	4
15 Pi	8	203	259	315	343	399	455	512	32	4
15 Pi	6	154	197	239	260	303	345	388	24	4
9 Pi	8	129	164	200	218	253	289	324	30	4
9 Pi	6	98	125	152	165	192	219	246	22	4

*Standard punching, four holes per foot in longitudinal seams; galvanized, AASHO 2-oz coating.

†For gages 12 to 5, bolt lengths are: 1¼" and 1½"; for gages 3 and 1: 1½" and 1¾".

Weight in pounds per hundred bolts only: 1¼" = 33; 1½" = 35; 1¾" = 37. Weight of one hundred nuts: 16 pounds.

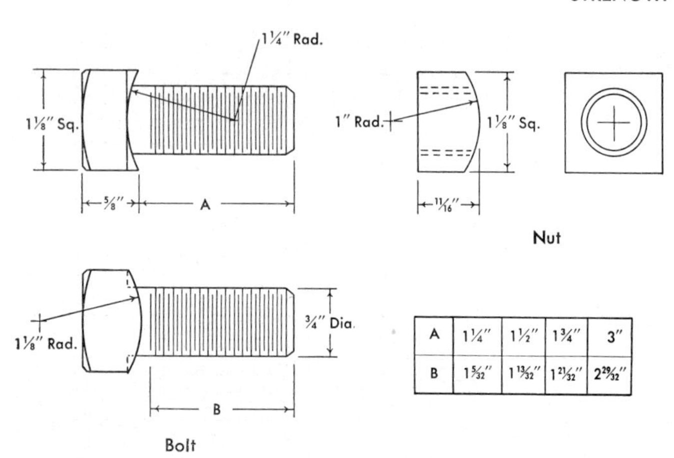

A	1¼"	1½"	1¾"	3"
B	1 5/32"	1 13/32"	1 21/32"	2 29/32"

Fig. 63. Dimensions and specifications for Multi-Plate bolts and nuts.

TABLE 8-10 WEIGHT OF MULTI-PLATE PIPE IN POUNDS PER FOOT OF PIPE

Diam. in Inches	*Number of Plates per Ring*			*Approximate Weight per Foot of Structure—in Pounds*						
	15 pi	*18 pi*	*21 pi*	*12 Gage*	*10 Gage*	*8 Gage*	*7 Gage*	*5 Gage*	*3 Gage*	*1 Gage*
60	4			111	139	167	181	209	237	265
66	2	2		120	151	181	197	227	258	289
72	2		2	130	163	196	213	246	280	313
78		2	2	139	175	211	228	264	301	336
84			4	148	187	225	244	283	321	360
90	6			166	208	250	271	313	356	398
96	4	2		175	220	265	287	332	377	422
102	4		2	185	232	279	303	350	398	445
108		6		194	244	294	319	369	420	469
114		4	2	204	256	309	335	387	441	493
120		2	4	213	268	323	351	406	461	516
126			6	223	280	338	366	424	482	540
132	6		2	240	301	363	393	455	517	578
138	2	6		249	313	377	409	473	538	602
144	4		4	259	326	392	425	492	560	625
150		6	2	268	338	407	441	510	581	649
156	2		6	278	350	421	457	528	601	672
162		2	6	287	362	436	473	547	622	696
168			8	297	373	450	488	565	643	719
174	6		4	314	395	475	515	596	677	758
180		10		324	407	490	531	615	700	782

Galvanized, with bolts, and based on three rings at 8′ and one at 6′ for 6″ x 2″ corrugation of 1⅛″ valley radius.

Bolted Assembly: Multi-Plate sections are delivered to the job ready for quick, easy field assembly. The sections are bolted together to form a full-round pipe, an elliptical pipe, an arch or a pipe-arch. Detailed instructions for assembly accompany each structure.

Galvanized ¾-in. diameter bolts made of special heat-treated (high tensile strength) steel are used in assembling Multi-Plate. The under side of the head is shaped to fit either the crest or valley of the corrugations, thereby giving a larger bearing area, a tighter seam and simplified erection (see Fig. 63). Only a few simple hand tools are needed to make the installation.

For arch seats, special unbalanced channels with anchor lugs are available (see Fig. 64).

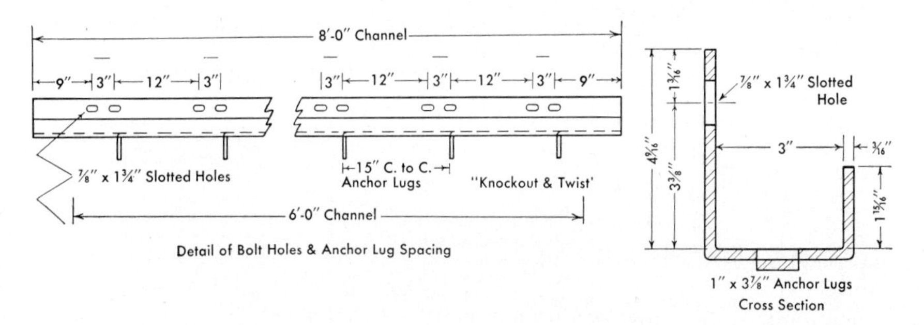

Fig. 64. Dimensions of unbalanced channel for arches.

PART ONE

DESIGN OF MULTI-PLATE PIPE

The Gage tables in Chapters 9 to 14 are for average conditions and take into account the fill loads, legal live loads and other forces likely to affect a culvert or conduit, with a factor of safety of 4 to take care of any unusual or unanticipated forces. They assume that *reasonable* care will be taken to provide a stable foundation, that proper backfill material will be used and compacted, and that other installation specifications will be followed. Where these conditions are carefully controlled, and where durability is not a limiting factor, lighter gages may be permissible. On the other hand, under unfavorable conditions, or where human life or large investment is endangered, heavier gages may be desirable. Strutting, as described elsewhere, may be an alternate means of preventing excessive deflection.

The strength of the joints, couplings or seams should be commensurate with the service conditions.

Multiple Gages. Where large Multi-Plate pipes are installed under high fills, certain economics are possible by using the heavier gages under the center of the fill

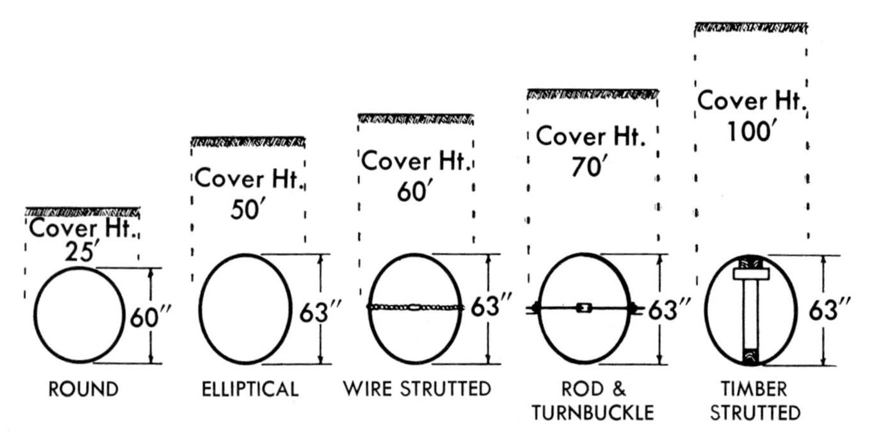

Fig. 65. How permissible heights of cover may be increased over a 60-in. 8 ga. corrugated metal pipe by changing the shape or strutting.

and lighter gages where the fill decreases in height. This is called "balanced design."

It is also accepted practice, from a durability standpoint, to use heavier gages of Multi-Plate in the bottom than on the sides and top.

Effect of Strutting

In selecting the gage of a pipe, there are other factors to consider besides the height of cover and the surface loads. One such factor consists of making the pipe in elliptical shape before the fill is consolidated. The methods include manufacturing the pipe in elliptical shape, or shortening the horizontal diameter by "shop strutting," with tie wires or rods, elongating the vertical diameter by field strutting with timbers.

The effect of these operations on the load-carrying capacity of a 60-in. 8-gage pipe is shown in Fig. 65.

Placing struts in a pipe serves to elongate the vertical diameter and to retard and reduce the vertical deflection as the fill is placed. Consolidation of the fill at the sides of the pipe before the struts are removed is a definite means of increasing the load-carrying capacity of the pipe. This is recognized in the gage tables that follow. Consequently the designer in many cases may choose between a heavier gage unstrutted or a lighter gage strutted.

See further details on strutting in Chapter 52 on Installation.

PART TWO

DESIGN OF MULTI-PLATE PIPE-ARCHES

THE USE of the pipe-arch is preferred in many cases because it provides the necessary base integrally with the arch. This expedites construction, especially under unfavorable weather or foundation conditions. It also permits building units of the structure on the bank and then lifting into place in the channel or trench.

The design of pipe-arches is largely by the use of the accompanying gage-versus-fill-height tables. See Chapters 9, 10, 11 and 13.

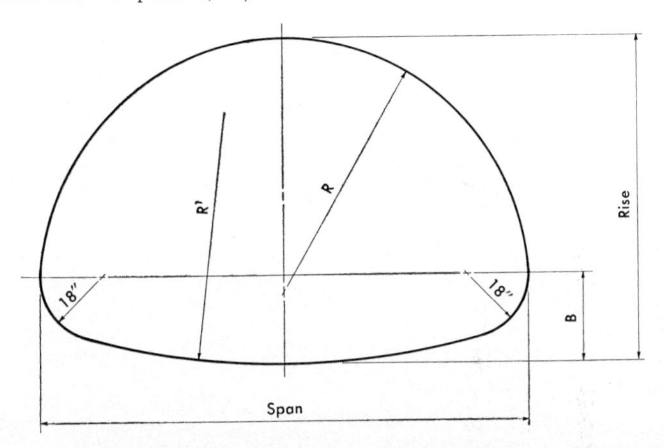

Fig. 66. Dimensions of Multi-Plate pipe-arches.

Fig. 67. One of the larger sizes of Multi-Plate pipe-arches for stream enclosure at McGuire Air Force Base, New Jersey.

TABLE 8-11 DIMENSIONS OF MULTI-PLATE *PIPE-ARCHES*

Nominal Dimensions				*Layout Dimensions in Inches*				
Span	*Rise*	*Area in Sq Ft*	*Total Periphery in Pi In.*	*B*	*Rise*	*½ Span*	*R*	*R′*
6′-1″	4′-7″	22	66	21.0	55.0	36.5	36.8	76.3
6′-4″	4′-9″	24	69	20.5	57.1	38.0	38.1	98.6
6′-9″	4′-11″	26	72	22.0	58.9	40.6	41.0	83.5
7′-0″	5′-1″	28	75*	21.4	61.1	42.1	42.3	104.2
7′-3″	5′-3″	31	78	20.8	63.2	43.5	43.5	136.2
7′-8″	5′-5″	33	81	22.4	65.0	46.2	46.5	109.8
7′-11″	5′-7″	35	84	21.7	67.2	47.6	47.7	137.9
8′-2″	5′-9″	38	87*	20.9	69.4	48.0	48.9	182.9
8′-7″	5′-11″	40	90	22.7	71.1	51.7	51.9	141.0
8′-10″	6′-1″	43	93	21.9	73.3	53.0	53.0	178.7
9′-4″	6′-3″	46	96	23.8	75.1	55.9	56.2	144.6
9′-6″	6′-5″	49	99	22.9	77.3	57.1	57.3	177.5
9′-9″	6′-7″	52	102	21.9	79.5	58.3	58.3	227.7
10′-3″	6′-9″	55	105	24.0	81.2	61.3	61.5	178.3
10′-8″	6′-11″	58	108	26.1	82.9	64.2	64.9	153.2
10′-11″	7′-1″	61	111	25.1	85.1	65.5	65.9	180.4
11′-5″	7′-3″	64	114*	27.4	86.9	68.4	69.4	157.9
11′-7″	7′-5″	67	117	26.3	89.1	69.7	70.2	183.2
11′-10″	7′-7″	71	120	25.2	91.3	70.9	71.1	216.4
12′-4″	7′-9″	74	123	27.5	93.0	73.9	74.7	186.5
12′-6″	7′-11″	78	126	26.4	95.2	75.1	75.5	216.8
12′-8″	8′-1″	81	129	25.2	97.4	76.2	76.4	257.4
12′-10″	8′-4″	85	132*	24.0	99.7	77.2	77.3	314.7
13′-5″	8′-5″	89	135	26.4	101.3	80.4	80.7	254.8
13′-11″	8′-7″	93	138	28.9	103.0	83.6	84.4	220.7
14′-1″	8′-9″	97	141	27.6	105.2	84.7	85.1	254.1
14′-3″	8′-11″	101	144	26.3	107.5	85.7	85.9	297.6
14′-10″	9′-1″	105	147	28.9	109.2	88.9	89.6	254.3
15′-4″	9′-3″	109	150*	31.6	110.8	92.0	93.4	226.8
15′-6″	9′-5″	113	153	30.2	113.1	93.2	94.0	255.7
15′-8″	9′-7″	118	156	28.8	115.3	94.2	94.7	291.5
15′-10″	9′-10″	122	159	27.5	117.6	95.2	95.5	338.1
16′-5″	9′-11″	126	162	30.1	119.2	98.5	99.2	290.9
16′-7″	10′-1″	131	165*	28.7	121.5	99.5	99.9	332.7

Dimensions are to inside crests and are subject to manufacturing tolerances.

*These structures are preferred because they give greatest area for given number of plates and bolts per ring. Each structure of less span than those marked provides correspondingly less area for the same number of plates and bolts.

TABLE 8-12 WEIGHT OF MULTI-PLATE *PIPE-ARCHES* IN POUNDS PER FOOT

Span	*Rise*	*Total Periphery in Pi Inches*	*Number of Plates per Ring*				*Approximate Weight per Ft of Structure—in Pounds*						
			9 Pi	*15 Pi*	*18 Pi*	*21 Pi*	*12 Gage*	*10 Gage*	*8 Gage*	*7 Gage*	*5 Gage*	*3 Gage*	*1 Gage*
6′-1″	4′-7″	66	2	2	1		124	156	187	202	234	265	297
6′-4″	4′-9″	69	2	2		1	129	162	194	210	243	276	309
6′-9″	4′-11″	72	2	1	1	1	134	168	202	218	252	287	321
7′-0″	5′-1″	75*	2		2	1	138	173	209	226	261	297	332
7′-3″	5′-3″	78	3	1	2		147	184	221	240	277	314	351
7′-8″	5′-5″	81	3	1	1	1	152	190	228	248	286	325	363
7′-11″	5′-7″	84	3	1		2	156	196	236	255	295	336	375
8′-2″	5′-9″	87*	2	2	1	1	161	202	243	263	304	346	386
8′-7″	5′-11″	90	3	3	1		170	213	255	277	320	363	406
8′-10″	6′-1″	93	3	3		1	175	219	262	285	329	374	418
9′-4″	6′-3″	96	3	2	1	1	179	225	270	293	338	375	430
9′-6″	6′-5″	99	3	1	2	1	184	231	277	301	347	395	441
9′-9″	6′-7″	102	3		3	1	189	237	285	309	356	406	453
10′-3″	6′-9″	105	3		2	2	194	243	292	316	366	416	465
10′-8″	6′-11″	108	2	1	3	1	198	249	299	324	375	427	477
10′-11″	7′-1″	111	2	1	2	2	203	255	306	332	385	437	488
11′-5″	7′-3″	114*	2	1	1	3	207	261	313	340	394	448	500
11′-7″	7′-5″	117	2	4	1	1	216	271	326	354	408	465	519
11′-10″	7′-7″	120	2	3	2	1	221	277	334	362	417	476	531
12′-4″	7′-9″	123	2	2	3	1	226	284	341	370	427	486	543
12′-6″	7′-11″	126	2	1	4	1	231	290	348	378	436	497	555
12′-8″	8′-1″	129	2	2	1	3	235	296	356	385	445	507	567
12′-10″	8′-4″	132*	2		4	2	240	302	363	393	455	517	578
13′-5″	8′-5″	135	3	1	4	1	249	312	375	407	470	535	597
13′-11″	8′-7″	138	3		5	1	254	318	383	415	479	546	609
14′-1″	8′-9″	141	3		4	2	258	324	390	423	489	556	621
14′-3″	8′-11″	144	3		3	3	263	330	397	431	498	566	633
14′-10″	9′-1″	147	2	2	2	3	268	336	404	439	507	576	645
15′-4″	9′-3″	150*	2	2	1	4	273	342	411	447	516	586	657
15′-6″	9′-5″	153	2	4	3	1	281	353	424	460	531	604	676
15′-8″	9′-7″	156	2	5		3	286	359	431	468	541	614	687
15′-10″	9′-10″	159	2	4	1	3	291	365	438	476	550	625	699
16′-5″	9′-11″	162	2	3	2	3	295	371	446	484	559	636	711
16′-7″	10′-1″	165*	2	1	5	2	300	377	453	492	568	646	723

*These structures are preferred because they give greatest area for given number of plates and bolts per ring. Each structure of less span than those marked provides correspondingly less area for the same number of plates and bolts. Galvanized, with bolts, and based on three rings at 8 feet and one at 6 feet.

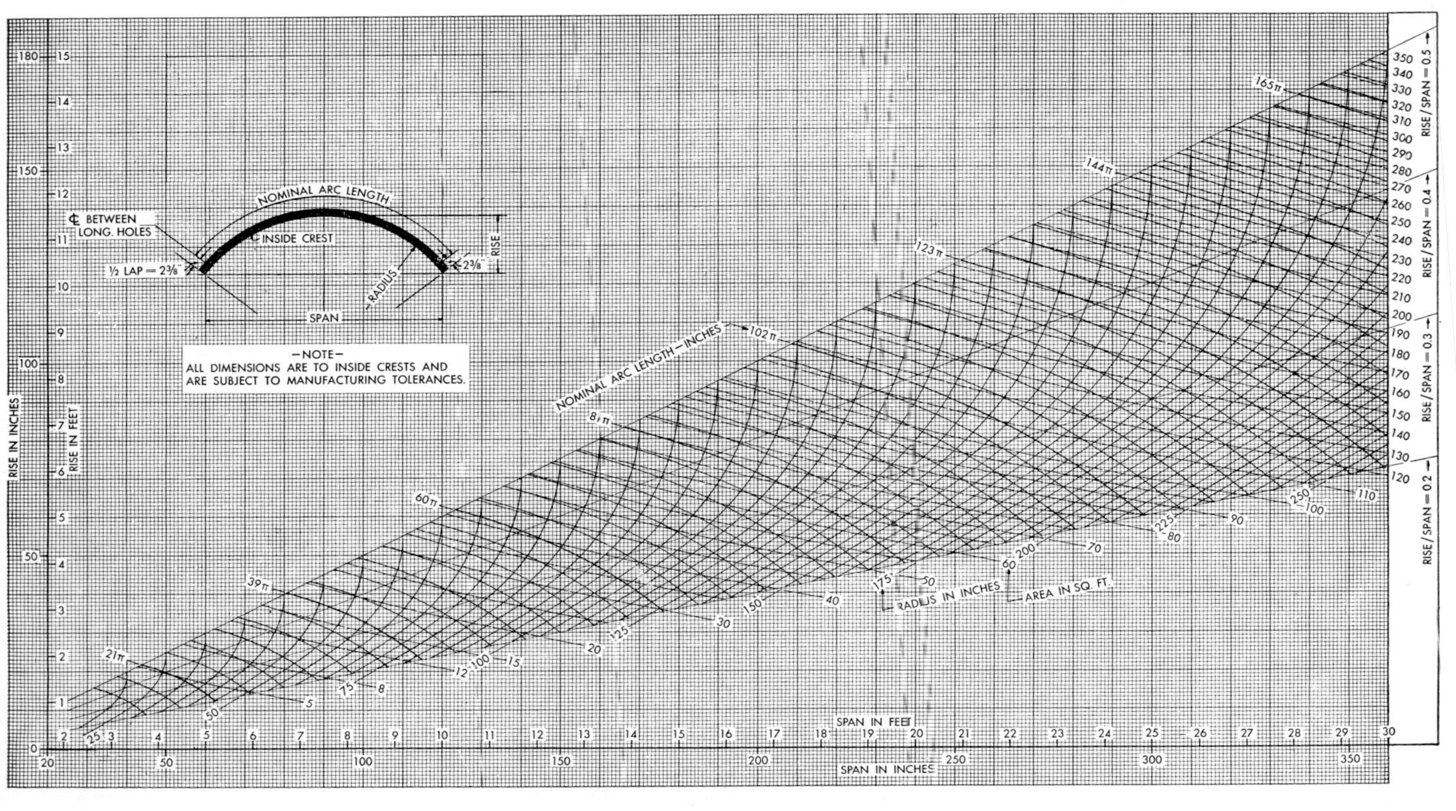

Fig. 68. Rise, span, radius and area of Multi-Plate arches.

PART THREE

DESIGN OF MULTI-PLATE ARCHES

WHEN THERE is not sufficient headroom for a pipe, or where esthetic considerations are important, an arch or a pipe-arch may be used.

Sizes of Arches

An almost unlimited number of combinations of Multi-Plate arch span and rise are available as shown in Fig. 68 and in the accompanying Table 8–14. The spans range from 5 to 30 ft in even feet. By varying the rise, the desired waterway area can be obtained. [Additional waterway can be provided by varying the abutment height. The nominal arc length is in increments of about 9½ in. (3 x pi)]. Fig. 69.

Plate Gages

The Multi-Plate arch is considered a two-hinged arch and is designed rationally by the theory of elastic analysis. In determining the loads on the ring, the vertical load from the fill and live load and the active horizontal components of those same loads are used. (For masonry arches, the practice is to use only the vertical loads.) The accompanying gage tables have been computed on the above theory, with a factor of safety.

Proper gages for arches under various highway loadings are shown in Tables 9-13, 9-14 and 9-15 for H-20, H-15 and H-10 loadings respectively.

For other than highway loadings, such as for pedestrian walkways or bridges for light maintenance equipment, the permissible gages can be lightened, provided care is taken in backfilling the arch to see that the original shape is maintained. Table 9-16 gives the recommended gages for "no live load" under various heights of cover.

Relining old structures with Multi-Plate arches is a special problem. Recommendation for maximum span and gage should be based on a study of local conditions.

For arches under railroads, see Tables 11-7 and 11-8.

Arches for sewers take the same gage as for equivalent highway loadings.

Effect of Shape on Strength

It might normally be assumed from the knowledge that flexible pipe is very strong due to side support developed by lateral deflection, that the strongest arch is a half circle because there is more area against which side support can act.

A flat arch may be stronger than a half circle under some conditions. Although an arch may develop some side support when it deflects under load, it also derives part of its strength from the abutments which resist lateral movement.

Naturally it is impossible to choose arbitrarily the ratio of rise over span (R/S) for every arch, but when this is possible, the following rules apply:

1. In cases where the cover over the arch is shallow and when, in addition, heavy trucks will pass over the arch, keep the shape as nearly a half-circle as conditions permit.

[*Text continued on page 93*]

TABLE 8-13 WEIGHT OF MULTI-PLATE *ARCHES* IN POUNDS PER FOOT

Arc Length of Arch in Pi Inches	*Number of Plates per Ring*				*Approximate Weight per Foot of Structure—in Lb*						
	9 Pi	*15 Pi*	*18 Pi*	*21 Pi*	*12 Gage*	*10 Gage*	*8 Gage*	*7 Gage*	*5 Gage*	*3 Gage*	*1 Gage*
24	1	1			46	57	69	75	86	98	109
27	1		1		51	63	76	82	95	108	121
30	1			1	55	69	83	90	104	119	133
33		1	1		60	75	90	98	113	129	145
36		1		1	65	81	98	106	123	140	156
39*			1	1	70	87	105	114	132	150	168
42	1	1	1		78	98	117	128	147	168	187
45	1		2		83	104	125	136	157	178	199
48		2	1		88	110	132	144	166	188	211
51		2		1	92	116	140	152	175	199	223
54		1	1	1	97	122	147	160	184	209	235
57			2	1	102	128	154	167	194	220	246
60*			1	2	107	134	161	175	203	231	258
63		3	1		115	145	173	189	218	249	277
66		2	2		120	151	181	197	227	259	289
69		1	3		125	157	188	205	236	269	301
72		2		2	130	163	196	213	246	279	313
75			3	1	135	169	203	221	255	290	324
78			2	2	139	175	211	228	264	301	336
81*			1	3	144	181	218	236	273	311	348
84		2	3		153	191	230	250	288	329	367
87		3		2	158	197	238	258	298	339	379
90		2	1	2	163	203	245	266	307	349	391
93			4	1	167	209	252	274	316	360	403
96			3	2	172	215	259	282	325	370	415
99			2	3	176	221	267	290	335	381	426
102*			1	4	181	227	275	298	344	391	438
105		2	3	1	189	238	287	311	359	409	457
108		3		3	194	244	294	319	369	419	469
111			5	1	199	250	301	327	378	430	481
114			4	2	204	256	309	335	387	441	493
117			3	3	209	262	316	343	396	451	505
120			2	4	213	268	323	351	406	461	516
123*			1	5	218	274	331	359	415	471	528
126		1	5	1	226	285	343	372	430	489	547
129			6	1	231	291	350	380	439	500	559
132			5	2	236	297	357	388	448	510	571
135			4	3	241	303	365	396	458	521	583
138			3	4	246	309	372	404	467	531	595
141			2	5	250	315	379	412	476	542	606

TABLE 8-13—(cont'd.) WEIGHT OF MULTI-PLATE *ARCHES* IN POUNDS PER FOOT

Arc Length of Arch in Pi	*Number of Plates per Ring*				*Approximate Weight per Foot of Structure—in Lb*						
	9 Pi	*15 Pi*	*18 Pi*	*21 Pi*	*12 Gage*	*10 Gage*	*8 Gage*	*7 Gage*	*5 Gage*	*3 Gage*	*1 Gage*
144*			1	6	255	321	386	420	485	552	618
147			7	1	263	331	398	433	500	570	637
150			6	2	268	337	407	441	510	581	649
153			5	3	273	343	414	449	519	591	661
156			4	4	277	349	421	457	528	601	673
159			3	5	282	355	428	465	537	611	685
162			2	6	287	362	436	473	547	622	696
165*			1	7	292	367	443	481	556	632	708
168			7	2	301	378	456	494	572	650	727
171			6	3	305	384	463	502	581	661	739
174			5	4	310	390	470	510	590	671	751
177			4	5	315	396	477	518	599	682	762

Galvanized, with bolts, and based on three rings at 8 ft and one at 6 ft.

*These structures are preferred because they give greatest area for given number of plates and bolts per ring. Each structure of less span than those marked provides correspondingly less area for the same number of plates and bolts.

Fig. 69. Multi-Plate arch being installed on concrete abutments.

TABLE 8-14 REPRESENTATIVE SIZES OF MULTI-PLATE ARCHES
With R/S Ratio from Approx. 0.3 to 0.5

Span in Feet*	*Rise in Feet and In.*	*Area in Sq Ft*	*Nominal Arc in Pi Inches*	*R/S*	*Radius in Inches*
6-0	1-9½	7½	27	0.30	41
	2-3½	10	30	.38	37½
	3-2	15	36	.53	36
7-0	2-4	12	33	.34	45
	2-10	15	36	.40	43
	3-8	20	42	.52	42
8-0	2-11	17	39	.37	51
	3-4	20	42	.42	48½
	4-2	26	48	.52	48
9-0	2-11	18½	42	.32	59
	3-10½	26½	48	.43	55
	4-8½	33	54	.52	54
10-0	3-5½	25	48	.35	64
	4-5	34	54	.44	60½
	5-3	41	60	.52	60
11-0	3-6	27½	51	.32	73
	4-5½	37	57	.41	67½
	5-9	50	66	.52	66
12-0	4-0½	35	57	.34	77½
	5-0	45	63	.42	73
	5-10	55	69	.48	72
	6-3	59	72	.52	72
13-0	4-1	38	60	.32	86½
	5-1	49	66	.39	80½
	5-11½	59	72	.46	78½
	6-9	70	78	.52	78
14-0	4-7½	47	66	.33	91
	5-7	58	72	.40	86
	6-5½	70	78	.46	84½
	7-3	80	84	.52	84
15-0	4-7½	50	69	.31	101
	5-8	62	75	.38	93
	6-7	75	81	.44	91
	7-9	92	90	.52	90

*Intermediate spans are available.
For end areas, see Fig. 68, page 86.

TABLE 8-14—(Cont'd) REPRESENTATIVE SIZES OF MULTI-PLATE ARCHES
With R/S Ratio from Approx. 0.3 to 0.5

Span in Feet*	*Rise in Feet and In.*	*Area in Sq Ft*	*Nominal Arc in Pi Inches*	*R/S*	*Radius in Inches*
16-0	5-2	60	75	0.32	105
	6-2	73	81	.39	99
	7-1	86	87	.45	97
	7-11	99	93	.49	96
	8-3	105	96	.52	96
17-0	5-2½	63	78	.31	115
	6-3	78	84	.37	107
	7-2	92	90	.42	103
	8-0	106	96	.47	102
	8-10	119	102	.52	102
18-0	5-9	75	84	.32	119
	6-9	90	90	.38	112
	7-8	104	96	.43	109
	8-6	119	102	.48	108
	8-11	126	105	.50	108
19-0	6-4	87	90	.33	123
	7-3½	102	96	.38	118
	8-2	118	102	.43	115
	9-0½	133	108	.48	114
	9-5½	140	111	.50	114
20-0	6-4	91	93	.32	133
	6-10	100	96	.35	128
	8-3½	124	105	.42	122
	9-2	140	111	.46	121
	10-0	157	117	.50	120
21-0	6-11	104	99	.33	137
	7-11	122	105	.38	131
	8-10	140	111	.42	128
	9-8	157	117	.46	126
	10-6	172	123	.50	126
22-0	6-11	109	102	.31	146
	7-11½	128	108	.36	138
	8-11	146	114	.40	135
	9-9	163	120	.44	133
	11-0	190	129	.50	132
23-0	6-11	114	105	.30	155
	8-0	134	111	.35	147

*Intermediate spans are available.
For end areas, see Fig. 68, page 86.

TABLE 8-14—(Cont'd) REPRESENTATIVE SIZES OF MULTI-PLATE ARCHES
With R/S Ratio from Approx. 0.3 to 0.5

Span in Feet*	*Rise in Feet and In.*	*Area in Sq Ft*	*Nominal Arc in Pi Inches*	*R/S*	*Radius in Inches*
23-0 (Con't)	8-11½	153	117	0.39	142
	9-10	171	123	.43	140
	10-8	189	129	.46	138
	11-6	208	135	.50	138
24-0	7-6	129	111	.31	160
	8-6	150	117	.35	152
	9-5½	169	123	.39	148
	10-4	188	129	.43	146
	11-2½	208	135	.47	144
	12-0	226	141	.50	144
25-0	7-6	133	114	.30	170
	8-6½	155	120	.34	160
	10-0	186	129	.40	153
	10-10½	207	135	.43	152
	11-8½	227	141	.47	150
	12-6	247	147	.50	150
26-0	8-1	150	120	.31	174
	9-1	172	126	.35	166
	10-6	204	135	.40	159
	11-5	226	141	.44	157
	12-3	246	147	.47	156
	13-0	265	153	.50	156
27-0	8-0½	155	123	.30	184
	9-1½	179	129	.34	174
	10-1½	201	135	.38	168
	11-6	234	144	.43	164
	12-4	256	150	.46	163
	13-7	288	159	.50	162
28-0	8-7	173	129	.31	188
	9-8	197	135	.35	179
	10-8	220	141	.38	174
	12-0	254	150	.43	170
	12-10	277	156	.46	169
	13-8	299	162	.49	168
	14-1	310	165	.50	168

*Intermediate spans are available.
For end areas, see Fig. 68, page 86.

TABLE 8-14—(Cont'd) REPRESENTATIVE SIZES OF MULTI-PLATE ARCHES
With R/S Ratio from Approx. 0.3 to 0.5

Span in Feet*	*Rise in Feet and In.*	*Area in Sq Ft*	*Nominal Arc in Pi Inches*	R/S	*Radius in Inches*
29-0	9-2	191	135	0.32	192
	10-3	217	141	.35	184
	11-2	240	147	.39	180
	12-1	263	153	.42	177
	12-11	287	159	.45	175
	13-9	310	165	.48	174
	14-7	332	171	.50	174
30-0	9-3	197	138	.31	202
	10-9	236	147	.36	189
	11-8½	260	153	.39	185
	12-7	284	159	.42	183
	13-5	308	165	.45	181
	14-3½	332	171	.48	180
	15-1	354	177	.50	180

[*Continued from page 87*]

2. In cases, such as stream enclosures, where there will be no live load on the arch, and in all cases where the fill above the crown will be more than 3 ft, flatten the arch so that the rise divided by the span will be less than 0.45, but in no case make the arch so flat that the rise divided by the span is less than 0.20.

Need for Adequate Foundations

Every structure built must have some kind of foundation, no matter how simple it may be. Corrugated metal pipe presents an example where little need be done ordinarily for foundation preparation except to see that the trench in which the pipe is laid is free from large stones and that the backfill is well tamped up to three-quarters of the height of the pipe. For very soft and unstable foundation conditions, a gravel sub-base or some form of timber grillage will probably be necessary.

If, however, the lower half of the pipe is removed, so to speak, leaving only the top half which is an arch, the foundation problem becomes more difficult.

The load to be carried is the same, but instead of leaving the curved bottom for foundation, all of the load is concentrated on two edges. In addition to the tendency of the edges to move downward, they also tend to spread sidewise, due, of course, to the vertical and horizontal components of the load. These tendencies must be resisted by equal and opposite vertical and horizontal reactions.

Effect of Shape on Reactions

Considering first the vertical reaction, the problem is merely to determine the total load on the arch, regardless of the shape of the arch, and proportion it between the two edges. If the live load is on the crown or center line, each vertical reaction will be the same (one-half of the vertical load), but in many cases the maximum vertical reaction is produced when the position of the live load is other than at the center.

The horizontal reaction is somewhat more difficult to determine because the reaction produced by a given load on the arch depends upon the shape of the arch and where the load is applied. For example, a load of 1000 lb on the crown of a half-circle arch (where rise divided by span, $R/S=0.5$) will produce a horizontal reaction of 320 lb, while the same load on a flatter arch, $R/S=0.2$, will produce 940 lb of horizontal thrust; that is, with the load on the crown. If this same load on the flat arch is applied at the quarter point, half way between the crown and the edge, the horizontal reaction is only 580 lb, whereas if applied at the exact edge, the horizontal reaction will be zero.

Therefore, with the horizontal reaction changing with the shape of the arch, and with the location and magnitude of the load, the equation expressing this relation is necessarily complicated. The ordinary solution requires a scale drawing of the arch and considerable calculating. However, the following tables and charts and their explanation enable the designer to obtain the reactions with a minimum of labor, after which the foundation can be designed.

Dead Load Reactions

In order to find the vertical reaction due to dead load (V_D) for any fill height, it is necessary first to find it for zero fill, or when the earth is level with the crown of the arch, and then add the reaction for any additional cover. (See Fig. 70.)

For example, if the vertical reaction due to dead load is wanted for 2 ft of cover on an arch of 15-ft span, enter the graph (Fig. 70) at the base at 15, trace vertically to Curve No. 1, then left to the zero cover reaction scale. After this reaction is established, follow the same procedure for 1 ft of cover, using Curve No. 2 and multiply that value by 2, then add it to the reaction from the zero cover.

Because the shape or R/S of the arch determines the amount of earth below the zero cover contributing to the reactions, the half circle arch when $R/S=0.5$ was used in developing Curve No. 1. For any other value of R/S the vertical reaction will be less than shown on this curve, therefore, the correction factor as shown in Curve No. 1A should be used.

Curve No. 2, for 1 ft of cover, is independent of the shape of the arch and needs no correction factor.

The horizontal reaction (H_D) is found the same way except that both values, H_0 for zero cover and H_1 for 1 ft of cover must be corrected for values of R/S, other than 0.5. (See Fig. 71.)

These dead-load graphs are based on a filling material weighing 100 lb per cu ft. For any other weight of material, multiply the reactions by that weight and divide by 100. A shorter method, for example, for 120-lb material, is to multiply the reaction by 1.2.

Live Load Reactions

The reactions due to live load are determined in a similar manner from Figs. 73–76 for *highway* and *railroad* loadings respectively. These curves show the live

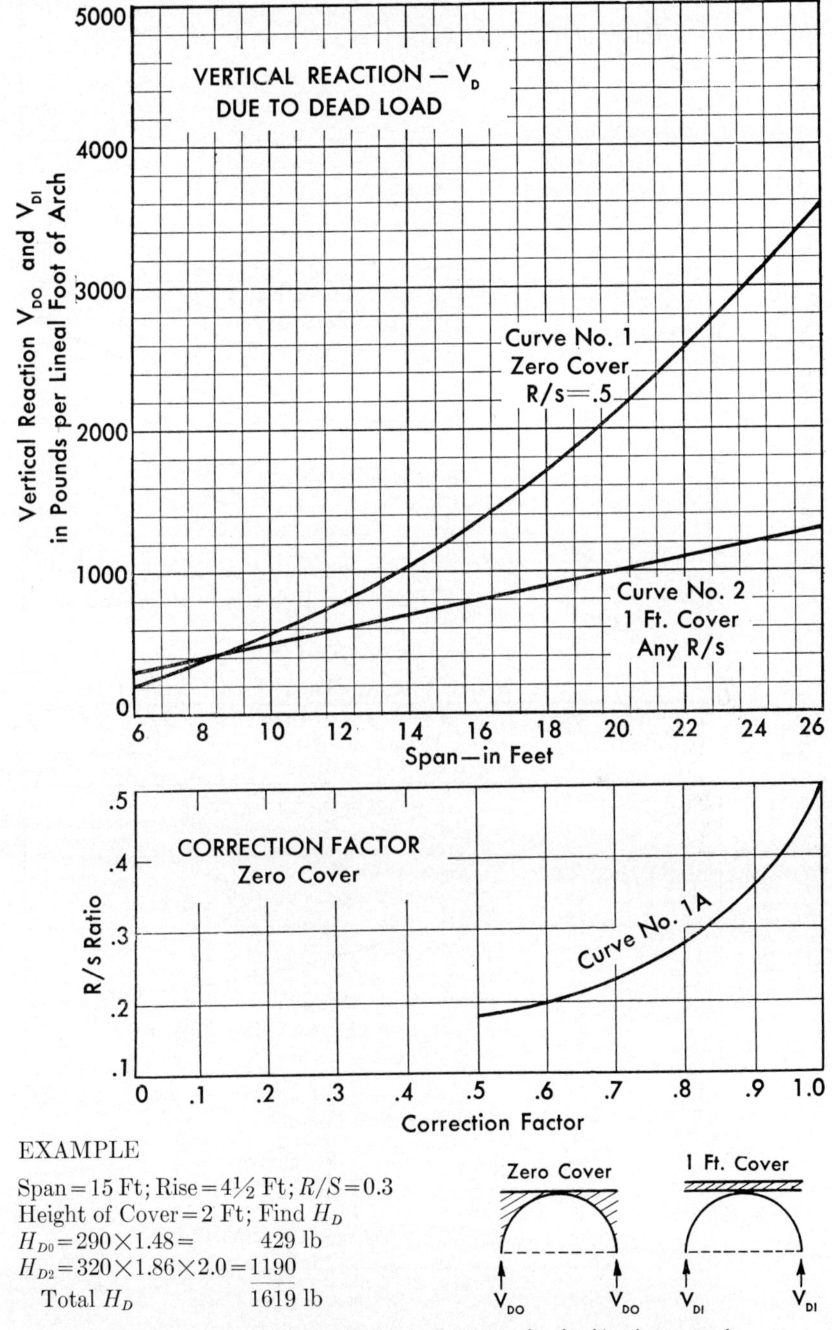

EXAMPLE

Span = 15 Ft; Rise = 4½ Ft; $R/S = 0.3$
Height of Cover = 2 Ft; Find H_D
$H_{D0} = 290 \times 1.48 =$ 429 lb
$H_{D2} = 320 \times 1.86 \times 2.0 =$ 1190
Total H_D 1619 lb

Fig. 70. Curves for determining *vertical* reactions for *dead* load on an arch.

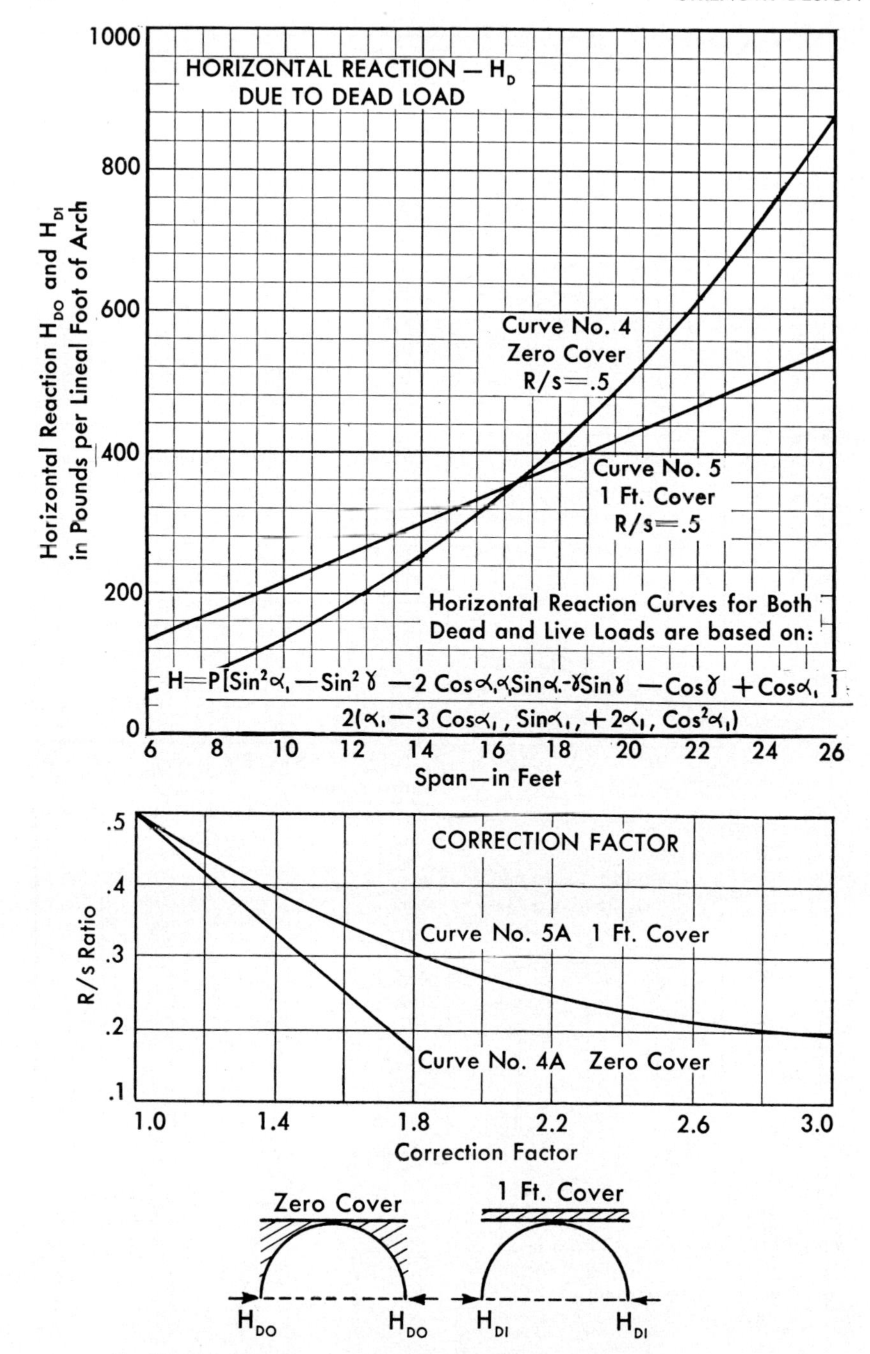

Fig. 71. Curves for determining horizontal reactions for *dead* load on an arch.

load decreasing with an increasing fill height due to the enlarging area over which the live load is distributed.

This dissipation of live load by means of distribution through the fill is sometimes limited in one direction by the length of the arch. Fig. 74, Curve No. 7, gives the maximum value of cover to be considered for all short length arches. For example, assume an arch with a span of 10 ft and a length of 20 ft, under a cover of 7 ft. Entering Curve No. 7 in Fig. 74, we find that for an arch 20 ft in length, the controlling depth of cover for distribution of live load is only 3 ft (rather than 7 ft). So in entering curve No. 3 in Fig. 73, with this governing height of cover (*HC*) and for a 10-ft span a vertical reaction due to live load (V_L) of approximately 1,580 lb is obtained (instead of only 1,200 lb as would have been the case if the 7-ft depth of cover had controlled).

The highway live load is based on two 20-ton trucks passing side by side with 80 per cent of the load on the rear axles. The wheels are spaced 6 ft apart and the trucks 3 ft apart, all according to the AASHO specification. For a live load other than H 20, vary the live load reactions proportionately.

Railroad live load is based on Cooper E 50 loading and for other live loads, vary the live load reactions proportionately.

Combining Reactions

The vertical and horizontal reactions for live load (V_L and H_L) are finally added to those for dead load (V_D and H_D), to obtain the total maximum vertical and horizontal reactions.

[*Continued on page 102*]

Fig. 72. Relining and extending twin arch with Armco Multi-Plate.

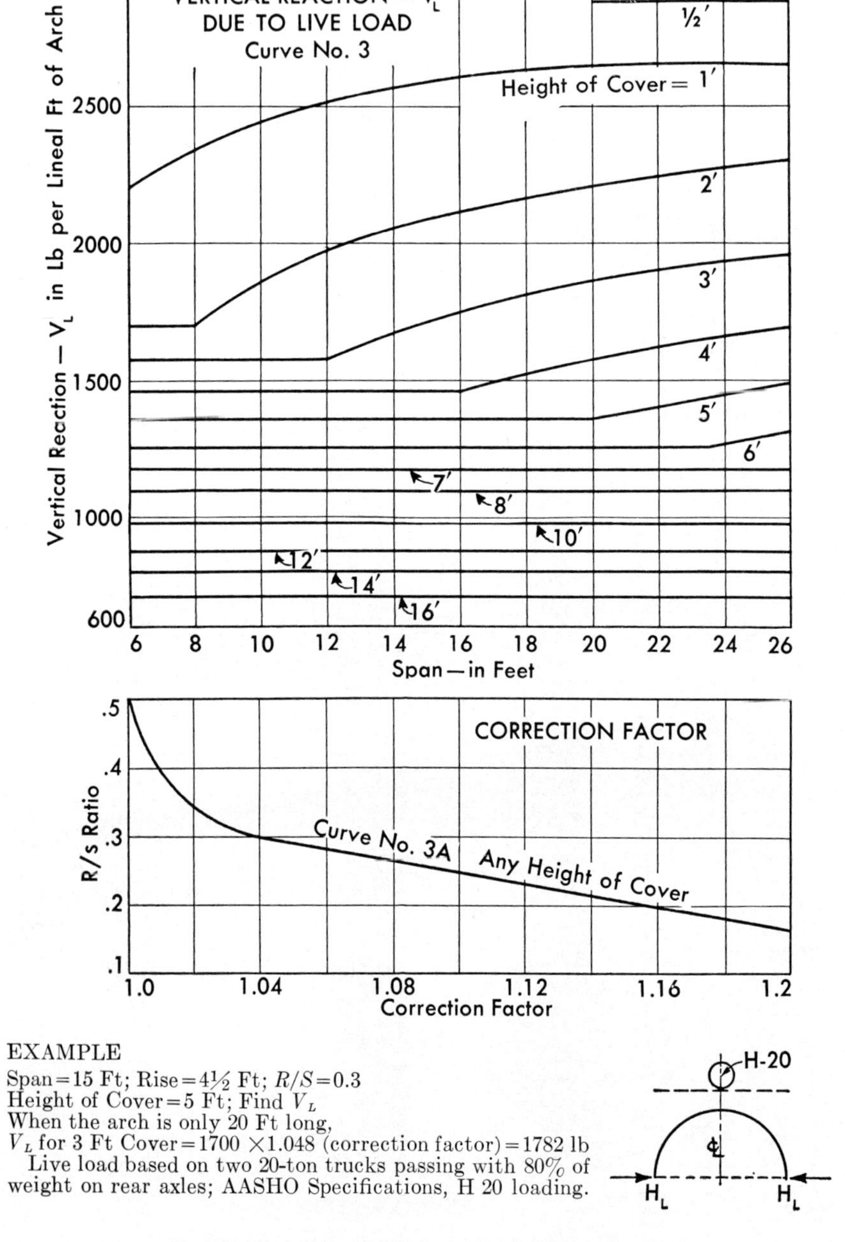

EXAMPLE
Span = 15 Ft; Rise = 4½ Ft; $R/S = 0.3$
Height of Cover = 5 Ft; Find V_L
When the arch is only 20 Ft long,
V_L for 3 Ft Cover = 1700 × 1.048 (correction factor) = 1782 lb
Live load based on two 20-ton trucks passing with 80% of weight on rear axles; AASHO Specifications, H 20 loading.

Fig. 73. *Vertical* reactions for *highway* live load on an arch.

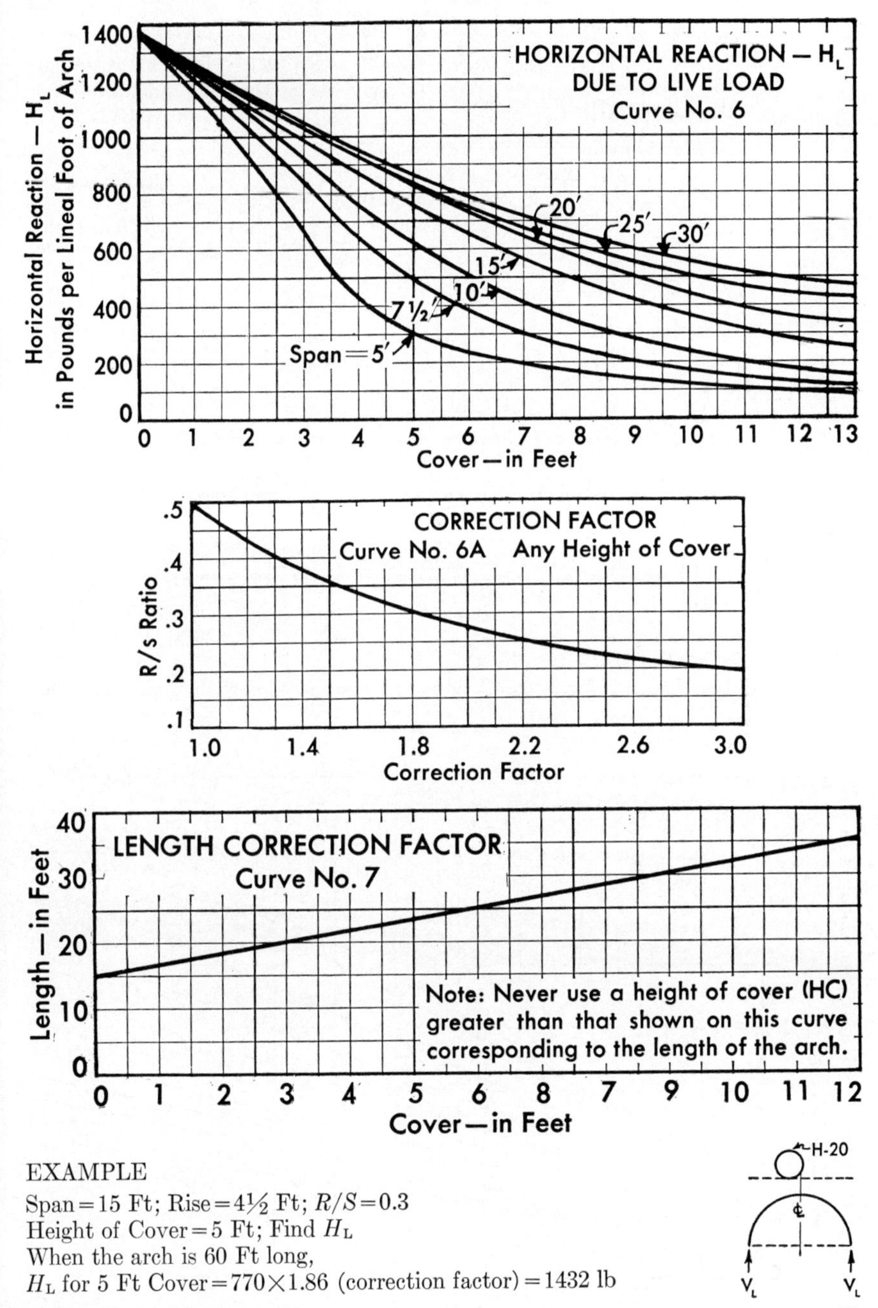

EXAMPLE

Span = 15 Ft; Rise = 4½ Ft; $R/S = 0.3$
Height of Cover = 5 Ft; Find H_L
When the arch is 60 Ft long,
H_L for 5 Ft Cover = 770 × 1.86 (correction factor) = 1432 lb

For explanation of Curve No. 7, see page 97.

Fig. 74. *Horizontal* reactions for *highway* live load on an arch.

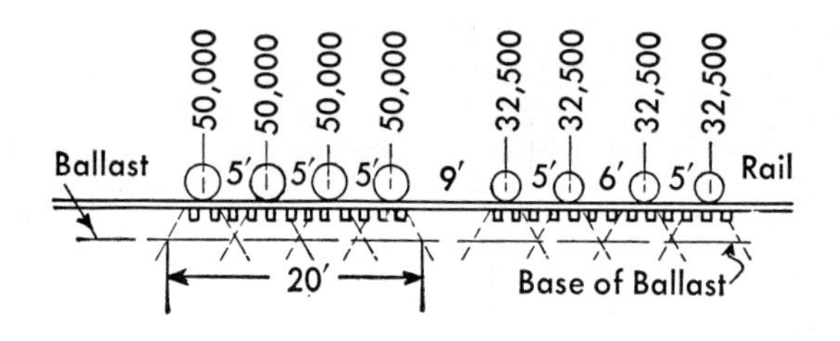

(A) Live load equivalent to Cooper E 50, or 10,000 lb per foot of track. Impact based on equation

$$I=1.0\frac{L}{L+D}L$$

Curves based on live load plus impact.

EXAMPLE—SINGLE TRACK

(B) Span = 15 Ft; Rise = 4½ Ft; Height of cover = 5 Ft. From chart below, $V_L+I=9{,}250$ lb

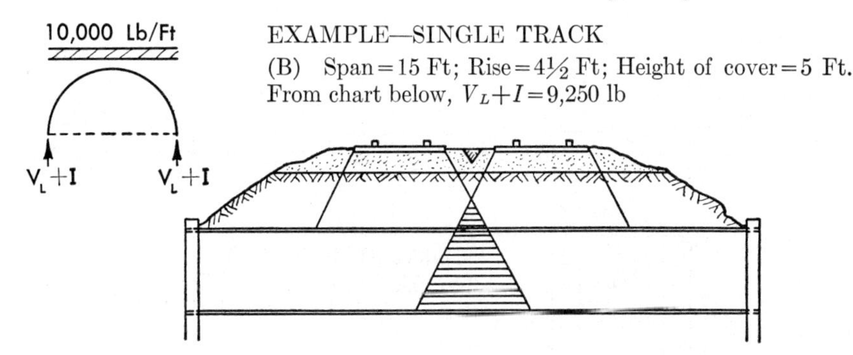

(C) In designing the foundation for an arch under double track, the center fifth of length should be designed for twice the load of the remainder of the foundation.*

*If locomotives pass on arch, shaded area in sketch above will receive load from both tracks.

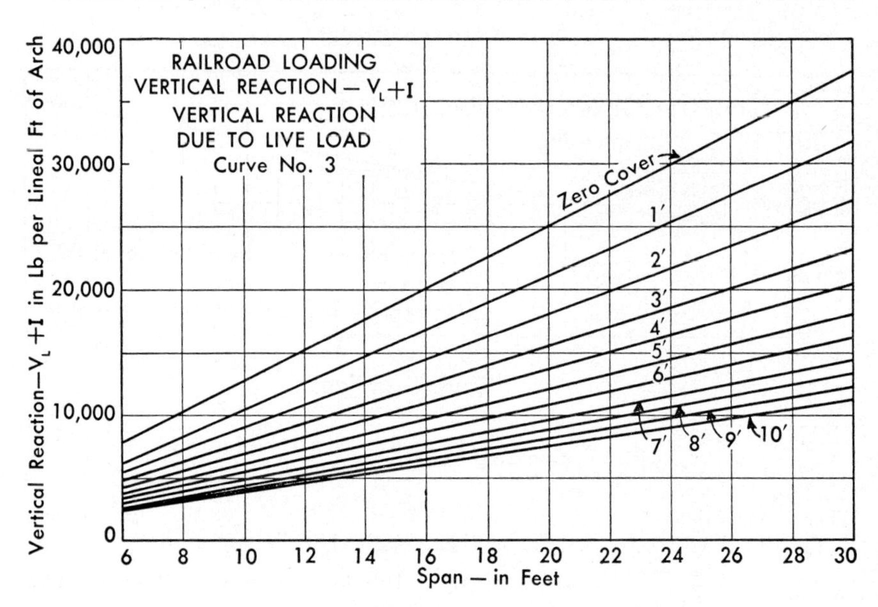

Fig. 75. *Vertical* reactions for *railway* live load on an arch.

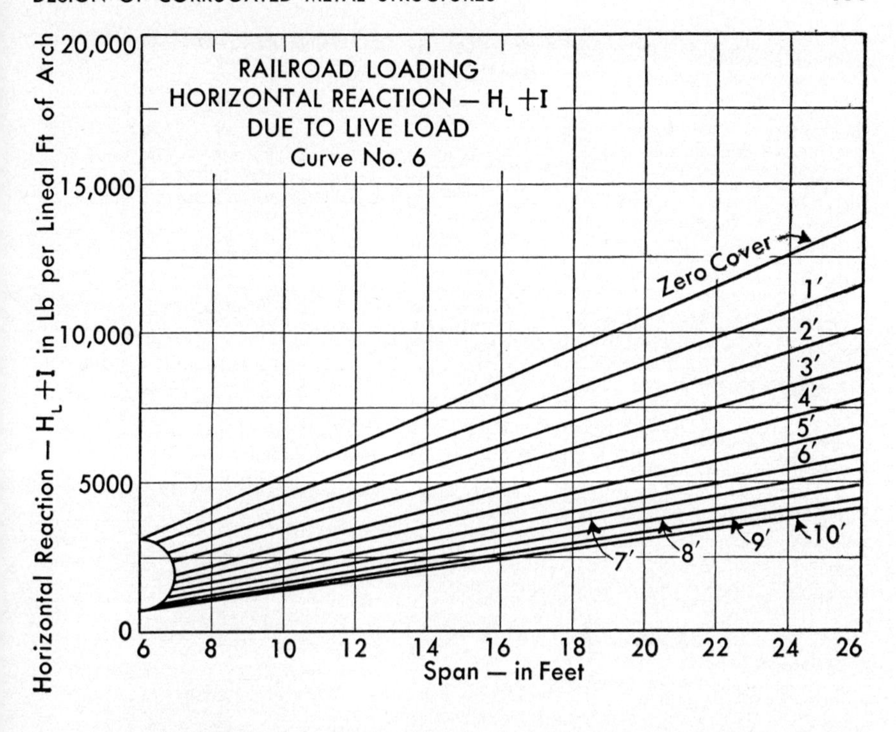

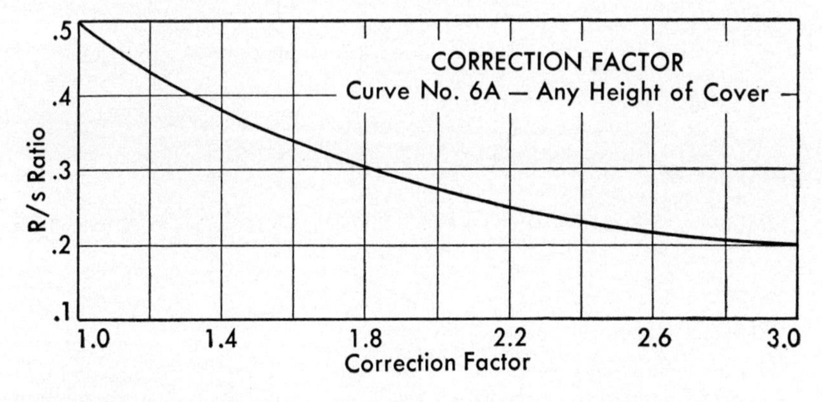

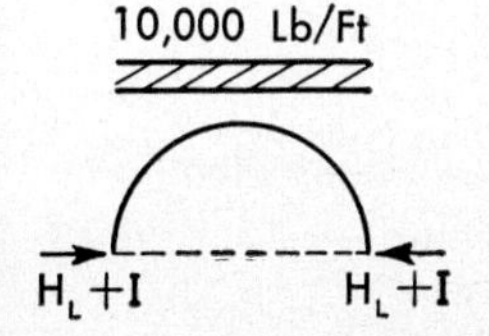

EXAMPLE—SINGLE TRACK

Span = 15 Ft; Rise = 4½ Ft; $R/S = 0.3$
Height of Cover = 5 Ft
$H_L + I = 4{,}000$ times correction factor, $1.86 = 7{,}440$ lb

Fig. 76. *Horizontal* reactions for *railway* live load on an arch.

TABLE 8-15 CALCULATION SHEET TO DETERMINE REACTIONS OF MULTI-PLATE ARCHES

Date__________

Location or
Name of Project____________________ Calcu. by________________

Rise (R)______ Span (S)______ $\frac{\text{Rise}}{\text{Span}}$ (R/S)______ Plates ________

Height of Cover (HC)_______ Live Load (L)_______ Length________

V_{DO} = (1)_______ x (R/S Factor-1A)_______ = _______

V_{DI} = (2)_______ x (HC) _______ = _______

Total V_D = _______ if backfill = 100 lb per cu ft

If not, times weight per cu ft ÷ 100 V_D _______

V_L* = (3)_______ x (R/S Factor-3A)_______ = _______
For H-20 loading. For other loading take proportional amount. V_L _______

Total V = _______

H_{DO} = (4)_______ x (R/S Factor-4A) _______ = _______

H_{Di} = (5)_______ x (R/S Factor-5A)_______ x (HC)_______ = _______

Total H_D_______ If backfill = 100 lb per cu ft

If not, times weight per cu ft ÷ 100 H_D = _______
H_L* = (6)_______ x (R/S Factor-6A)_______ = _______
For H-20 loading. For other live load, take proportional amount. H_L = _______

Total H = _______

$\frac{V}{H}$ = _______ $V + H$ = _______

*NOTE: Length of arch must be taken into consideration (7) as length of arch affects the reactions due to live load.

[*Continued from page 97*]

This procedure may seem complicated but by using the sample data sheet, Table 8-15, and filling in each space from the curves indicated, the problem is solved by simple multiplication and addition.

Selecting Type of Foundation

For arches of 15-ft span or less, the foundation may consist of a slab type of concrete or a timber base. These and larger arches may also be supported on independent footings, abutments or piers. The economy depends on local soil or channel conditions.

If the over-all depth of the abutment as determined by requirements for waterway area, depth for scour and depth for frost is small, a non-reinforced gravity type of construction is economical. Forces acting on this abutment are (1) the horizontal and vertical reactions of the arch and (2) the vertical pressure and the active pressure on the sloping backs of the abutment from the column of earth above it. Generally, any active pressure of the earth in front of the abutment is considered negligible. A width of footing can then be assumed, the weight of concrete computed and the soil pressure diagram determined. Adjustments are then made in the base dimensions of this abutment until the soil pressure diagram has satisfactory distribution.

High Abutments

When the abutment is relatively high, the same procedure can be followed; but quite often results in too large a mass of unreinforced concrete to be economical. Under this condition it becomes possible to design the abutment as a reinforced cantilever type of abutment. Further economy can be obtained by utilizing the passive pressure on the back of the abutment, provided the specifications require as good compaction as would be obtained in building a first-class highway embankment.

If such adequate compaction of material against the metal arch ring is assured, the effect of the arch ring distorting slightly and utilizing passive pressures can be taken into consideration. This serves to counteract the horizontal thrust of the arch to such an extent that it will result in further economy in the abutment.

Pier Design

In the design of piers for multiple-span metal arches, the horizontal reactions of the arch rings are usually considered as balanced. Sometimes there are slight differences in these horizontal components from heavy live loads even when equal arches are on either side of a pier. However, these differences are generally momentary application and so slight that they are not considered as affecting the pier. Hence the pier can be designed as a simple pedestal to accommodate the vertical reactions from both rings.

A distance of about 2 ft should be maintained between the base channels of the arch rings on the pier so as to furnish adequate room for compaction of the spandrel fill. Appearance, too, is improved.

By means of his specification, the designer should in all cases control the installation of the arch so the resultant arch ring is of true shape. This may call for occasional bracing of the metal ring while the spandrel fill is compacted. When this is done, metal plate arches can be designed as very economical structures to operate under the heaviest highway loads.

REFERENCES

1. "The Structural Design of Flexible Pipe Culverts," by M. G. Spangler, Bulletin 153, Iowa Engineering Experiment Station, 1941.
2. "Underground Conduits—an Appraisal of Modern Research," by M. G. Spangler, Paper No. 2337 (Appendix A in this Handbook) and discussion by G. E. Shafer and others. ASCE Transactions, Vol. 113, pp. 341, 355, June 1947, Proceedings of ASCE.

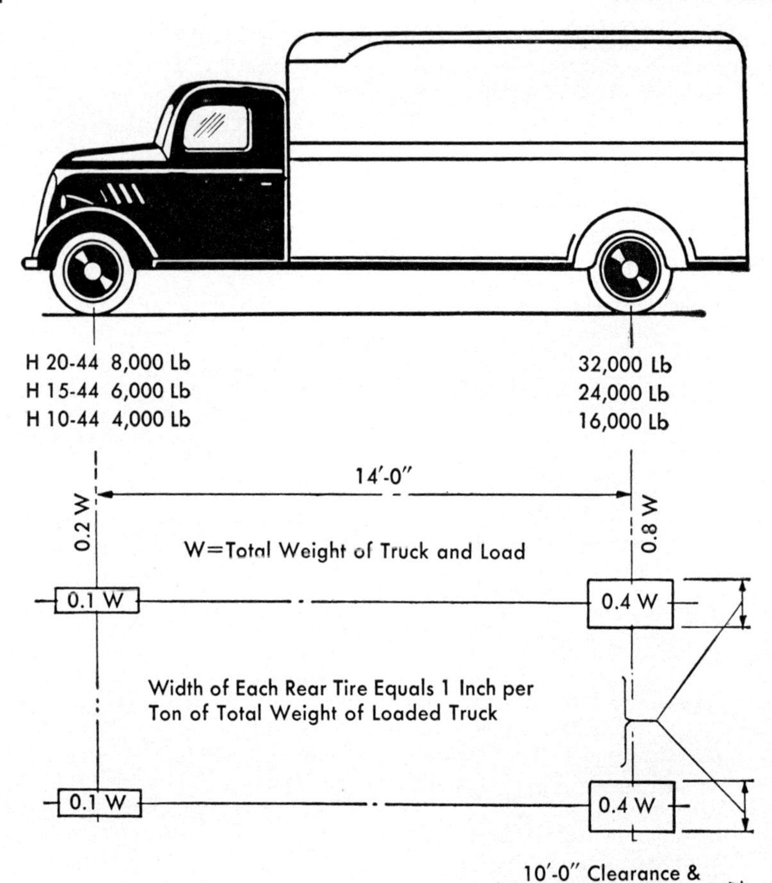

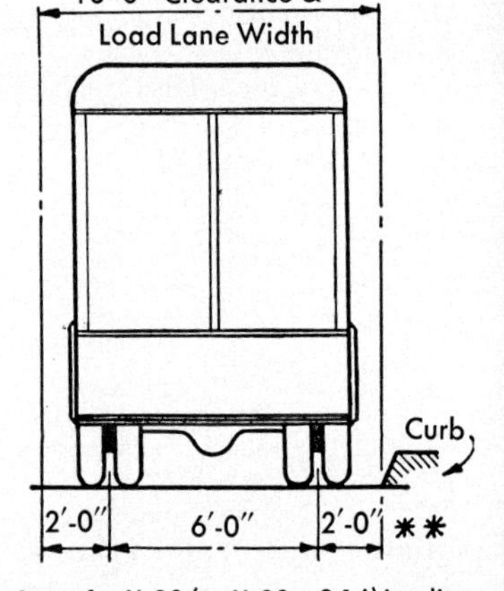

* In the design of floors (concrete slabs, steel grid floors, and timber floors) for H 20 or H 20—S 16 loading, one axle load of 24,000 pounds or two axle loads of 16,000 pounds each, spaced 4 feet apart may be used, whichever produces the greater stress, instead of the 32,000 pound axle shown.

** For slab design the center line of wheel shall be assumed to be 1 foot from face of curb (See Art. 3. 3. 2. (b).)

Fig. 77. Standard highway loadings. In the design of bridge floors for H 20 (or H 20—S 16) loading, one axle of 24,000 lb or two axle loads of 16,000 lb each, spaced 4 ft apart may be used, whichever produces the greater stress, instead of the 32,000 lb axle shown.—Reproduced from *Standard Specifications for Highway Bridges, AASHO, 1953.*

CHAPTER NINE

Highway Loadings and Gages

Highway Loadings

In addition to the dead load of an embankment, highway culverts or drains may be subject to live loads and impact, both during construction and while in normal service. Gage tables are based on specific heights of cover and legal live loads.

Live loads vary greatly. During construction the concentrated wheel loads of heavy equipment may be greater than the service loads after a pavement is placed. Proper installation practice avoids running such construction equipment directly over a structure until it has been backfilled and tamped to a point above the structure. This minimum protective cover may be more than that shown on Fig. 78.

The legal load limit varies from 18,000 lb to 22,400 lb maximum axle on state highway road surfaces.* (One exception is the New Jersey Turnpike, opened in 1952, which is based on a 36,000 lb maximum axle loading. This highway carried a peak count of 104,000 vehicles per day on its 4 and 6-lane surfaces.)

Increases of trucks and tractor-trucks on highways in the United States have been phenomenal. The increase was from 4,513,340 in 1944 to 7,667,000 in 1949. Loaded truck combinations averaged 39,455 lb in 1948, an increase of 47 per cent over the 1941 figure. In 1947 the eastern states had an average of twenty-nine axles in excess of 22,000 lb, per 1000 trucks and combinations, while the western states' average was only three per 1000. In 1948, there were fifty-five overloaded trucks per 1000 vehicles, with six being 30 per cent overloaded and one 50 per cent above the legal axle-load limit.*

Where private industries such as mining companies operate only over their own private roads, they may use giant draglines, shovels, scraper equipment and 30-cu yd trucks which place great total loads on road surfaces and structures. However, the unit wheel or axle loads are usually reduced by huge pneumatic tires, or wide metal treads with a large number of contacts on the road.

Highway departments issue special permits for occasional super-loads to cross or travel over their highways. On the other hand, during the spring break-up periods, they may restrict load limits for several weeks to reduce the amount of possible damage to road surfaces.

Although the legal load limits on *road surfaces* are established between 18,000 and 22,400 lb per axle, the design of bridges and culverts is based on gross loadings that vary with the class of road.† The loadings illustrated in Fig. 77 are designated "H" followed by a number indicating the gross weight in tons of the standard truck. These are known as H-20, H-15 and H-10 based on standard trucks or "lane loads" which are equivalent to truck trains. The "H-S" loadings, consisting of a tractor truck with a semi-trailer, are not illustrated. The "H-S" loadings have no effect on the majority of culvert installations, because corrugated metal structures are usually of such diameter or span that only one axle or pair of

*"The Truck Weight Problem in Highway Transportation," Highway Research Board Bulletin No. 26, Table 9, July 1950.

†"Standard Specifications for Highway Materials and Methods of Sampling and Testing," AASHO, 1950, p. 80.

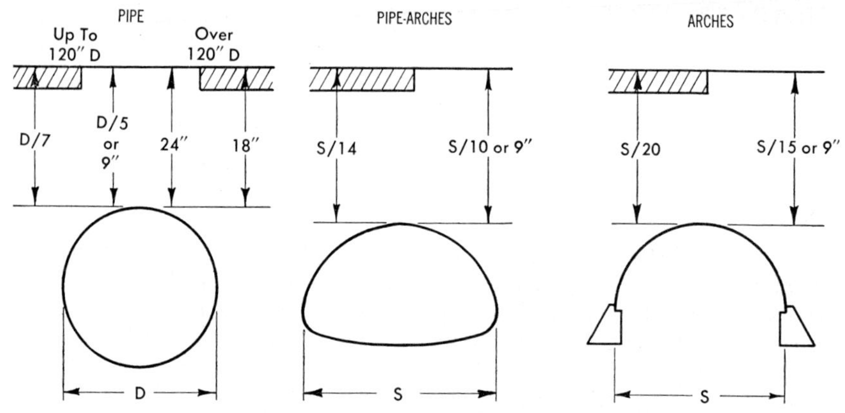

NOTES—Minimum cushion of 3″ under slab and 9″ under unpaved surface. Covers shown are for finished construction. During construction cover must be provided to protect the structure from damage.

Fig. 78. Minimum height of cover for corrugated metal structures under H-15 or H-20 highway loadings, for rigid or flexible pavements and unpaved surfaces.

TABLE 9-1 RECOMMENDED MINIMUM HEIGHT OF COVER* FOR CORRUGATED METAL STRUCTURES UNDER HIGHWAYS

Load	*Surface*	*Base of Measurement*	*Round or Elliptical Pipe*		*Arches*	*Pipe-Arches*
			Up to 120-in. Diam.	*Over 120-in. Diam.*		
H-10 or less	Unpaved, and flexible pavements	Top of surface	D/10 or 6 in. min.	12 in. minimum	S/25 or 6 in. min.	S/15 or 6 in. min.
H-15 and H-20	Unpaved, and flexible pavements	Top of surface	D/5 or 9 in. min.	24 in. minimum	S/15 or 9 in. min.	S/10 or 9 in. min.
	Rigid pavements	Top of slab	D/7 or	18 in. min.	S/20	S/14
			(minimum of 3-in. cushion under slab)			

*Covers shown are for finished construction. During construction, adequate cover must be provided to protect the structure from damage.

axles is over the structure. The culvert designer is interested only in the maximum axle load rather than the total weight of the truck and its load. The policy of the AASHO states that "No axle shall carry a load in excess of 18,000 lb."

TABLE 9-2 GAGES OF CORRUGATED METAL *PIPE* (*UNSTRUTTED*) FOR H-20 LIVE LOAD

Diam. in Inches	*Area in Sq Ft*	*Height of Cover Above Top of Culvert—in Feet*												
		1–10	*11–15*	*16–20*	*21–25*	*26–30*	*31–35*	*36–40*	*41–45*	*46–50*	*51–60*	*61–70*	*71–80*	*81–100*
15	1.2	16	16	16	16	16	16	16	16	16	14	14	12	12
18	1.8	16	16	16	16	16	16	16	14	14	14	12	12	12
21	2.4	16	16	16	16	16	16	14	14	14	12	12	12	10
24	3.1	16†	16†	14	14	14	14	14	14	12	12	12	10	10
30	4.9	14	14	14	14	14	12	12	12	10	10	10	8*	8*
36	7.1	14†	14†	12	12	12	10	10	10	8	8	8*	8*	8*
42	9.6	12	12	12	12	10	10	8	8	8	8*	8*	8*	8*
48	12.6	12	12	12	10	8	8							
54	15.9	12	12	10	8	8								
60	19.6	10	10	8	8									
66	23.8	10	10	8										
72	28.3	10	8											

For values not shown, use Table 9-3.

†Not in accord with AASHO.
*Make a trench one diameter deep in original soil or in compacted fill. The gages shown are the minimum with adequate backfill. For recommended *minimum* height of cover, see Table 9-1.

TABLE 9-3 GAGES OF CORRUGATED METAL *PIPE* (*STRUTTED*) FOR H-20 LIVE LOAD

Diam. in Inches	*Area in Sq Ft*	*Height of Cover Above Top of Culvert—in Feet*										
		1–20	*21–25*	*26–30*	*31–35*	*36–40*	*41–45*	*46–50*	*51–60*	*61–70*	*71–80*	*81–100*
48	12.6		12	10	10	10	10	10	10	10	8	8
54	15.9	12	10	10	10	10	10	10	8	8	8	8
60	19.6	10	10	10	10	10	10	8	8	8	8	
66	23.8	10	10	10	10	8	8	8	8	8		
72	28.3	10	10	8	8	8	8	8	8			
78	33.2	8	8									
84	38.5	8										

The gages shown are the minimum with adequate backfill.
For recommended *minimum* height of cover, see Table 9-1.

AASHO Highway Gage Tables

The American Association of State Highway Officials adopted (originally in 1932) a table of gages for riveted corrugated metal pipe in diameters from 8 to 84-in. without express limitation as to fill height. (Designation: M36-47). This table is in agreement in most respects with that of corrugated pipe manufacturers.

In 1952 this Association revised its specification (originally adopted in 1941) on corrugated structural plate pipe and arches.* Pipe-arches were included in the 1952 specification. This specification is based on extensive research described in Chapter 5.†

Individual state highway departments for the most part follow the AASHO specification, which agrees with the manufacturers' standard recommendations.

County and other highway departments usually follow the practice of the states in which they are located.

The U. S. Bureau of Public Roads and the AASHO are in agreement on specifications for federal aid primary, secondary and rural roads. In addition, the Bureau of Public Roads has a forests and parks standard specification (FP-41) quite similar to the AASHO specification (except that 72 and 84-in. diameters are not included).

Examples of Highway Gage Selection

Example No. 1

Kind of highway:	state or federal-aid primary
Size of opening:	60-in. diameter
Type of structure:	riveted corrugated metal pipe
Depth of cover:	3 ft
Live Load:	H-20
Table to use:	Table No. 9-2, page 107
Gage selected:	No. 10—pipe need not be strutted

TABLE 9-4 GAGES OF CORRUGATED METAL *PIPE-ARCHES* FOR H-20 LIVE LOAD

Diam. of Pipe of Equal Periph. in Inches	*Span in Inches*	*Rise in Inches*	*Height of Cover—in Feet*				
			1	*2–4*	*5–9*	*10–15*	*16–20*
15	18	11	16	16	16	16	16
18	22	13	16	16	16	16	16
21	25	16	16	16	16	16	16
24	29	18	14	14	14	14	14
30	36	22	14	14	14	14	14
36	43	27	12	12	12	12	12
42	50	31	12	12	12	12	10
48	58	36	10	12	12	10	10
54	65	40	10	12	12	10	8
60	72	44	8	10	10	8	—

The gages shown are the recommended minimum.
For recommended *minimum* height of cover, see Table 9-1.

---

*"Standard Specifications for Highway Bridges," AASHO, Sec. 2.23, 3.10, 3.11 and 4.19, 1953.

†"Load Deflection Tests on Corrugated Metal Sections," Michigan Engineering Experiment Station Bulletin 109, 1951, pp. 62.

Example No. 2

Kind of highway:	state or local
Size of opening:	72-in. diam.
Type of structure:	corr. metal pipe
Depth of cover:	40 ft
Live Load:	(not important under this fill)
Table to use:	Table No. 9-3
Gage selected:	No. 8—pipe should be strutted

Example No. 3

Kind of highway:	state or local
Size of opening and structure:	65 in. x 40 in. pipe-arch
Depth of cover:	3 ft
Live Load:	H-15
Table to use:	Table No. 9-4
Gage selected:	No. 12 (no strutting)

TABLE 9-5 GAGES OF MULTI-PLATE *PIPE* (*UNSTRUTTED*) FOR H-20 LIVE LOAD

Diameter in Inches	*Height of Cover—in Feet*															
	1–5	*6–10*	*11–15*	*16–20*	*21–25*	*26–30*	*31–35*	*36–40*	*41–45*	*46–50*	*51–55*	*56–60*	*61–70*	*71–80*	*81–90*	*91–100*
60	12	12	12	12	12	10	10	10	10	10	8	8	8	7	5	5
66	12	12	12	12	10	10	10	10	8	8	8	8	8	7	5	3
72	12	12	12	10	10	10	10	8	8	8	8	7	7	5	3	1
78	12	12	12	10	10	10	8	8	8	8	7	7	5	3	1	—
84	10	12	10	10	10	8	8	8	8	7	7	5	5	3	1	
90	10	12	10	10	8	8	8	7	7	7	5	5	3	1	—	
96	10	12	10	10	8	8	8	7	7	5	5	5	3	1		
102	10	10	10	8	8	8	7	7	5	5	5	5	1	—		
108	10	10	10	8	8	7	7	5	5	5	5	3	1			
114	10	10	10	8	8	7	5	5	5	3	3	3	1			
120	8	10	8	8	7	5	5	5	3	3	3	1	—			
126	8	10	8	7	7	5	5	3	3	3	1	1				
132	8	10	8	7	5	5	5	3	3	3	1	1				
138	8	10	8	7	5	5	3	3	3	1	1	—				
144	8	8	8	7	5	5	3	3	1	1	—					
150	7	8	7	5	5	3	3	1	1	1						
156	7	8	7	5	5	3	3	1	1	—						
162	7	8	7	5	3	3	1	1	1							
168	5	8	5	5	3	1	1	—	—							
174	5	7	5	3	3	1	1									
180	5	7	5	3	3	1	—									

The gages shown are the minimum structural requirements for use with adequate backfill. For additional footnotes on Multi-Plate pipe, see following tables.

Example No. 4	Kind of highway:	state or local
	Size of opening:	10-ft diam.
	Type of structure:	Multi-Plate pipe
	Depth of cover:	4 ft
	Live Load:	H-20
	Table to use:	Tables, No. 9-5, 9-6
	Gage selected:	8 gage if unstrutted
		10 gage if strutted

TABLE 9-6 GAGES OF MULTI-PLATE *PIPE* (*STRUTTED*) FOR H-20 LIVE LOAD

Diameter in Inches	*Height of Cover—in Feet*																*Height of Cover Limit 1 Gage—6 Bolts*
	1–5	*6–10*	*11–15*	*16–20*	*21–25*	*26–30*	*31–35*	*36–40*	*41–45*	*46–50*	*51–55*	*56–60*	*61–70*	*71–80*	*81–90*	*91–100*	
60	12	12	12	12	12	12	12	12	12	12	10	10	8	7	5	5	200
66	12	12	12	12	12	12	12	12	12	10	10	8	8	7	5	3	180
72	12	12	12	12	12	12	12	12	10	10	8	8	7	5	3	1	165
78	12	12	12	12	12	12	12	10	10	8	8	8	5	3	1	—	150
84	12	12	12	12	12	12	12	10	10	8	8	7	5	3	1		140
90	12	12	12	12	12	12	10	10	8	8	7	5	3	1	—		130
96	12	12	12	12	12	10	10	10	8	7	7	5	3	1			125
102	12	12	12	12	10	10	10	8	8	7	5	5	1	—			115
108	12	12	12	10	10	10	10	8	7	5	5	3	1				110
114	10	12	10	10	10	10	8	8	7	5	5	3	1				105
120	10	12	10	10	10	10	8	7	5	5	3	1	—				100
126	10	12	10	10	10	10	8	7	5	3	3	1					95
132	10	10	10	10	10	8	8	7	5	3	1	1					90
138	10	10	10	10	10	8	7	5	3	3	1	—					85
144	10	10	10	10	8	8	7	5	3	1	1						80
150	10	10	10	8	8	8	7	5	3	1	—						80
156	10	10	10	8	8	8	5	3	1	1							75
162	10	10	10	8	8	7	5	3	1	—							70
168	10	10	10	8	8	7	5	3	1								70
174	8	10	8	8	8	7	5	3	1								65
180	8	10	8	8	8	5	3	1	—								65

For structures in this zone use 1 gage with six bolts per foot of longitudinal seam with height of cover limits as shown in column at right.

The gages shown are the minimum structural requirements for use with adequate backfill. Bottom plates are frequently designed of heavier gage to resist wear.

Gages are for finished construction; during construction adequate cover must be provided to protect the structure from damage.

For minimum height of cover, see table "Recommended Minimum Height of Cover." Table 9-1.

The last column shows the greatest height of cover that can be placed on pipes specially fabricated to have six bolts per foot in each longitudinal seam in 1 gage metal.

Pipe diameters are to inside crests and are subject to manufacturing tolerances.

For lighter H-loadings, the manufacturer recommends the use of the above table.

TABLE 9-7 GAGES OF MULTI-PLATE *PIPE* (*UNSTRUTTED*) FOR NO LIVE LOAD

Diameter in Inches	*Height of Cover—in Feet*				
	1–5	*6–10*	*11–15*	*16–20*	*21–25*
60	12	12	12	12	12
66	12	12	12	12	10
72	12	12	12	10	10
78	12	12	12	10	10
84	12	12	10	10	10
90	12	12	10	10	8
96	12	12	10	10	8
102	10	10	10	8	8
108	10	10	10	8	8
114	10	10	10	8	8
120	10	10	8	8	7
126	10	10	8	7	7
132	10	10	8	7	5
138	8	10	8	7	5
144	8	8	8	7	5
150	8	8	7	5	5
156	8	8	7	5	5
162	8	8	7	5	3
168	7	8	5	5	3
174	7	7	5	3	3
180	7	7	5	3	3

The gages shown are the minimum structural requirements for use with adequate backfill.

TABLE 9-8 GAGES OF MULTI-PLATE *PIPE* (*STRUTTED*) FOR NO LIVE LOAD

Diameter in Inches	*Height of Cover—in Feet*				
	1–5	*6–10*	*11–15*	*16–20*	*21–25*
60	12	12	12	12	12
66	12	12	12	12	12
72	12	12	12	12	12
78	12	12	12	12	12
84	12	12	12	12	12
90	12	12	12	12	12
96	12	12	12	12	12
102	12	12	12	12	10
108	12	12	12	10	10
114	10	12	10	10	10
120	10	12	10	10	10
126	10	12	10	10	10
132	10	10	10	10	10
138	10	10	10	10	10
144	10	10	10	10	8
150	10	10	10	8	8
156	10	10	10	8	8
162	10	10	10	8	8
168	10	10	10	8	8
174	10	10	8	8	8
180	8	10	8	8	8

See also footnotes under Table 9-6.

Example No. 5	Kind of highway:	state or federal-aid
	Size of opening:	12-ft diam.
	Type of structure:	Multi-Plate pipe
	Depth of cover:	60 ft
	Live Load:	(not important)
	Table to use:	No. 9-6
	Gage selected:	No. 1 strutted—with 6 bolts per ft of longitudinal seam

TABLE 9-9 GAGES OF MULTI-PLATE *PIPE-ARCHES* FOR H-20 LIVE LOAD

Span	*Height of Cover—in Feet*														
	1	*2*	*3*	*4*	*5*	*6*	*7*	*8*	*9*	*10*	*11*	*12*	*13*	*14*	*15*
5′-0″	12	12	12	12	12	12	12	12	12	12	12	12	12	12	12
5′-6″	12	12	12	12	12	12	12	12	12	12	12	12	12	12	12
6′-0″	12	12	12	12	12	12	12	12	12	12	12	12	12	12	12
6′-6″	12	12	12	12	12	12	12	12	12	12	12	12	12	12	10
7′-0″	10	12	12	12	12	12	12	12	12	12	12	12	12	10	10
7′-6″	10	10	12	12	12	12	12	12	12	12	12	12	10	10	10
8′-0″	10	10	10	12	12	12	12	12	12	12	12	10	10	10	10
8′-6″	10	10	10	10	10	10	10	10	10	10	10	10	10	10	8
9′-0″	10	10	10	10	10	10	10	10	10	10	10	10	10	8	8
9′-6″	8	10	10	10	10	10	10	10	10	10	10	10	8	8	8
10′-0″	8	8	10	10	10	10	10	10	10	10	10	8	8	8	7
10′-6″	8	8	8	10	10	10	10	10	10	10	10	8	8	8	7
11′-0″	8	8	8	10	10	10	10	10	10	8	8	8	7	7	5
11′-6″	7	8	8	8	10	10	10	10	8	8	8	8	7	7	5
12′-0″	7	8	8	8	8	8	8	8	8	8	8	7	5	5	3
12′-6″	7	7	8	8	8	8	8	8	8	8	7	7	5	5	3
13′-0″	5	7	8	8	8	8	8	8	8	7	7	5	5	3	1
13′-6″	5	5	7	8	8	8	8	8	8	7	5	5	5	3	1
14′-0″	5	5	7	7	8	8	8	7	7	5	5	3	3	1	1
14′-6″	3	5	5	7	7	7	7	7	7	5	5	3	3	1	1
15′-0″	3	5	5	7	7	7	7	7	5	3	3	1	1	—	—
15′-6″	3	3	5	5	7	7	7	7	5	3	3	1	1	—	—
16′-0″	1	3	5	5	7	7	7	5	3	3	1	1	—	—	—
16′-6″	1	3	3	5	5	5	5	3	3	1	1	—	—	—	—

The gages shown are the minimum structural requirements for use with adequate backfill. Bottom plates are frequently designed of heavier gage to resist wear.

Gages are for finished construction; during construction adequate cover must be provided to protect the structure from damage.

Plates are standard 6″ x 2″ corrugation of 1⅛″ valley radius with four bolts per foot in each longitudinal seam. Bolts are ¾″ diameter, high strength to meet ASTM: A325-52T and galvanized to meet ASTM: A153-49.

Pipe-Arches are available in a range of spans, rises and areas; tabular values are for gage determination.

For recommended *minimum* height of cover, see Table 9-1.

Example No. 6	Kind of highway:	local
	Size of opening:	14-ft span
	Type of structure	Multi-Plate pipe-arch 14 ft 1 in. x 8 ft 9 in.
	Depth of cover:	2 ft
	Live Load:	H-15
	Table to use:	No. 8-11 and 9-11
	Gage selected:	No. 7

TABLE 9-10 GAGES OF MULTI-PLATE *PIPE-ARCHES* FOR H-15 LIVE LOAD

Span	*Height of Cover—in Feet*														
	1	*2*	*3*	*4*	*5*	*6*	*7*	*8*	*9*	*10*	*11*	*12*	*13*	*14*	*15*
5′-0″	12	12	12	12	12	12	12	12	12	12	12	12	12	12	12
5′-6″	12	12	12	12	12	12	12	12	12	12	12	12	12	12	12
6′-0″	12	12	12	12	12	12	12	12	12	12	12	12	12	12	12
6′-6″	12	12	12	12	12	12	12	12	12	12	12	12	12	12	10
7′-0″	10	12	12	12	12	12	12	12	12	12	12	12	12	10	10
7′-6″	10	12	12	12	12	12	12	12	12	12	12	12	10	10	10
8′-0″	10	10	12	12	12	12	12	12	12	12	12	12	10	10	10
8′-6″	10	10	12	12	12	12	12	12	10	10	10	10	10	10	8
9′-0″	10	10	10	12	12	12	12	10	10	10	10	10	10	8	8
9′-6″	10	10	10	10	10	12	10	10	10	10	10	10	8	8	8
10′-0″	8	10	10	10	10	10	10	10	10	10	10	10	8	8	7
10′-6″	8	8	10	10	10	10	10	10	10	10	10	8	8	8	7
11′-0″	8	8	10	10	10	10	10	10	10	10	8	8	8	7	5
11′-6″	8	8	8	10	10	10	10	10	10	8	8	8	7	7	5
12′-0″	8	8	8	10	10	10	10	10	8	8	8	8	7	5	5
12′-6″	7	8	8	8	10	10	10	8	8	8	8	7	5	5	3
13′-0″	7	8	8	8	8	8	8	8	8	8	8	7	5	5	3
13′-6″	7	7	8	8	8	8	8	8	8	8	7	5	5	3	3
14′-0″	5	7	8	8	8	8	8	8	8	7	7	5	3	3	1
14′-6″	5	5	7	8	8	8	8	8	8	7	5	5	3	3	1
15′-0″	5	5	7	7	8	8	8	8	7	7	5	5	3	1	1
15′-6″	3	5	5	7	7	8	8	7	7	5	5	3	1	1	1
16′-0″	3	5	5	7	7	7	7	7	5	5	5	3	1	1	—
16′-6″	3	3	5	5	7	7	7	7	5	5	3	1	1	—	

The gages shown are the minimum structural requirements for use with adequate backfill. For additional footnotes, see Table 9-9.

TABLE 9-11 GAGES OF MULTI-PLATE *PIPE-ARCHES* FOR H-10 LIVE LOAD

Span	*Height of Cover—in Feet*														
	1	*2*	*3*	*4*	*5*	*6*	*7*	*8*	*9*	*10*	*11*	*12*	*13*	*14*	*15*
5′-0″	12	12	12	12	12	12	12	12	12	12	12	12	12	12	12
5′-6″	12	12	12	12	12	12	12	12	12	12	12	12	12	12	12
6′-0″	12	12	12	12	12	12	12	12	12	12	12	12	12	12	12
6′-6″	12	12	12	12	12	12	12	12	12	12	12	12	12	12	12
7′-0″	12	12	12	12	12	12	12	12	12	12	12	12	12	12	10
7′-6″	12	12	12	12	12	12	12	12	12	12	12	12	10	10	10
8′-0″	12	12	12	12	12	12	12	12	12	12	10	10	10	10	10
8′-6″	12	12	12	12	12	12	12	12	10	10	10	10	10	10	10
9′-0″	12	12	12	12	12	12	12	10	10	10	10	10	10	10	10
9′-6″	12	12	12	12	12	12	10	10	10	10	10	10	10	10	8
10′-0″	10	12	12	12	10	10	10	10	10	10	10	10	10	8	8
10′-6″	10	10	10	10	10	10	10	10	10	10	10	8	8	8	8
11′-0″	10	10	10	10	10	10	10	10	10	10	8	8	8	8	7
11′-6″	10	10	10	10	10	10	10	10	10	8	8	8	8	8	7
12′-0″	10	10	10	10	10	10	10	10	8	8	8	8	8	7	7
12′-6″	8	10	10	10	10	10	10	8	8	8	8	8	7	7	5
13′-0″	8	10	10	10	10	10	8	8	8	8	8	8	7	7	5
13′-6″	8	8	10	10	10	8	8	8	8	8	8	7	7	5	5
14′-0″	7	8	8	10	8	8	8	8	8	8	7	7	5	5	3
14′-6″	7	7	8	8	8	8	8	8	8	8	7	7	5	5	3
15′-0″	7	7	8	8	8	8	8	8	8	7	7	7	5	3	3
15′-6″	5	7	7	8	8	8	8	8	7	7	7	5	3	3	3
16′-0″	5	7	7	8	8	8	8	7	7	7	5	5	3	3	1
16′-6″	5	5	7	7	8	8	8	7	7	7	5	3	3	1	—

The gages shown are the minimum structural requirements for use with adequate backfill. Bottom plates are frequently designed of heavier gage to resist wear.

Gages are for finished construction; during construction adequate cover must be provided to protect the structure from damage.

For minimum height of cover, see table "Recommended Minimum Height of Cover." Table 9-1.

Plates are standard 6″ x 2″ corrugation of 1⅛″ valley radius with four bolts per foot in each longitudinal seam. Bolts are ¾″ diameter, high strength to meet ASTM: A325-52T and galvanized to meet ASTM: A153-49.

Pipe-Arches are available in a range of spans, rises and areas; tabular values are for gage determination.

TABLE 9-12 GAGES OF MULTI-PLATE *PIPE-ARCHES* FOR NO LIVE LOAD

Span	*Height of Cover—in Feet*														
	1	*2*	*3*	*4*	*5*	*6*	*7*	*8*	*9*	*10*	*11*	*12*	*13*	*14*	*15*
5′-0″	12	12	12	12	12	12	12	12	12	12	12	12	12	12	12
5′-6″	12	12	12	12	12	12	12	12	12	12	12	12	12	12	12
6′-0″	12	12	12	12	12	12	12	12	12	12	12	12	12	12	12
6′-6″	12	12	12	12	12	12	12	12	12	12	22	12	12	12	12
7′-0″	12	12	12	12	12	12	12	12	12	12	12	12	12	12	10
7′-6″	12	12	12	12	12	12	12	12	12	12	12	12	10	10	10
8′-0″	12	12	12	12	12	12	12	12	12	12	10	10	10	10	10
8′-6″	12	12	12	12	12	12	12	12	10	10	10	10	10	10	10
9′-0″	12	12	12	12	12	12	12	10	10	10	10	10	10	10	10
9′-6″	12	12	12	12	12	12	10	10	10	10	10	10	10	10	8
10′-0″	10	12	12	12	10	10	10	10	10	10	10	10	10	8	8
10′-6″	10	12	10	10	10	10	10	10	10	10	10	8	8	8	8
11′-0″	10	10	10	10	10	10	10	10	10	10	8	8	8	8	8
11′-6″	10	10	10	10	10	10	10	10	10	8	8	8	8	8	8
12′-0″	10	10	10	10	10	10	10	10	8	8	8	8	8	8	8
12′-6″	10	10	10	10	10	10	10	8	8	8	8	8	8	8	7
13′-0″	10	10	10	10	10	10	8	8	8	8	8	8	8	7	7
13′-6″	10	10	10	10	10	8	8	8	8	8	8	8	7	7	7
14′-0″	10	10	10	10	8	8	8	8	8	8	7	7	7	7	5
14′-6″	10	10	10	8	8	8	8	8	8	8	7	7	7	5	5
15′-0″	8	10	10	8	8	8	8	8	8	7	7	7	5	5	5
15′-6″	8	10	8	8	8	8	8	8	7	7	7	5	5	5	5
16′-0″	8	8	8	8	8	8	8	7	7	7	5	5	5	5	5
16′-6″	8	8	8	8	8	8	8	7	7	7	5	5	5	5	3

The gages shown are the minimum structural requirements for use with adequate backfill. Bottom plates are frequently designed of heavier gage to resist wear.

Gages are for finished construction; during construction adequate cover must be provided to protect the structure from damage.

For recommended *minimum* height of cover, see Table 9-1.

Plates are standard 6″ x 2″ corrugation of 1⅛″ valley radius with four bolts per foot in each longitudinal seam. Bolts are ¾″ diameter, high strength to meet ASTM: A325-52T and galvanized to meet ASTM: A153-49.

Pipe-Arches are available in a range of spans, rises and areas; tabular values are for gage determination.

TABLE 9-13 GAGES OF MULTI-PLATE *ARCHES* FOR H-20 LIVE LOAD

Span in Feet	Height of Cover—in Feet									
	1	*2*	*3*	*4*	*5*	*6*	*7*	*8*	*9*	*10*
4 to 10	12	12	12	12	12	12	12	12	12	12
11	10	10	10	12	12	12	12	12	12	12
12	10	10	10	12	12	12	12	12	10	10
13	8	8	10	12	12	12	12	10	10	8
14	7	8	8	10	10	10	10	8	8	8
15	5	7	8	10	10	10	10	8	8	7
16	5	5	7	8	8	10	8	7	7	5
17	3	5	5	7	8	8	8	7	5	3
18	3	3	5	7	7	8	7	5	3	3
19	1*	1*	3	5	5	7	5	3	3	1
20	—	1*	1*	3	5	5	5	3	1	—
21	—	—	1*	3	3	5	3	1	—	—
22	—	—	—	1	3	3	3	1	—	—
23	—	—	—	—	1	3	1	—	—	—
24	—	—	—	—	—	1	1	—	—	—
25	—	—	—	—	—	1	—	—	—	—

*Use only when R/S is 0.3 or more.

The gages shown are the minimum structural requirements for use with adequate backfill.

Gages are for finished construction; during construction adequate cover must be provided to protect the structure from damage.

For recommended minimum height of cover, see Table 9-1.

Plates are standard 6″ x 2″ corrugation of 1⅛″ valley radius with four bolts per foot in each longitudinal seam. Bolts are ¾″ diameter, high strength to meet ASTM: A325-52T and galvanized to meet ASTM: A153-49.

TABLE 9-14 GAGES OF MULTI-PLATE *ARCHES* FOR H-15 LIVE LOAD

Span in Feet	Height of Cover—in Feet									
	1	*2*	*3*	*4*	*5*	*6*	*7*	*8*	*9*	*10*
4 to 10	12	12	12	12	12	12	12	12	12	12
11	12	12	12	12	12	12	12	12	12	12
12	12	12	12	12	12	12	12	12	12	10
13	10	10	12	12	12	12	12	10	10	10
14	10	10	10	12	12	12	10	10	8	8
15	8	10	10	12	12	10	10	8	8	7
16	8	8	8	10	10	10	10	8	7	7
17	7	8	8	10	10	10	8	7	7	5
18	7	7	7	8	8	8	8	7	5	3
19	5	5	7	8	8	8	7	5	3	3
20	3	5	5	7	8	8	5	5	3	1
21	3	3	5	5	7	7	5	3	3	—
22	1*	3	3	5	5	7	5	3	1	—
23	1*	1*	3	3	5	5	3	1	—	—
24	—	1*	1	3	3	5	3	1	—	—
25	—	—	—	1	3	3	3	—	—	—
26	—	—	—	1	1	3	1	—	—	—
27	—	—	—	—	1	1	1	—	—	—
28	—	—	—	—	—	1	—	—	—	—

Continued from section at left

Range of rise to span is from 0.2 to 0.5.

Arches are available in a range of sizes; tabular values are for gage determination.

TABLE 9-15 GAGES OF MULTI-PLATE *ARCHES* FOR H-10 LIVE LOAD

Span in Feet	*Height of Cover—in Feet*									
	1	*2*	*3*	*4*	*5*	*6*	*7*	*8*	*9*	*10*
4 to 10	12	12	12	12	12	12	12	12	12	12
11	12	12	12	12	12	12	12	12	12	12
12	12	12	12	12	12	12	12	12	12	10
13	12	12	12	12	12	12	12	12	10	10
14	12	12	12	12	12	12	12	10	10	8
15	12	12	12	12	12	12	12	10	8	8
16	10	10	12	12	12	12	10	10	8	7
17	10	10	10	12	12	12	10	8	8	7
18	10	10	10	12	10	10	10	8	7	5
19	8	8	10	10	10	10	8	7	5	3
20	8	8	10	10	10	10	8	7	5	3
21	8	8	8	10	10	10	8	5	3	1
22	7	7	8	8	8	8	7	5	3	1
23	5	7	7	8	8	8	7	3	1	—
24	3	5	7	7	8	8	5	3	1	—
25	1	5	5	7	7	8	5	3	1	—
26	—	5	5	5	5	7	5	3	—	—
27		3	3	5	5	5	3	1	—	—
28		1	3	3	3	5	3	1	—	—
29		1	1	3	3	3	3	1	—	—
30		—	1	1	1	3	1	1	—	—

The gages shown are the minimum structural requirements for use with adequate backfill.

For additional footnotes, see page 116.

TABLE 9-16 GAGES OF MULTI-PLATE *ARCHES* FOR NO LIVE LOAD

Span in Feet	*Height of Cover—in Feet*									
	1	*2*	*3*	*4*	*5*	*6*	*7*	*8*	*9*	*10*
4 to 12	12	12	12	12	12	12	12	12	12	12
13	12	12	12	12	12	12	12	12	12	10
14	12	12	12	12	12	12	12	12	10	10
15	12	12	12	12	12	12	12	10	10	8
16	12	12	12	12	12	12	12	10	8	8
17	12	12	12	12	12	12	12	10	8	7
18	12	12	12	12	12	12	10	8	8	5
19	10	12	12	12	12	12	10	8	7	5
20	10	10	10	12	12	10	8	8	5	3
21	8	10	10	10	10	10	8	7	5	3
22	7	8	8	10	8	8	7	5	3	1
23	5	8	8	8	8	8	7	5	3	1
24	3	7	7	8	8	7	5	5	3	1
25	1	5	7	7	7	5	5	3	1	—
26	—	5	5	7	5	5	5	3	1	
27		3	5	5	5	5	3	3	1	
28		1	5	5	5	5	3	1	1	
29		1	3	3	3	3	3	1	—	
30		—	3	3	3	3	1	1		

CHAPTER TEN

Sewer Loadings and Gages

Sewer and Street Culvert Loadings; Gage Tables

Sewers, culverts and other conduits under streets are subject to about the same surface loads (live loads) as highway culverts. However, because of more favorable installation conditions such as trenching and drier foundation soils (in many cases), the gages for municipal installation may usually be made lighter with equal safety.

Stream enclosures or sewers across open lands may or may not be subject to repeated live loads. Sewers across residential property are not likely to be subject to surface loads as are those across industrial or commercial property. Fig. 79.

For aerial sewers on bents or hung from brackets, the gage will be a minimum. See Table 15-1, page 145, on safe spans for pipe running full under beam loading.

For sewer work, see Tables 10-1 to 10-9.

These gage tables are acceptable to sewer designers, consulting engineers and others and are in common use.

TABLE 10-1 GAGES OF CORRUGATED METAL SEWER PIPE FOR H-10 LIVE LOAD—TRENCH CONDITION

Diam. in Inches	*Area in Sq Ft*	*Height of Cover Above Top of Pipe—in Feet*								
		1.0–2.9	*3.0–6.9*	*7.0–10*	*11–15*	*16–20*	*21–25*	*26–30*	*31–35*	*36–40*
8	0.35	16	16	16	16	16	16	16	16	16
10	0.55	16	16	16	16	16	16	16	16	16
12	0.79	16	16	16	16	16	16	16	16	16
15	1.23	16	16	16	16	16	16	16	16	16
18	1.77	16	16	16	16	16	16	16	16	16
21	2.41	16	16	16	16	16	16	16	16	14
24	3.14	16	16	16	16	14	14	14	14	14
30	4.91	16	16	16	14	14	14	14	12	12
36	7.07	16	16	14	14	14	12	12	10	10
42	9.62	14	14	14	12	12	12	10	10	8
48	12.6	14	14	14	12	12	12	10	10	8
54	15.9	12	14	14	12	12	10	10	10	8
60	19.6	12	14	12	10	10	10	10	8	8
66	23.8	12	12	12	10	10	8	8	8	8
72	28.3	10	12	10	10	8	8	8	8	
78	33.2	10	12	10	8	8	8	8		
84	38.5	10	10	8	8	8	8	8		

For recommended *minimum* height of cover, see Table 9-1.

Unless installed under favorable conditions, pipe in gages shown below heavy black should be strutted according to the manufacturers' recommendations.

For installations larger than 84-in. diameter, write for recommendations of manufacturer.

TABLE 10-2 GAGES OF CORRUGATED METAL SEWER PIPE FOR H-20 LIVE LOAD—TRENCH CONDITION

Diam. in Inches	*Area in Sq Ft*	*Height of Cover Above Top of Pipe—in Feet*								
		1.0–2.9	*3.0–6.9*	*7.0–10*	*11–15*	*16–20*	*21–25*	*26–30*	*31–35*	*36–40*
8	0.35	16	16	16	16	16	16	16	16	16
10	0.55	16	16	16	16	16	16	16	16	16
12	0.79	16	16	16	16	16	16	16	16	16
15	1.23	16	16	16	16	16	16	16	16	16
18	1.77	16	16	16	16	16	16	16	16	16
21	2.41	16	16	16	16	16	16	16	16	14
24	3.14	16	16	16	16	14	14	14	14	14
30	4.91	14	14	14	14	14	14	14	12	12
36	7.07	14	14	14	14	14	12	12	10	10
42	9.62	12	14	14	12	12	12	10	10	8
48	12.6	12	14	12	12	12	12	10	10	8
54	15.9	12	14	12	12	12	10	10	10	8
60	19.6	12	12	12	10	10	10	10	8	8
66	23.8	10	12	10	10	10	8	8	8	8
72	28.3	10	12	10	10	8	8	8	8	
78	33.2	8	10	8	8	8	8	8		
84	38.5	8	10	8	8	8	8	8		

For recommended *minimum* height of cover, see Table 9-1.

Unless installed under favorable conditions, pipe in gages shown below heavy black should be strutted according to the manufacturers' recommendations.

For installations larger than 84-in. diameter, write for recommendations of manufacturer.

TABLE 10-3 GAGES OF CORRUGATED METAL SEWER *PIPE-ARCH* FOR H-10 LIVE LOAD*—TRENCH CONDITION

Size		*Area in Sq Ft*	*Height of Cover Above Top of Pipe-Arch—in Feet*				
Span in Inches	*Rise in Inches*		*1.0–1.9*	*2.0–4.9*	*5.0–9.9*	*10–15*	*16–20*
18	11	1.1	16	16	16	16	16
22	13	1.6	16	16	16	16	16
25	16	2.2	16	16	16	16	16
29	18	2.8	16	16	16	14	14
36	22	4.4	16	16	14	14	14
43	27	6.4	14	14	14	12	12
50	31	8.7	14	14	14	12	10
58	36	11.4	12	14	12	10	10
65	40	14.3	12	12	12	10	8
72	44	17.6	10	12	10	8	—

*For H 20 live load, see Table 9-4.

For recommended *minimum* height of cover, see Table 9-1.

TABLE 10-4 GAGES OF MULTI-PLATE *SEWER PIPE* FOR H-10 LIVE LOAD—TRENCH CONDITION

Diam. in Inches	*Area in Sq Ft*	*Height of Cover Above Top of Pipe—in Feet*							
		1–5	*6–10*	*11–15*	*16–20*	*21–25*	*26–30*	*31–35*	*36–40*
60	19.6	12	12	12	12	12	10	10	10
66	23.8	12	12	12	12	10	10	10	10
72	28.3	12	12	12	10	10	10	10	8
78	33.2	12	12	12	10	10	10	8	8
84	38.5	12	12	10	10	10	8	8	8
90	44.2	12	12	10	10	8	8	8	7
96	50.3	12	12	10	10	8	8	8	7
102	56.7	10	10	10	8	8	8	7	7
108	63.6	10	10	10	8	8	7	7	5
114	70.9	10	10	10	8	8	7	5	5
120	78.5	10	10	8	8	7	5	5	5
126	86.6	10	10	8	7	7	5	5	3
132	95.0	10	10	8	7	5	5	5	3
138	104	8	10	8	7	5	5	3	3
144	113	8	8	8	7	5	5	3	3
150	123	8	8	7	5	5	3	3	1
156	133	8	8	7	5	5	3	3	1
162	143	8	8	7	5	3	3	1	1
168	154	7	8	5	5	3	1	1	—
174	165	7	7	5	3	3	1	1	
180	177	7	7	5	3	3	1	—	

TABLE 10-5 GAGES OF MULTI-PLATE *SEWER PIPE* FOR H-20 LIVE LOAD—TRENCH CONDITION

Diam. in Inches	*Area in Sq Ft*	*Height of Cover Above Top of Pipe—in Feet*							
		1–5	*6–10*	*11–15*	*16–20*	*21–25*	*26–30*	*31–35*	*36–40*
60	19.6	12	12	12	12	12	10	10	10
66	23.8	12	12	12	12	10	10	10	10
72	28.3	12	12	12	10	10	10	10	8
78	33.2	12	12	12	10	10	10	8	8
84	38.5	10	12	10	10	10	8	8	8
90	44.2	10	12	10	10	8	8	8	7
96	50.3	10	12	10	10	8	8	8	7
102	56.7	10	10	10	8	8	8	7	7
108	63.6	10	10	10	8	8	7	7	5
114	70.9	10	10	10	8	8	7	5	5

[*Continued on next page*]

TABLE 10-5—(cont'd) GAGES OF MULTI-PLATE *SEWER PIPE* FOR H-20 LIVE LOAD—TRENCH CONDITION

Diam. in Inches	*Area in Sq Ft*	*Height of Cover Above Top of Pipe—in Feet*							
		1–5	*6–10*	*11–15*	*16–20*	*21–25*	*26–30*	*31–35*	*36–40*
120	78.5	8	10	8	8	7	5	5	5
126	86.6	8	10	8	7	7	5	5	3
132	95.0	8	10	8	7	5	5	5	3
138	104	8	10	8	7	5	5	3	3
144	113	8	8	8	7	5	5	3	3
150	123	7	8	7	5	5	3	3	1
156	133	7	8	7	5	5	3	3	1
162	143	7	8	7	5	3	3	1	1
168	154	5	8	5	5	3	1	1	—
174	165	5	7	5	3	3	1	1	
180	177	5	7	5	3	3	1	—	

Gages may often be lighter than those shown in table if field strutting methods are used to increase the load supporting ability of the structure.

For recommended *minimum* height of cover, see Table 9-1.

The gages shown are the minimum structural requirements for use with adequate backfill.

Gages are for finished construction; during construction, adequate cover must be provided to protect the structure from damage.

Bottom plates are frequently designed of heavier gage to resist wear.

Fig. 79. Industrial sewer of 66-in. Armco Asbestos-Bonded Paved-Invert Pipe. The section under the railroad tracks is inside a liner plate tunnel.

TABLE 10-6 GAGES OF MULTI-PLATE *SEWER PIPE-ARCHES* FOR H-10 LIVE LOAD

*Representative Sizes**		*Area in Sq Ft*	*Periphery in Pi In.*	*Height of Cover Above Top of Pipe-Arch—in Feet*														
Span	*Rise*			*1*	*2*	*3*	*4*	*5*	*6*	*7*	*8*	*9*	*10*	*11*	*12*	*13*	*14*	*15*
6′-1″	4′-7″	22	66	12	12	12	12	12	12	12	12	12	12	12	12	12	12	12
7′-0″	5′-1″	28	75	12	12	12	12	12	12	12	12	12	12	12	12	12	12	10
8′-2″	5′-9″	38	87	12	12	12	12	12	12	12	12	12	12	10	10	10	10	10
9′-6″	6′-5″	49	99	12	12	12	12	12	12	10	10	10	10	10	10	10	10	8
11′-5″	7′-3″	64	114	10	10	10	10	10	10	10	10	10	8	8	8	8	8	7
12′-10″	8′-4″	85	132	8	10	10	10	10	10	8	8	8	8	8	8	7	7	5
15′-4″	9′-3″	109	150	5	7	7	8	8	8	8	8	7	7	7	5	3	3	3
16′-7″	10′-1″	131	165	5	5	7	7	8	8	8	7	7	7	5	3	3	1	—

TABLE 10-7 GAGES OF MULTI-PLATE *SEWER PIPE-ARCHES* FOR H-20 LIVE LOAD

*Representative Sizes**		*Area in Sq Ft*	*Periphery in Pi In.*	*Height of Cover Above Top of Pipe-Arch—in Feet*														
Span	*Rise*			*1*	*2*	*3*	*4*	*5*	*6*	*7*	*8*	*9*	*10*	*11*	*12*	*13*	*14*	*15*
6′-1″	4′-7″	22	66	12	12	12	12	12	12	12	12	12	12	12	12	12	12	12
7′-0″	5′-1″	28	75	10	12	12	12	12	12	12	12	12	12	12	12	12	10	10
8′-2″	5′-9″	38	87	10	10	10	12	12	12	12	12	12	12	12	10	10	10	10
9′-6″	6′-5″	49	99	8	10	10	10	10	10	10	10	10	10	10	10	8	8	8
11′-5″	7′-3″	64	114	7	8	8	8	10	10	10	10	8	8	8	8	7	7	5
12′-10″	8′-4″	85	132	5	7	8	8	8	8	8	8	8	7	7	5	5	3	1
15′-4″	9′-3″	109	150	3	5	5	7	7	7	7	7	5	3	3	1	1	—	—
16′-7″	10′-1″	131	165	1	3	3	5	5	5	5	3	3	1	1	—	—	—	—

*Information on other sizes available on request to manufacturer.

For recommended *minimum* height of cover, see Table 9-1.

The gages shown are the minimum structural requirements for use with adequate backfill. During construction, adequate cover must be provided to protect the structure from damage.

TABLE 10-8 GAGES OF MULTI-PLATE SEWER ARCHES FOR H-10 LIVE LOAD

Representative Spans in Feet	*Height of Cover Above Crown of Arch—in Feet*									
	1	*2*	*3*	*4*	*5*	*6*	*7*	*8*	*9*	*10*
4-10	12	12	12	12	12	12	12	12	12	12
11	12	12	12	12	12	12	12	12	12	12
12	12	12	12	12	12	12	12	12	12	10
13	12	12	12	12	12	12	12	12	10	10
14	12	12	12	12	12	12	12	10	10	8
15	12	12	12	12	12	12	12	10	8	8
16	10	10	12	12	12	12	10	10	8	7
17	10	10	10	12	12	12	10	8	8	7
18	10	10	10	12	10	10	10	8	7	5
19	8	8	10	10	10	10	8	7	5	3
20	8	8	10	10	10	10	8	7	5	3

TABLE 10-9 GAGES OF MULTI-PLATE SEWER ARCHES FOR H-20 LIVE LOAD

Representative Spans in Feet	*Height of Cover Above Crown of Arch—in Feet*									
	1	*2*	*3*	*4*	*5*	*6*	*7*	*8*	*9*	*10*
4-10	12	12	12	12	12	12	12	12	12	12
11	10	10	10	12	12	12	12	12	12	12
12	10	10	10	12	12	12	12	12	10	10
13	8	8	10	12	12	12	12	10	10	8
14	7	8	8	10	10	10	10	8	8	8
15	5	7	8	10	10	10	10	8	8	7
16	5	5	7	8	8	10	8	7	7	5
17	3	5	5	7	8	8	8	7	5	3
18	3	3	5	7	7	8	7	5	3	3
19	1‡	1‡	3	5	5	7	5	3	3	1
20	—	1‡	1‡	3	5	5	5	3	1	—

Arches are available in a range of sizes. See Table 8-14. Values here are for gage determination.

For recommended *minimum* height of cover, see Table 9-1.

Armco "Economy-Type" footings may be used on spans up to 15 ft.

The gages shown are the minimum structural requirements for use with adequate backfill. During construction, adequate cover must be provided to protect the structure from damage.

‡Use only when R/S is 0.3 or more.

CHAPTER ELEVEN

Railway Loadings and Gage Tables

UNDER fill heights of 12 ft or less, live loads and impact are of importance. Fig. 82. Beyond 13 ft they have little or no effect, although vibration may be a factor. When a conduit is not under track, the requirements are less. The minimum recommended height of cover for corrugated metal structures under track is shown in Fig. 80.

Concentrated loads of heavy construction equipment are an important consideration, especially if they are heavier than the design loading. Either the gage should be heavier or sufficient fill should be made with light equipment before running the heavy construction equipment over the structure.

Railway live loadings on bridges consist of standard "Cooper loadings." These are Cooper E 72, illustrated in Fig. 81, page 126 and Cooper E 50, page 100. They are based on two locomotives followed by a uniform load representing the weight of the heaviest car. For a Cooper E 50 loading, the weight on the axle of each driver is 50,000 lb. For a Cooper E 72 loading, the weight is 72,000 lb, and so on. Wheel spacings are the same for all Cooper loadings.

More than one axle load may be over a corrugated metal structure, and this is taken into account in establishing the gages.

The American Railway Engineering Association has adopted and uses standard specifications and gage tables for riveted corrugated metal pipe (first in 1930, reapproved in 1953; page 1-4-6 of AREA 1953 Manual); and for structural plate pipe culverts (first in 1943, reapproved in 1953; page 1-4-25).

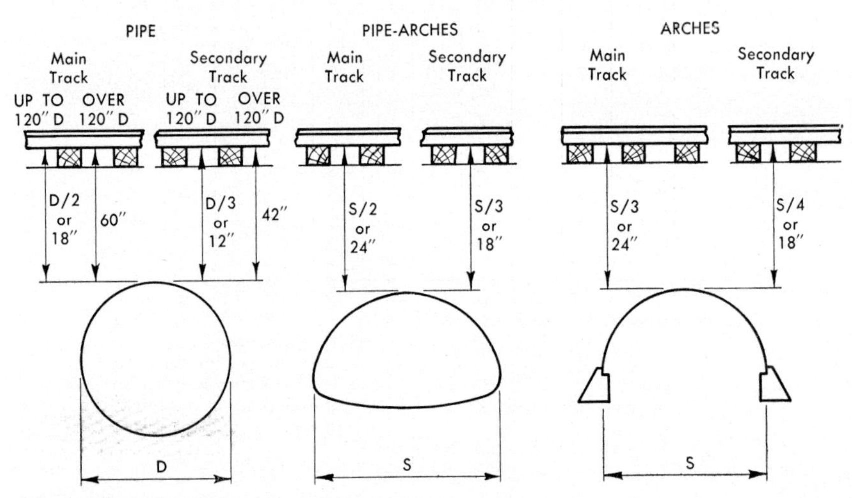

Fig. 80. Minimum height of cover for corrugated metal structures under Cooper E 50 to E 70 railroad loadings, for main and secondary tracks.

TABLE 11-1 GAGES OF CORRUGATED METAL PIPE (UNSTRUTTED AND STRUTTED)‡ FOR COOPER E 70 LIVE LOAD

Diam. in Inches	*Area in Sq Ft*	*Height of Cover Above Top of Culvert—in Feet*									
		1–10	*11–20*	*21–30*	*31–40*	*41–50*	*51–60*	*61–70*	*71–80*	*81–90*	*91–100*
18	1.8	14	14	14	14	14	14	12	12	12	12
21	2.4	14	14	14	14	14	12	12	12	10	10
24	3.1	14	14	14	14	12	12	12	10	10	10
30	4.9	14	14	12	12	10	10	10	8*	8*	8*
36	7.1	12	12	12	10	8	8	8*	8*	8*	8*
42	9.6	12	12	10	8	8					
‡42	9.6						8	8*	8*	8*	8*
‡48	12.6	10	10	8	8	8	8	8*	8*	8*	8*
‡54	15.9	8	8	8	8	8*	8*	8*	8*		
‡60	19.6	8	8	8	8	8*					
‡66	23.8	8	8	8*							
‡72	28.3	8	8*								

*Make a trench one diameter deep in original soil or in compacted fill.
The gages shown are the minimum structural requirements for use with adequate backfill.
For recommended *minimum* height of cover, see Fig. 80.
‡Values below line are based on strutting of pipe.

TABLE 11-2 GAGES OF CORRUGATED METAL PIPE-ARCHES FOR COOPER E 70 LIVE LOAD

Diam. of Pipe of Equal Periph. in Inches	*Span* in Inches*	*Rise* in Inches*	*Height of Cover—in Feet*			
			2	*3–4*	*5–7*	*8–15*
			Recommended Minimum Gage			
15	18	11	14	14	14	14
18	22	13	14	14	14	14
21	25	16	12	14	14	14
24	29	18	12	12	14	14
30	36	22	10	12	12	12
36	43	27	8	10	10	12
42	50	31		8	10	10
48	58	36			8	8
54	65	40				8
60	72	44				8

*Manufacturing tolerance = plus or minus one (1) inch.
The gages shown are the recommended minimum.

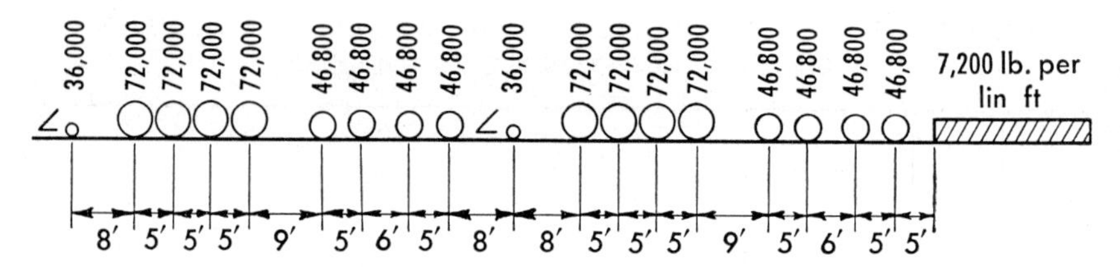

Fig. 81. Spacing of wheels and loads per axle for a standard Cooper E 72 locomotive loading. Axle loads are decreased for lighter loads in direct proportion to the E loads. After AREA Manual, 1953.

TABLE 11-3 GAGES OF MULTI-PLATE *PIPE* (UNSTRUTTED) FOR COOPER E 70 LIVE LOAD

Diameter in Inches	*Height of Cover—in Feet*															
	1–5	*6–10*	*11–15*	*16–20*	*21–25*	*26–30*	*31–35*	*36–40*	*41–45*	*46–50*	*51–55*	*56–60*	*61–70*	*71–80*	*81–90*	*91–100*
60	10	12	12	12	12	10	10	10	10	10	8	8	8	7	5	5
66	8	12	12	12	10	10	10	10	8	8	8	8	8	7	5	3
72	8	10	10	10	10	10	10	8	8	8	8	7	7	5	3	1
78	7	10	10	10	10	10	8	8	8	8	7	7	5	3	1	—
84	7	10	10	10	10	8	8	8	8	7	7	5	5	3	1	
90	5	10	10	10	8	8	8	7	7	7	5	5	3	1	—	
96	5	8	10	8	8	8	8	7	7	5	5	5	3	1		
102	5	8	8	8	8	8	7	7	5	5	5	5	1	—		
108	5	8	8	8	8	7	7	5	5	5	5	3	1	—		
114	3	8	8	8	7	7	5	5	5	3	3	3	1			
120	3	7	8	7	7	5	5	5	3	3	3	1	—			
126	3	7	7	7	7	5	5	3	3	3	1	1				
132	1	7	7	7	5	5	5	3	3	3	1	1				
138	1	5	7	5	5	5	3	3	3	1	1	—				
144	1	5	5	5	5	5	3	3	1	1	—					
150	—	5	5	5	5	3	3	1	1	1						
156	—	5	5	5	3	3	3	1	1	—						
162	—	5	5	5	3	3	1	1	1	—						
168	—	3	5	3	3	1	1	—	—	—						
174	—	3	3	3	3	1	1	—	—							
180	—	3	3	3	1	1	—	—	—							

The gages shown are the minimum structural requirements for use with adequate backfill. Bottom plates are frequently designed of heavier gage to resist wear.

Gages are for finished construction; during construction adequate cover must be provided to protect the structure from damage.

For recommended *minimum* height of cover, see Fig. 80.

Pipe diameters are to inside crests and are subject to manufacturing tolerances.

Although the AREA tables permit the choice of various gages for various diameters of riveted and structural pipe, most of the railroads in the United States and Canada adhere to the manufacturers' tables of recommended gages under various heights of cover.

Railroads prefer slightly heavier gages than do highway and airport engineers, partly from the standpoint of added durability but mostly because of added assurance against structural failure, costly interruption to service, and possible lawsuits.

Examples of gage selection are not given here but are made the same way as those shown on pages 108-113.

TABLE 11-4 GAGES OF MULTI-PLATE *PIPE* (STRUTTED) FOR COOPER E 70 LIVE LOAD

Diameter in Inches	*Height of Cover—in Feet*																*Height of Cover Limit 1 Gage—6 Bolts*
	1–5	*6–10*	*11–15*	*16–20*	*21–25*	*26–30*	*31–35*	*36–40*	*41–45*	*46–50*	*51–55*	*56–60*	*61–70*	*71–80*	*81–90*	*91–100*	
60	12	12	12	12	12	12	12	12	12	12	10	10	8	7	5	5	200
66	12	12	12	12	12	12	12	12	12	10	10	8	8	7	5	3	180
72	12	12	12	12	12	12	12	12	10	10	8	8	7	5	3	1	165
78	10	12	12	12	12	12	12	10	10	8	8	8	5	3	1	—	150
84	10	12	12	12	12	12	12	10	10	8	8	7	5	3	1	—	140
90	10	12	12	12	12	12	10	10	8	8	7	5	3	1	—		130
96	8	12	12	12	12	10	10	10	8	7	7	5	3	1	—		125
102	8	10	12	12	10	10	10	8	8	7	5	5	1	—			115
108	8	10	10	10	10	10	10	8	7	5	5	3	1	—			110
114	8	10	10	10	10	10	8	8	7	5	5	3	1				105
120	8	10	10	10	10	10	8	7	5	5	3	1	—				100
126	8	10	10	10	10	10	8	7	5	3	3	1					95
132	8	10	10	10	10	8	8	7	5	3	1	1					90
138	8	8	10	10	10	8	7	5	3	3	1	—					85
144	7	8	10	10	8	8	7	5	3	1	1	For structures in this zone use 1 gage with six bolts per foot of longitudinal seam with height of cover limits as shown in column at right.					80
150	7	8	10	8	8	8	7	5	3	1	—						80
156	7	8	8	8	8	8	5	3	1	1							75
162	7	8	8	8	8	7	5	3	1	—							70
168	7	8	8	8	8	7	5	3	1								70
174	7	8	8	8	8	7	5	3	1								65
180	7	8	8	8	8	5	3	1	—								65

The gages shown are the minimum structural requirements for use with adequate backfill. Bottom plates are frequently designed of heavier gage to resist wear.

Gages are for finished construction; during construction adequate cover must be provided to protect the structure from damage.

For recommended *minimum* height of cover, see Fig. 80.

The last column shows the greatest height of cover that can be placed on pipes specially fabricated to have six bolts per foot in each longitudinal seam in 1 gage metal.

Pipe diameters are to inside crests and are subject to manufacturing tolerances.

TABLE 11-5 GAGES OF MULTI-PLATE *PIPE-ARCHES* FOR COOPER E 70 LIVE LOAD

Span	*Height of Cover—in Feet*												
	2–3	*4*	*5*	*6*	*7*	*8*	*9*	*10*	*11*	*12*	*13*	*14*	*15*
5′-0″	8	10	12	12	12	12	12	12	12	12	12	12	12
5′-6″	8	10	10	10	12	12	12	12	12	12	12	12	12
6′-0″	8	10	10	10	10	10	10	10	10	10	10	10	10
6′-6″	7	8	10	10	10	10	10	10	10	10	10	10	10
7′-0″	5	8	8	10	10	10	10	10	10	10	10	10	10
7′-6″	5	7	8	8	8	8	8	8	10	10	10	10	10
8′-0″	3	5	7	7	8	8	8	8	8	8	8	8	8
8′-6″	1	5	5	7	7	7	8	8	8	8	8	8	8
9′-0″	1	3	5	5	5	7	7	7	7	7	7	7	7
9′-6″	—	3	3	5	5	5	5	5	7	7	7	7	7
10′-0″		1	1	3	3	5	5	5	5	5	5	5	5
10′-6″		—	1	1	3	3	3	5	5	5	5	5	5
11′-0″			—	1	1	3	3	3	3	3	3	3	3
11′-6″				—	1	1	1	1	3	3	3	3	3
12′-0″					—	—	1	1	1	1	1	3	3
12′-6″							—	1	1	1	1	1	1
13′-0″								—	—	1	1	1	1
13′-6″										—	—	—	1

See footnotes on opposite page.

Fig. 82. Under shallow cover the flexibility of corrugated metal structures is an advantage.

TABLE 11-6 GAGES OF MULTI-PLATE *PIPE-ARCHES* FOR COOPER E 50 LIVE LOAD

Span	*Height of Cover—in Feet*												
	2–3	*4*	*5*	*6*	*7*	*8*	*9*	*10*	*11*	*12*	*13*	*14*	*15*
5′-0″	10	12	12	12	12	12	12	12	12	12	12	12	12
5′-6″	10	12	12	12	12	12	12	12	12	12	12	12	12
6′-0″	10	10	10	12	12	12	12	12	12	12	12	12	12
6′-6″	10	10	10	10	10	10	10	10	10	10	10	10	10
7′-0″	8	10	10	10	10	10	10	10	10	10	10	10	10
7′-6″	8	10	10	10	10	10	10	10	10	10	10	10	10
8′-0″	8	8	8	10	10	10	10	10	10	10	10	10	10
8′-6″	7	8	8	8	8	10	10	10	10	10	10	10	10
9′-0″	7	8	8	8	8	8	8	8	8	8	8	8	8
9′-6″	5	7	8	8	8	8	8	8	8	8	8	8	8
10′-0″	5	7	7	8	8	8	8	8	8	8	8	8	8
10′-6″	3	5	7	7	8	8	8	8	8	8	8	8	8
11′-0″	3	5	5	7	7	7	7	8	8	8	8	8	8
11′-6″	1	3	5	5	5	7	7	7	7	7	7	7	7
12′-0″	1	3	3	5	5	5	5	7	7	7	7	7	7
12′-6″	—	1	3	3	5	5	5	5	5	5	5	7	7
13′-0″		1	1	3	3	5	5	5	5	5	5	5	5
13′-6″		—	1	1	3	3	3	5	5	5	5	5	5
14′-0″			—	1	1	3	3	3	3	3	5	5	5
14′-6″				—	1	1	3	3	3	3	3	3	3
15′-0″					1	1	1	1	3	3	3	3	3
15′-6″					—	1	1	1	1	1	3	3	3
16′-0″						—	—	1	1	1	1	1	1
16′-6″								—	—	1	1	1	1

The gages shown are the minimum structural requirements for use with adequate backfill.

Bottom plates are frequently designed of heavier gage to resist wear.

Gages are for finished construction; during construction adequate cover must be provided to protect the structure from damage.

For recommended *minimum* height of cover, see Fig. 80.

Plates are standard 6″ x 2″ corrugation of $1\frac{1}{8}$″ valley radius with four bolts per foot in each longitudinal seam. Bolts are $\frac{3}{4}$″ diameter, high strength to meet ASTM: A325-52T and galvanized to meet ASTM: A153-49.

Pipe-arches are available in a range of spans, rises and areas; tabular values are for gage determination.

TABLE 11-7 GAGES OF MULTI-PLATE *ARCHES* FOR COOPER E 70 LOADING

Span	*Height of Cover—in Feet*								
	2	*3*	*4*	*5*	*6*	*7*	*8*	*9*	*10*
6′-0″	12	12	12	12	12	12	12	12	12
7′-0″	12	12	12	12	12	12	12	12	12
8′-0″	10	10	10	10	10	12	12	12	12
9′-0″	8	8	8	8	10	10	10	10	10
10′-0″	5	5	5	7	8	8	8	8	8
11′-0″	1	3	3	5	5	5	7	7	7
12′-0″	—	—	1	3	3	3	5	5	5
13′-0″			—	—	1	1	3	3	3
14′-0″					—	—	—	—	1

TABLE 11-8 GAGES OF MULTI-PLATE *ARCHES* FOR COOPER E 50 LOADING

Span	*Height of Cover—in Feet*								
	2	*3*	*4*	*5*	*6*	*7*	*8*	*9*	*10*
6′-0″	12	12	12	12	12	12	12	12	12
7′-0″	12	12	12	12	12	12	12	12	12
8′-0″	12	12	12	12	12	12	12	12	12
9′-0″	10	10	10	12	12	12	12	12	12
10′-0″	8	8	10	10	10	10	10	10	10
11′-0″	7	8	8	8	8	10	10	10	10
12′-0″	5	5	7	7	8	8	8	8	8
13′-0″	1	3	5	5	7	7	7	7	8
14′-0″	1	1	3	3	5	5	5	5	7
15′-0″	—	—	1	1	3	3	3	3	5
16′-0″			—	—	1	1	3	3	3
17′-0″					—	1	1	1	1
18′-0″						—	—	—	1

The gages shown are the minimum structural requirements for use with adequate backfill.

Gages are for finished construction; during construction adequate cover must be provided to protect the structure from damage.

For recommended *minimum* height of cover, see Fig. 80.

Plates are standard 6″ x 2″ corrugation of 1⅛″ valley radius with four bolts per foot in each longitudinal seam. Bolts are ¾″ diameter, high strength to meet ASTM: A325-52T and galvanized to meet ASTM: A153-49.

Range of rise to span is from 0.2 to 0.5.

Arches are available in a range of sizes; tabular values are for gage determination.

TABLE 11-9 GAGES OF MULTI-PLATE *ARCHES* FOR INSTALLATION INSIDE EXISTING ARCH-TYPE STRUCTURES FOR COOPER E 70 LOADING—$R/S = 0.3$ to 0.5

Height of Cover—in Feet	*3*			*6*			*9*			*12*			*15*			*18*			*21*			*24*			*27*			*30*			*Span in Feet*
*Class of Installation** / *Span in Feet*	*A*	*B*	*C*	*A*	*B*	*C*	*A*	*B*	*C*	*A*	*B*	*C*	*A*	*B*	*C*	*A*	*B*	*C*	*A*	*B*	*C*	*A*	*B*	*C*	*A*	*B*	*C*	*A*	*B*	*C*	
6	10	10	8	10	10	8	10	10	8	10	10	8	10	10	8	10	10	8	10	10	8	10	10	8	10	8	8	10	8	8	6
7	10	10	8	10	10	8	10	10	8	10	10	8	10	10	8	10	10	8	10	10	8	10	8	7	10	8	7	10	8	7	7
8	10	8	8	10	8	7	10	8	8	10	8	8	10	8	7	10	8	7	10	8	7	10	8	7	10	8	7	8	7	5	8
9	10	8	7	10	8	7	10	8	7	10	8	7	10	8	7	10	8	7	10	8	7	8	7	5	8	7	5	8	7	5	9
10	10	8	7	10	8	7	10	8	7	10	8	7	10	8	7	10	8	7	8	7	5	8	7	5	8	7	5	8	7	5	10
11	8	7	5	8	7	7	8	8	7	8	8	7	8	7	7	8	7	5	8	7	5	8	7	5	8	7	5	7	5	3	11
12	8	7	5	8	7	5	8	7	7	8	7	5	8	7	5	8	7	5	8	7	5	7	5	3	7	5	3	5	3	1	12
13	8	7	5	8	7	5	8	7	7	8	7	5	8	7	5	8	7	5	7	5	3	7	5	3	7	5	3	5	3	1	13
14	7	5	3	7	7	5	8	7	5	8	7	5	7	7	5	7	5	3	7	5	3	7	5	3	5	3	1	5	3	1	14
15	7	5	3	7	5	3	7	7	5	7	5	5	7	5	3	7	5	3	7	5	3	5	3	1	5	3	1	5	3		15
16	7	5	3	7	5	3	7	5	5	7	5	3	7	5	3	7	5	3	5	3	1	5	3	1	5	3		3	1		16
17	5	3	1	7	5	3	7	5	3	7	5	3	7	5	3	5	3	1	5	3	1	5	3	1	5	1		3	1		17
18	5	3	1	5	3	3	7	5	3	5	5	3	5	3	1	5	3	1	5	3	1	5	1		3	1		3			18
19	5	3	1	5	3	1	5	5	3	5	3	3	5	3	1	5	3	1	3	1		3	1		3			1			19
20	3	1		5	3	1	5	3	3	5	3	1	5	3	1	3	1	1	3	1		3	1		1			1			20
21	3	1		5	3	1	5	3	1	5	3	1	3	3	1	3	1		3	1		1			1						21
22	3	1		3	1		5	3	1	3	3	1	3	1		3	1		1			1									22
23	1			3	1		3	3	1	3	1		3	1		1	1		1			1									23
24	1			3	1		3	1	1	3	1		3	1		1			1												24
25	1			1			3	1		3	1		1			1															25

*CLASSES OF INSTALLATION

(A) Condition of existing structure FAIR with space between existing structure and metal structure to be completely filled with soundly placed pressure grout of 1–3 mix or richer.

(B) Condition of existing structure POOR with space between existing structure and metal structure to be completely filled with soundly placed pressure grout of 1–3 mix or richer.

(C) Condition of existing structure FAIR with space between existing structure and metal structure to be completely filled with SAND or pressure grout of 1–4 mix or leaner.

Fig. 83. Installation of corrugated metal pipe under a Missouri River levee calls for watertight joints, diaphragms, drainage gates and metal end sections.

Fig. 83A. Installing Armco drainage gates and building headwall on triple 72-in. Paved-Invert corrugated culvert under Mississippi River levee near Ft. Chartres, Ill.

CHAPTER TWELVE

Design for Levee Loadings

LEVEE HEIGHTS range up to 40 ft or more above the surrounding ground. Consequently, culverts placed in channels may be required to carry from 40 to 50 ft or more of cover. The Corps of Engineers, Department of the U. S. Army, specifies and uses riveted corrugated culverts from 36 to 72 in. in diameter. Because of the generally poor foundation conditions and because of the method of strutting required for the pipe, a special table of gages is used (see Table 12-1). Fig. 83.

On projects under access highways and railways and where there are no surface loads, U. S. Engineers usually specify the gages and materials used by local highway departments and railways.

TABLE 12-1 GAGES OF STANDARD CORRUGATED METAL PIPE FOR USE UNDER LEVEES & DAMS*

Diameter of Pipe in Inches	*Gage No.*	*Cross-Sectional Area in Sq Ft*	*Maximum Height of Cover in Feet*
12	10	0.8	140
18	10	1.2	120
21	10	1.8	100
24	10	2.4	100
30	10	3.1	70
36	8	7.1	60
42	8	9.6	50
‡48	8	12.6	105
‡54	8	15.9	85
‡60	8	19.6	70
‡66	8	23.8	60
‡72	8	28.3	52

*See AASHO or AREA for gages for appurtenant structures.
‡These sizes are all to be strutted.

CHAPTER THIRTEEN

Design for Airport Loadings

THE DESIGN of an airport requires first the determination of the type and extent of activities it is expected to serve, and especially the size and weight of the planes that will use it. Civil airports are divided into the following classes:*

Secondary—Airports for larger (2,000-lb to 15,000-lb) aircraft in nonscheduled flying activities.

Feeder—Airports to serve certificated feeder airlines.

Trunk Line—Airports to serve smaller cities on airline trunk routes.

Express—Airports at important cities or junction points on trunk routes.

Continental—Airports serving aircraft making long nonstop domestic flights.

Intercontinental—Airports terminating long international flights.

Intercontinental Express—Airports serving the highest type of transoceanic flights.

The design standards shown in Table 13-1 are recommended by the Civil Aeronautics Administration as general guides for airport design.

The usual design practice is to consider the gross weight of the airplane as divided between the two main wheels or groups of wheels, disregarding that portion of the load carried by the tail wheel or nose wheel.

It will be noted that the heaviest wheel load provided for in Table 13-1 is 125,000 lb. Military planes have still greater weights. Experimental planes in operation have gross weights up to 300,000 lb. The U. S. Air Force B-36 bomber has a gross

*"Airport Design," Civil Aeronautics Admin., U. S. Dept. of Commerce, Jan. 1949.

Fig. 84. Giant cargo airplane, C-124-A, of the United States Air Force has a maximum weight of 210,000 lb—*Courtesy Wright-Patterson Air Force Base.*

TABLE 13-1 AIRPORT DESIGN STANDARDS

Type of Service	*Minimum Widths in Feet*			*Maximum Grades in Per Cent*		*Pavement Loading per Wheel (in 1000 lb.)*	
	Runway Length in Feet	*Landing Strip*	*Runway*	*Longitudinal*	*Transverse*	*Single Wheel*	*Dual Wheel*
Secondary.......	1500 to 3000	250	75	2	2		
Feeder..........	3001 to 3500	300	100	1½	1½	15	20
Trunk Line......	3501 to 4200	400	150	1½	1½	30	40
Express.........	4201 to 5000	500	150	1½	1½	45	60
Continental	5001 to 5900	500	150	1½	1½	60	80
Intercontinental..	5901 to 7000	500	200	1½	1½	75	100
Intercontinental Express.......	7001 to 8400	500	200	1½	1½	100	125

Source: Airport Design, Civil Aeronautics Admin., Wash., D.C., Jan. 1949. 64 pp.

weight of 340,000 lb. It is necessary to guard the landing surface, the service areas, and the underground structures against the wheel loads expected on the airport that is being designed. Fig. 84.

Impact and Vibration

There is some difference of opinion as to whether a parked airplane with its motors not rotating, transmits a greater dead load to the pavement than the impact load when the plane is landing. Some consider the impact load factor to be less than 1; others use an impact factor of 1.25 to 2.

Some disagreement on the effect of airplane wheel loads on pavement and subgrade is reflected in the Canadian Department of Transport and the U. S. Navy design for a thickness of only a fraction of that required by the U. S. Engineers.*

Vibration at the ends of runways and other warm-up or "revving" areas when the propellers are revolving at high speeds can impose a severe stress on underground conduits. Corrugated metal structures because of their flexible nature are not usually adversely affected.

Recommended Minimum Cover

Depth of cover or "height of cover" is measured from bottom of pavement to top of conduit. If there is no pavement, the required minimum cover is increased by zero to 1 ft.

Cover for pipes in airfield areas outside of landing or taxiway strips and on similar non-traffic areas is designed for a 30,000-lb plane load by both the CAA and the U. S. Engineers. Cover for pipes within aircraft traffic areas should be provided as shown in Table 13-2 of the CAA (revised April 1951). The CAA and the U. S. Engineers require that pipes placed under concrete pavements on airfields should have a minimum cover below the slab of 1.0 ft for single wheel loads of 60,000 lb, and 2.0 ft for single wheel loads of 150,000 lb.

*"Canadian Pavement Design Defended," by Norman W. McLeod, Canadian Dept. of Transp., *Engineering News-Record*, Aug. 9, 1951 pp. 35–38.

TABLE 13-2 MINIMUM HEIGHT OF COVER FOR *PIPE* UNDER AIRPORTS—IN FEET
Recommended by Civil Aeronautics Administration (Dwg. No. 892, April, 1951)

Kind of Pipe	*No. of AASHO Specifications*		*Diameter of Pipe, in Inches* — *15,000 Lb Wheel Load*									*30,000 Lb Wheel Load*									*60,000 Lb Wheel Load*									*100,000 Lb Wheel Load*								
		Gage	*6*	*10*	*12*	*18*	*24*	*30*	*36*	*48*	*60*	*6*	*10*	*12*	*18*	*24*	*30*	*36*	*48*	*60*	*6*	*10*	*12*	*18*	*24*	*30*	*36*	*48*	*60*	*6*	*10*	*12*	*18*	*24*	*30*	*36*	*48*	*60*
V.C. Sewer Pipe Stand. Strength	M65-49		1.5	2.5	3.0	3.0	3.0	3.5	3.5			2.5	3.5								4.0	5.0								5.5	6.0							
V.C. Culv. Pipe Extra Strength	M65-49		1.5	1.5	1.5	1.5	1.5	2.0	2.0			1.5	2.0	2.5	3.0	3.0	3.0	3.0			2.5	3.5	3.5	4.0	4.5	4.5	4.5			4.0	4.0							
Concrete Sewer Pipe	M86-49		1.5	2.0	2.5	3.0	3.0					2.5	3.0	3.5							4.0	4.5								5.0	5.5							
R.C. Sewer Pipe	M87-49				2.0	3.0	3.0	3.5	3.5	4.0	4.0			3.0	3.5																							
R.C. Culvert Pipe Stand. Strength	M41-49 Table I				1.5	2.0	2.0	2.0	2.0	2.0	2.0			2.0	2.5	2.5	3.0	3.0	3.0	3.0			3.0	4.0	4.0	4.5	4.5					3.5	4.5	5.0	5.0	5.5		
R.C. Culvert Pipe Extra Strength	M41-49 Table II						1.0	1.0	1.0	1.0	1.0					2.0	2.0	2.0	2.0	2.0					3.0	3.0	3.5	3.5	3.5					4.0	4.0	4.5	4.5	5.0
Corrugated Metal Pipe	M36-47 or M136-47 for Underdrains	18	1.0	1.0	1.5							1.0	1.5	2.0							2.0									2.5								
		16	1.0	1.0	1.0	1.5	1.5					1.0	1.0	1.5	1.5	2.0					1.5	2.0	2.5	3.5	4.0					2.0	2.5	3.0	4.5	5.0				
		14			1.0	1.0	1.0	1.5	2.0						1.0	1.5	2.0	2.5					2.0	2.5	3.0	3.5	4.0					2.5	3.5	4.0	5.0	5.5		
		12						1.0	1.0	2.0							1.5	2.0	3.0				1.5	2.0	2.5	2.5	3.5	4.0						3.5	4.5	5.0	5.5	
		10								1.0	1.5							1.5	2.0	2.5					2.0	2.5	3.0	3.5	4.0					3.0	3.5	4.5	5.0	5.5
		8									1.0							1.0	1.5	2.0							2.5	3.0	3.5							4.0	4.5	5.0

Note 1. Cover for pipe in airfield areas not used by aircraft traffic shall be designed for a single wheel load of 15,000 pounds.

Note 2. Cover for pipes within runway or taxiway strips and other aircraft traffic areas shall be provided in accordance with the above table except as provided for rigid pavements in Note 3.

Note 3. Pipe placed under concrete pavements on airfields shall have a minimum cover measured below the slab of one foot for single wheel loads of 60,000 pounds and two feet for single wheel loads of 150,000 pounds.

V.C. = Vitrified clay R.C. = Reinforced concrete

Design Examples

The accompanying table of CAA (Table 13-2) includes rigid types as well as corrugated metal pipe, and is for wheel load and not for plane load.

Example: Class 4 Airport
120,000 lb plane
8-in. corr. metal pipe, 18 gage
min. cover = 2.0 ft

Example: Class 3 Airport
74,000 lb plane
120-in. Multi-Plate pipe
min. cover (depth below slab) = 1.5 ft
gage to use = No. 8. (Table 13-7, page 139)

TABLE 13-3 MINIMUM HEIGHT OF COVER—IN FEET
FOR *CORRUGATED METAL PIPE-ARCHES*
UNDER *RIGID* AIRFIELD PAVEMENT

Span—in Feet	*1*			*2*			*3*			*4*			*5*			*6*		
Plane Weight in Thousand Pounds	*100*	*200*	*300*	*100*	*200*	*300*	*100*	*200*	*300*	*100*	*200*	*300*	*100*	*200*	*300*	*100*	*200*	*300*
16 gage	0.5	1.0	1.0	0.5	1.0	1.0												
14 gage	0.5	1.0	1.0	0.5	1.0	1.0	0.5	1.0	1.0									
12 gage	0.5	1.0	1.0	0.5	1.0	1.0	0.5	1.0	1.0	1.0	1.5	2.0	1.0					
10 gage	0.5	1.0	1.0	0.5	1.0	1.0	0.5	1.0	1.0	0.5	1.0	1.0	0.5	1.0	1.0	1.5		
8 gage	0.5	1.0	1.0	0.5	1.0	1.0	0.5	1.0	1.0	0.5	1.0	1.0	0.5	1.0	1.0	1.0	1.5	2.0

TABLE 13-4 MINIMUM HEIGHT OF COVER—IN FEET
FOR *CORRUGATED METAL PIPE-ARCHES*
FROM SURFACE OF *FLEXIBLE* AIRFIELD PAVEMENT

Span—in Feet	*1*			*2*			*3*			*4*			*5*			*6*		
Plane Weight in Thousand Pounds	*100*	*200*	*300*	*100*	*200*	*300*	*100*	*200*	*300*	*100*	*200*	*300*	*100*	*200*	*300*	*100*	*200*	*300*
16 gage	1.5	2.0	3.0	3.0	4.0													
14 gage	1.0	2.0	2.5	2.5	3.0	4.5												
12 gage	1.0	2.0	2.5	2.0	2.5	3.5	3.0	4.0										
10 gage				1.0	2.0	2.5	2.0	3.5	4.5	3.0	4.0	5.0	4.0	5.0	6.0	5.0		
8 gage							1.0	2.5	4.0	2.0	3.0	3.5	3.5	4.0	4.5	4.0	4.5	5.0

Strength of Underdrains

Underdrains or subdrainage pipes are no different than other conduits or culverts insofar as loading conditions are concerned. Some of these underdrains are of riveted corrugated metal pipe, but for the most part are of the Hel-Cor type in diameters from 6 to 18 inches. The foregoing gage tables, particularly those for airfield loadings, are applicable.

TABLE 13-5 MINIMUM HEIGHT OF COVER—IN FEET
FOR *MULTI-PLATE PIPE-ARCHES*
UNDER *RIGID* AIRFIELD PAVEMENT

Span—in Feet	*6*			*8*			*10*			*12*			*14*			*16*		
Plane Weight in Thousand Pounds	*100*	*200*	*300*	*100*	*200*	*300*	*100*	*200*	*300*	*100*	*200*	*300*	*100*	*200*	*300*	*100*	*200*	*300*
12 gage	2.0	2.5	3.0	2.5	3.5	4.0	3.5	4.5		4.5								
10 gage	1.5	2.0	2.5	2.0	3.0	3.0	3.0	3.5	4.0	3.5	4.5	5.0	4.5					
8 gage	1.5	2.0	2.0	2.0	2.5	2.5	2.5	3.0	3.0	3.0	3.5	3.5	3.5	4.0	4.5	4.0		
7 gage	1.0	1.5	1.5	1.5	2.0	2.0	2.0	2.0	2.5	2.0	2.5	3.0	2.5	3.5	3.5	3.5	4.0	
5 gage	1.0	1.0	1.5	1.0	1.5	1.5	1.5	1.5	2.0	1.5	2.0	2.5	2.0	2.5	3.0	2.5	3.0	4.0
3 gage	0.5	1.0	1.5	1.0	1.0	1.5	1.0	1.5	1.5	1.5	1.5	2.0	1.5	2.0	2.5	2.0	2.5	3.0
1 gage	0.5	1.0	1.5	0.5	1.0	1.5	1.0	1.0	1.5	1.0	1.5	1.5	1.5	1.5	2.0	1.5	2.0	2.5

TABLE 13-6 MINIMUM HEIGHT OF COVER—IN FEET
FOR *MULTI-PLATE PIPE-ARCHES*
FROM SURFACE OF *FLEXIBLE* AIRFIELD PAVEMENT

Span—in Feet	*6*			*8*			*10*			*12*			*14*			*16*		
Plane Weight in Thousand Pounds	*100*	*200*	*300*	*100*	*200*	*300*	*100*	*200*	*300*	*100*	*200*	*300*	*100*	*200*	*300*	*100*	*200*	*300*
12 gage	3.0	3.5	4.5	3.5	4.5													
10 gage	2.0	3.0	4.0	3.0	4.0	4.5	4.5	5.0		5.0								
8 gage	2.0	3.0	3.5	2.5	3.5	4.0	3.5	4.0	5.0	4.0	5.0	5.5	4.5			5.0		
7 gage	1.5	2.5	3.0	2.0	3.0	3.5	2.5	3.5	4.5	3.0	4.0	5.0	3.5	5.0	5.5	4.5		
5 gage	1.5	2.0	3.0	1.5	2.5	3.5	2.0	3.0	4.0	2.5	3.5	4.5	3.0	4.0	5.0	3.5	4.5	
3 gage	1.0	2.0	2.5	1.5	2.0	3.0	1.5	2.5	3.5	2.5	3.0	4.0	2.5	3.5	4.5	3.0	4.0	5.0
1 gage	1.0	2.0	2.5	1.0	2.0	3.0	1.5	2.0	3.0	2.0	3.0	3.5	2.5	3.0	4.0	2.5	3.5	4.5

TABLE 13-7 RECOMMENDED MINIMUM HEIGHT OF COVER—IN FEET FOR *MULTI-PLATE PIPE* UNDER AIRPORTS

Wheel Load	*Gage*	*For Pipe Under Concrete Pavement Depth Below Slab*						*For Pipe Under Compacted Earth Backfill— No Pavement*					
		Diameter in Inches						*Diameter in Inches*					
		60	*72*	*84*	*96*	*108*	*120*	*60*	*72*	*84*	*96*	*108*	*120*
15,000 Lb	12	0.5	0.5	1.0				1.0	1.5	2.0			
	10			0.5	0.5	0.5	1.5		1.0	1.5	1.5	2.0	2.5
	8						0.5			1.0	1.0	1.5	2.0
	7											1.0	2.0
	5												1.0
	3												
	1												
40,000 Lb	12	0.5	2.0	3.5				2.0	2.5	4.0			
	10		0.5	1.0	1.5	2.5	5.0	1.0	1.5	2.0	2.5	3.5	5.0
	8			0.5	0.5	1.0	1.5		1.0	1.5	2.0	2.0	2.5
	7					0.5	1.0			1.0	1.5	1.5	2.0
	5						0.5				1.0	1.0	1.5
	3												1.0
	1												
60,000 Lb	12	1.0	2.5					2.5	3.5				
	10	0.5	0.5	1.5	2.5	4.0		1.5	2.0	2.5	3.5	4.0	
	8			0.5	1.0	1.5	2.5	1.0	1.5	1.5	2.0	2.5	3.5
	7				0.5	1.0	1.5		1.0	1.5	1.5	2.0	2.5
	5					0.5	0.5			1.0	1.0	1.5	2.0
	3											1.0	1.5
	1												1.0
150,000 Lb	12	3.0						3.5					
	10	1.0	2.0	3.5				2.0	3.0	4.0			
	8		1.0	1.5	2.5	4.0		1.5	2.0	2.5	3.5	4.0	
	7			1.0	1.5	2.5	4.0		1.5	2.0	2.5	3.5	4.0
	5				1.0	1.0	2.0			1.5	1.5	2.0	3.0
	3						1.0					1.5	2.0
	1												1.5

CHAPTER FOURTEEN

Tunnel Liner Plate Gages

(CORRUGATED, LAP JOINT TYPE)

Gage Tables for Liner Plate

Experience is the best guide for determining dimensions and proper gages for liner plate under various conditions of soil, water and care of installation. The accompanying Tables 14–1 to 14–5 may be used as a guide for permanent installations under constructed embankments.

TABLE 14-1 GAGES OF ARMCO LINER PLATE FOR CONTINUOUS LOAD-CARRYING STRUCTURES

Under H-20 Loading

Neutral Axis Diam. in Inches	*Height of Cover—in Feet*														
	2-5	*6-10*	*11-15*	*16-20*	*21-25*	*26-30*	*31-35*	*36-40*	*41-45*	*46-50*	*51-55*	*56-60*	*61-70*	*71-80*	*81-100*
48	12	12	12	12	12	12	12	12	10	8	7	5	5	5	5
54	12	12	12	12	12	12	12	10	8	7	5	5	5	5	3
60	12	12	12	12	12	12	10	8	7	5	5	5	5	5	
66	12	12	12	12	12	10	8	8	5	5	5	5	5	3	
72	12	12	12	12	12	10	8	7	5	5	5	5	3		
78	12	12	12	12	10	8	7	5	5	5	5	5			
84	12	12	12	10	10	8	5	5	5	5	5	3			
90	12	12	10	10	10	7	5	5	5	5	3				
96	10	12	10	10	8	5	5	5	5	5					
102	10	12	10	10	8	5	5	5	5	3					
108	10	10	10	10	7	5	5	5	3						
114	10	10	10	8	5	5	5	5	3						
120	10	10	10	8	5	5	5	3							
126	8	10	8	8	5	5	5	3							
132	8	10	8	7	5	5	5								
138	8	10	8	7	5	5	3								
144	8	8	8	5	5	5	3								
150	8	8	8	5	5	5									
156	8	8	8	5	5	5									
162	8	8	8	5	5	3									
168	8	8	8	5	5	3									
174	8	8	7	5	5	3									
180	7	8	7	5	5										

Notes:
1. Interpolate for intermediate diameters. Diameters are available in increments of 2 in.
2. Lighter gages are often used for temporary load-carrying structures. 14 Gage plates are available for use when conditions permit.
3. The determination of gages for liner plate for tunneling in natural ground involves so many variables that no single table can adequately cover all situations. Investigations at the site must be made to obtain knowledge of the geological origin of the soil and present physical properties. Knowledge gained from these investigations, combined with experience in practical tunneling will enable the selection of an adequate and economical structure.

TABLE 14-2 GAGES OF ARMCO LINER PLATE FOR CONTINUOUS LOAD-CARRYING STRUCTURES
Under Cooper E 70 Loading

Neutral Axis Diam. in Inches	*Height of Cover—in Feet*														
	4-5	*6-10*	*11-15*	*16-20*	*21-25*	*26-30*	*31-35*	*36-40*	*41-45*	*46-50*	*51-55*	*56-60*	*61-70*	*71-80*	*81-100*
48	12	12	12	12	12	12	12	12	10	8	7	5	5	5	5
54	12	12	12	12	12	12	12	10	8	7	5	5	5	5	3
60	12	12	12	12	12	12	10	8	7	5	5	5	5	3	
66	10	12	12	12	12	10	8	7	5	5	5	5	5		
72	10	12	12	12	12	10	8	5	5	5	5	5	3		
78	8	10	10	10	10	8	7	5	5	5	5	5			
84	8	10	10	10	10	8	5	5	5	5	5	3			
90	7	8	8	8	8	7	5	5	5	5	3				
96	5	8	8	8	8	5	5	5	5	3					
102	5	8	8	8	8	5	5	5	5	3					
108	5	7	7	7	5	5	5	5	3						
114	5	5	5	5	5	5	5	5	3						
120	5	5	5	5	5	5	5	3							
126	5	5	5	5	5	5	5	3							
132	5	5	5	5	5	5	5								
138	5	5	5	5	5	5	3								
144	5	5	5	5	5	5	3								
150	5	5	5	5	5	5	3								
156	5	5	5	5	5	5									
162	3	5	5	5	5	3									
168	3	5	5	5	5	3									
174	3	5	5	5	5	3									
180		5	5	5	5										

Fig. 85. Installing steel liner plate for storm sewer tunnel in city of Los Angeles. Finished tunnel is horse-shoe shaped with 3,200 ft length having inside diameter of 11 ft 6 in. and 1,700 ft of 9 ft 3 in. diameter.

TABLE 14-3 RECOMMENDED MINIMUM GAGES OF ARMCO LINER PLATE ARCHES FOR INSTALLATIONS INSIDE EXISTING ARCH STRUCTURES

Under Cooper E 70 Loading $R/S=0.3$ to 0.5

Height of Cover in Feet	*3*			*6*			*9*			*12*			*15*			*18*			*21*			*24*			*27*			*30*			*Span in Feet*
*Class of Installation**	*A*	*B*	*C*	*A*	*B*	*C*	*A*	*B*	*C*	*A*	*B*	*C*	*A*	*B*	*C*	*A*	*B*	*C*	*A*	*B*	*C*	*A*	*B*	*C*	*A*	*B*	*C*	*A*	*B*	*C*	
Span in Feet																															
6	10	10	8	10	10	8	10	10	8	10	10	8	10	10	8	10	10	8	10	10	8	10	8	7	10	8	7	10	8	7	6
7	10	8	8	10	8	7	10	8	8	10	8	8	10	8	7	10	8	7	10	8	7	10	8	7	10	8	7	8	7	5	7
8	10	8	7	10	8	7	10	8	7	10	8	7	10	8	7	10	8	7	10	8	7	8	7	5	8	7	5	8	7	5	8
9	10	8	7	10	8	7	10	8	7	10	8	7	10	8	7	10	8	7	8	7	5	8	7	5	8	7	5	8	7	5	9
10	8	7	5	8	7	7	8	8	7	8	8	7	8	7	7	8	7	5	8	7	5	8	7	5	8	7	5	7	5	3	10
11	8	7	5	8	7	5	8	7	7	8	7	5	8	7	5	8	7	5	8	7	5	7	5	3	7	5	3	5	3		11
12	8	7	5	8	7	5	8	7	7	8	7	5	8	7	5	8	7	5	7	5	3	7	5	3	7	5	3	5	3		12
13	7	5	3	7	7	5	8	7	5	8	7	5	7	7	5	7	5	3	7	5	3	7	5	3	5	3		5	3		13
14	7	5	3	7	5	3	7	7	5	7	5	5	7	5	3	7	5	3	7	5	3	5	3		5	3		5	3		14
15	7	5	3	7	5	3	7	5	5	7	5	3	7	5	3	7	5	3	5	3		5	3		5	3		3			15
16	5	3		7	5	3	7	5	3	7	5	3	7	5	3	5	3		5	3		5	3		5			3			16
17	5	3		5	3	3	7	5	3	5	5	3	5	3		5	3		5	3		5			3			3			17
18	5	3		5	3		5	5	3	5	3	3	5	3		5	3		3			3			3						18
19	3			5	3		5	3	3	5	3		5	3		3			3			3									19
20	3			5	3		5	3		5	3		3	3		3			3												20
21	3			3			5	3		3	3		3			3															21

*Classes of Installations

A. Condition of existing structure FAIR with space between existing structure and metal structure to be completely filled with soundly placed pressure grout of 1:3 mix or richer.

B. Condition of existing structure POOR with space between existing structure and metal structure to be completely filled with soundly placed pressure grout of 1:3 mix or richer.

C. Condition of existing structure FAIR with space between existing structure and metal structure to be completely filled with sand or pressure grout of 1:4 mix or leaner.

TABLE 14-4 GAGES OF ARMCO ELLIPTICAL LINER PLATE UNDERPASSES
For H-20 Loading

Under-pass No.	*Height of Cover in Feet*							
	4-5	*6-10*	*11-15*	*16-20*	*21-30*	*31-40*	*41-50*	*51-60*
1	12	12	12	12	8	5	5	5
2	12	12	12	10	8	5	5	3
3	12	12	10	10	7	5	5	
4	12	12	10	10	7	5	5	
5	10	12	10	10	5	5	5	
6	10	12	10	10	5	5	3	
7	10	12	10	10	5	5	3	
8	10	10	10	8	5	5		
9	10	10	10	8	5	3		
10	8	10	8	8	5	3		

TABLE 14-5 GAGES OF ARMCO ELLIPTICAL LINER PLATE UNDERPASSES
For Cooper E 70 Loading

Under-pass No.	*Height of Cover in Feet*							
	2-5	*6-10*	*11-15*	*16-20*	*21-30*	*31-40*	*41-50*	*51-60*
1	8	10	10	10	8	5	5	5
2	8	10	10	10	8	5	5	3
3	7	10	10	10	7	5	5	
4	7	8	8	8	7	5	5	
5	5	8	8	8	5	5	5	
6	5	8	8	8	5	5	3	
7	5	8	8	8	5	5	3	
8	5	7	7	7	5	5		
9	5	5	5	5	5	3		
10	5	5	5	5	5	3		

CHAPTER FIFTEEN

Miscellaneous Loadings

Safe Spans for Aerial Pipe

For exposed corrugated metal sewers and other pipe lines carrying sewage or water, the table of safe spans (opposite) gives the allowable spacing between saddles or brackets, when the pipe is flowing full. It is not necessary to support the pipe on beams or rails between the piers. Fig. 86.

Where exposed pipe serves to carry air or gases, the spans may be increased.

Column Strength

Column strength of smooth and corrugated metal pipe is of importance where such pipe are "jacked" as conduits, driven as pile shells or caissons, or where they support superloads. The same is true of vertical storage bins.

The ultimate strength of short columns of standard riveted corrugated metal pipe for various diameters and gages is shown in Fig. 53, page 62. By using a suitable factor of safety, the desired gage can be read from the curves (see example).

Example: From chart (Fig. 53,) a 48-in. diam. 12 gage riveted corrugated metal pipe will carry approximately 550 lb per in. of periphery.
Therefore 550 x 48 x 3.1416 = 82,938 lb ultimate strength.
(This is with no factor of safety).

Results of compression tests on a few 10-ft lengths of 6 and 8-in. diameter helical and standard corrugated pipe are shown in Table 15–2.

Fig. 86. Aerial sanitary sewer of 48-in. Asbestos-Bonded pipe with watertight joints.

TABLE 15-1 SAFE SPANS OR BENT SPACING —IN FEET

For Standard Corrugated Metal Pipe Flowing Full of Water

Diameter in Inches	*Gage of Pipe*				
	16	*14*	*12*	*10*	*8*
12	12	13.5	15.5		
15	12	13.5	15.5		
18	12.5	14	15.5		
21	12.5	14	16		
24	13	14.5	16.5		
30		14.5	16.5	19	20.5
36		14.5	17	19	21
42		14.5	17	19	21
48		15	17.5	19.5	21
54		15	17.5	19.5	21.5
60			17.5	19.5	21.5
66			17.5	20	21.5
72			17.5	20	22
84				20	22

TABLE 15-2 END COMPRESSION STRENGTH OF CORRUGATED METAL PIPE

Kind of Corrugation	*Diameter in Inches*	*Gage*	*Average Max. Load in Lb*
Helical.	6	18	9,325
Helical.	6	16	10,312
Helical.	8	18	9,133
Helical.	8	16	14,875
Standard.	8	16	10,690

Fig. 87. Test culvert made up of various kinds of pipe, being installed in marshy soil near Portland, Maine.

SECTION THREE

DURABILITY STUDIES

ON METALS AND PROTECTIVE COATINGS

CHAPTER SIXTEEN

Methods of Determining Durability

Summary

Although considerable research has been and is being carried on, there is little published information on the durability or life expectancy of drainage structures. Field inspections give the surest answer on durability. Inspections of large numbers of structures indicate two pathways of deterioration—structural and material. Interpretation of the results is not an exact science but is a helpful guide in predicting durability. Corrugated metal drainage structures under various service conditions and with various degrees of protection give long and ample service life for modern construction.

Destructive Forces

Any engineering structure to be satisfactory for a designed use must possess sufficient but not wasteful durability. This durability implies resistance both to structural forces and material deterioration, including:

1. Excessive loads from any cause, impact, undermining, etc.
2. Longitudinal forces tending to pull the structure apart.
3. Corrosion, deterioration, rotting, disintegration and other chemical or electrolytic actions.
4. Erosion or abrasive action by hydraulic traffic through the structure.

Research on the first two items has been discussed in preceding chapters. The third and fourth items are discussed here.

Nature of Research

Research on material durability has been of several kinds—(1) laboratory tests, (2) special field installations and (3) inspection and evaluation of actual existing structures. Extensive tests have been made and are constantly underway by the American Society for Testing Materials, the U. S. Bureau of Standards and by other engineering associations, industries and materials producers. Those investigations cover not only the basic materials but also protective coatings, linings, etc.

1. Laboratory Tests. Laboratory tests on material durability are useful in that they enable the factors to be varied and controlled. Also, they permit accelerating the aging conditions, thereby giving data within days or weeks which otherwise might require years. Researchers, however, are wary about making any predictions as to the comparative or absolute service life expectancy of any material as the result of these accelerated tests, which at best can serve only as a rough guide. It is practically impossible to predict actual service behavior from such accelerated tests as they cannot be designed to include all the factors encountered in actual service.

For example, in 1907 the American Society for Testing Materials inaugurated the "acid corrosion test" to simulate atmospheric corrosion of metal. These tests were renounced by this same organization in 1909 and 1911. Again, in 1930, this organization "concluded that an acid test conducted by the procedure followed by the committee is not capable of consistent repetition. Further, the data from such an acid test should not be used to forecast the relative life of ordinary ferrous or other materials in the atmosphere."[1] Another general conclusion was that life expectancy under atmospheric and underground conditions were not comparable.

2. Special Field Installations. Research projects are constantly underway to determine the comparative durability of various materials. These are not accelerated tests, nor are they full-scale tests of actual structures. Rather they involve the exposure of many samples of materials to atmospheric, water immersion or underground conditions in various typical geographical areas.[2] Fig. 87.

These tests cover long periods of time. Data obtained from them are definitely more reliable than those from accelerated tests, but are not necessarily convertible to all service conditions.

3. Field Investigations. The most reliable way to estimate the life expectancy of a conduit or other engineering structure is to examine the records of a large number of these structures that have served their full useful life. Unfortunately such complete records of structures under various service conditions are not available. However, many structures of various ages have been examined, and by applying a widely accepted method of predicting life expectancy discussed hereafter, it is possible to reach reasonable conclusions.

Prompted by the report over three decades ago that corrugated metal culverts were rusting out (failing materially), the Armco Steel Corporation (then The American Rolling Mill Co.) started a nationwide survey of various drainage structures.[3] This marked the initiation of a "Look Under Your Roads" campaign to learn first-hand how the various types of drainage structures were performing under actual service conditions. Armco has continued ever since to cooperate with various groups in this research on durability.

A number of state highway departments and, later, the Highway Research Board became vitally interested in field investigations. In 1925, the Tennessee State Highway Department launched the first comprehensive study to learn more about culvert performance. During the next few years similar studies were made by more than a dozen states. This work was reviewed in the June 5, 1930, issue of *Engineering News-Record*[4] by S. B. Slack of the Georgia State Highway Department, who conducted investigations in that state in 1926, 1928 and 1930. In this article Slack quotes from a report by E. F. Kelley, chief of Division of Tests, Bureau of Public Roads:

1. The rating schedule used in this survey for measuring the relative behavior in service of corrugated sheet metal culverts is sound in principle.

Fig. 88. The "look under your roads" method of examining culverts is considered the best way of determining durability. Above 42-in. Armco culvert was installed 1912 near Mt. Healthy, Ohio. Age of culvert, 41 years.

2. The use of such a schedule may be expected to yield results having a degree of accuracy sufficient for the purpose and its use by different observers may be expected to yield comparable results.

Thousands of culverts of all types were examined and re-examined at intervals. Definite ideas of performance in the major conditions of service developed from these investigations and replaced the somewhat erroneous theories which prevailed previous to that time. Fig. 88.

Uniform Methods

It was necessary to set forth a definite inspection procedure, capable of being duplicated by a number of competent investigators with a reasonable degree of accuracy. Among the more important points of an investigation are:

1. The inspection of all culverts under a given number of roads according to a previously determined program, and by a competent and unbiased inspection crew.
2. A written record of each culvert inspected.
3. A percentage rating assigned to each culvert based on its present condition.
4. An average life expectancy computed for each culvert type or material in each variation of service.

By examining a sufficient number of existing structures in service and predicting the number of years of service remaining, based on their condition and age, a much clearer picture of culvert life expectancy can be gained.

Rating programs employed in field investigations of culverts are founded on the theory that a galvanized metal structure is subject to a uniform rate of deterioration to failure.* Percentage values for the stages of deterioration are determined from field observations of structures of the principal types in all conditions of deterioration and of various ages. The rating program is then based on these stages of deterioration and applied to each culvert examined. The average percentage rating for each type in each service together with the average service age furnishes the basis for estimating the total probable durability for that type and condition.

Two Pathways of Deterioration

All of the culvert rating programs developed during the early state highway culvert investigations were unanimous in recognizing two distinct pathways of deterioration—structural and material. Structures of all types tend to follow both pathways to failure but there exists a difference in rates of the two.

Structural deterioration of a conduit occurs as a result of excessive loads, impact,

*This theory, while proved satisfactory for comparing the durability of drainage conduits, is more conservative than the U. S. Bureau of Standards' approach to measuring exterior corrosive effects on underground pipe lines. In the latter, greatest corrosion occurs early in the life of the conduit and then tapers off.

TABLE 16-1 CULVERT RATING CHART
CORRUGATED METAL PIPE

Rating Per Cent	*Structural Condition*	*Rating Per Cent*	*Material Condition*
90	Perfect line, joints and shape.	90	Spelter entirely intact.
75	Bands or lugs loosening, slight sag or change in alignment, flattening 1/10 diameter or less.	75	Spelter just gone and thin rust beginning to form in places, no abrasion and no pitting.
50	Joints opening at bands or lugs. Considerable sagging, faulting, and change of alignment. Flattening less than 1/10 diameter.	50	Complete loss of spelter and considerable loss of metal in invert. Pitting and some abrasion.
30	Heavy sagging and change of alignment. Joints opening considerably and pipe flattening less than 1/5 D.	30	Decided pitting and abrasion. Heavy loss of metal in invert.
10	Pipe flattening more than 1/5 D. Joints pulled entirely apart. Heavy sagging and very bad alignment. Decided faulting.	10	Metal corroded and abraded through invert in small spots. Very heavy rust and deep pitting general over invert.
0	A zero per cent rating can only be given when pipe has practically quit functioning and needs replacing.	0	Entire invert gone.

foundation faults and other forces. It is the characteristic pathway to failure for the rigid type structures and occurs to a limited extent in the flexible type.

Material deterioration is the reaction of the material in the structure to the disintegrating substances in the hydraulic traffic, to freezing and thawing, to alternate wet and dry conditions, to weathering, aging and other conditions. As applied to corrugated metal and concrete, this deterioration is accounted for chiefly through erosion and corrosion of the invert.

Rating *charts* used by the Tennessee State Highway Department for their culvert investigations are reproduced here. See Tables 16-1 and 16-2.

Combined Rating

After a culvert has been assigned a percentage rating for both structural and material condition, it is necessary to combine these ratings. An equation that has given reasonable results is:

$$F = L + K\,(H - L)$$

where F = composite rating of present condition in per cent
L = low rating, either structural or material
H = high rating, either structural or material
K = empirical compensating constant (1/10 in Tennessee investigations)

TABLE 16-2 CULVERT RATING CHART
RIGID PIPE

Rating Per Cent	*Structural Condition*	*Rating Per Cent*	*Material Condition*
90	Straight alignment, tight joints and no cracked sections.	90	No weathering or disintegration and no softening from acid or alkali or other causes.
75	No cracked sections. Some faulting and opening of joints. Poor alignment.	75	Some weathering or spalling and disintegration. Slight erosion of invert.
50	Sections cracked but cracks not opened to any extent. Poor alignment. Joints opening and faulting. Slight flattening.	50	Decided disintegration or erosion in invert. General weathering and spalling. Softening due to alkali or acid.
30	Cracks opening and pipe flattening considerably. Poor alignment and joints opening and faulting considerably.	30	Decided disintegration throughout pipe. Considerable weathering and spalling. Softening due to alkali or acid.
10	Sections broken and crushed partly in; joints badly faulted. Line very poor. Culvert still functioning.	10	Extreme distintegration and spalling. Material very soft due to acid or alkali.
0	Section crushed so that pipe needs replacing.	0	Disintegration through pipe. Reinforcing exposed.

Having obtained the final rating, not of one but of a large number of any type of culverts, and knowing the service ages at the time of the investigation, the life expectancy of that group may be determined. The following method is used:

$$u=\frac{100-F}{A} \text{ and } E=\frac{100}{U}$$

where F = final rating, in per cent
A = age or years of service to date
E = life expectancy, in years for any culvert type
u = unit deterioration, in per cent per year
U = average unit deterioration for all the culverts in one service classification

Example: Assume $F=33$ per cent (for single culvert)
and $A=24$ years

then $u=\frac{100-33}{24}=2.79$ per cent deterioration per year

and $\frac{100}{2.79}=36$ years = total ultimate life for culvert

Assume a group of culverts with $U=3.78$ per cent

then, $E=\frac{100}{3.78}=26.4$ years = average useful life of group

A large number of structures is necessary in applying the law of averages. Note from the above example that while it is entirely possible to rate one culvert, it is not a safe practice to predict an average life expectancy on one structure. Only where a sufficient number of structures, sixty to seventy-five or more under one service condition, have been investigated can the results be considered reasonably conclusive.

Conclusions

A number of general conclusions can be drawn from culvert investigations:

1. No one type of culvert of those investigated is the ideal one for all conditions.
2. Past opinions of culvert durability are in many cases erroneous.
3. The weaknesses of existing culvert types have been brought out.
4. Sufficient data on durability are available to make economic selection of culverts possible.

Because there is a wide variation in performance with every variation in service condition, and because erroneous conclusions might be drawn in attempting to apply the results from one major service condition to another, it seems advisable to make culvert investigations of as many culvert types as possible serving under various major conditions, in order that true durability comparisons can be made.

TABLE 16-3 DATES OF INTRODUCTION OF FABRICATED METAL PRODUCTS

Structure	*Year*	*Remarks*
Corrugated metal pipe	1895	Patented May 1896. Some of earliest structures still in use
Armco Ingot Iron Pipe	1906	Hundreds of early culverts and sewers still in service
Bituminous Paved-Invert Pipe	1926	Developed to resist erosion in bottom —gives a pipe of "balanced design"
Multi-Plate Pipe and Arches	1931	Field assembled, bolted construction
Metal Retaining Walls	1931	Cribbing; replaced by bin-type
Beam-type Guardrail	1933	Corrugated plate rail
Asbestos-Bonded Pipe	1934	Developed to give better adhesion of bituminous coating and pavement. Found to give superior resistance to corrosion
Liner Plates	1935	For tunneling or relining
Pipe-Arch	1937	For limited headroom. Found to be more efficient hydraulically
Sheeting	1937	Interlocking and flange types
Foundation Pipe	1939	Piles and pile shells
Bridge Plank	1946	Replacement of old bridge flooring

REFERENCES

1. Proceedings of the Thirty-fourth Annual Meeting, American Society for Testing Materials, 1931, Vol. 31, pp. 176–180.
2. "Causes of Underground Corrosion" Chapter III of Circular C450—Underground Corrosion, published by National Bureau of Standards, U. S. Department of Commerce, 1945, pp. 10–13.
3. "Report of Culvert Investigations, 1921 and 1922," by A. J. Sheldon, Armco Culvert & Flume Mfrs. Assn., Middletown, Ohio, p 140.
4. "Studies in Pipe Culvert Durability and Performance," by Searcy B. Slack, *Engineering News-Record*, June 5, 1940, pp. 938–939.

CHAPTER SEVENTEEN

Highway Culvert Inspections

West Virginia Inspection of Paved Pipe

Information gained from the early culvert investigations conducted by the highway departments provided Armco engineers with valuable data for improving their products. It enabled them to design drainage structures of a "balanced design." For example, it was learned from these investigations that where the structure must carry heavy hydraulic traffic, the invert of any culvert is vulnerable to considerable erosion. This led to the development of the bituminous paved invert.

In 1934 the Engineering Experiment Station of the University of West Virginia published Research Bulletin No. 13 entitled, "A Survey of Culverts in West Virginia".[5, 6] Between four and five hundred bituminous Paved-Invert corrugated metal structures were included in the inspection. The following quotation from this bulletin summarizes the results:

> "There is reason to believe it (paving the invert) may more than double the life of plain corrugated metal pipe."

Fig. 89. Paved-Invert culvert installed in Roane Co., W. Va. in 1928 in acid mine water service. In very good condition when photographed 24 years later.

Fig. 90. Reinspection of 60-in. Armco Paved-Invert culvert under the Pennsylvania Turnpike in 1948 showed the pavement successfully resisting erosion.

The life of the Paved-Invert (single pavement) corrugated metal pipe in these inspections was estimated at forty-nine years.

Many of the culverts inspected in 1934 were reinspected by Armco engineers in 1952.[7] The findings substantiated those of the 1934 inspection:

> "The most outstanding feature noticed in this reinspection was the value of the pavement in the corrugated metal pipe. In the report by Professor Downs in 1934, he estimated the average life of single Paved-Invert corrugated metal pipe at forty-nine years. We feel that the pipe will reach that figure. On the other hand, had these pipes been full coated and multiple paved (over a greater portion of periphery), a very high percentage would attain many more years of useful service life than predicted by Professor Downs." Fig. 89.

Bureau of Public Roads' Inspection of Paved-Invert Culverts

Engineers from the U. S. Bureau of Public Roads (formerly the Public Roads Administration) made an extensive investigation of the performance of bituminous coated and Paved-Invert corrugated metal culverts used for cross-drains under the Blue Ridge Parkway in North Carolina and Virginia in 1945. The structures inspected had been installed during the period 1936–1941. Included were culverts furnished by Armco and other manufacturers. This investigation[8] indicates that the proper application of coating and paved-invert can substantially increase the service life of corrugated culverts.

Pennsylvania Turnpike Culverts

In 1941, Armco engineers made a study of the performance of corrugated metal drainage structures installed a few years earlier on the original Pennsylvania Turnpike. In 1948 these structures were reinspected. Fig. 90. Little change from the condition reported in 1941 could be noted. Quoting from the earlier report:[9]

"The invert pavements were, with a few minor exceptions, in excellent or very good condition.

"The coatings in the upper portions of all Armco culverts were examined and tested for adhesion . . . The coatings adhered tenaciously and, using a putty knife, it was impossible to expose base metal."

From an article,[10] written after the 1948 inspection of these same installations, the following is quoted:

"The need for a 'balanced design' in culverts, i.e. extra material where the wear is greatest, is dramatically demonstrated by the structures under the Pennsylvania Turnpike. No evidence of erosion damage to Armco Pipe was found, but in many places small chips were missing from the pavement surfaces, indicating that the water flowing through the structures carried considerable gravel and other debris. Without the protection of the bituminous pavement, the galvanized coating on the pipe would have been worn away under the continuous flow observed."

Culverts in New Mexico Alkali Soils

Inspection was made by Armco engineers, in 1948, of a number of highway culverts at several locations in New Mexico. The purpose was to determine the effect of alkali soils on the durability of galvanized corrugated metal structures. Fig. 91.

Most of the culverts were 24, 30 and 36-in. pipe and small pipe-arches. However,

Fig 91. Installed in 1927 under a state highway south of Gallup, N. Mex., this 24-in. Armco culvert showed no loss of spelter when inspected 21 years later.

Fig. 92. Twenty years of service on this Multi-Plate pipe in Georgia shows some discoloration but otherwise is perfect materially and structurally.

a twin 60-in. pipe and a 90-in. Multi-Plate pipe were included. Ages varied from eighteen months to twenty years. The soil at all locations was tested for water soluble salts including sulphates and chlorides. Sulphates varied from 0.01 to 2.84 per cent.

Although there was some corrosion of the base metal on the outside of some of the culverts, there was no deterioration on the inside. The report reads, "There is no correlation to be found between the sulphate content of the soils and the apparent corrosion of the corrugated metal pipe after periods of service varying from eighteen months to more than twenty years."

Multi-Plate Pipe and Arch Inspections

The first extensive study made to learn the performance being given by the larger Multi-Plate structures was in 1943–1944.[11] Since this was the first comprehensive investigation of installations of the size range of Multi-Plate, considerable thought was given to the development of an inspection form which would furnish the desired information and insure uniformity of results regardless of the number of investigators taking part. In drawing up the inspection forms, full use was made of the experience gained during the previous investigations of smaller pipe. Fig. 92.

Ages of the structures inspected range from four to twelve years, with an over-all average of 7.7 years. It was realized that this was a comparatively short hindsight to use as a basis of predicting average life expectancy. Therefore, every effort was made to be conservative. Quoting from a published article:[12]

> "Only structures where circumstances permitted a thorough examination were included in making up the weighted averages, and the material ratings were based on the worst condition and not on the average conditions of the entire structure. With these precautions in mind, the estimate of an average of at least fifty years for all gages and all conditions of service may be said to be a conservative one based on the most complete performance data which could be secured. . . .

"Service conditions for arches, with respect to the effect on the plates vary greatly from those of pipes. Arches, except for a few in the smaller sizes, have no bottom except the streambed, and, where possible, the springline of the arch is usually kept above the normal water level.

"Because of the uniformly good material condition of the arches, it is believed that in the majority of cases, the life of corrugated arches will be determined by the life of the foundations."

REFERENCES

5. "A Survey of Culverts in West Virginia," by W. S. Downs, Research Bulletin No. 13, West Virginia University, Dec. 15, 1934.
6. "Durability of Culvert Types Under Service Conditions," by W. S. Downs, *Engineering News-Record,* March 14, 1935, p. 384.
7. "Inspection of Older Coated and Paved Pipe in West Virginia," by Armco Drainage & Metal Products, Inc., July 17, 1952.
8. "A Study of Bituminous-Coated Corrugated Sheet Metal Culverts," by J. Y. Welborn and C. J. Serafin, Public Roads, Federal Works Agency, Public Roads Administration, July-August-September 1946, pp. 227–238.
9. "A Brief Report on Condition of Paved-Invert Corrugated Pipe Culverts Under the Pennsylvania Turnpike," by W. H. Spindler, Armco Drainage Products Association, July 1941.
10. "Ten Years Under the Pennsylvania Turnpike," by Max H. Bailey, *The Highway Magazine,* October 1949, p. 224.
11. "Summary of Inspections of Armco Multi-Plate Pipe and Arches," Armco Drainage & Metal Products, Inc., 1943–1944.
12. "Probable Life of Corrugated Culverts," by G. E. Shafer, and W. J. Kropf, *Engineering News-Record* October 18, 1945, pp. 10–13.

CHAPTER EIGHTEEN

Railway Culvert Inspections

Railroads in the United States and Canada make it a practice to examine annually all of the culverts under their lines—a very commendable practice. While this does not result in "rating" the culverts and measuring their service life, it gives the engineers an answer to the question of culvert performance and durability.

These inspections have led to confidence in and widespread use of corrugated metal culverts in a wide range of sizes and under even the severest of service conditions.

Fig. 93. Veteran 24-in. 16 gage Armco culvert installed under 25 ft of fill on the Santa Fe Railway in Arizona in 1911. Condition good when photographed 37 years later.

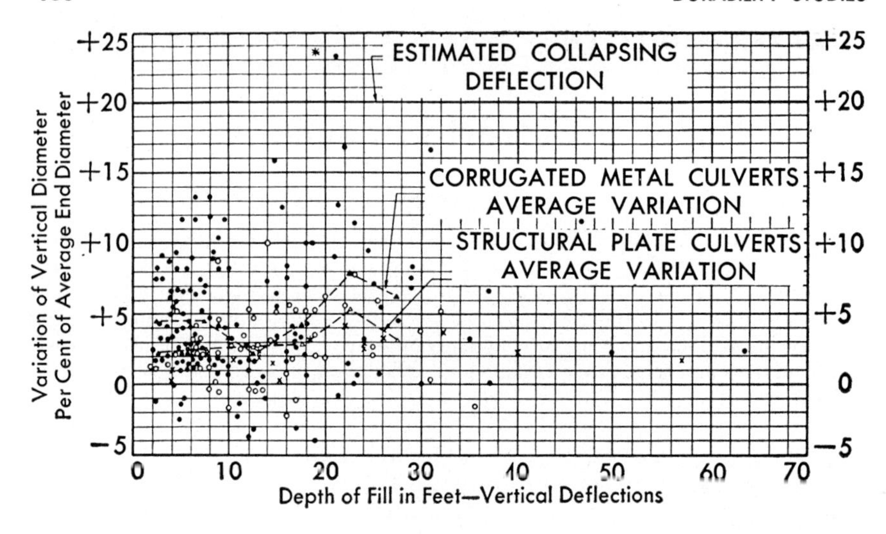

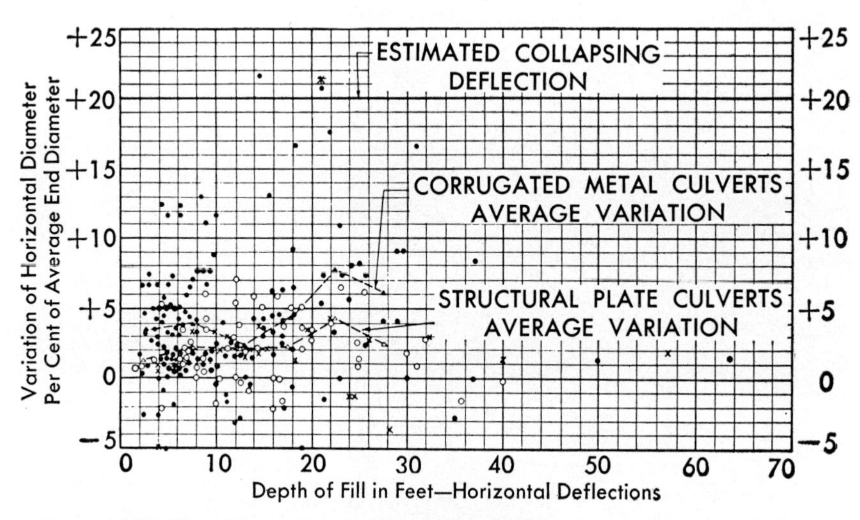

Note: *Fill Is Wet, Water Seeping Through Joints. Loss of Lateral Resistance Has Resulted in Excessive Deflection But Complete Failure Not Imminent.

●—Corrugated Metal Culverts
o—Structural Plate Culverts
x—Tunnel Liner
△—Average Variation—Corrugated Metal Culverts
△—Average Variation—Structural Plate Culverts

Fig. 94. Charts showing vertical and horizontal deflections of approximately 300 corrugated metal culverts 5 ft in diameter and larger installed in various ways under numerous U. S. railroads. Excessive deflections occurred in only a few cases.—*Courtesy AREA, Jan. 1953.*

American Association of Railroads, Inspections of 1949-1952

The American Railway Engineering Association Committee 15, Iron and Steel Structures, in January 1953 issued a progress report on the inspection of some 300 corrugated metal pipe 60 in. and larger.[13] The purpose was to examine "the structural performance of existing field installations with the hope that their performance would show either that the present design practice is sound or that it should be revised. Member roads of the AREA were asked to report the vertical and horizontal deflections of a representative number of structures 5 ft or more in diameter. The 300 corrugated metal pipes were "of riveted and bolted construction installed with and without strutting, in compacted and non-compacted embankments. Approximately one-fourth of the structures were installed by jacking or tunneling the structure through the existing embankment."

Fig. 94 indicates the vertical and horizontal deflections of all pipes under all installation and service conditions. The report says: "In general, the average deflection supports the design criteria for flexible structures in common use. Excessive deflection in a few cases has been checked and satisfactorily explained by unusual installation conditions."

Material Durability Data

Detailed studies of material durability are continually made by various railroads and by Armco, independently or jointly, to see how various materials and coatings perform under different service conditions. These conditions include swamps, tidal coastlands, steep hilly country, mine-water streams, alkali country, and many others.

A typical inspection of 139 installations in 1946 on one railroad in eastern Kentucky included riveted corrugated metal pipe and pipe-arches, Multi-Plate pipe, liner plate, cast iron and concrete pipe. In areas of highly corrosive mine waters the importance of additional protective coatings was illustrated by the deterioration of concrete pipe and rusting of plain galvanized metal culverts and cast iron.

Another inspection on a mid-western railroad in 1952 included 125 structures in four states, with ages of ten to twenty-five years, under a wide variety of service conditions. Here are a few typical conclusions from the report:[14]

1. Plain galvanized pipe twenty to twenty-five years old can be expected to give fifteen to twenty-five years more of service.
2. The area most affected by corrosion is in the bottom twenty-five per cent of the invert.
3. The Asbestos-Bonded pipe inspected ranged in age from five to sixteen years. None of these pipes has been affected by erosion or corrosion.
4. Until such time as signs of deterioration are evident, the expected life of Asbestos-Bonded pipe is too far in the future to be estimated.
5. Chief installation faults were grade lines too low, resulting in silting; inclusion of cinders in backfill material and installing multiple pipes too close together.

In general, inspections are helpful in revealing the results of improper manufacture and installation practices and eliminating them on subsequent installations.

REFERENCES

13. "Design of Metal Culverts of 60-in. Diam. and Larger," Progress Report of Comm. 15, AREA—Bulletin 506, January 1953, pp. 918–929.

14. "Inspection of Metal Drainage Structures," by R. C. Baker, Armco Research Laboratories, December 1952, 130 pp.

CHAPTER NINETEEN

Sewer Inspections

Inspection of Sanitary and Combined Sewers—1940, 1950

Armco engineers have been very active in the investigation of drainage structure performance from the earliest inspections to the present time. Every year hundreds of corrugated metal drainage structures, both culverts and sewers in all types of service, are inspected and rated. Many of these investigations are reinspections of the same installations to learn if the rates of deterioration originally assigned to them are substantially correct for a particular service exposure. Fig. 95.

A review of a few of the more important investigations made during the period 1940–1950 is given for its general interest.

In 1940, the first comprehensive field study of the performance of corrugated metal sanitary and combined sewer structures was made on approximately forty-five bituminous coated and Paved-Invert installations in five states to learn the effect of sewage on the coating and paving material.[15] The coating and pavement were found to be entirely unaffected by the sewage flow and were giving good protection to the structures. Again in 1950, these same installations plus an additional

Fig. 95. Inspecting sewers requires proper equipment. Here in a Wisconsin city, such inspection led to relining a monolithic sewer with 1800 ft of 62-in. Asbestos-Bonded pipe.

200 structures representing nearly every state were inspected. The results of the repeat investigation indicated that the rates of deterioration originally assigned were too conservative. The following quotations are from the 1950 summary:[16]

"Ten to twenty years is added to the average life of Armco corrugated metal sewer pipe by the bituminous coating and pavement.

"Even much longer service life is assured by Armco Asbestos-Bonded Pipe. It is definitely proving itself to be a superior sewer material because of the additional protection provided by the asbestos layer to the underlying galvanized coating and base metal. Excellent bituminous coating adhesion is another advantage.

"In every instance the bituminous pavements were found to be in excellent condition with good adhesion to the base metal. This is conclusive evidence that sanitary sewage is in no way harmful to asphalt.

"Sewer gases and their condensates were found to have little effect on the bituminous coating in the top of the pipe. Inspection of the galvanizing under the bituminous coating showed that it was always in excellent condition, thereby further substantiating this conclusion.

"The concentration of active industrial wastes normally found in sewage is so dilute that premature failure of the bituminous coating and pavement from this source is remote."

Sewers in Salt Water Service, 1949

A study of the performance of corrugated metal sewers in the State of Florida was made in 1949. Many of these structures are installed in coastal areas through soils containing a high percentage of decaying vegetable matter and are subject to tidal inundation twice daily. Even in these rather severe corrosive conditions, the material performance of the installations is considered to be generally excellent.

The report[17, 18] carries the following statement:

"Field inspection of Asbestos-Bonded installations along the Florida Coast and elsewhere show them to be giving excellent service in salt water.

"Besides the direct attack of salt and brackish water on metals, Armco research engineers have observed other harmful conditions surrounding installations along or near the seacoast. Decaying vegetation may add active chemicals to the ground water flowing through low marsh lands. Oxidation produces active gases and aggressively attacks drainage structures."

REFERENCES

15. "Inspection Report on Sanitary and Combined Sewers of Armco Paved-Invert Pipe," by R. W. Martens, Armco Drainage Products Association, 1940.

16. "1950 Inspection of Armco Sanitary and Combined Sewers," by Max H. Bailey, Armco Drainage & Metal Products, Inc., 1950.

17. "Armco Asbestos-Bonded Corrugated Metal Pipe in Salt Water Service," Armco Drainage & Metal Products, Inc., 1951.

18. "The 'Balanced Design' Pays Off in Sewers," by Max H. Bailey, *The Highway Magazine*, September 1951, pp. 211–214.

Fig. 96. This galvanized corrugated metal culvert has been serving under a paved state highway in Ohio for forty years.

SECTION FOUR

DURABILITY DESIGN

CHAPTER TWENTY

Soil and Water Conditions

Summary

Durability is an essential part of economy. It should be commensurate with the expected service life of the structure. Rapidly changing conditions make it impractical to anticipate needs beyond fifty years and in many cases beyond twenty or thirty years. Plain galvanized metal drainage structures have service records of twenty-five to fifty years. With the many developments in coating materials in recent years, the tendency is to regulate durability by means of protective coatings and pavements.

PART ONE

PRACTICAL DURABILITY

How Much Durability?

Design engineers are practical economists. They are more interested in the economy of a structure than in monumental permanence. Fig. 96.

Materials that may be expected to endure perpetually, from the standpoint of physical performance, may never have that opportunity in the service for which they were constructed. However, this possibility does not justify substandard construction on the chance that the structure may become obsolete before it wears out. Neither can justification be found for extravagant cost to secure visionary perpetual service. A material or structure that can be adapted to changing conditions may prove to be the most economical over a period of time.

How long should a structure be designed to last? Is the service temporary—a few days or weeks, or a few years, or fifty? How inconvenient or costly is it to replace the structure if it fails or proves inadequate? Are methods available for making replacements at reasonable cost and inconvenience? What are the methods of financing maintenance and replacements?

To establish a reasonable design life expectancy for a drainage structure, it is well to know the relative importance of the roadway, its location and the possibility of relocation or obsolescence due to changing traffic conditions. The national system of interstate highways in the United States is designed to be adequate to handle safely and efficiently the traffic expected twenty years from the date of construction.[1] However, the culverts on that system are required to be strong enough for H20-S16 design loadings and have a material durability of not less than fifty years.[2, 3]

The American Association of State Highway Officials on April 1, 1946, adopted a policy concerning maximum dimensions, weights and speeds of motor vehicles. If all legislative bodies would adopt this policy, "the variation between vehicle and road design can be reduced and uneconomic obsolescence and overdesign can be eliminated to a major degree."[4]

Obsolescence problems of the railroad design engineer are less acute due to uniform established standards of the American Railway Engineering Association. In other words, there is a semblance of unified control of all elements of railroad equipment such as weight, size, power, speed and other operating conditions. Nonetheless, major line changes on railroads today are not uncommon, so that obsolescence due to relocation or abandonment may be a factor.

Committee 2 of the American Railway Bridge and Building Association in 1948 stated* that "the service life (for corrugated metal pipe, standard and Multi-Plate

*"Types of Bridges for Replacing Timber Trestles," Report of Committee 2, American Railway Bridge and Building Assn., 1948. Reprinted in *Railway Engineering and Maintenance*,—1948.

Fig. 97. Invert of 36-in. corrugated metal and of concrete culvert showing severe erosion and corrosion. Remainder of pipes are in good condition, indicating need for invert protection to give "balanced design."

type) was estimated at forty to sixty years." Also, "The service life of (extra-strength reinforced) concrete culvert pipe was reported at forty to sixty years, or longer, if properly installed."

Sewer designers also have the problem of determining how long their structures should last. Except for those smaller communities that have ceased to grow, the experience of the past half century should be helpful. Experience shows that changes in conditions and requirements are so continuous that usually it is unwise to design for a period longer than fifty years. (Such things as air conditioning and garbage disposal were hardly dreamed of twenty-five years ago.) That is the figure used by many city and consulting engineers in their current plans.

PART TWO

SERVICE CONDITIONS

What Affects Durability

Whereas obsolescence is an important yet unpredictable element in the useful service life of a structure, there are two other factors that can be measured more accurately. These are the material and structural durability. (See page 150 on the two pathways of deterioration.)

Corrosion is one of the principal causes of *material deterioration* of metal structures.[5] Other materials such as concrete and wood are likewise subject to corrosion and rot, as well as attack by corrosion producing organisms. Corrosion of metal is basically an electro-chemical action in the presence of moisture, oxygen and soil salts or other chemicals.

The following theories on corrosion are extracts from printed literature of the U. S. Bureau of Standards[6] based on numerous tests of buried specimens.

> "The relative importance of the factors that affect corrosion underground is so difficult to evaluate and the conditions under which corrosion occurs are so poorly defined that the theory is often more helpful in explaining corrosion that has already taken place than it is in predicting what may be expected . . .
>
> "Although a very large number of chemical elements exist in soils, most of them are combined in difficultly soluble compounds, which exert little chemical influence on corrosion . . . As a rule, soils containing considerable quantities of salts in solution are corrosive . . .
>
> "The physical properties of soils that are of importance in corrosion are chiefly those which determine the aeration of the soil and its retentiveness for water . . ."

The foregoing has to do principally with corrosion in contact with soils. However, the experience with drainage structures is that corrosion on the exterior is usually of less consequence than that from hydraulic traffic on the inside. Fig. 97.

Since the surface water passing through a drainage structure usually derives its chemical constituents from the soils through and over which it flows, a general classification of the primary chemically active constituents of the soil will serve as a *guide* in judging service conditions. The major chemical classifications of soils and water for drainage structure service are: mineral, acid, alkali, salt, normal, arid and special. (For domestic and industrial sewage see page 170.)

Mineral Waters

Sulphur-bearing coal mines and certain other mining operations such as copper and zinc mines produce waters which are corrosive to nearly all materials normally used for drainage structures. This is due to the free acid or acid forming elements carried in the waters. Drainage from high sulphur-bearing coal strata has relatively the same effect.

Every stream in a mining area is not necessarily contaminated with chemical constituents that are harmful to structures through which they flow. Investigations indicate that relatively few streams not actually issuing from mines or coal-bearing strata are so contaminated. A determination should be made at the specific stream in question if there is doubt. Where analysis shows concentrations of free sulphuric acid or the presence of the sulphate radical (SO_4) in the water, additional protection is recommended for corrugated metal and concrete.

Acid Waters

This classification encompasses many of the conditions mentioned above. In addition it refers to aggressive waters caused by contamination with organic acids present in marsh and swamp land and other locations where vegetable matter is decaying in quantities. The generally unstable nature of organic acids causes them to be difficult to identify by laboratory analysis. Such conditions are often found with soft and unstable foundations and they tend to increase the difficulties of drainage construction.

Fig. 98. Twin Asbestos-Bonded culvert under Missouri River levee south of Omaha, Nebr. The levee is incomplete here.

Additional protection for all drainage structure materials is recommended when they are to be used in this type of exposure.

Alkali Soils and Waters

"Alkali" is a rather vague term when used to describe certain salts present in many of the arid and semi-arid soils of the western section of the United States. The word was originally used to describe the adverse effect of these salts on the ability to raise agricultural crops on these soils.

Alkali regions are generally classified as being white or black; the former usually contains sufficient quantities of sulphates, or carbonates which on evaporation leave a white deposit on the surface of the ground. The black alkali—sodium carbonate—does not leave this white "snow" upon evaporating.

The white alkalis, particularly the sulphates, deteriorate ordinary portland cement concrete quite rapidly. Drainage structures made of this material normally fail to provide satisfactory service in the presence of this soil type. These alkalis will also attack the zinc coating on metal pipe much more rapidly than does normal soil.

The black alkalis and the chloride-salt alkalis are injurious to underground structures of both metal and concrete. These alkalis are much less common than the white alkalis.

Where soil is known to be highly alkaline, additional protective coatings for all drainage structures are recommended.

Salt and Salt Marsh

In sea water the chlorides are primarily responsible for the corrosion of metal, while certain magnesium salts are thought to cause deterioration of concrete. The chemical deterioration of concrete in sea water is accelerated by the mechanical disintegration resulting from alternate wetting and drying and frost action in cold climates. All ordinary culvert materials exposed to sea water should carry additional protective coatings.

Normal and Arid Conditions

Normal soil conditions are prevalent in the greater Mississippi Valley area and the eastern states in sections removed from the effects of coastal conditions. Many areas in the western United States can be classified in this category. Percentage-wise, the normal areas are considerably greater than the more severe areas mentioned above. In normal areas no additional protection to the ordinary drainage structure is required for the material to have a reasonable life expectancy.

The arid and semi-arid regions with annual rainfall of 20 in. or less, except in the alkali soil locations, are even more favorable than the normal condition for long life expectancy of drainage structures. Much of the eastern slope of the Rocky Mountains illustrates this region. Galvanized corrugated metal culverts installed in these normal, arid and semi-arid regions will have a great many years of life expectancy.

Cinders

Occasions arise when it is necessary to install drainage structures in cinder contaminated embankments. Cinder fills are very corrosive to metal and concrete, especially when they are in direct contact with the structure. Considerable protection can be obtained by placing a 2 to 3-in. layer of sand, gravel or clay around the outside of the structure before backfilling.

Fig. 99. Interior of Armco storm sewer installed at Pocatello, Idaho in 1914. Note perfect structural condition.

PART THREE

SEWER SERVICE CONDITIONS

SEWERS, in addition to encountering the various soils and exterior service conditions described in the preceding, Part 2, are subject to the action of the "hydraulic traffic" they carry. Therefore, special consideration is given here to sewers.

Sewer Types

Sewer systems are classified as separate or combined, depending on whether storm water and sanitary sewage are carried in the same conduit or separately.

A *storm sewer* carries storm and surface water and street wash, exclusive of domestic and industrial wastes. The water is little if any more corrosive than rural watershed runoff. Erosion by the hydraulic traffic may be a factor. Fig. 99.

A *sanitary sewer* is designed to carry domestic sewage and the discharge from commercial and light industrial plants. The general nature of fresh sanitary sewage is usually slightly alkaline or neutral and usually well-diluted.[7] Hence, in any well designed and normally maintained sanitary sewer system, if the velocity of flow is sufficient to carry the sewage to its point of disposal before putrefaction processes begin, the problem of corrosion is minimized.

In older sewers, where flow is sluggish or stagnant due to incorrect design or because of low points caused by settlement in grade, putrescible organic material may accumulate. In such cases, if the temperature and the concentration of sewage are sufficiently high and the atmosphere deficient in oxygen, bacterial action will take place and "sewer gases" will be released. If bacterial action takes place in the presence of high sulphate waters, hydrogen sulphide gas (H_2S) results.

This gas, in sufficient quantities, can be fatal to humans. When combined with moisture and oxygen in the atmosphere of the sewer, it forms sulphurous or sulphuric acid, both of which are very corrosive. Corrosive attack of this type occurs above the water line of the sewer. Where possible, sanitary sewers should be designed with adequate velocities to avoid deposits of any solids.

Combined sewers, common in many communities, have the advantage of dilution and flushing by occasional storm waters. Some sanitary sewers are designed for periodic flushings.

Industrial wastes may be handled in sanitary or combined sewers, or in some cases are handled in sewers built especially to cope with highly corrosive wastes. Although hydrogen-ion concentration (pH) determinations of domestic sanitary sewage have little significance, they are helpful in studying the corrosive nature of tannery, pickling, plating, refinery or other industrial wastes.[7] In fact, many governmental agencies have in recent years adopted ordinances regulating the minimum and maximum pH of industrial wastes to prevent damage to sewer installations. Control of the pH values is also important to the efficient operation of sewage treatment plants.[8]

REFERENCES

1. "A Policy on Design Standards," by American Association of State Highway Officials, "Policies on Geometric Highway Design," reprinted in Vol. 1, 1950, p. 1.
2. "Interregional Highways," U. S. House of Representatives Document No. 379, Jan. 12, 1944, p. 157.
3. The Oklahoma Turnpike Authority has based its design and financing of the Oklahoma City-Tulsa toll road on a life expectancy of forty years. (*Ohio Public Works,* Sept. 1951, p. 26).
4. "Highway Design and Construction," by A. G. Bruce and J. Clarkeson, Third Edition, 1950, pp. 88–89.
5. "Corrosion in Relation to Engineering Structures," by James Aston, Esq., in Transactions of American Society of Civil Engineers, Vol. 102, 1937.
6. "Underground Corrosion," Circular of the Bureau of Standards, C 450, Washington, D. C., 1945, pp. 10–24.
7. "Sewerage and Sewage Treatment," by W. A. Hardenbergh, 3rd Edition, 1950, pp. 3, 237, 409.
8. "Municipal Sewer Ordinances," Manual of Practice No. 3, by the Federation of Sewage Works Assns., 1949.

CHAPTER TWENTY-ONE

Durability of Metals and Coatings

PART ONE

CORRUGATED METAL STRUCTURES

LABORATORY and field methods of determining durability of drain materials were described in Chapter 16, Research on Durability, page 148. The conclusion was that actual service records of structures serving under conditions like those for the proposed structures are the best means of designing for durability.

Ferrous metals are given a protective metallic coating before installation in drainage structures. A tightly adhering coating excludes the elements essential to corrosion, namely air, moisture, soil salts or other chemicals. Once this coating is removed, corrosion is accelerated. Service conditions are important, but the life of the metal depends also on its composition, uniformity and its gage (thickness). The invert of drainage structures is where service is usually most severe. In Multi-Plate pipe and pipe-arches, the gage of the bottom plates may be made heavier than on the sides and top in order to give equal or balanced durability.

TABLE 21-1 CHEMICAL COMPOSITION OF BASE METALS BY LADLE ANALYSIS

Elements *(Max. per Cent Except as Noted)*	*Kind of Base Metal*					*Tolerance by Check Analysis of Finished Sheets*
	Pure Iron	*Copper Bearing Pure Iron*	*Copper Iron*	*Copper Molybdenum Iron*	*Copper Steel*	
Carbon	....	....	....	....	....	....
Manganese	....	....	....	....	....	....
Phosphorus	.015	.015	.015	.015	....	....
Sulphur	.040	.040	.040	.040	.050	.010
Silicon	....	....	....	....	....	....
Copper, Min. Per Cent	....	.20	.20	.40	.20	.02
Molybdenum, Min. Per Cent	....	....	....	.05	....	....
Sum of First 5 Elements	....	.10	.25	.25	.70	.04
Sum of First 6 Elements	.10	....	....	....	....	.04

From AREA and AASHO Specifications.

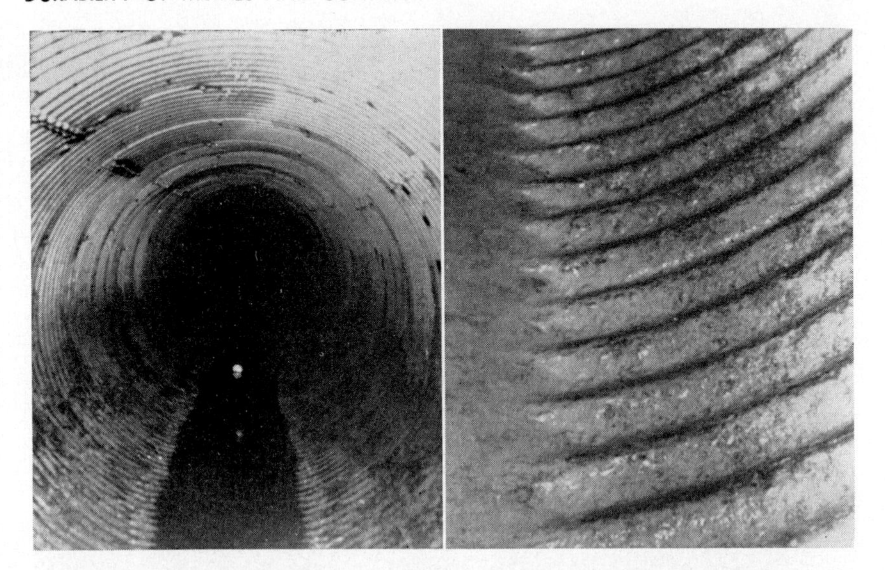

Fig. 100. Installed in 1907 under the streets of an Ohio city, this 36 and 39-in. Armco storm sewer is an excellent example of service rendered by plain galvanized metal. Close-up shows tight rust in invert.

Base Metals

Corrugated metal pipe (standard riveted and Multi-Plate) and other fabricated metal products are made from ferrous metal sheets or plates. These ferrous base metals are made by the open-hearth process and conform in chemical properties to one of the classes listed in Table 21-1.

Galvanized Coatings

Corrosion of metal is a *surface* reaction. Protecting or treating that surface is a logical method of combatting such reaction and thereby giving longer life. Common practice for many years on underground and aboveground structures has been to use a zinc coating (galvanizing) on ferrous base metals, both because of its effectiveness and low cost. The galvanizing not only directly protects the underlying iron or steel, but by virtue of its electro-chemical nature, it sacrifices itself and protects the base metal at scratches in the coating. This behavior is unlike that of nickel, chromium, tin, copper or lead coatings on steel or iron. These metals, being lower in the electro-chemical series, tend to accelerate the corrosion of exposed areas of iron or steel where exposed. The sacrificial effect of galvanizing is illustrated by the fact that where sheets are sheared or punched after galvanizing, the raw edges have no influence on the service life of the structure.*

The life of a galvanized coating (2 oz per sq ft total on both sides of sheet) in normal intermittent culvert flow conditions may be a decade or more. Where not subject to erosion and flow, it may last indefinitely.

Many plain galvanized corrugated metal pipe culverts and sewers have under normal conditions given up to forty-five years of satisfactory service. Fig. 100.

*"It is impossible to find any case in which the life of the pipe is decreased due to these ungalvanized sheared edges." Proc. of the Amer. Railway Eng. Assn., 1943, Vol. 44, p. 698.

Fig. 101. Cut-away section of Paved-Invert pipe showing how smooth bituminous pavement protects the bottom of pipe where greatest wear occurs.

This is in excess of the original estimated design life of thirty-six years (for ingot iron), based on the uniform rating schedules described in Chapter 16.

Recommendation: Where a drainage structure is subject to normal intermittent flow, and the soil and water are not particularly corrosive, a pipe with galvanized coating is usually economically satisfactory, as proved by many field inspections.

Non-Metallic Coatings

Where a metal structure is completely accessible, its life may be prolonged indefinitely by repeated painting or coating. Where not accessible, as in the case of many culverts, sewers and drains, the coating must be applied before installation.

Bituminous coatings are preferably applied over a galvanized coating as additional protection against corrosion. Such a coating "insulates" the metal from its environment. To be effective, this type of coating must adhere well to the underlying metal. Materials generally used consist of asphalts, tars, rubber and plastic compounds.

Paved-Invert Pipe

Field inspections (Chapter 17) show that where erosion is a serious factor, structures such as culverts and sewers *generally wear out* in the bottom or invert whereas the upper three-fourths may remain in good condition. In order to protect the bottom against erosion and to give it a well-balanced design, a heavy bituminous pavement was developed by Armco engineers. (1926)[9]

When used on corrugated metal pipe, this pavement fills the valleys of the corrugations and covers the crests a minimum of ⅛-in. to provide a smooth, tough wearing surface in the invert. This is known as Paved-Invert pipe and is available in diameters up to 96 in. The pipe above the pavement may or may not be bituminous coated. Fig. 101.

Recommendation: For streams carrying silt, sand, gravel or other erosive material, or having a continuous flow, the Paved-Invert extends the life of the pipe many years.

Asbestos-Bonded Pipe

Bituminous coatings and pavements in the invert have added measurably to the service life of galvanized corrugated metal pipe.[10] To further increase the durability, especially under more severe corrosive conditions, Asbestos-Bonded metal pipe was developed by Armco engineers. It is suitable for culverts and other drainage structures in highly corrosive areas, and for sanitary and industrial sewers where the effluent may be extremely corrosive. It is also suitable for uses where extra long life is desirable.[11, 12]

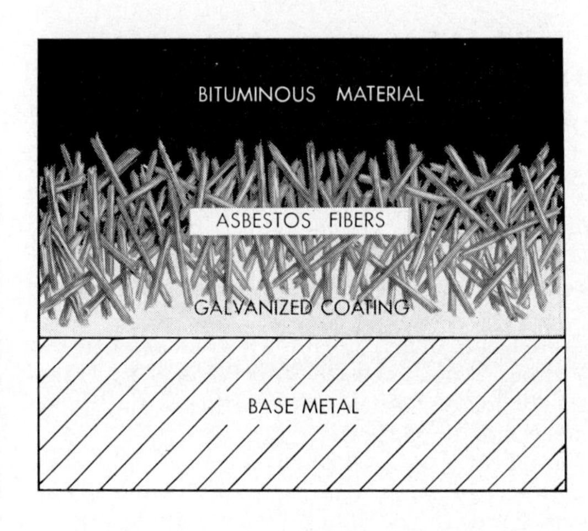

Fig. 102. Cross-sectional drawing of Asbestos-Bonded sheet showing how asbestos fibers are imbedded in the galvanized coating to provide a permanent bond for bituminous coating or pavement.

The make-up of Asbestos-Bonded sheets is illustrated in Fig. 102. The bonding is accomplished by pressing inert, rot-proof asbestos fibers into the molten metallic zinc coating during the manufacture of the sheet. The fibers thus become imbedded in the zinc as it solidifies. The sheets are then passed through specially designed equipment that thoroughly saturates the mass of fibers with a bituminous material that is compatible with non-metallic coatings which may be added later.

After the excess saturant is squeezed out, the sheets are corrugated and formed into pipe. Further treatment of the pipe may consist of a non-metallic seal coat or asphaltic coating and a paved invert of the same material.

Recommendation: For severely corrosive conditions such as highly acid soils, mine drainage, tidal drainage or certain industrial wastes, the use of Asbestos-Bonded pipe is recommended.

Cathodic Protection

Because corrosion is an electro-chemical process, it can be combatted by using a "sacrificial anode" in the process to divert corrosion from the structure to be protected. There are two variations of cathodic protection. One, called the galvanic method, is a natural battery action between metals based on their relative positions in the electro-chemical series. The other, known generally as the impressed current method, requires an external source of current.[13]

Corrosion of steel pipe lines and other large structures is sometimes counteracted by means of cathodic protection. Sewers or culverts in corrosive areas are protected with a bituminous coating. This provides insulation between the individual pipe sections and permits only short electrical circuits as compared with those possible in long steel pipe lines. Cathodic protection is therefore seldom, if ever, used for sewers or culverts.

PART TWO

MISCELLANEOUS PRODUCTS AND SERVICE CONDITIONS

Subdrainage. Water carried in a subdrainage system is usually from underground sources. It is filtered and ordinarily not corrosive, nor does it carry erosive sediment. Moisture and temperature conditions inside the subdrain are fairly constant.

Material durability of the pipe used is therefore usually a minor factor in the design of a subdrainage or underdrain system. On the other hand, structural strength, the ability to maintain tight joints, and adequacy of the layout under changing service conditions are much more important.

Plain galvanized metal pipe has been entirely satisfactory on many subdrainage installations for over twenty-five years, with many years of useful life remaining. For localized areas where corrosive or erosive conditions are known to exist, bituminous coated subdrain pipe is recommended.

Metal End Sections. Being attached to the ends of culverts, storm drains and spillways, metal end sections are readily accessible. They may be of the same gage or of a lighter gage than the conduit, and are ordinarily supplied with a standard 2-oz galvanized coating. This assures ample durability.

Bin-Type Retaining Walls. Metal retaining walls are supplied with a galvanized finish. Where soil or atmospheric conditions are known to be corrosive, the units comprising the wall may be furnished of Asbestos-Bonded metal. Galvanized bolts are used and these may be painted with asphalt.

Liner Plates. Where used as a tunnel lining or temporary lining to be backed up or covered with other materials, bare metal plates of adequate strength are used. For permanent linings or conduits, the plates may be hot-dip galvanized or may be asphalt coated either directly on the bare metal or over a galvanized coating.

Sheeting. Steel sheeting or sheet piling used as temporary sheeting or cofferdam work is generally pulled and re-used. Material durability is less of a factor than structural strength. However, for permanent dams, cutoff walls and the like, the sheeting may be galvanized or bituminous coated, or both.

Guard Rail. Most guard rail is painted to increase its visibility for warning purposes. Therefore, instead of being galvanized, it is given a mill coat of paint primer to prevent rusting until it can be installed and painted.

Gates. Water control gates are usually of cast iron, cast steel or structural steel, and are treated with a bituminous coating. Small irrigation gates are of galvanized sheet steel. Where corrosive conditions are likely to interfere with the proper seating of the gate, bronze facings and other parts are commonly used.

REFERENCES

9. "The 'Balanced Design' Pays Off in Sewers," by Max H. Bailey, *The Highway Magazine*, Sept. 1951, pp. 211–214.

10. "Armco Corrugated Metal Pipe, a Type for Every Need," Manual CMS-5850, Armco Drainage & Metal Products, Inc., p. 8.

11. "Armco Asbestos-Bonded Corrugated Metal Pipe in Salt Water Service," Armco Drainage & Metal Products, Inc., 1951.

12. "Armco Sewers for Efficiency and Economy," Manual CMS-17350, Armco Drainage & Metal Products, Inc., 1950, p. 44.

13. "Fighting Corrosion With Corrosion," by J. L. Gilliland and N. G. Noonan, U. S. Bur. of Reclama., in *The Reclamation Era*, Dec. 1951, p. 266.

Fig. 103. Quadruple line of 8-ft diam. Multi-Plate pipe was assembled on the bank in 40-ft lengths. Each line is 316 ft long and serves to enclose a canal in Derby, Conn.

SECTION FIVE

ECONOMIC FACTORS

CHAPTER TWENTY-TWO

Installation Costs

THROUGH the joint efforts of engineers, contractors and manufacturers, construction methods and materials are being constantly improved. Especially significant is the increase of "pre-engineered" and prefabricated structures, with consequent reduction of on-the-job labor. This has a three-way effect. (1) It gives factory controlled quality under more ideal working conditions. (2) In reducing design and inspection time, it enables the engineer to concentrate on the larger features of his job. And (3) although the product cost is probably higher, the installed cost may be less than fully field-constructed structures. Fig. 103.

An accurate appraisal of related economic factors is of utmost importance in the proper selection of methods and materials from the wide variety available today. Dependable cost data enable the engineer to design economically and estimate accurately. This permits the contractor to bid competitively and realize the profit which his investment and risk justify. By balancing the costs of alternate methods and materials against the ends to be achieved, the maximum of service per construction dollar to be expended can be realized.

Scope

Costs will vary in different sections of the country and even from job to job depending on soil, water, weather, labor efficiency, wage scales, topography, design standards and construction practice. Therefore, even when costs are given in machine and man hours, they are of value only when accompanied by a description of the conditions applying to that particular job.

Average costs, of value in making general comparisons, are likely to be misleading if applied to a specific job. Unit prices bid on past work likewise are a poor basis for bidding future work unless tempered by judgment, experience and some knowledge of the circumstances applicable in each case.

In view of these limitations, this chapter is devoted principally to a general analysis of the various cost factors that collectively make up the total installed cost of the products described in this handbook. By relating these factors to the materials or structures involved and also to current local prices and practices, their relative economy can be generally determined.

Where approximate estimating figures are given on items directly applicable to the products described herein, they are in the form of man hours to permit the application of prevailing labor rates. In each case, such man hour figures include direct labor only. No provision is made for insurance, supervision, overhead, equipment, profit, etc. The man hour figures, based on records of typical jobs, are given as a range between high and low cost jobs rather than an average of all jobs. Whether the high, low or an intermediate figure will apply to a particular job will depend on the size of the job, working conditions, amount of equipment used, efficiency of local labor and other factors which of necessity will require the judgment of the estimator and his knowledge of applicable conditions.

Cost Items Included

The true first cost of any structure is the sum total of all the items involved in readying it to perform fully the function for which it is intended. In general, the total cost is made up of all or part of the following items:

1. Material cost
2. Engineering, including design and inspection
3. Transportation and handling
4. Excavation and backfill
5. Removing old structure
6. Placing new structure
7. Replacing traffic surface
8. Equipment and tools
9. Supervision, overhead, contingencies and insurance
10. Detours and slow orders
11. Miscellaneous factors
    a. Effects of weather
    b. Dewatering trench
    c. Special foundation preparation, piling, cradles, etc.

Additional factors, not part of the first cost, are maintenance and salvage value.

While some of the above items apply more particularly to the installation of drainage structures, all that are applicable to a given situation or structure, need to be considered in an accurate cost appraisal. Maintenance and salvage value have little effect on the original installed cost, but are often important factors in the cost of the service rendered by a structure and therefore merit thought in the final selection from the alternates under consideration.

1. Material Cost

Material cost or the purchase price often is taken as a measure of the final cost. Obviously, this is unsound. A material is not a structure until it receives all of the operations necessary to adapt it to the requirements of a given situation. On this basis, a material could well have the lowest purchase price, yet have the highest finished cost when ready for service.

For example, the material costs of a structure completely assembled on the job site will probably be considerably less than a comparable prefabricated, pre-engineered structure. However, the difference in the cost of assembling and placing will often prove the prefabricated structure the more economical on a completely installed basis.

2. Engineering and Inspection

The cost of engineering, including design and inspection, should be considered in figuring over-all costs even when not chargeable directly to a given job. With a large selection of functionally-designed factory-produced materials available to-

Fig. 104. Concentric nesting of corrugated metal pipe at Guelph, Ont. plant shows how large quantities can economically be shipped by rail or truck.

day, it is often possible to select a pre-engineered structure which meets the exact requirements. Where this is possible, design costs are reduced. Because such a structure is built under carefully controlled factory conditions, inspection is less costly than for a structure which is completely constructed at the job site. By using such a structure, many time-consuming details are avoided and engineering time is made available for other important functions.

3. Transportation and Handling

The cost of getting materials to the job site is determined principally by weight, bulk, distance involved, methods of transportation available, and accessibility of the job site. By custom the loading, unloading, rehandling and breakage (of fragile materials) are usually included in this item. Transportation costs are a factor even when prices are quoted f.o.b. destination, because in such event, the transportation charges are included in the quoted price. Often, the manufacturer's volume and nature of the material make special equipment practical. By using such equipment and avoiding unnecessary rehandling by delivery direct to the point of use, the supplier's transportation costs may be lower.

Railroad Freight

Freight charges vary according to the weight of the material, distance and the freight classification, with weight usually being the most important factor. For heavy massive materials, the load capacity of a freight car is the controlling factor. This is also true of materials with a light unit weight but designed so the individual sections can be nested, Fig. 104, or made into compact bundles. Multi-Plate pipe, arches and pipe-arches, corrugated steel sheeting and Flex-Beam guardrail are typical

Fig. 105. Vast quantities of corrugated metal pipe, and Multi-Plate, were "airlifted" to speed the construction of the Quebec, North Shore and Labrador Railway to the iron ore deposits in northeastern Canada.

of materials falling into the latter class. For light-weight bulky materials, the cubic capacity of the freight car is the limiting element.

Since freight charges vary with weight, substantial freight savings can be made by the selection of light-weight materials.

Hauling by Truck

The cost of truck transportation is affected by the following factors:

1. Type, condition and capacity of the vehicle
2. Length and time of haul
   a. In traffic
   b. On open road
   c. Over job site
3. Condition of roads traveled
4. Depreciation on the vehicle
5. Accessibility of the job site

The common measure of truck hauling costs is the ton mile. It is recognized because of the diversity of conditions affecting the factors listed above, there will be considerable variation in ton mile costs. However, once the rate is established, the cost of transportation by truck is proportionate to the weight of the material. Typical weights are given in the following table. Table 22-1 and Fig. 105.

4. Excavation and Backfill

Excavation is an item of major importance in the installed cost of many structures. Because of the wide variation in types of soil encountered and equipment used, no attempt will be made to give typical costs on this item.

However, there are a number of general factors which should receive careful consideration. Hand versus machine methods is one of them. Because of higher labor costs, together with increased efficiency and greater mobility in excavating

TABLE 22-1 APPROXIMATE WEIGHTS OF VARIOUS PIPE

Pounds per lineal foot

Diam. in Inches	*Corr. Metal Pipe Plain Galv. Riveted*	*Concrete Culv. Pipe* ASTM C 76-41 Stand Str. 4500 psi.*	*Cast Iron† AWWA Class "C"*	*Ex. Str. Vit. Clay‡*
12	10.5	79	91.7	55.5
15	13.0	111	—	89.5
18	15.5	131	175.0	116.0
24	25.5	217	279.2	218.0
30	31.0	324	400.0	344
36	51.5	435	545.8	505
42	60.5	561	716.6	
48	68.5	727		
54	100.	887		
60	110.	1064		
72	159.5	1532		
84	186.5	2085		
96	212.	2906(3500 psi)		

*From Concrete Pipe Handbook, 1951.
†From Handbook of Cast Iron Pipe.
‡From published literature.

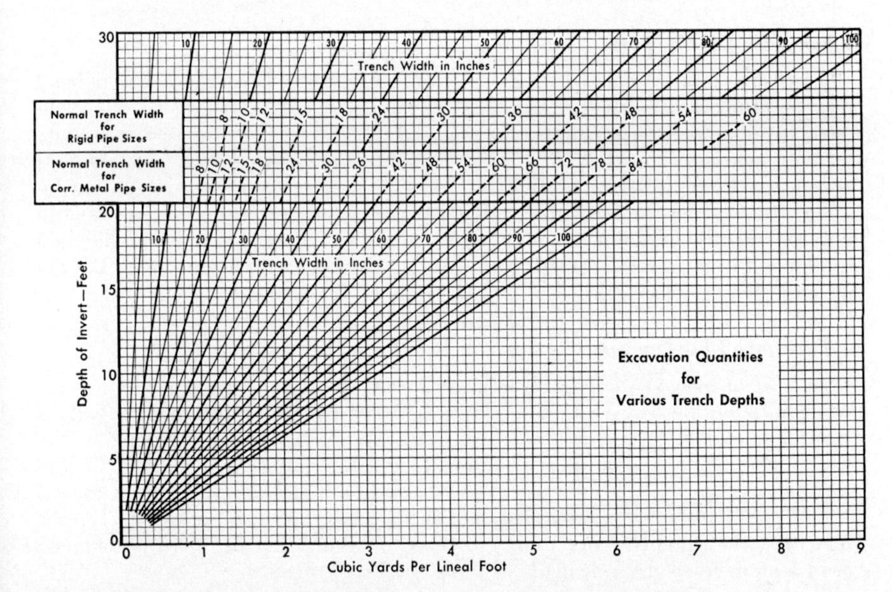

Fig. 106. Chart showing excavation quantities and comparative trench widths for corrugated metal and rigid pipes of equal inside diameters.

equipment, machine methods are more economical for most jobs. Where the amount of excavation is small, and equipment is not required for other purposes such as placing heavy materials, the cost of moving a machine to and from the site could more than offset the savings it would make possible.

On small jobs where hand methods are employed or on long lines such as sewers, water mains, etc., one factor is the width and depth of the trench, which is often influenced by the type of pipe used. Fig. 106. Where excavation and backfill costs are on a cubic yard basis, the use of a product which requires less excavation may be an important factor. For example, data on pipe cover requirements for airfields prepared by the U. S. Engineers (see page 136) permits lower heights of cover and consequently less excavation and backfill for corrugated metal pipe than for the rigid types of drains. In the case of subdrains where a pervious backfill is often required, the saving in special backfill due to a narrower and shallower trench is an additional factor to be considered.

Sheeting of an excavation is an added detail where it is required by safety regulations or where soil conditions, lack of space, or cost will not permit an excavation with sloping sides. For information on sheeting see pages 389–396.

Preparing Bed

In the installation of culverts and longer pipe lines, the cost of preparing the bed to grade, depends upon the soil, slope, size, type and weight of the structure, the length of the individual sections, and the type of joints used. Hence, the cost of preparing the bed is usually considered as a separate item. If a material is available in long lengths, has a uniform cross section, and a high beam strength it is not necessary to grade every foot of the trench accurately. If, however, the material is in short sections with enlarged joints, greater care is required and the cost of bed preparation is greater.

5. Removing Old Structure

The cost of removing an existing structure, when that is necessary, will depend largely on the type of structure involved. Generally speaking, the cost of removing a structure originally made up by the field assembly of smaller prefabricated units will be much less than that of a heavy monolithic structure which must first be broken up. Prefabricated materials can often be salvaged and used in another location. In some cases, particularly with drainage structures, it may be possible to avoid the expense of removing an old structure which has proved to be of adequate size but not of adequate strength by threading the new structure through the old (see page 465 on relining).

6. Placing the New Structure

The cost of placing the new structure will vary with the type of structure and the installation method used. The choice between hand and machine methods is determined largely by the unit weight of the material or its component parts, the availability and cost of suitable equipment, and the quantity of material in the job. As a general rule, where quantities are small, a material which can be placed by hand will cost much less to install than one requiring equipment. On larger quantities, the same rule may apply, although the unit savings may be reduced because more efficient use is made of the equipment. Fig. 107.

Where the same equipment may be used for both excavating and handling materials, those materials requiring the minimum time for placing will make more

Fig. 107. Moderate size equipment can economically handle large sections of pre-assembled metal structures.

machine hours available for excavation, which is usually the pace setting operation for the job.

For some types of structures, such as those of monolithic concrete, the cost of placing is a large portion of the installed cost. The skilled labor required for building forms, setting steel, equipment operation, etc., although usually included in the unit prices for both concrete and steel, are the basic reasons for the high cost of placing such structures. In direct contrast, the cost of placing prefabricated materials with only a small amount of unskilled labor is a comparatively small portion of their total cost. Higher labor rates accentuate this basic difference between field assembled and prefabricated types of materials.

A substantial item of expense sometimes occasioned by the time required in placing structures is the delay due to lack of coordination of various operations. With equipment increasing in size and cost, its continued, uninterrupted operation is essential to over-all job economy. The possibility of costly delays can be reduced by the selection of materials that can be placed quickly and which require no extended curing period before they are usable.

Laying, Lining and Joining Pipe

On long lines such as sewers and stream enclosures, the cost of laying, lining and joining pipe is an important item and one which offers opportunities for effecting economies through the choice of materials. Primary factors affecting this item are the length of sections, their weight and the type of joints. Obviously, long light-weight sections such as are available in corrugated metal pipe can be placed at a lower cost because of their ease and speed of handling and fewer joints required, as compared with heavier materials available only in shorter lengths. The availability of different types of joints, which permits selecting one most suitable to the conditions at the job, can be a factor in reducing costs.

In subdrain construction, which normally requires pipe of small diameters, the long, light-weight lengths of corrugated metal pipe together with the positive joints make it possible to join the pipe on the surface prior to lowering in the trench. This permits the use of a narrower trench with less excavation and consequently less special pervious backfill material.

The effect of the above factors on the costs of laying, lining and coupling corrugated metal pipe is best reflected in unit bid prices submitted on similar types of work. See Fig. 108 and Table 22-2.

Estimated man hours of direct labor only required to lay, line and join corrugated metal pipe range from .01 to .05 man hour per lineal ft per ft of diameter.

Example 1:

Assume 30-in. diam. standard corrugated metal pipe in 20-ft lengths to be installed under good working conditions. Select a value of .02 man hour per lineal ft per ft of diameter to lay, line and join the pipe.

Solution: $.02 \times 20 \times \frac{30}{12} = 1.0$ man hour for 20 ft

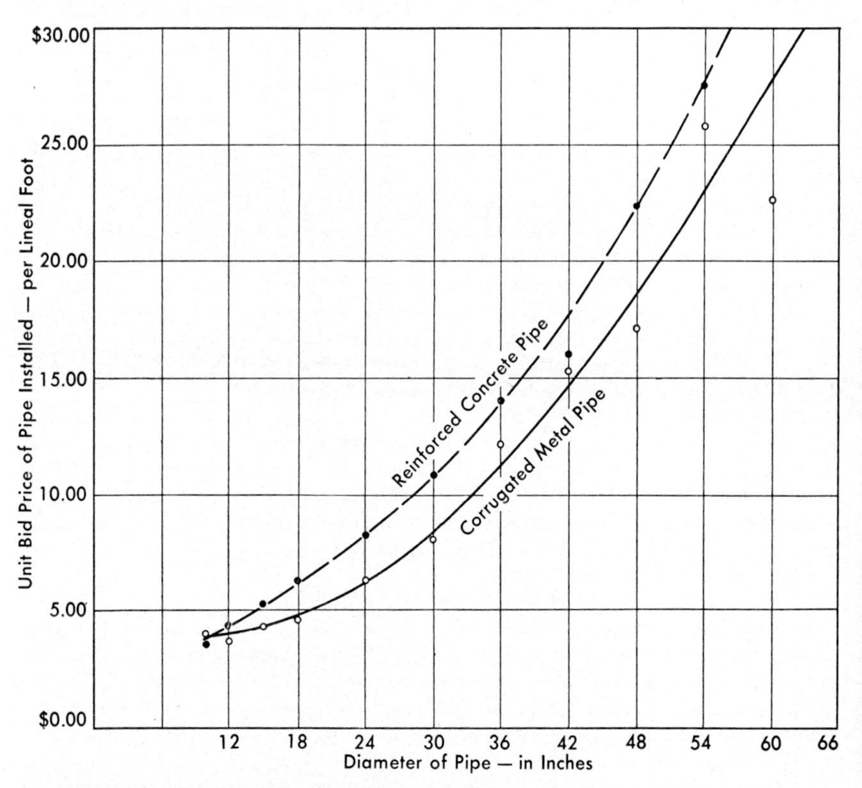

Fig. 108. Comparison of average unit bid prices on rigid and flexible pipe installed. From data compiled by San Francisco Dist., U. S. Corps of Engineers, from Jan. to June 1953. Published in *Engineering News-Record*, October 8, 1953.

TABLE 22-2 UNIT BID PRICES FOR PIPE INSTALLED, PER LINEAL FOOT
Far West, Jan.–June 1953 Average

Diameter in Inches	Corrugated Metal Pipe				Reinforced Concrete Pipe			
	No. of Jobs	High	Low	Average	No. of Jobs	High	Low	Average
10	12	$6.05	$2.97	$4.06	5	$5.33	$1.93	$3.52
12	62	6.00	2.50	3.61	57	8.48	2.13	4.38
15	21	6.71	3.03	4.37	36	9.67	3.02	5.18
18	89	7.75	3.20	4.62	65	12.90	3.60	6.25
24	76	10.52	4.58	6.46	60	14.75	5.34	8.22
30	41	14.08	6.08	8.12	60	17.53	6.15	10.84
36	49	20.33	9.25	12.20	42	20.78	10.22	13.94
42	11	22.29	11.45	15.35	26	20.00	11.75	15.88
48	25	24.33	13.50	17.14	36	32.48	16.21	22.27
54	11	38.50	17.00	25.83	7	30.93	21.40	27.46
60	5	26.00	18.34	22.55	12	42.68	23.50	32.48
66	1	.....	.....	32.27				
72	7	51.17	27.83	36.77	12	69.38	37.32	60.76

From *Engineering News-Record*, Oct. 8, 1953, p. 205.

Example 2:

Assume 48-in. diam. coated and paved corrugated metal pipe in 20-ft lengths to be installed under fair working conditions. Select a value of .035 man hour to lay, line and join.

Solution: $.035 \times 20 \times \frac{48}{12} = 2.8$ man hour for 20 ft

Assembling Multi-Plate Structures

Multi-Plate pipe, arches and pipe-arches require field assembly by bolting of curved plates (see page 440). Such assembly costs vary with the size of the job, conditions at the job site and the equipment used. Where the quantities involved are substantial, the work will be expedited by the use of some type of power lifting equipment and power wrenches. On smaller jobs, simple lifting equipment, such as an A frame with chain falls or block and tackle and hand wrenches are sufficient. In either case, only unskilled labor is required for the actual assembly.

Where working conditions are suitable, the structure can be erected in place. If water or other conditions make this impossible, the structure may be assembled on the bank and rolled or lifted into place. In some cases, structures are assembled at a central point where labor and equipment are available and then hauled to the job and placed as a unit.

The commonly used unit of measurement in computing assembly costs for

Multi-Plate is man hours of direct labor per plate ft. For rough estimating purposes this ranges from 0.25 to 0.50 man hour per plate ft. The total number of plate ft in a structure equals the number of plates required to make the ring, multiplied by the total length of the structure in ft.

Example:

Assume an 84-in. pipe 50 ft long. What is the installation cost in man hours of direct labor?

Solution: An 84-in. pipe requires *four* 21 pi wide plates to make the ring.
The number of plate ft in the structure is $50 \times 4 = 200$
Assume 0.3 man-hour per plate ft
Then $0.3 \times 200 = 60$ man hours

Strutting

On large diameter pipe where fill heights require it, field strutting (see page 443) is part of the installation costs. Field strutting may be required for either standard riveted pipe or Multi-Plate pipe, which is assembled in the field. Riveted pipe may be shop strutted, either by wire or rods, the cost of which is included in the purchase price of the pipe. Direct labor only required for strutting will range from 0.09 to 0.14 man hour per linear ft of pipe per ft of diameter.

7. Replacing Street Road or Track Surface

Where the installation of culverts or drains requires the removal of street, road or track surfaces, the cost of replacing the surface is an important item and should be included in the total cost. Such costs, together with more intangible items such as inconvenience to traffic and possible loss of trade or business, should be taken into account in the consideration of alternate methods and materials, which would not involve disturbing the surface or require future maintenance.

8. Use of Equipment and Tools

The savings and speed resulting from the application of power equipment make its use increasingly necessary in the interest of over-all economy. The extent to which equipment should be employed is determined by conditions of the individual job. Although modern construction equipment increases efficiency, it is expensive to own and operate. Equipment expense can be reduced by the selection of materials that will require the minimum of machine time for handling and other operations.

Regardless of the extent to which equipment is employed, it is important from a cost accounting standpoint that the actual expense be charged to the particular operation on which it is used. Unless this is done accurately, distorted and unrepresentative costs will result. This observation applies to small tools such as picks, shovels, form clamps, etc., as well as major pieces of equipment.

9. Cost of Detours

The construction or replacement of smaller drainage structures, particularly on highways or streets, was once a common cause for detours. Fig. 109. However, engineers cognizant of the heavy increase in traffic, now avoid the expense and inconvenience of detours wherever possible by the selection of methods and materials that either avoid detours entirely or at least keep the time they are in effect to a minimum.

Fig. 109. Long-time detours for replacement of small drainage structures are not in the interest of safety or public good will.

A common method of constructing openings under highways and railroads is the Armco jacking method of installing corrugated metal pipes for culverts, conduits, etc. (see page 455). Where conditions are not suitable for jacking, or a larger structure is required, tunneling with Armco liner plate also provides a solution which does not interfere with traffic (see page 462). The same desirable results can be achieved for smaller openings by utilizing boring equipment (see page 460).

Often the need for a complete replacement with the attendant detour can be avoided by threading a new structure inside the old before failure has become too far advanced (see page 465).

With many types of structures, it is often possible to install one half at a time, thereby permitting at least one-way traffic. Sometimes it is possible to completely place the new structure under or within the old, thereby closing the road only for the short time required to remove the old structure and backfill. In some cases, the old structure can be utilized as a ramp for backfilling operations.

If, however, a detour is necessary, the actual cost of providing it should be charged to the improvement. Detour costs will usually include: the cost of constructing a temporary structure or putting a road in condition and marking it, maintaining the detour in a serviceable condition and the extra operating expense to traffic. While this third item of expense is borne by the public and cannot therefore be charged to the job, it should be considered as an important item in the selection of alternate methods.

Slow Orders

Closely akin to detours are slow orders required on railroad construction. Since slow orders represent a direct expense to the railroad, the total cost of construction is made up of the installation cost plus the increased operating cost during the construction period. The elimination or reduction of slow orders by any of the methods referred to above under "detours" will therefore result in reduced overall costs.

10. Supervision and Overhead

Other factors being equal, materials which are simple to place or install will require less supervision than those of a more involved nature. Shortened construction time also reduces overhead—a major item on any construction job. In the interest of accurate cost accounting it is important that each phase of the project be charged with its true share of these items. It is only by doing so that a realistic evaluation of the comparative economy of alternate materials and methods can be determined.

11. Miscellaneous Factors

Weather can be an important factor in affecting costs. Some materials require protection from freezing weather. If so, such protective measures should be included in their total cost. Floods and other emergencies often cause additional expense by loss of formwork or other damage. The choice of materials which can be installed quickly and which by their nature are less susceptible to damage will reduce such hazards. Some operations like tunneling or jacking pipe are carried on largely underground and are therefore less affected by weather conditions. For this reason, they are well suited to winter use and offer work for crews released from operations of a more seasonable nature.

Depending on soil conditions and water table levels, dewatering an excavation can be a major item of expense. The expense of cofferdams, well points, pumping, etc., can often be either eliminated or reduced by selecting a material that can either be assembled on the bank and placed as a unit or which is of such nature that complete dewatering of the excavation is not required for properly placing the material. Fig. 110.

Where foundation conditions are not the most suitable, substantial economies can often be made by selecting a material which will either eliminate or reduce the

Fig. 110. First of two 12-ft diam. pipes 1400 ft long pre-assembled on the bank and then launched into place. U. S. Engineer job at McChord Field, Tacoma, Wash.

Fig. 111. Placing a metal end section on corrugated metal culvert in Minnesota is quickly done with a shovel and wrenches.

TABLE 22-3 TIME REQUIRED TO INSTALL METAL END SECTIONS

Round Pipe		*Pipe-Arch*	
Diam. in Inches	*Man Hours per End*	*Span x Rise in Inches*	*Man Hours per End*
12	0.71		
15	0.88	18 x 11	0.65
18	1.03	22 x 13	0.74
		25 x 16	0.93
24	1.61	29 x 18	1.32
30	3.08	36 x 22	2.18
36	4.93	43 x 27	3.59
42	6.33	50 x 31	4.60
48	7.38	58 x 36	5.57
		65 x 40	7.24
		72 x 44	9.90

Based on cost studies in Middle West where end sections are used extensively.

Includes only direct labor and supervision on following operations: handling at site, preparing bed, attaching to culvert, tamping and grading (but not sodding), and travel time to and from job and between installation sites.

need for special bedding, piling, cradles or other foundation work. For example, because it meets these requirements, paved and coated corrugated metal pipe is widely used for openings through flood control levees. Furthermore, it can be securely joined together and can be installed on a camber to allow for unequal settlement.

Culvert End Finish

The total cost of a culvert installation should include the cost of headwalls or other end treatment that may be required for proper, maintenance-free performance. Headwalls are necessary with some culvert materials to prevent progressive undermining due to scour at the outlet end or prevent separation of the sections because of transverse pressures. The cost of such headwalls should be included in making an economic comparison with a material of such a nature that headwalls are not essential for satisfactory service.

The Armco End Section was designed for those locations where some form of end finish is necessary with corrugated metal pipe to provide the improved appearance, lack of obstruction to mowing and snow removal equipment, protection from erosion and other requirements of modern highway design. It is a factory assembled unit that is quickly attached in the field to provide a complete culvert installation. Fig. 111. Representative man hours of direct labor required to install sections based on the average experience of contractors in a state where they are specified in large quantities are listed in Table 22-3.

Bin-Type Retaining Walls

The total cost of placing an Armco bin-type retaining wall will vary considerably with the amount of excavation required, working conditions and availability and type of backfill as they apply to individual jobs. However, once excavation is completed, direct labor required for the actual erection of the wall will be affected largely by the following factors: working conditions, amount of wall to be erected and labor efficiency. Other factors being equal, the unit costs for erecting a larger wall should be less than for a smaller wall. Estimated man hours of direct labor only for fine grading the foundation, and erection exclusive of backfill will range from 0.2 to 0.4 man hour per sq ft of facial area. Fig. 112.

Fig. 112. Assembling of bin-type retaining wall in Texas. Large walls can be installed at a lower unit cost than small walls.

Installation Costs for Guardrail

The cost of installing guardrail will vary considerably with the type used. A beam type rail which requires no special brackets for attaching to posts or special end anchorages will require less labor than a tension type rail. Post spacing and the type of posts used are also factors.

Because of the above variables together with the quantity involved, actual direct man hours required to place posts, erect guardrail and paint on a number of representative jobs ranged from 0.4 to 0.9 man hour per lineal ft of laying length. This labor estimate applies only to Flex-Beam Guardrail. End anchorages and other appurtenances required with a tension type rail would normally require additional labor.

Maintenance is an important factor in the over-all cost of guardrail protection. Generally speaking a beam type guardrail which will permit the easy removal and replacement of damaged sections will cost less to maintain than a tension type of rail where the entire line can be affected by an impact at one point.

Maintenance

Maintenance items include those operations necessary to keep a structure in serviceable condition after the original installation is completed. While such items have no effect on the first or installed cost, they do contribute to the cost of the service performed by the structure. Therefore, estimated maintenance costs for structures of various types is an important factor in the final selection. For example, railroads are reducing operating costs substantially by eliminating the maintenance costs of trestles by replacing them with culverts and fills. The same is true on highways where many obsolete structures are being replaced with underfill structures which require little or no upkeep.

Salvage Value

The service cost of structures not adaptable to relocation or extension is often increased by changing conditions which make it impossible for them to serve their normal life expectancy.

All construction is subject to constantly changing conditions. For example, many highways, adequate for the traffic of only a relatively few years ago, need to be widened and relocated and structures strengthened and lengthened to meet modern needs.

No one can anticipate accurately what changes may become necessary. However, future losses due to obsolescence can be either eliminated or reduced by selecting materials which can readily be extended or otherwise adapted to changing conditions, or salvaged and moved to a new location. Use of under-fill structures will provide a margin of safety for live loads of the future.

Fig. 113. Because of the many variables in runoff from precipitation, the design of drainage structure sizes is still an approximation. Corrugated culvert and end section in Yosemite National Park.

SECTION SIX

DESIGN PRINCIPLES AND PRACTICES

CHAPTER TWENTY-THREE

Hydrology

Summary

Hydrology deals with precipitation and runoff; hydraulics is the science dealing with the flow of water. Fig. 114. This handbook is concerned with the control and disposal of water in order to protect engineering works and property in general.

The vagaries and variables of precipitation (weather) are better known than understood. Research continues and progress is being made, but the determination of adequate floodways and culvert and sewer sizes is still more a matter of engineering judgment than of science.

Various factors are herein discussed and formulas given for determining the amount of flow to be expected. Methods are indicated on how to design the various culverts, sewers and appurtenances to handle that flow economically. It should be emphasized, however, that with the present state of knowledge, all methods of computing sizes are only an approximation. Fig. 113.

Current Studies

How much, how fast, and how frequently water reaches his structures, are questions the engineer must answer before he can properly design those structures. Gaging stations have been established at about 6,000 locations in the United States to measure rainfall and stream flow, and to determine the magnitude and frequency of peak floods. Yet relatively meager information is available for designing the smaller structures.

Few highway departments, municipalities or railways have established hydrologic and hydraulic departments to make the studies that are necessary if design of culverts and other drainage structures is to be more exact. However, some of these groups along with governmental agencies and educational institutions are carrying on much-needed research in this field.

In addition to routine gagings and meteorologic records, studies are being made on: runoff from small drainage areas; hydraulics of curbs and gutter inlets and gratings; hydraulics of culverts and their entrances and outlets; flow in open channels; erosion and silting; and many other related hydrologic and hydraulic factors.

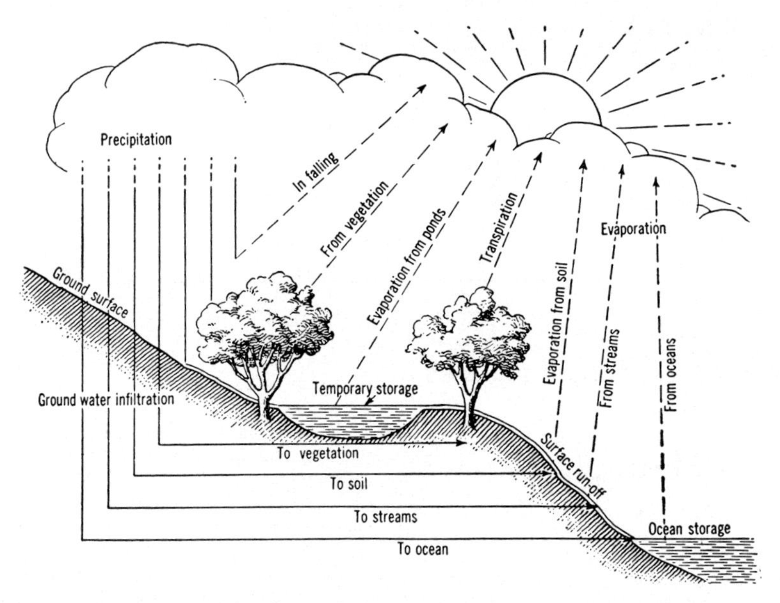

Fig. 114. The hydrologic cycle—showing where water comes from and where it goes.—From M. G. Spangler's "Soil Engineering."

The theories of statistics and of probability are being employed in hydrology to an increasing extent, just as in business, agriculture and other pursuits.

Statement of the Problem

There are two general methods of determining the required size of a drainage structure:

1. If a structure exists at or near the site, make a study of its adequacy over a period of ten to fifty years—the longer the better. Study of structures upstream and downstream will likewise be helpful.
2. Based on rainfall records for the watershed and for an assumed frequency, use an empirical or rational formula to determine the peak rate of runoff and how quickly it will reach the site.

Some empirical formulas give the size of waterway opening directly; others determine the amount of flow from which the size is computed by hydraulic formulas.

Rainfall Distribution or Intensity

Precipitation is caused by some type of atmospheric disturbance or storm. Rainfall is measured in total inches of depth either for a given storm or time period, or at the rate of so many inches an hour during a storm. Tables 23-1 and 23-2.

Frequency and amount of rainfall vary widely from month to month, from year to year and even within a given area for a single storm. There is an element of error if only a few scattered gages are read. Isohyetal maps are used to show equal depths of precipitation (much the same as contour lines show equal elevations). Fig. 115.[1]

TABLE 23-1 WORLD'S GREATEST OBSERVED POINT RAINFALLS

Duration	*Depth in Inches*	*Station*	*Date*
1 min	0.65	Opid's Camp, Calif.	Apr. 5, 1926
5 min	2.48	Porto Bello, Panama	Nov. 29, 1911
8 min	4.96	Füssen, Bavaria	May 25, 1920
14 min	3.95	Galveston, Tex.	June 4, 1871
15 min	7.80	Plumb Point, Jamaica	May 12, 1916
20 min	8.10	Curtea-de-Argés, Roumania	July 7, 1889
40 min	9.25	Guinea, Va.	Aug. 24, 1906
42 min	12.00	Holt, Mo.	June 22, 1947
1 hr	10.00	Catskill, N. Y.	July 26, 1819
1 hr, 20 min	11.50	Campo, Calif.	Aug. 21, 1891
2 hr, 10 min	19.00	Rockport, W. Va.	July 18, 1889
2 hr, 45 min	22.00	D'Hanis, Tex. (17 miles NNW)	May 31, 1935
3 hr	16.00	Concord, Pa.	Aug. 5, 1843
4 hr	23.00	Bassetere, St. Kitts, West Indies	Jan. 12, 1880
4 hr, 30 min	30.8+	Smethport, Pa.	July 18, 1942
12 hr	26.58	Baguio, Philippine Islands	July 15, 1911
15 hr	34.50	Smethport, Pa.	July 17–18, 1942
18 hr	36.40	Thrall, Tex.	Sept. 9, 1921

Source: Monthly Weather Review, Jan. 1950, p. 4, U. S. Weather Bureau, Washington, D. C.

Note: Maximum recorded U. S. point rainfall for 207 first-order stations in the U. S. for periods of 5 min. to 24 hrs. can be found in Technical Paper No. 2, April 1947, of the U. S. Weather Bureau.

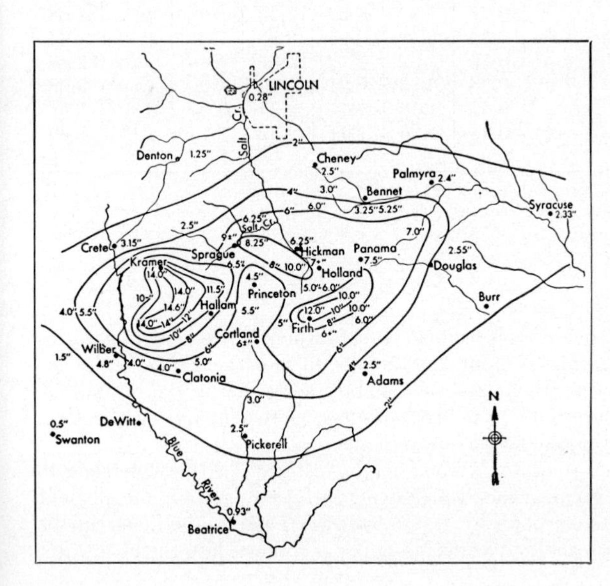

Fig. 115. Isohyetal map of storm of May 10–11, 1942, near Lincoln, Nebr. Contours indicate areas of equal rainfall.—From E. E. Foster's "Rainfall and Run-off."

TABLE 23-2 MAXIMUM RECORDED U. S. POINT RAINFALLS
In Inches

City*	Minutes					Hours	
	5	10	15	30	60	2	24
Bismarck, N. Dak.	0.75	1.10	1.40	2.31	3.07	3.35	3.76
Boston, Mass.	0.56	0.91	1.12	1.45	1.80	2.45	6.04
Cairo, Illinois	0.63	1.01	1.33	1.89	3.15	3.67	5.69
Charleston, S. C.	0.63	1.05	1.51	2.42	4.11	6.64	10.57
Chicago, Illinois	0.64	1.11	1.31	1.81	2.81	3.67	6.19
Cincinnati, Ohio	0.81	1.45	1.92	2.57	2.63	2.85	5.22
Cleveland, Ohio	0.78	1.20	1.46	1.81	1.95	2.25	4.97
Denver, Colorado	0.91	1.36	1.54	1.72	2.20	2.54	6.53
Detroit, Michigan	0.86	1.40	1.86	2.44	3.09	3.86	4.75
Helena, Montana	0.47	0.64	0.76	0.84	1.06	1.34	3.67
Indianapolis, Ind.	0.83	1.30	2.00	2.65	3.20	3.27	6.80
Key West, Florida	0.65	1.03	1.52	2.68	4.30	7.09	13.54
Knoxville, Tenn.	0.58	0.99	1.37	2.57	3.52	3.57	6.20
Little Rock, Ark.	0.63	1.01	1.35	1.92	2.42	3.23	9.58
Los Angeles, Calif.	0.44	0.66	0.81	1.12	1.51	1.99	7.36
New York, N. Y.	0.75	1.26	1.63	2.34	2.48	3.50	9.40
Omaha, Nebraska	1.00	1.49	1.86	2.32	2.62	3.17	7.03
Phoenix, Ariz.	0.43	0.61	0.86	1.16	1.41	2.20	4.98
Portland, Oregon	0.40	0.70	0.93	1.10	1.31	1.74	7.66
Saint Paul, Minn.	0.61	1.01	1.33	2.13	2.60	3.00	5.69
Salt Lake City, Utah	0.40	0.66	0.82	1.25	1.62	1.63	2.72
San Antonio, Texas	0.77	1.22	1.62	2.38	3.07	4.60	7.08
San Francisco, Calif.	0.33	0.51	0.65	0.83	1.07	1.29	4.67
Santa Fe, N. Mex.	0.46	0.62	0.77	1.03	1.16	1.65	2.83
Spokane, Wash.	0.46	0.72	0.81	0.83	1.02	1.09	2.22
Topeka, Kans.	0.67	1.08	1.44	2.24	3.27	3.82	8.08
Vicksburg, Miss.	0.83	1.20	1.41	2.32	3.11	4.17	7.99

Source: U. S. Weather Bureau Technical Paper No. 2, Washington, D. C., April 1947.
*Data available on 207 first-order stations.
Records from cooperative stations in many states are roughly double those of first-order station maximum records.

An engineer designing large bridges or flood control works is interested in storms covering large areas and lasting for hours and days. On the other hand, in designing culverts and storm sewers, the engineer is mainly interested in the rainfalls of high intensity of short duration—from five minutes to two hours, or the time necessary to reach a peak or sustained flow. Fig. 116.

The time required for a raindrop from the remotest part of the watershed to reach the culvert or sewer is called the "time of concentration." This time element is needed if designing is to be done by the so-called rational method. It can be determined by such a simple method as dropping paper confetti into the headwater

TABLE 23-3 AVERAGE PRECIPITATION IN THE UNITED STATES

City	*Average Precipitation in Inches*				
	Jan.–Mar.	*Apr.–June*	*July–Sept.*	*Oct.–Dec.*	*Annual*
Bismarck, N. Dak.	1.55	6.66	5.26	1.93	15.40
Boston, Mass.	9.86	9.85	9.41	9.65	38.76
Cairo, Illinois	12.53	11.89	9.13	10.10	43.65
Charleston, S. C.	8.93	10.10	19.89	7.07	45.99
Chicago, Illinois	6.10	10.63	9.15	6.84	32.72
Cincinnati, Ohio	10.06	11.23	9.96	8.09	39.34
Cleveland, Ohio	7.60	9.19	9.33	7.38	33.50
Denver, Colorado	2.22	5.89	3.87	2.22	14.20
Detroit, Michigan	6.63	9.42	8.31	6.67	31.03
Helena, Montana	1.64	4.63	3.07	1.96	11.30
Key West, Florida	4.75	9.23	14.96	10.58	39.52
Little Rock, Ark.	14.03	13.44	9.10	10.81	47.38
Los Angeles, Calif.	8.11	1.50	.30	4.64	14.54
New York, N. Y.	10.15	10.43	12.25	9.20	42.03
Omaha, Nebraska	3.04	9.41	9.62	3.83	25.90
Portland, Oregon	14.45	5.92	2.86	16.68	39.91
Saint Paul, Minn.	3.37	9.63	8.56	4.04	25.60
Salt Lake City, Utah	4.48	4.58	2.28	4.47	15.81
San Antonio, Texas	5.51	9.74	7.26	5.42	27.93
San Francisco, Calif.	9.35	1.82	.13	6.13	17.43
Spokane, Wash.	4.52	3.20	1.78	5.42	14.92
Vicksburg, Miss.	16.61	12.37	8.44	12.21	49.63

Source: From Monthly Normal Temperatures, Precipitation and Degree Days, bulletin of the U. S. Weather Bureau, Washington, D. C.

Normals based on 30-yr period, 1921 through 1950, adjusted to represent observations taken at the present station location.

Fig. 116. The designer is interested in the time required for water from all parts of a watershed to reach a culvert or a given point in a sewer. Photo shows relined sewer of egg-shape.

TABLE 23-4 TIME OF RAINFALL CONCENTRATION FOR TYPICAL AGRICULTURAL WATERSHEDS IN ROLLING COUNTRY

Size of Watershed, in Acres	*Time of Minimum Concentration, in Minutes*	*Size of Watershed, in Acres*	*Time of Minimum Concentration, in Minutes*
1	1.4	100	17
3	3.0	200	23
5	3.5	300	29
10	4.0	400	35
20	4.8	600	47
30	8.0	800	60
50	12.0	1000	75

during periods of rainfall. As an alternative, a survey can be made to determine the velocity of flow in various sections and channels of the watershed.

Values of times of concentration for typical agricultural watersheds in rolling country are given in Table 23-4. These are based on a large number of runoff measurements on small agricultural areas over a period of twenty years or more by C. E. Ramser, U. S. Department of Agriculture. They apply to watersheds with about 5 ft of fall per 100 ft and a length about twice the average width.

The time of concentration will be shorter for paved or graded areas where "sheet flow" occurs and in ditches and gutters as compared with cultivated land.

Rainfall Frequency

The engineer is interested not only in knowing the peak flow but how often it occurs. For economic reasons he may not be justified in designing for an intensity of rainfall that may occur only once in fifty or 100 years. The greater the intensity of rainfall, the less frequently it will occur. Accompanying charts, Figs. 118–121[2] are typical of fifty-six charts showing rainfall expectancy during brief time periods once every so many years.

Example: Suppose the engineer wants to determine the maximum rainfall to be expected on a watershed near Des Moines, Iowa, once every five years. The time of concentration is estimated at ten minutes. On the upper left chart in Fig. 119, the rainfall in Iowa would be interpolated at about 0.7 in. or 4.2 in. an hour. On a once in fifty years basis, it would be about 1.2 in. or 7.2 in. an hour.

The curves in Fig. 117 represent average conditions in the United States east of the Rocky Mountains and are of interest as showing the relation between the intensity of storms of various durations and their average frequency of recurrence.

Runoff; Watershed Characteristics

Having determined the rainfall expectancy, the second step for the designer is to estimate what portion of it must be handled as surface runoff. Watershed characteristics that govern the amount and rate of runoff are:

1. Kind and extent of vegetation or cultivation.
2. Condition of soil—dry, saturated, frozen—retentive or repellent.
3. Steepness and length of slopes.

TABLE 23-5 VALUES OF RELATIVE IMPERVIOUSNESS

Type of Surface	*Factor "I"*
For all watertight roof surfaces	.75 to .95
For asphalt runway pavements	.80 to .95
For concrete runway pavements	.70 to .90
For gravel or macadam pavements	.35 to .70
*For impervious soils (heavy)	.40 to .65
*For impervious soil, with turf	.30 to .55
*For slightly pervious soils	.15 to .40
*For slightly pervious soils, with turf	.10 to .30
*For moderately pervious soils	.05 to .20
*For moderately pervious soils, with turf	.00 to .10

*For slopes from 1% to 2%

4. Size and shape of watershed.
5. Number, arrangement, slope and condition of drainage channels on the watershed.

Table 23-5, above, gives values of relative imperviousness.

The changes of land use during the lifetime of a drainage structure may increase the coefficient of runoff as much as 50 to 100 per cent. Runoff characteristics may vary widely even for watersheds which are in close proximity to each other.

REFERENCES

1. "Rainfall and Runoff," by Edgar E. Foster, The McMillan Co., New York, 1948, 487 pp. This book has a 200 item bibliography.
2. "Rainfall Intensity-Frequency Data," by D. L. Yarnell, Publication No. 204, U. S. Dept. of Agriculture, 1935.

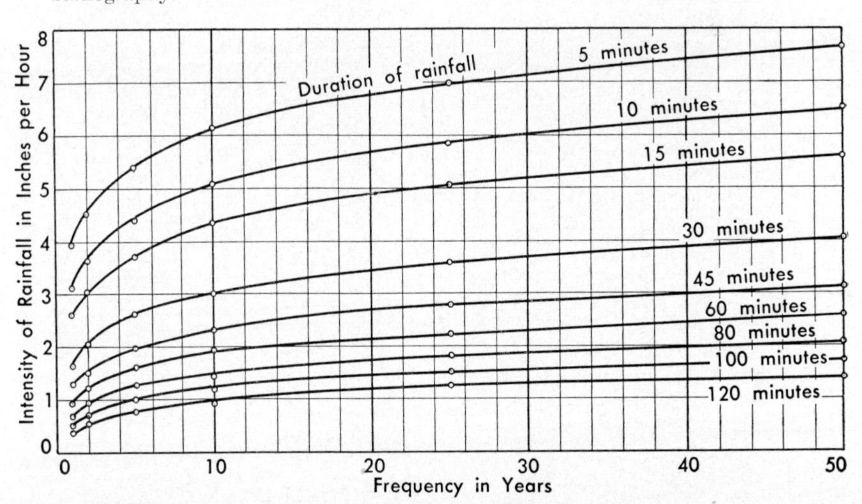

Fig. 117. Relationship between intensity of storms and their frequency of recurrence.—From Journal of Agricultural Research, 1927.

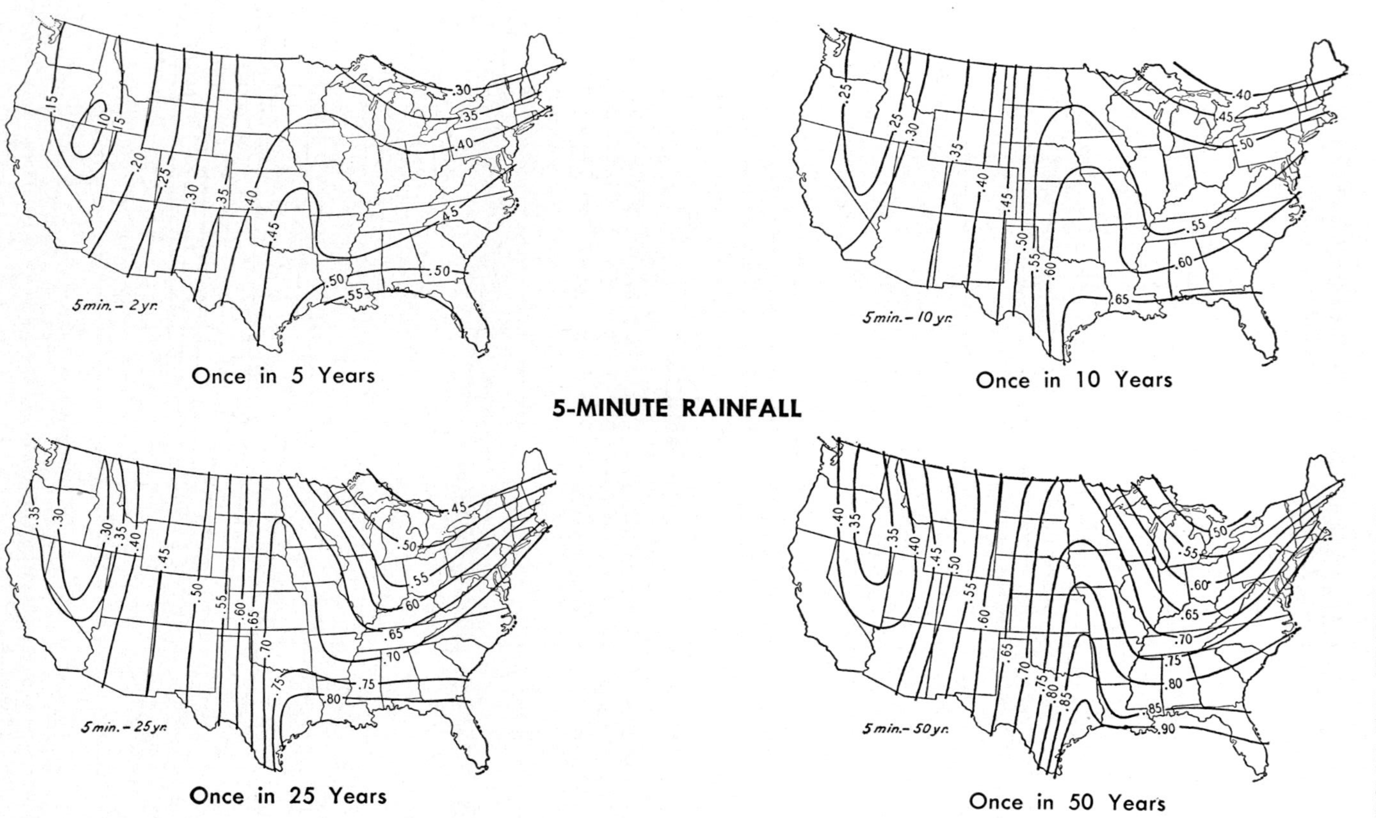

Fig. 118. Inches of rainfall during *5-minute* period to be expected once in 5, 10, 25 and 50 years.—U. S. Dept. of Agri. Misc. Publica. No. 204, 1935.

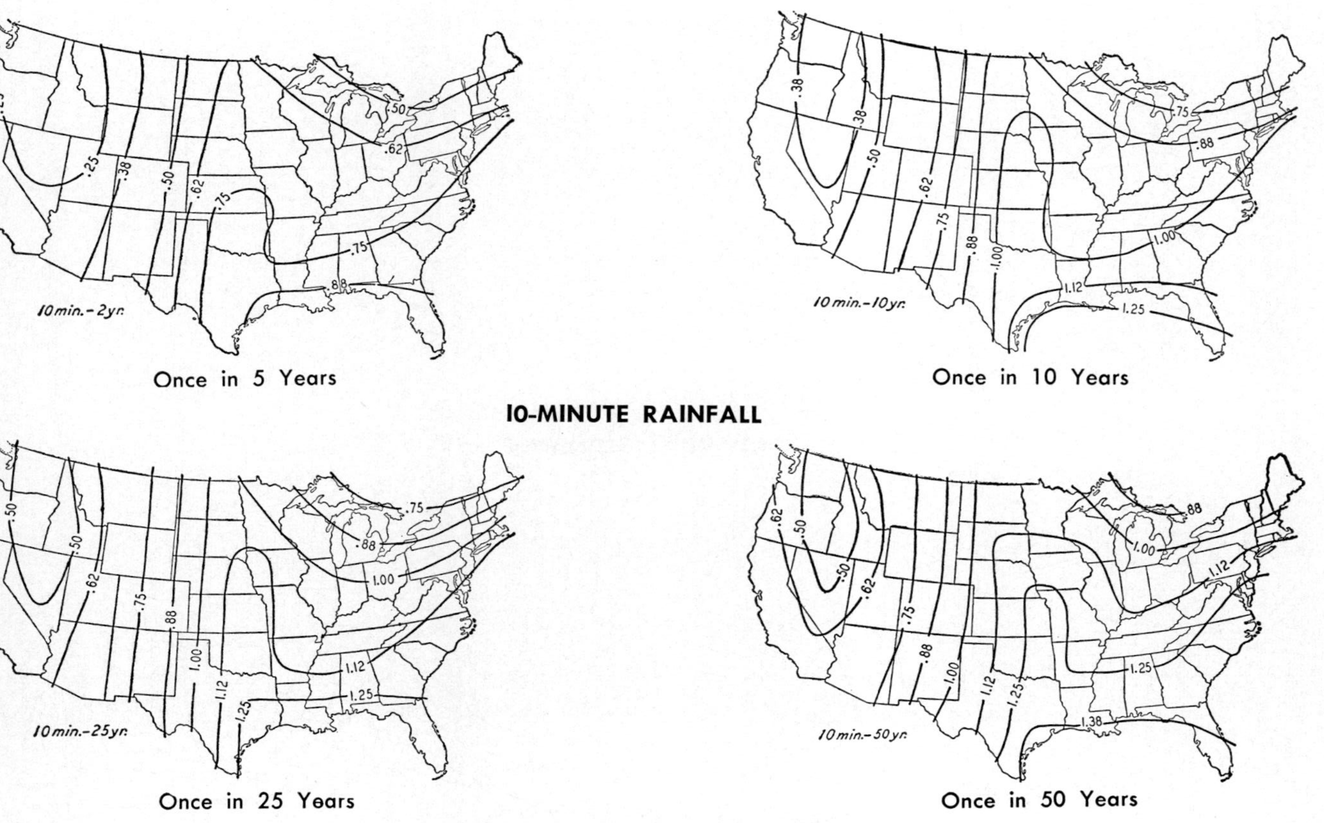

Fig. 119. Inches of rainfall during 10-*minute* period.

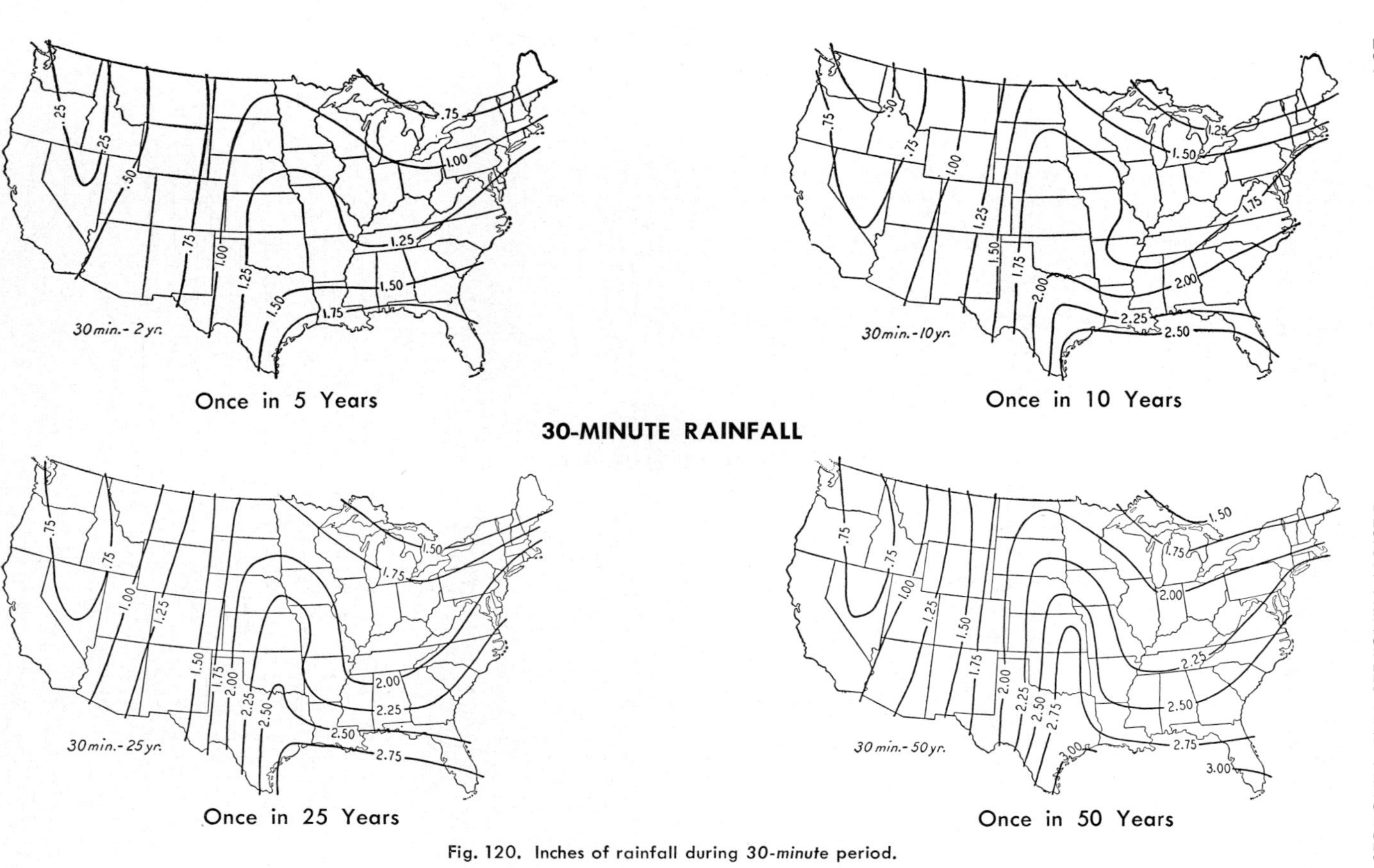

Fig. 120. Inches of rainfall during 30-*minute* period.

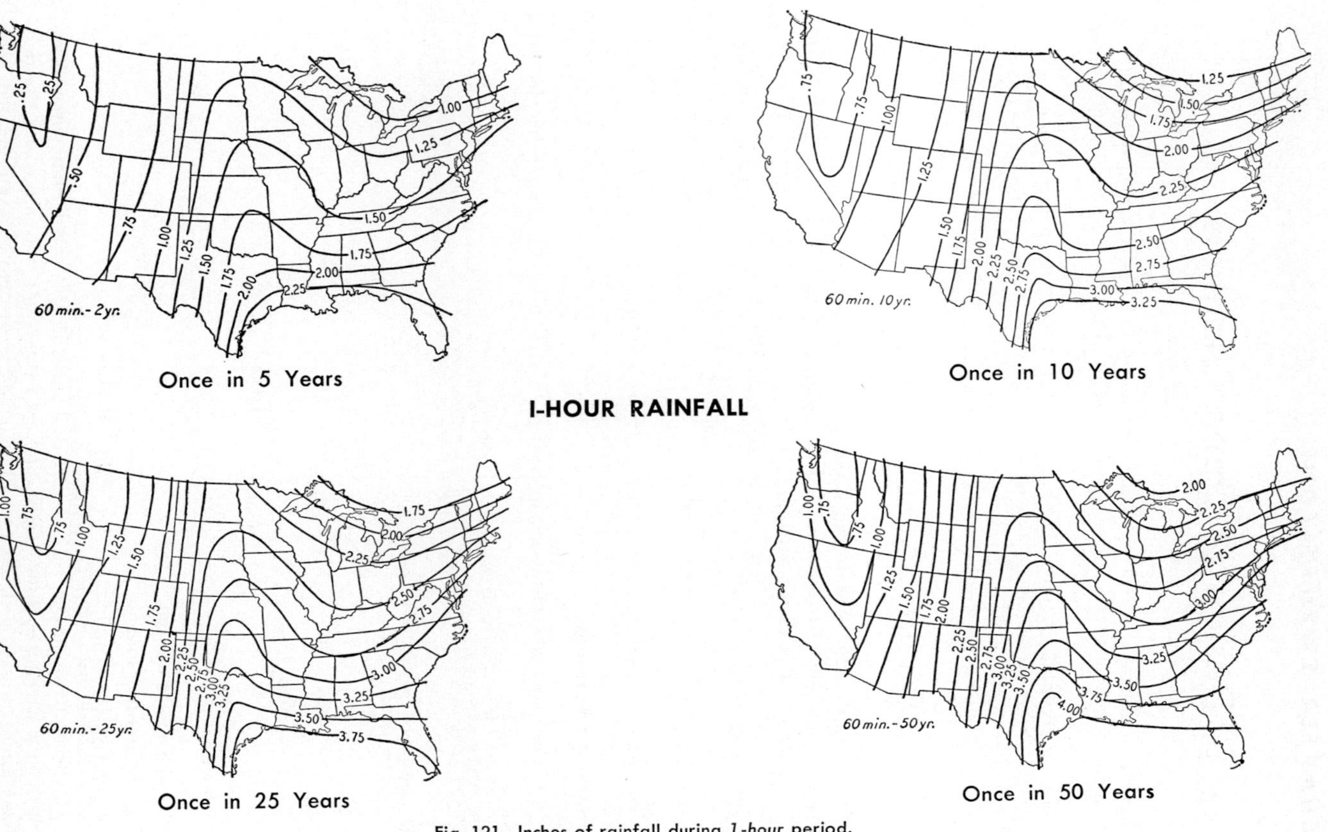

Fig. 121. Inches of rainfall during 1-hour period.

CHAPTER TWENTY-FOUR

Design of Open Channels

BEFORE designing culverts and other drainage structures, it is well to consider the design of ditches, gutters and other channels in which the drainage structures may be placed.

A basic hydraulic formula developed by Chezy for determining the flow of water particularly in open channels is written as follows:

$$V=c\sqrt{RS} \qquad Q=AV \qquad \text{and } Q=Ac\sqrt{RS}$$

in which:

Q = discharge in cu ft per sec
A = cross-sectional area of flow in sq ft
V = mean velocity of water, in ft per sec
c = a coefficient of roughness whose value depends upon the character of surface over which water is flowing

R = mean hydraulic radius in ft $= \dfrac{\text{area of section}}{\text{wetted perimeter}}$

S = slope, or grade in ft per 100 ft

This fundamental formula is the basis of most capacity formulas.

Manning's Formula

Manning's formula, published in 1890, gives the value of c in the Chezy formula as:

$$c=\frac{1.486}{n}R^{\frac{1}{6}}$$

the complete Manning formula being:

$$V=\frac{1.486}{n}R^{\frac{2}{3}}S^{\frac{1}{2}}$$

and

$$Q=A\,\frac{1.486}{n}R^{\frac{2}{3}}S^{\frac{1}{2}}$$

in which:

S = slope in ft per ft
R = hydraulic radius in ft
n = coefficient of roughness (see Table 24-1)

The accompanying charts, Figs. 122, 123 and 124 give the discharge, depth and velocity for various bottom widths, and for various flat side slopes. Intermediate values may be obtained from additional charts or may be interpolated. The reader is also referred to capacity tables in King's "Handbook of Hydraulics";

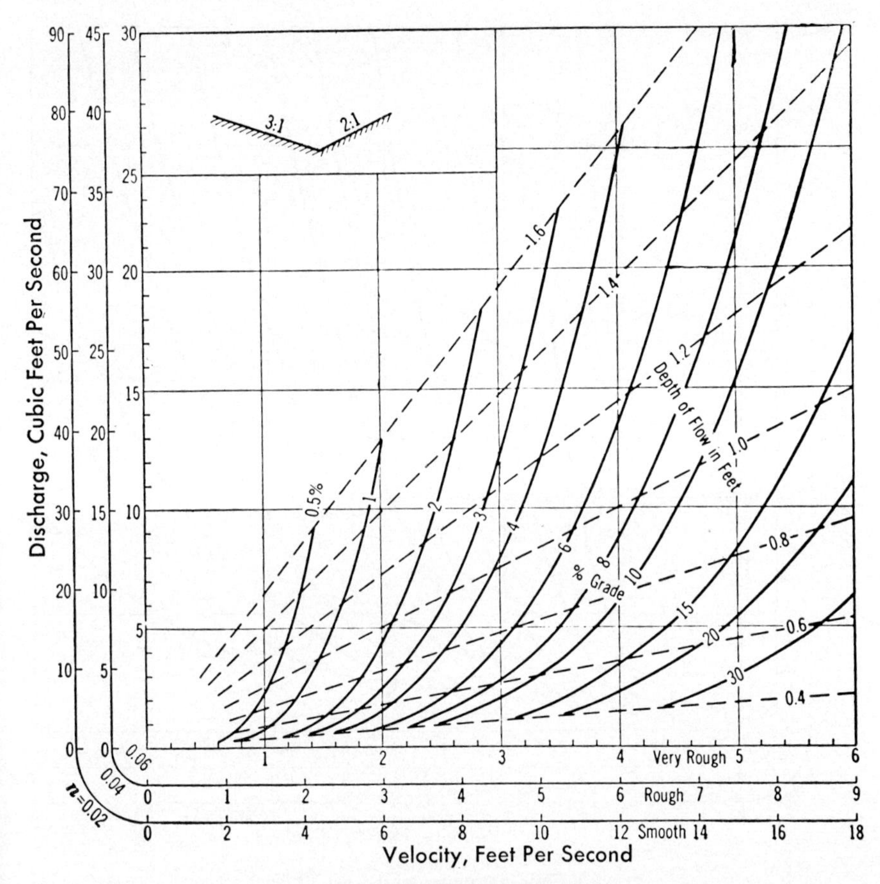

Fig. 122. Flow in triangular channel.

U. S. Bureau of Reclamation Hydraulic and Excavation Tables; and J. B. Brown, U. S. Dept. of Agriculture and Univ. of Calif. Extension Service, "Hydraulic Elements of Trapezoidal Channels."

Safe Velocities

The ideal situation is one where the velocity of water will cause neither silting nor erosion. Fortier and Scobey* point out that there is no such sharp line of demarcation, but it is believed there is a distinction between ditch bottoms that have aged or seasoned and other types of exposed surfaces. Table 24-2 gives the allowable velocities for canal beds after aging.

It will be noted that streams transporting sand, gravel or rock fragments are more erosive than clear water or water carrying colloidal silts.

*"Permissible Canal Velocities," by Samuel Fortier and F. S. Scobey in Report of the Special Committee on Irrigation Hydraulics, Trans. ASCE, Vol. 89, 1926.

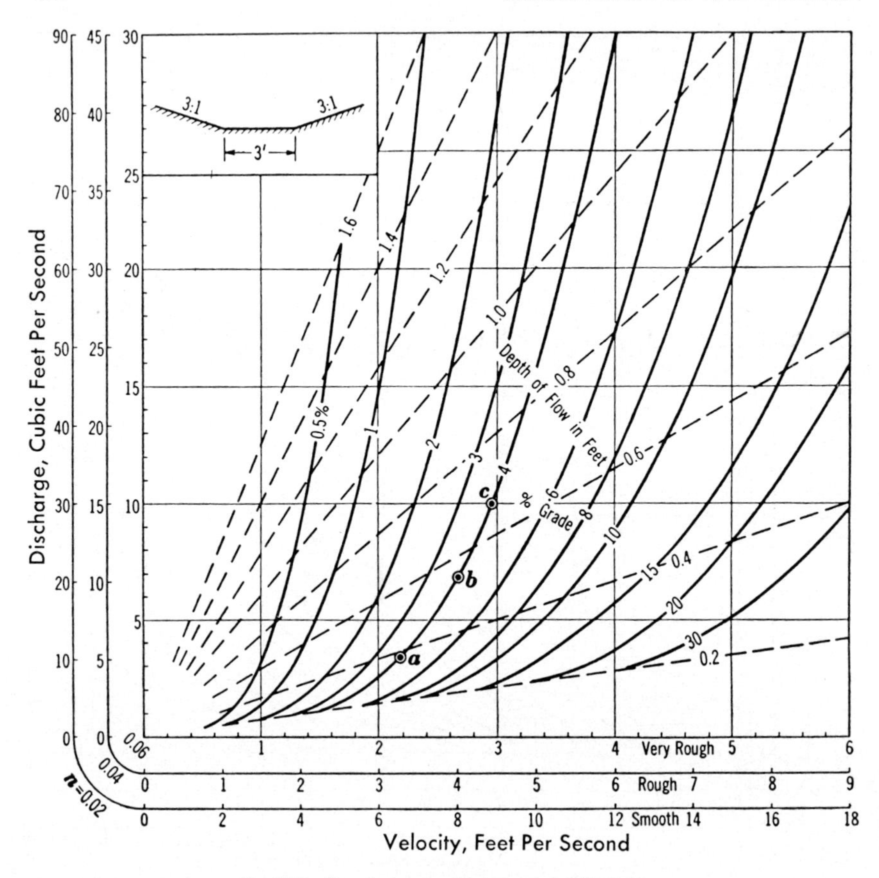

Fig. 123. Flow in trapezoidal channel 3 ft wide.

TABLE 24-1 VALUES OF *n* FOR DITCHES

Type of Lining	*n (Manning)*
Ordinary earth, smoothly graded	.02
Sod, depth of flow over 6 in.	.04
Sod, depth of flow under 6 in.	.06
Type A riprap, rough	.04
Concrete paved gutter	.016

From Ohio Hydraulic Treatise, 1947

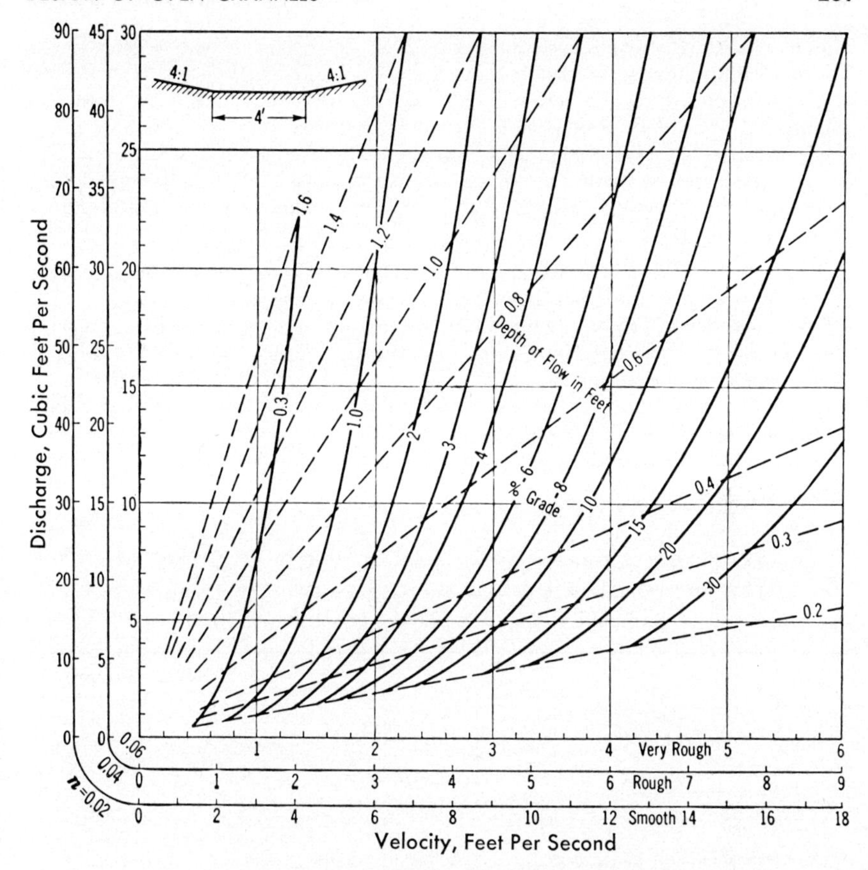

Fig. 124. Flow in trapezoidal channel 4 ft wide.

General Design of Side Ditches

Side ditches along a roadway serve to intercept surface water from the roadway and (in cut sections) from the backslope. In snow country, the side ditch provides storage space for fallen or plowed snow. Side ditches are of limited value in lowering the ground water under a roadway.

Where side ditches are objectionable or unsafe, it may be desirable to pave the ditch, use a stream enclosure or storm drain, or place an intervening guardrail.

Ditches are usually V-shaped or trapezoidal. The V-ditch can be made and maintained with a blade grader. While such maintenance may be satisfactory on unimportant roads, proper erosion prevention measures and grassing of the ditch bottom makes blading objectionable. The trapezoidal ditch is a more natural shape and has greater capacity.

The depth of small roadside ditches is usually 12 to 24 in. or more below the shoulder (see highway cross-sections, page 251). If a pervious base extends the full width of the roadway, the ditch bottom should be at least several inches lower.

Capacity of a ditch can better be increased by widening than by deepening the channel. In that way velocity and erosion are reduced.

Cautionary Note: The design of side ditches cannot be exact and therefore some allowance should be made for non-uniformity in cross section and slope, silting, erosion, obstructions and other factors which may change during the life of the roadway. Fig. 125.

In studying various handbooks and textbooks on hydraulics, one cannot fail to be impressed by the great array and complexity of hydraulic formulas. There is little agreement even on the basic formulas as they are applied to experiments in the laboratory or in the field under uniform and closely controlled conditions. Consequently, under ordinary conditions in the field, with numerous variables, the engineer should settle on a few simple formulas and use them constantly enough to become acquainted with the various coefficients and other factors which will give him reasonable results over moderate periods of time for the locality served.

TABLE 24-2 COMPARISON OF LIMITING WATER VELOCITIES AND TRACTIVE FORCE VALUES FOR THE DESIGN OF STABLE CHANNELS

Straight Channels After Aging. Canal Depth, 3 Ft

Material	*n*	*For Clear Water*		*Water Transporting Colloidal Silts*	
		Velocity ft/sec	*Tractive* Force lb/sq ft*	*Velocity ft/sec*	*Tractive* Force lb/sq ft*
Fine sand colloidal	0.020	1.50	0.027	2.50	0.075
Sandy loam noncolloidal	.020	1.75	.037	2.50	0.075
Silt loam noncolloidal	.020	2.00	.048	3.00	0.11
Alluvial silts noncolloidal	.020	2.00	.048	3.50	0.15
Ordinary firm loam	.020	2.50	.075	3.50	0.15
Volcanic ash	.020	2.50	.075	3.50	0.15
Stiff clay very colloidal	.025	3.75	.26	5.00	0.46
Alluvial silts colloidal	.025	3.75	.26	5.00	0.46
Shales and hardpans	.025	6.00	.67	6.00	0.67
Fine gravel	.020	2.50	.075	5.00	0.32
Graded loam to cobbles when noncolloidal	.030	3.75	.38	5.00	0.66
Graded silts to cobbles when colloidal	.030	4.00	.43	5.50	0.80
Coarse gravel noncolloidal	.025	4.00	.30	6.00	0.67
Cobbles and shingles	.035	5.00	.91	5.50	1.10

Table is from "Progress Report on Results of Studies on Design of Stable Channels," U. S. Bureau of Reclamation, Report No. Hyd-352, 1952, 60 pp.

*"Tractive force" or shear is the force which the water exerts on the periphery of a channel due to the motion of the water. The tractive values shown were computed from velocities given by S. Fortier and Fred C. Scobey and the values of *n* shown.

The tractive force values are valid for the given materials regardless of depth. For depths greater than 3 ft, higher velocities can be allowed and still have the same tractive force.

Fig. 125. Side ditches and entrance culverts should be adequate to provide free flow and should not endanger the roadway.

TABLE 24-3 ANGLE OF REPOSE OF COARSE, NON-COHESIVE MATERIAL

Material	*Angle of Repose*	*Authority*	*Remarks*
Gravel	30°	Anderson	34-per cent voids
Gravel	30°–48°	American Civil Engineers Pocket-book	Round to angular
Gravel	39°–48°	Rankine's Applied Mechanics	
Gravel or soil	37°	Massey	Dry
Cobbles	39°	Massey	Dry
Gravel	31°	Paaswell	
Shingle and gravel	35°–48°	Trautwine	
Dense sand and gravel	34°	Plummer and Dore	
Gravel	30°–48°	Urquhart	Round to angular
Gravel ½ in	25°	Goodrich	
Gravel ¼ in	19°	Goodrich	

Source: Bureau of Reclamation, 1952.

CHAPTER TWENTY-FIVE

Theory of Critical Flow

THE FLOW of water in a pipe with a free outlet, and with a slope sufficient to create no backwater effect, is based on well-established hydraulic theory, and is controlled by the "critical velocity" and the "critical section."

This can best be explained for a conduit with a rectangular opening. Assume a square box with the upstream pond water surface at the same elevation as the top of the inside of the box. (See Fig. 126.) If we consider a free discharge of the box into the atmosphere, and if we consider the friction as being negligible, there will be a drop-down curve from the pond level to the critical depth, so that one-third the total head becomes velocity head, as demonstrated mathematically on the opposite page. There are examples of this drop-down phenomenon in common, every-day hydraulics. Perhaps the best known example is where the depth of water is reduced as the water falls over a dam partly submerged by high water. The reason for this reduction in depth is due to the increased velocity as the water starts to fall over the crest. Before the water falls over the crest, there is comparatively very little velocity and part of the depth is used to create the new velocity of the falling water.

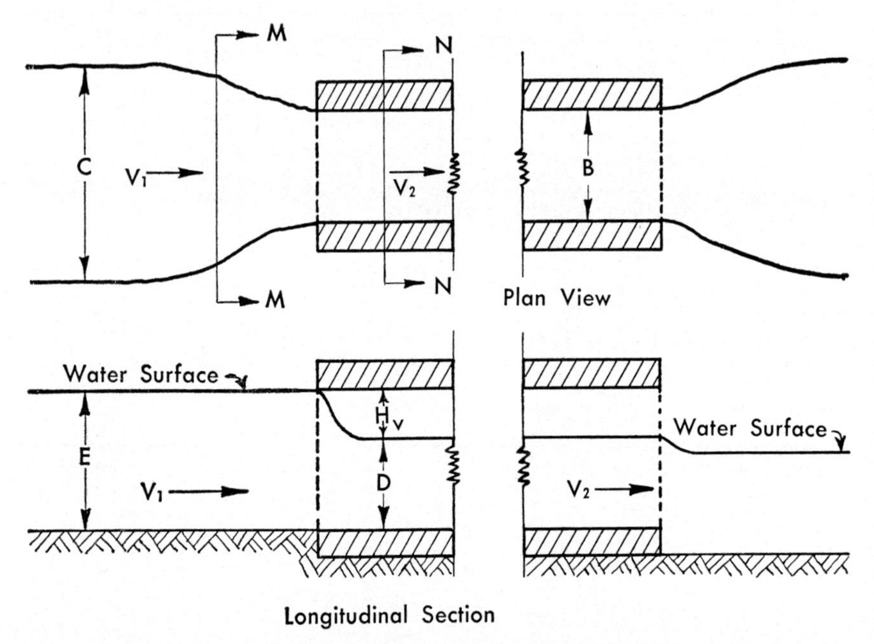

Fig. 126. Plan and longitudinal section of a rectangular conduit under critical flow.

In general, it may be said that the total energy or head of a flowing stream of water may be considered as made up of two parts: potential energy as represented by depth, and kinetic energy as represented by velocity head. The two kinds of energy are readily interchangeable wherever conditions favorable to such changes are encountered.

The explanation of why the drop down is one-third the original depth in such cases is as follows:

Assume a pond and channel as in Fig. 126:

The quantity of water that can pass section M-M is no greater than the quantity that can pass section N-N and the total discharge $=Q=AV=CEV_1=BDV_2$

$$E=Hv+D \tag{1}$$

$$Hv=\text{velocity head } =\frac{V^2}{2g} \tag{2}$$

but since $Q=AV$, $V=\frac{Q}{A}$ and $V^2=\frac{Q^2}{A^2}$

and since $A=B\times D$, $V^2=\frac{Q^2}{B^2D^2}$

Substituting in (2) for V^2

$$Hv=\frac{Q^2}{2gB^2D^2} \tag{3}$$

and substituting in (1) for the value of Hv

$$E=\frac{Q^2}{2gB^2D^2}+D \tag{4}$$

or

$$\frac{Q^2}{2gB^2D^2}=E-D$$

and

$$\frac{Q^2}{2g}=EB^2D^2-B^2D^3 \tag{5}$$

If the headwater depth E is maintained constant, the maximum discharge which can pass section N-N is found by differentiation of equation (5).

$$\frac{d}{dD}\frac{(Q^2)}{(2g)}=2\ EB^2D-3\ B^2D^2=0 \tag{6}$$

Solving, $2\ EB^2D=3\ B^2D^2$

Dividing both sides by B^2D

$$2E=3D$$

$$\text{or } D=\tfrac{2}{3}\ E$$

and $Hv=E-D=\tfrac{1}{3}\ E$ (7)

$$V=\sqrt{2gH}=\sqrt{\frac{2}{3}g\ E}$$

$$Q=AV=BD\sqrt{\frac{2}{3}g\ E}$$

This result may be summarized in the following statement: The maximum discharge which can pass the constricted or critical section of a frictionless rectangular channel with constant headwater level, is that due to a critical velocity-head of ⅓, and a critical depth of ⅔ of the depth of the headwater above the floor of the constricted section.

For this condition, there is the same energy in section M-M as in section N-N. Section N-N represents a condition of uniform flow. Waves might form at that section but would have no effect upon the quantity of water passing the section.

When this phenomenon exists, the amount of drop-down creates a definite velocity. This velocity is commonly called the *critical* velocity and can be calculated from the velocity head equation, $H=\frac{V^2}{2g}$. Since the drop-down is a certain portion of the depth, the remaining depth and the area can easily be calculated. With the area and velocity known, the quantity of discharge can be determined.

Law Applied to Circular Pipe

This same principle that has been applied to the rectangular frictionless channel can also be applied to circular pipe. For the circular pipe, the calculations are somewhat more complicated because the sections are not uniform in horizontal projection. To determine the critical depth in a circular conduit, the law of critical velocity must be considered. The law as stated in the report "Hydraulics of the Miami Flood Control Project," by Sherman M Woodward, Technical Report No. 7, page 149, is:

> "The critical velocity for maximum discharge at any cross section of a channel is that due to a head equal to half the average depth of the water at the cross section."

Applying this law to a circular pipe, the head causing the critical velocity is found to be equal to $0.3113D$, when D is the diameter of the pipe in feet. This equation is true only when the surface of the water in the pond is coincident with the top of the pipe and when the pipe is placed on such a grade that there will be no backwater effect due to friction.

With the equation for head known, and the relationship that exists between the head and the velocity, the critical velocity can then be determined. By mathematical analysis, the critical velocity is found to be equal to $4.475D^{\frac{1}{2}}$ where D = diameter of pipe.

$$V=\sqrt{2gH}$$

$$Hv=\tfrac{1}{3}E=.3113D$$

Then, $$V=\sqrt{2\times 32.2\times .3113D}=4.475D^{\frac{1}{2}}$$

(In this special case the symbols "D" and "E" are interchangeable.)

This equation gives the critical velocity at the critical section where the depth is $(1-.3113D)$ or $.6887D$. (See Fig. 127.)

With the area and velocity of the critical section known, the critical discharge can be determined. This is found to be equal to $2.58D^{\frac{5}{2}}$.

$$Q=AV$$

$$A=\text{area for depth of } .6887D=.5768D^2$$

Then, $$Q=.5768D^2\times 4.475D^{\frac{1}{2}}=2.58D^{\frac{5}{2}}$$

This equation gives the discharge at the critical section when the slope is sufficient to remove the water without affecting the critical section.

Effect of Slope

The next step in this problem is to determine the slope that will take care of the water passing through the critical section, and not cause any backwater effect.

In the solution of this step of the problem it will be necessary to use some fundamental equation for flow based upon the friction in the pipe. Manning's equation was used in determining the slope necessary to remove the quantity of water passing through the critical section.

By substituting the critical velocity in the Manning equation, it was found that the critical slope was equal to $\frac{2.04}{D^{\frac{1}{3}}}$ per cent. The computation follows:

$$V=\frac{1.486}{n}R^{\frac{2}{3}}\,S^{\frac{1}{2}} \text{ (Manning's formula)}$$

$$\text{then, } S=\frac{V^2}{70.76^2\,R^{\frac{4}{3}}}$$

$$R=\text{hydraulic radius}=\frac{\text{area}}{\text{wetted perimeter}}=\frac{.5768D^2}{1.9578D}=\frac{.5768D}{1.9578}$$

Substituting

$$S=\frac{4.475^2D}{70.76^2\left(\frac{.5768}{1.9578}\right)^{\frac{4}{3}}D^{\frac{4}{3}}}=\frac{2.04}{D^{\frac{1}{3}}}$$

This equation gives the per cent slope on which a pipe must be placed so that the water passing through the critical section is taken away without any backwater effect.

Maximum Discharge at Critical Slope

At this point, it is necessary to understand that the velocity at the critical section is the velocity at which maximum discharge can be attained in any given pipe. That is to say that the head causing this is a constant and cannot be increased. Increasing the slope of a culvert beyond the critical slope does not increase the dis-

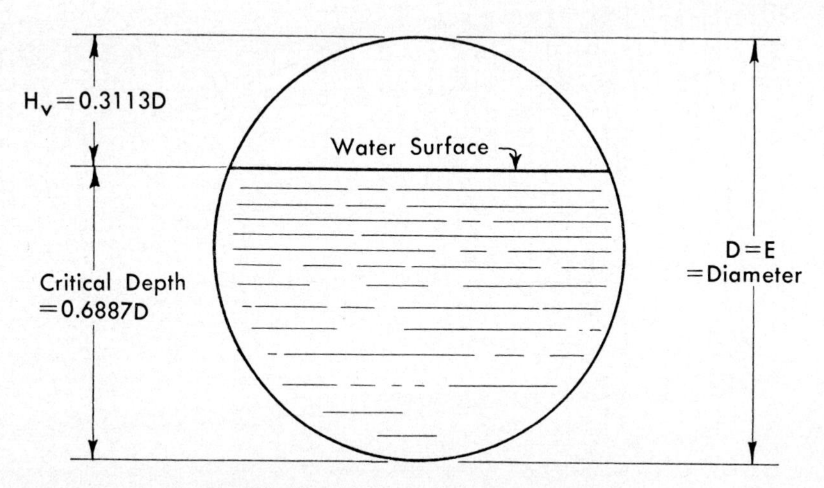

Fig. 127. Elements of critical flow in round pipes.

CAPACITY-VELOCITY CURVES

For Pipe on Various Slopes—*Outlets Unsubmerged*
Water Surface at Inlet Same Elevation as Top of Pipe
Computed by Manning's Formula

Note: Upper limit of curves is critical slope, beyond which the discharge is constant.

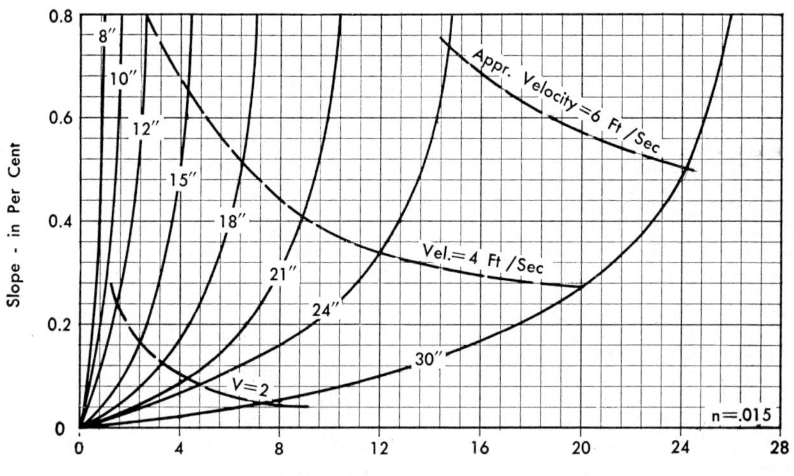

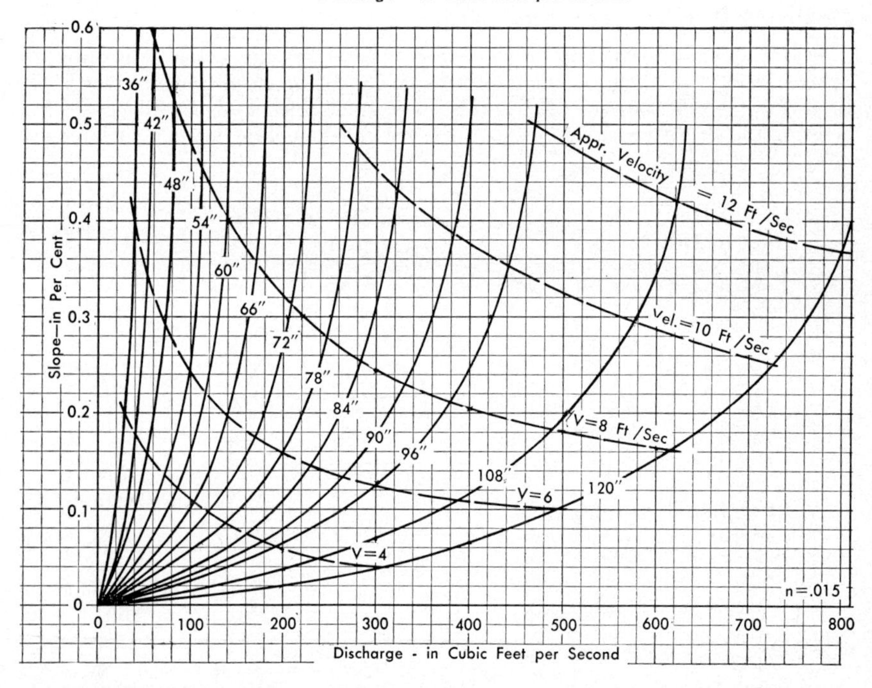

Figs. 128–129. Curves showing capacity and velocity for various slopes—outlets unsubmerged. For $n=.015$.

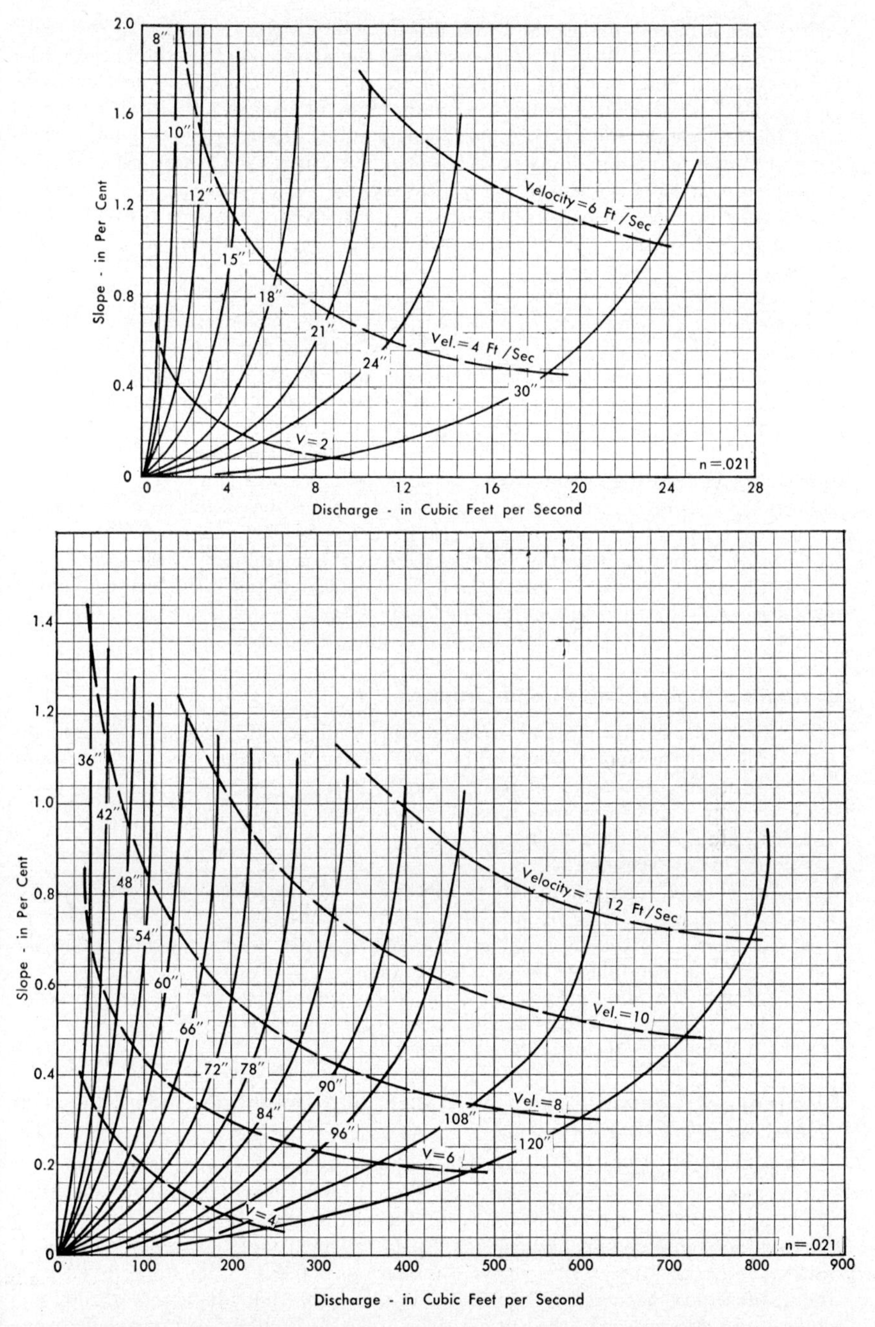

Figs. 130–131. Curves showing capacity and velocity for various slopes—outlets unsubmerged. For $n = .021$.

charge, but it merely makes the water flow at a depth less than the critical depth and at a greater velocity. This gives rise to the statement that discharge under this condition is limited by the amount of water that can enter the pipe. It might be said that the discharge is limited by the amount of water that can be forced through the pipe due to a certain head which is not dependent upon grade. This being true, the maximum discharge is obtained at a critical slope, and a slope greater than the critical slope will not increase the discharge. Therefore, the only remaining part of this problem to be solved is to find the discharge for slopes less than the critical slope, because for these slopes friction will have a retarding effect upon the discharge.

This is accomplished by choosing various values of depths at the critical section and determining the velocity caused by a head equal to the remaining depth and from this velocity finding the discharge for the various depths from critical depth to full depth. For various depths, a curve can be plotted showing the discharge with different values of slope. From these graphs or curves the discharge for even depths and slopes can be taken off and put in tabular form.

From Table 26-2, page 230, and Table 33-2, page 278, the discharge can be taken directly for various diameters of pipe on various slopes up to and including critical slopes. Velocities are also shown. Figures 128–131, in the accompanying series of graphs, give the same information in graphical form. These tables and charts are based on the condition that the water surface at the inlet end is at the same elevation as the top of the pipe. This is the usual condition found in culverts and storm sewers because they are seldom designed to flow under a head. Head, in this case, means height of water above the top of the pipe at the inlet.

Example of Use of Tables and Graphs:

A—Required: (1) the critical or maximum discharge, (2) critical slope and (3) approximate velocity for a 30-in. pipe having a value of $n = .021$ with water surface at inlet same elevation as top of pipe.

From Fig. 130 all requirements can be read directly.

(1) Max. or critical discharge = 26 cfs

(2) Critical slope = 1.6%

(3) Velocity = approximately 6 to 8 fps

These results may be obtained also from Table 26-2, page 230.

B—Required: (1) the discharge and (2) approximate velocity if the pipe in the preceding example is laid on 0.6% grade.

From the same graph and table, the requirements can be read directly.

(1) Discharge at 0.6% = 20.8 cfs

(2) Velocity = approximately 4.5 fps

Discharge of Conduits with Free Outlets and Operating Under Heads at Inlet from 0.2 to 5.0 Ft

Occasionally, it may be permissible to increase the discharge of a culvert or storm sewer by flow under pressure or head. Under this condition, the elevation of the water at the inlet end is above the top of the pipe.

From the accompanying figures, Nos. 132 to 139 inclusive, the discharge for heads varying from 0.2 ft to 5.0 ft inclusive, (in intervals of 0.2 ft for the first foot of head, and 1.0 ft intervals thereafter) can be obtained for various diameters of pipe and slopes up to and including the critical slope. The maximum discharge occurs when the pipe is laid on the critical slope or steeper. Any greater slopes will not increase

CAPACITY-VELOCITY CURVES

For Pipe on Various Slopes—Outlets Unsubmerged
Computed by Manning's Formula for $n = .021$

Note: Upper limit of curves is critical slope, beyond which discharge is constant.
Lower limit of curves is slope below which pipe flows full.
Number at top of each curve represents diameter in inches.
Numbers on straight lines represent approximate velocities in feet per second.

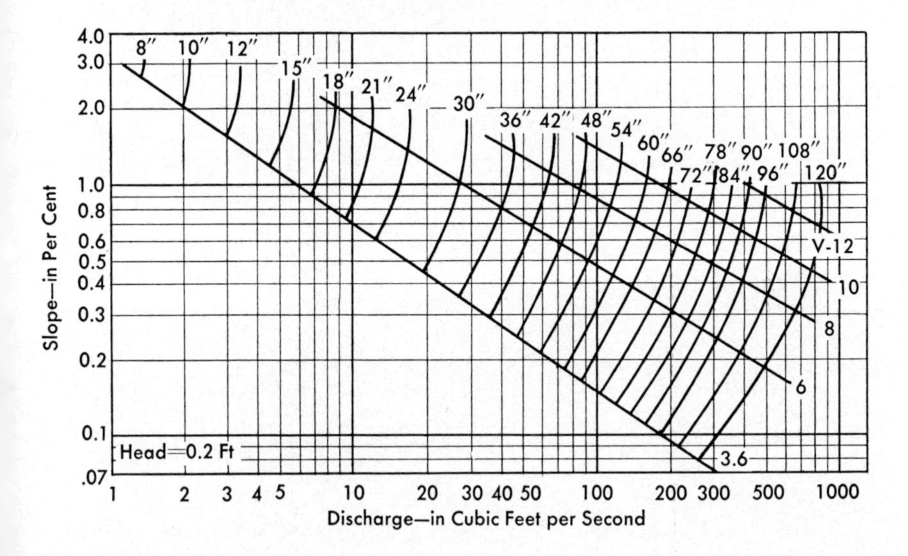

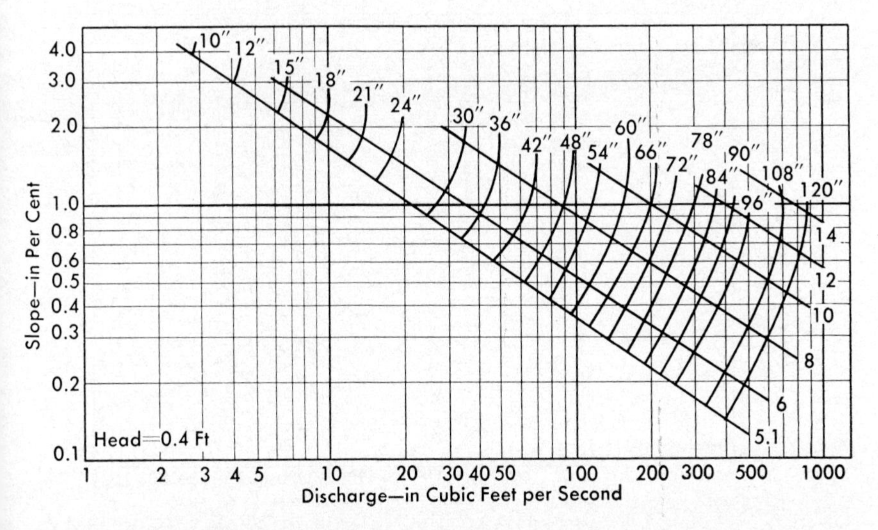

Figs. 132–133. Curves showing capacity and velocity for various slopes—outlets unsubmerged. For heads of 0.2 and 0.4 ft.

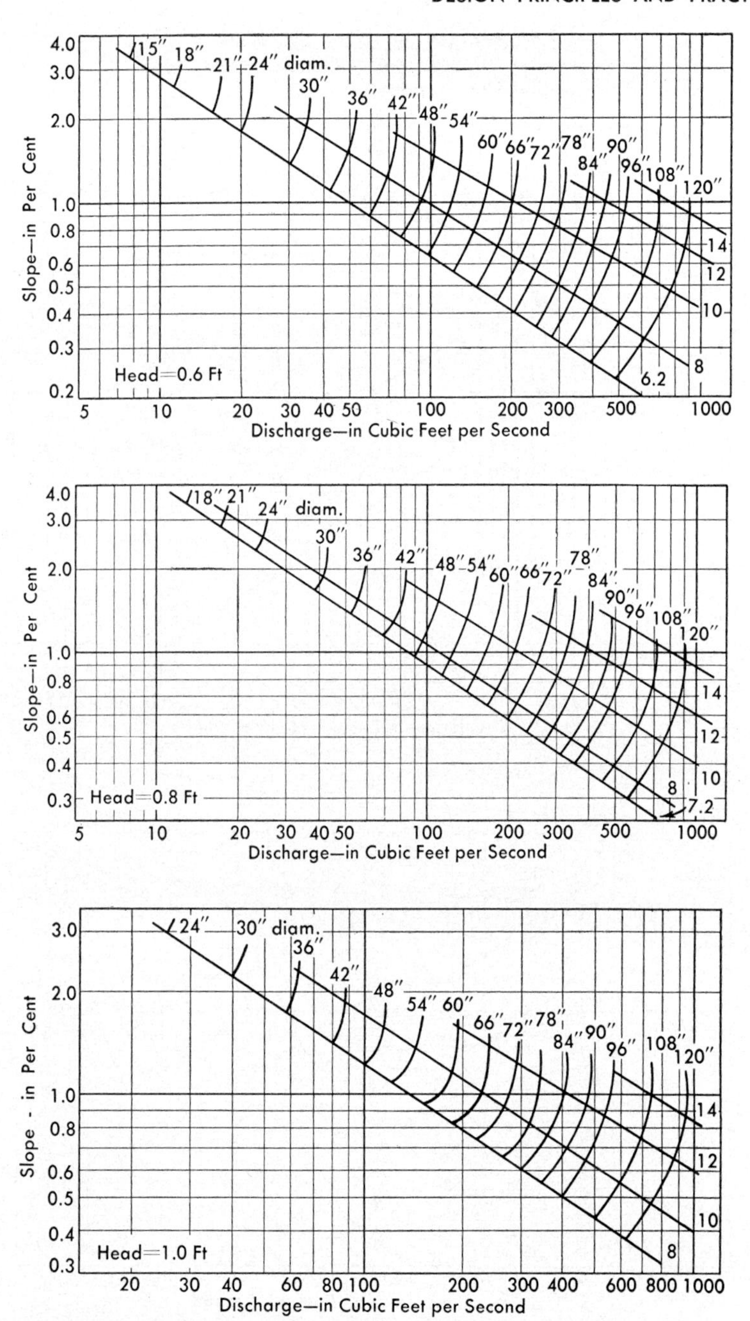

Figs. 134–136. Curves showing capacity and velocity for various slopes—outlets unsubmerged. For heads of 0.6, 0.8 and 1.0 ft.

CAPACITY-VELOCITY CURVES

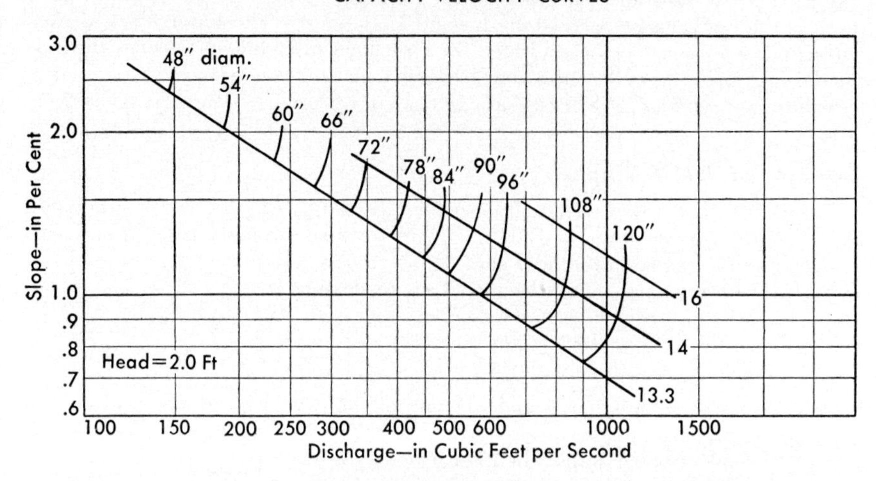

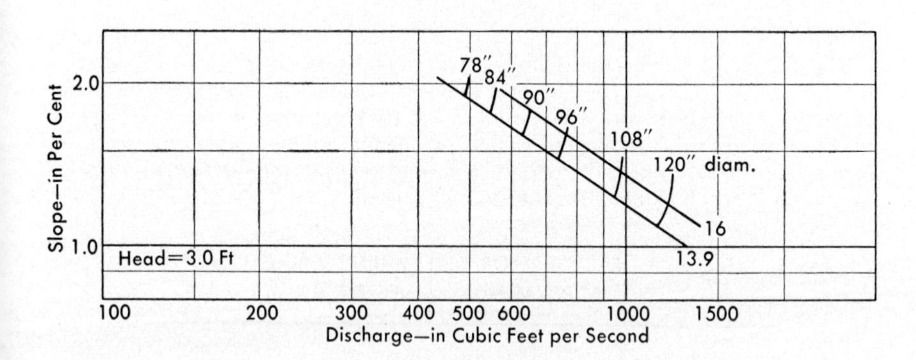

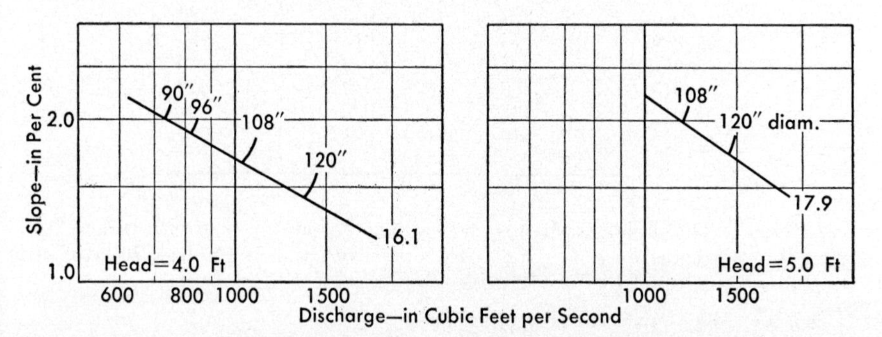

Figs. 137–139. Curves showing capacity and velocity for various slopes—outlets unsubmerged. For heads of 2, 3 and 4 ft.

the capacity of the pipe. The maximum possible discharge is the upper limit of each curve. Discharge is constant beyond that point. The lower limit of each curve indicates the slope below which the pipe flows full. For such slopes the pipe will always flow full and methods which apply for this condition must be used in computing discharge. Velocities are indicated by straight-line curves on each graph.

Example of Use of Graphs:

A—Required: (1) the maximum or critical discharge, (2) the critical grade and (3) the velocity for a pipe 60 in. in diameter with a value of $n = .021$ and with a head of 0.6 ft on the inlet end.

From Fig. 134, the requirements are read directly.

(1) Max. or critical discharge = 172 cfs
(2) Critical slope = 1.36%
(3) Velocity = approximately 11 fps

B—Required: (1) discharge and (2) approximate velocity if the pipe in the preceding example is laid on 0.8% grade.

From the same graph, the requirements are read directly.

(1) Discharge at 0.8% grade = 157 cfs
(2) Velocity = approximately 8 fps

Other Values of *n*

The discharge of a pipe varies inversely as *n*, and varies directly as the square of the slope. The accompanying curves, Figs. 132 to 139 inclusive, are based on a value of $n = .021$. For pipes with other values of *n*, the discharge, or the slope required to obtain an equivalent discharge, can be obtained by applying a per cent correction factor as given in Table 25-1. In no case, however, can the discharge exceed the maximum shown for the upper limit of each curve.

TABLE 25-1 FACTORS FOR DETERMINING CRITICAL SLOPES FOR VARIOUS VALUES OF *n*

n	*Decimal Per Cent*	*n*	*Decimal Per Cent*
.010	.227	.016	.580
.011	.274	.017	.656
.012	.327	.018	.735
.013	.383	.019	.819
.014	.445	.020	.907
.015	.510	.021	1.000

Examples: The problems on this and on page 218 are for pipe with an *n* of .021. Now the question is, on what slope would a pipe with an *n* of .017 have to be placed to give an equal discharge of 172 cfs?

Answer: Slope × per cent correction factor
= 1.36% × .656
= .89% (The velocity remains the same)

Fig. 140. Culvert with "free outlet," to which the theory of critical flow applies.

On the other hand, suppose that the discharge is desired for an 84-in. diameter pipe with a value of n of .015, placed on a grade of .4% and $H = 1.0$ ft

Answer: Slope ÷ per cent correction factor

= .4%. ÷ .51

= .785% (= grade for pipe with an n of .021 to produce an equal discharge)

Then, from Fig. 136, the discharge for the 84-in. pipe on a grade of .785% = 375 cfs.

CHAPTER TWENTY-SIX

Design of Culverts or Cross Drains for Size and Shape

THE DESIGN of culverts for size and shape is done by several acceptable methods. These vary greatly, depending on local precedent and experience. The results are equally variable.

Definition. A culvert is defined as a conduit to convey water through an embankment. It is a "grade separation" for the water and the traffic above it.

Distinction between a highway culvert and a bridge is that the top of a culvert does not ordinarily form a part of the roadway surface. On the other hand, a bridge is a link in a roadway. For the administration of federal-aid highway funds, all structures 20 feet or less between abutments are classified as culverts. Some states and railroads consider much smaller structures as bridges.

Importance Cost-wise

The U. S. Bureau of Public Roads[1] estimates that approximately $400 million is being spent annually on new drainage structures by federal, state and local agencies in the United States. Also, about 10 per cent of the total cost of constructing highways, or about $160 million a year goes into small drainage structures—culverts.

Add to this the cost of railroad culverts, levee culverts, industrial drainage and other uses of small drainage structures and the total cost is boosted considerably. Therefore, there is a need to avoid wasteful over-designing. On the other hand, if culverts are deficient, they may result in premature destruction of the roadway or other engineering structures they were intended to protect. The more important and costly the road, and the heavier the traffic, the more liberal should be the design. Some engineers purposely over-design culverts so that when replacement is necessary, this can be done by threading a new structure inside the old one and still have adequate waterway area.

Hydraulic Considerations

Surface water should be conducted across and away from a roadway as promptly as possible.

Proper alignment, grade, and installation methods, as discussed in later paragraphs, are important in determining the adequacy of a culvert or cross drain. If a culvert silts up, pulls apart or washes out, it will not have the capacity nor give the service intended.

A culvert usually constricts the waterway, thereby causing some ponding of the water at the inlet and an increase in velocity inside and beyond the culvert. The outlet may need protection against scour and undermining.

Culverts should not be designed to flow full or with the headwater submerging the entrance oftener than once every twenty-five years. On minor, lightly traveled roads, overtopping of the roadway once every few years may be of no consequence if the embankment is protected. For heavily traveled roads and on railroads, the size of the culvert opening should be such that while submerging the entrance may occur on rare occasions, overtopping of the roadway will not occur at any time.

There is an economic relationship between (1) providing a large culvert opening, (2) repairing the roadway in case of overtopping, (3) maintenance of culvert and channel, (4) interference with heavy traffic and (5) safety. Fig. 141.

Drainage Survey

Determining culvert size may require a drainage survey, including the following:[2]

1. Information as to runoff producing characteristics of drainage area (shape, slope, present and prospective land use, etc.).
2. Acreage of watershed. The use of U. S. Geological Survey maps or other topographical maps is satisfactory. Small areas may be estimated if visible.
3. Profile of existing inlet and outlet channels.
4. Cross-sections of the outlet channel.
5. Cross-section of the proposed embankment at the culvert site.
6. Contours of inlet basin up to maximum headwater elevation to determine storage capacity.
7. High water elevation of flood plain below culvert where flooding is probable from a stream or river below roadway.
8. Information on resistance to erosion of channel soil.
9. Possibility of and kind of drift.

Aerial surveys and photographs, if available, are satisfactory and may be less costly than ground surveys for determining several of the above items. Expensive surveys are not justified for small culverts but may be for large culverts and bridges.

An engineer is less likely to be criticized if he builds his drainage structures with capacity on the liberal side than if he makes them too small—particularly where accurate data are not available.

Fig. 141. Culverts should not be designed to flow full. Twin 9-ft corrugated metal culvert under 100 ft of fill on U. S. Route 10 near Cabinet Gorge Dam in Montana.

Methods of Determining Size

There are three general methods in use for determining the required size of a culvert:

1. Inspection of old structure at the site, or structures up and downstream.
2. Use of an empirical formula to determine directly the size of opening required.
3. Use of a formula to determine the amount of water reaching the culvert, then a second formula to determine the size of culvert required to carry this amount of water.

1. *Determining Size by Inspection*

Existing Structure. One of the most practical ways of determining proper size is by inspection of an existing structure at the site, (also upstream and downstream) even though its size may have been established by guess. Note the size and shape and the condition of the channel above and below. Was it adequate or oversize at peak flood-flow over a period of twenty-five years or more? Long-time local residents or maintenance men may have information as to high water marks and adequacy. Structures built during drought years may be inadequate later. Local residents may be concerned about keeping drainage openings on the liberal side and may testify accordingly.

2. *Talbot Formula*

Because of its simplicity in giving culvert size directly, the Talbot formula continues to be popular. It is an empirical formula based on a large number of observations in the Middle West. It does not take into account the intensity of rainfall (inches per hour), velocity of flow or other rational factors. The maximum rainfall for these observations is not known, but is assumed to have been about 4 in. per hour. The velocity of flow was variable—something less than 10 ft per second.

The Talbot formula gives the area of the culvert opening directly:

$$A = C\sqrt[4]{M^3}$$

where

A = waterway necessary, in sq ft
M = area drained, in acres
C = coefficient

The coefficient C depends upon the contour of the land drained, and the following values are recommended for various conditions of topography.

$C = 1$, for steep and rocky ground with abrupt slopes.
$C = 2/3$, for rough hilly country of moderate slopes.
$C = \frac{1}{2}$, for uneven valleys, very wide as compared to length.
$C = 1/3$, for rolling agricultural country where the length of valley is three or four times the width.
$C = 1/5$, for level district not affected by accumulated snow or severe floods. For still milder conditions or for subdrained lands, decrease C as much as 50 per cent; but increase C for steep side slopes or where the upper part of the valley has a much greater fall than the channel of the culvert.

Example: Required, the cross-sectional area of a culvert suitable for draining 75 acres in level country. Assuming 1/5 as the value of C, locate the intersection of the 75-acre line with the first curve of Fig. 142, then trace directly down to the base line. This point lies almost exactly at 5 sq ft.

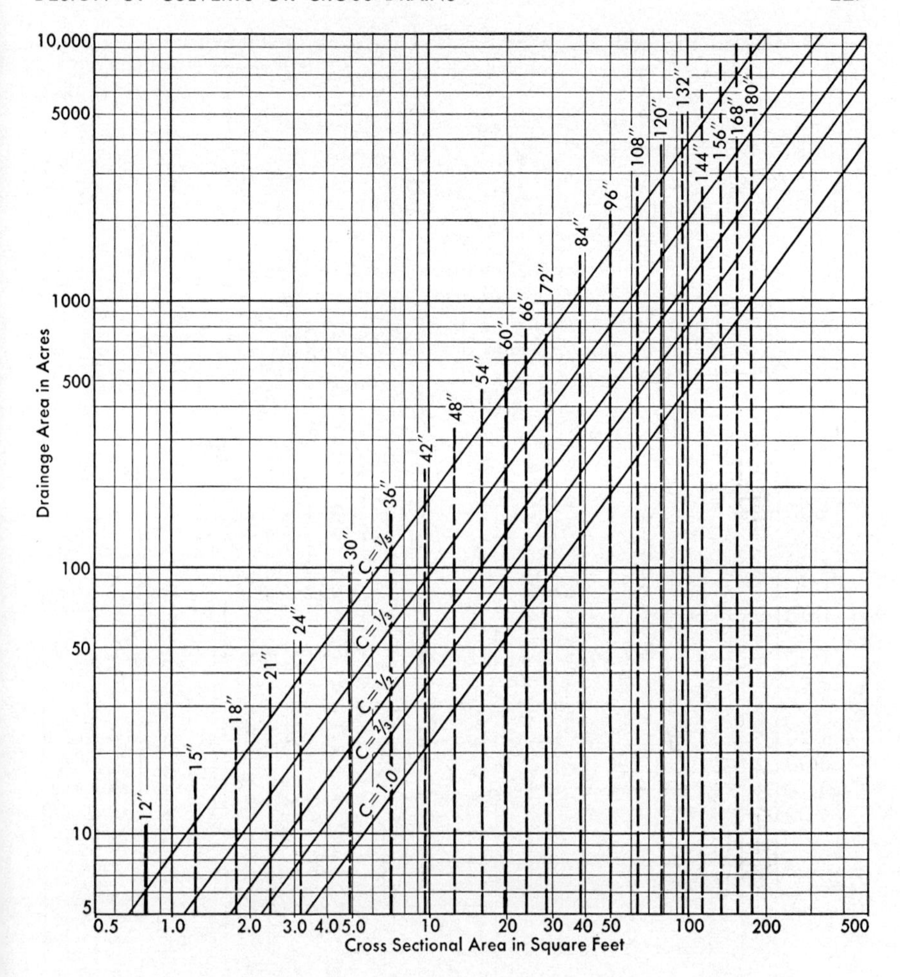

Fig. 142. Diagram for solution of Talbot formula for culvert sizes.

From Table 26-1 find the nearest waterway opening corresponding to 5.0, in this case 4.91. A 30-in. culvert is the nearest stock size.

A handy drainage calculator (slide rule) is also available for solving the Talbot formula.

Engineers have in some cases modified the factors in this formula, based on experience with it in their own section of the country.

3. *Jarvis-Myers Formula*

Dozens of other empirical formulas have been devised to fit peak flows in various parts of the country. These generally give the answer in quantity of flow expected for peak discharge. The second part of the problem then consists of designing the culvert by hydraulic methods—a size to carry the peak discharge within limits set up for headwater elevation and outlet velocity (based on formula $Q = AV$).

The Jarvis-Myers formula was based on studies in several sections of the United States and is applicable to large culverts and small bridges.

Jarvis-Myers formula: $Q = 10{,}000\ P\sqrt{M}$

in which Q = total flow in cu ft per sec
P = a coefficient, normally less than 1
M = the drainage area in sq mi

Solution for this formula is given in Fig. 143, from Water Resources Review of U. S. Geological Survey.[3] Two guide lines are shown giving percentage (100 and 50) in terms of the Jarvis-Myers formula. It is, of course, possible to plot lines of smaller percentages that will fall closer to some of the lower points.

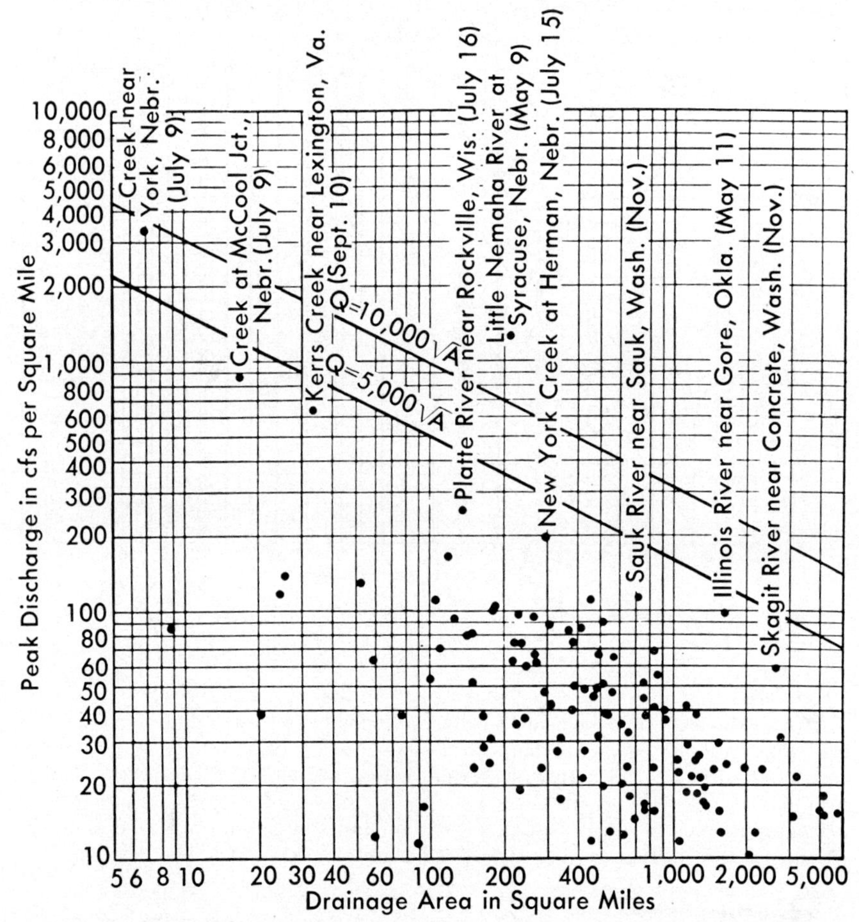

Fig. 143. Flood discharges in relation to drainage areas. Sloping guide lines give percentage in terms of Jarvis-Myers formula.—Chart from Water Resources Review of U. S. Geological Survey, 1950. Please note that the discharge values at the left are per square mile, and these must be multiplied by the drainage area in square miles.

TABLE 26-1 ACRES DRAINED BY CULVERTS OF VARIOUS DIAMETERS (Talbot Formula)

Diameter of Culvert in Inches	*Area of Waterway Opening in Sq Ft*	*Mountainous Country C=1*	*Rolling Country C=⅓*	*Level Country C=⅕*
12	.79	¾	3	6
15	1.23	1	6	11
18	1.77	2	9	18
21	2.40	3	14	28
24	3.14	5	20	39
30	4.91	8	36	71
36	7.07	14	59	115
42	9.62	20	89	175
48	12.6	29	125	250
54	16.0	40	175	345
60	19.6	55	230	455
66	23.8	70	295	585
72	28.3	85	375	735
78	33.2	105	460	910
84	38.5	130	560	1110
90	44.2	160	680	1340
96	50.3	190	800	1590
102	56.7	220	940	1860
108	63.6	250	1100	2170
114	70.9	290	1270	2510
120	78.5	340	1450	2870
126	86.6	380	1660	3270
132	95.0	430	1880	3710
138	103.9	490	2110	4180
144	113.1	550	2370	4680
150	122.7	610	2640	5210
156	132.7	680	2930	5780
162	143.1	750	3240	6400
168	153.9	820	3570	7050
174	165.1	910	3920	7740
180	176.7	990	4290	8480

Other formulas, including the rational formula (page 266) may be used for determining culvert sizes. The results may vary considerably. The engineer knows that exact results are not obtainable but that he must depend on his experience and judgment in deciding which formula and what size structure to use.

The Talbot formula gives the area of the culvert opening directly and simply and therefore has wide usage. Where other formulas are used, it is necessary to determine the size of culvert opening needed to carry the computed discharge.

TABLE 26-2 CAPACITY OF CULVERTS WITH *FREE* OUTLET
WITH WATER SURFACE AT INLET SAME ELEVATION AS TOP OF PIPE, AND OUTLET UNSUBMERGED

Values are in cubic feet per second

Slope in Per Cent	*Diameter of Pipe, in Inches*																				
	8	*10*	*12*	*15*	*18*	*21*	*24*	*30*	*36*	*42*	*48*	*54*	*60*	*66*	*72*	*78*	*84*	*90*	*96*	*108*	*120*
.1	0.2	0.4	0.6	1.3	2.1	3.3	4.7	8	12	20	25	36	47	67	85	110	130	160	190	270	330
.2	0.3	0.6	1.0	2.0	3.1	4.7	6.8	12	19	30	42	57	77	100	130	160	190	230	270	380	500
.3	0.4	0.8	1.3	2.4	3.9	5.9	8.3	15	25	37	53	72	97	120	150	190	230	280	330	450	600
.4	0.5	0.9	1.5	2.8	4.4	6.8	9.5	17	28	42	62	83	110	140	180	220	270	320	380	510	670
.5	0.6	1.0	1.7	3.0	4.9	7.5	10.	19	31	46	68	90	120	150	190	240	290	340	410	560	730
.6	0.6	1.1	1.9	3.3	5.4	8.1	11.	21	33	50	72	97	130	160	210	250	300	360	430	580	770
.8	0.8	1.2	2.1	3.7	6.1	9.0	13	23	37	55	77	100	140	180	220	270	320	390	460	620	**810**
1.0	0.8	1.4	2.3	4.0	6.5	9.6	14	24	39	57	80	**110**	140	180	**230**	**280**	**330**	**400**	**470**	**630**	810
1.2	0.8	1.5	2.4	4.3	6.8	10.	14	25	**40**	**59**	82	110	**150**	**190**	230	280	330	400	470	630	810
1.4	**0.9**	**1.6**	2.5	4.4	7.0	10	**15**	25	40	59	**83**	110	150	190	230	280	330	400	470	630	810
1.6	0.9	1.6	**2.6**	4.5	**7.1**	10	15	**26**	40	59	83	110	150	190	230	280	330	400	470	630	810
1.8	0.9	1.6	2.6	**4.6**	7.1	**11**	15	26	40	59	83	110	150	190	230	280	330	400	470	630	810
2.0	0.9	1.6	2.6	4.6	7.1	11	15	26	40	59	83	110	150	190	230	280	330	400	470	630	810
2.2	0.9	1.6	2.6	4.6	7.1	11	15	26	40	59	83	110	150	190	230	280	330	400	470	630	810
2.4	0.9	1.6	2.6	4.6	7.1	11	15	26	40	59	83	110	150	190	230	280	330	400	470	630	810

Note: The values in bold face type indicate discharge at the approximate "critical slope," when $n = .021$. Steeper slopes than "critical" do not result in increased discharge.

The "stairs" of heavy horizontal lines indicate approximate velocities of 2, 4, 6, 8 and 10 feet per second.

Free Outlet Condition

The amount of water a culvert will carry is controlled by several things: the slope of the flow line and streambed above and below, the elevation of the headwater (at inlet), the type of inlet, roughness of culvert interior, and height of the tailwater or backwater. Fig. 144.

If a culvert were the same size as the channel above and below, the design problem would be simple. However, a culvert is usually a constriction in the channel, and during flood flow the water will pond upstream from the culvert. If the culvert has a free discharge and sufficient slope, there will be a drop down of the water surface at the inlet; the velocity increases but the culvert does not run full. The minimum slope of the culvert that permits the maximum discharge of water is called the "critical slope."

For slopes less than critical, the discharge may be less for a given level of water at the culvert inlet. Slopes steeper than critical will not increase the discharge for any type of culvert, regardless of friction unless it is made to run full by some artificial means. For such cases, the discharge is limited by the amount of water that can enter the pipe.

For culverts under this free outlet condition, the required size can be determined from Table 26-2. This table assumes a pipe of any length, with the headwater or pond at the crown elevation of the pipe. It gives values of discharge for various diameters and slopes. This table, prepared under the direction of Professor S. M. Woodward, formerly of the University of Iowa, is based on the hydraulic theory of backwater and critical flow.[4]

Example: Assume that the runoff has been computed to be 40.3 cu ft per sec. Assume the slope of the streambed at this location is 1.0 per cent, and the outlet will be "free." What size pipe is required to pass this amount of water safely?

Answer: From Table 26-2 it will be seen that a 36-in. culvert will carry 39 cu ft per sec. and a 42-in. culvert will carry 57 cu ft per sec. The 42-in. size should be chosen because it gives a factor of safety over and above the required capacity.

Fig. 144. Culvert with "free outlet."

TABLE 26-3 CAPACITY OF CORRUGATED METAL PIPE WITH *SUBMERGED* OUTLET CULVERT FLOWING FULL—STRAIGHT ENDWALL ENTRANCE CULVERT LENGTH 30.6 FEET

Values are in cubic feet per second

Head on Pipe in Feet	*Diameter of Pipe*								
	12 inch	**15 inch*	*18 inch*	**21 inch*	*24 inch*	*30 inch*	**36 inch*	**42 inch*	**48 inch*
.01	0.31	.52	.79	1.13	1.54	2.57	3.92	5.60	7.62
.02	.44	.73	1.12	1.60	2.17	3.64	5.55	7.92	10.8
.03	.54	.90	1.37	1.96	2.66	4.46	6.79	9.70	13.2
.04	.62	1.04	1.58	2.26	3.07	5.15	7.84	11.2	15.2
.05	.69	1.16	1.77	2.52	3.44	5.76	8.77	12.5	17.0
.06	.76	1.27	1.94	2.77	3.76	6.30	9.61	13.7	18.7
.07	.82	1.37	2.09	2.99	4.07	6.82	10.4	14.8	20.2
.08	.88	1.47	2.24	3.19	4.35	7.28	11.1	15.8	21.5
.09	.93	1.56	2.38	3.39	4.61	7.72	11.8	16.8	22.9
.1	.98	1.64	**2.50**	**3.57**	**4.86**	**8.14**	**12.4**	**17.7**	**24.1**
.2	**1.39**	**2.32**	3.54	5.05	6.87	11.5	17.5	25.0	34.1
.3	1.70	2.84	4.33	6.18	8.42	14.1	21.5	30.7	41.8
.4	1.96	3.28	5.00	7.14	9.72	16.3	24.8	**35.4**	**48.2**
.5	2.19	3.67	5.59	7.98	10.9	**18.2**	**27.7**	39.6	53.9
.6	2.40	4.02	6.13	8.75	**11.9**	19.9	30.4	43.4	59.1
.7	2.59	4.34	**6.62**	**9.45**	12.9	21.5	32.8	46.9	63.8
.8	2.77	**4.64**	7.07	10.1	13.8	23.0	35.1	50.1	68.2
.9	2.94	4.92	7.51	10.7	14.6	24.4	37.2	53.1	**72.3**
1.0	**3.10**	5.19	7.91	11.3	15.4	25.7	**39.2**	**56.0**	76.2
1.2	3.40	5.69	8.66	12.4	16.8	**28.2**	43.0	61.3	83.5
1.4	3.67	6.14	9.36	13.4	**18.2**	30.5	46.4	66.3	90.2
1.6	3.92	6.57	10.00	**14.3**	19.4	32.6	49.6	70.8	96.4
1.8	4.16	6.96	**10.60**	15.2	20.6	34.5	52.6	75.1	102.0
2.0	4.38	**7.34**	11.20	16.0	21.7	36.4	55.5	79.2	108
2.2	**4.60**	7.70	11.74	16.8	22.8	38.2	58.2	83.1	113
2.4	4.80	8.04	12.25	17.5	23.8	39.9	60.8	86.8	118
2.6	5.00	8.37	12.81	18.2	24.8	41.7	63.0	90.3	123
2.8	5.19	8.69	13.24	18.9	25.7	43.1	65.6	93.7	128
3.0	5.37	8.99	13.70	19.6	26.6	44.6	67.9	97.0	132
3.2	5.55	9.29	14.26	20.2	27.5	46.1	70.2	100.2	136
3.4	5.72	9.57	14.60	20.8	28.4	47.5	72.3	103.5	141
3.5	5.80	9.71	14.80	21.1	28.8	48.2	73.4	105.0	143

Note: This table is based on the formula $Q = 3.10\ D^{2.31}\ H^{0.50}$ for corrugated pipe in which Q = discharge in cu ft per sec. D = diameter of pipe in ft and H = head on pipe in ft = difference in elevation of water surface at inlet and outlet ends.

*No experiments made on these sizes—Quantity computed by formula.

This capacity table is compiled from figures obtained through a series of tests made by the Bureau of Public Roads at the Hydraulic Testing Plant of the University of Iowa. Note that capacities are for 30.6-ft lengths of pipe.

The figures in bold face type are for velocities of approx. 2, 4 and 6 ft per second, reading downwards.

Fig. 145. A flared entrance and outlet on a culvert enable it to carry more water.

Submerged Outlet

In level country or other cases where the water does not have a quick get-away, as when obstructed by flood waters, the outlet of the culvert may be submerged. In this case the culvert *may* run full, and when this is true, the required size of culvert can be determined from Table 26-3.

This table is based on experiments only on the 12, 24 and 30-in. sizes, so the other values, especially in the larger sizes, are subject to error. This table is based on a length of 30.6 ft only.

Example: Assume as in the above problem that the runoff is 40.3 cu ft per sec.; the streambed at this location has a slope of 1.0 per cent; and the outlet is "submerged," with the water at the inlet just 0.4 ft higher than at the outlet.

Answer: The slope of the streambed and the culvert has no effect on the capacity of the pipe, the "head" being the controlling factor. In column 1 of Table 26-3 will be found a head of 0.4 ft. Reading to the right, we find that a 42-in. pipe has a capacity of 35.4 cu ft per sec., but a 48-in. pipe has a capacity of 48.2 cu ft per sec. The 48-in. pipe allows a factor of safety and consequently should be chosen. It will be seen that a slight variation in head gives an appreciable variation in capacity; and since the head cannot always be determined accurately in advance, it pays to be conservative and allow a sufficient factor of safety.

Effect of Inlet on Capacity

Experiments show that flared types of inlets are more efficient hydraulically than are straight headwalls, square edge entrances and entrances where the culvert projects out into the inlet pond. In other words, a flared entrance admits more water into a culvert with a free outlet and consequently increases its capacity. Fig. 145.

The actual amount of benefit from a flared entrance is variable, depending on its actual shape and conditions prevalent at this point. Various tests have been made for individual conditions, and inlet losses are usually expressed in terms of velocity head. Flared types may be as low as 0.1 of the velocity head loss, whereas projecting sharp entrances may be several times higher.

TABLE 26-4 CROSS-SECTIONAL AREAS FOR DROP-INLET CULVERTS

Watershed Area in Acres	*Cross-Sectional Area of Culvert in Square Feet*					
	Rolling Land			*Hilly Land*		
	Cultivated C = 1.0	*Pasture 0.6*	*Woods 0.3*	*Cultivated 1.4*	*Pasture 0.8*	*Woods 0.4*
1	1.9	1.1	0.6	2.7	1.5	0.8
2	2.1	1.3	0.6	2.9	1.7	0.8
4	2.5	1.5	0.8	3.5	2.0	1.0
6	2.9	1.7	0.9	4.1	2.3	1.2
8	3.4	2.0	1.0	4.8	2.7	1.4
10	3.8	2.3	1.1	5.3	3.0	1.5
15	4.8	2.9	1.4	6.7	3.8	1.9
20	5.8	3.5	1.7	8.1	4.6	2.3
30	7.8	4.7	2.3	10.9	6.2	3.1
40	9.7	5.8	2.9	13.6	7.8	3.9
50	11.5	6.9	3.5	6.1	9.2	4.6
75	15.9	9.5	4.8	22.3	12.7	6.4
100	20.0	12.0	6.0	28.0	16.0	8.0
125	23.8	14.3	7.1	33.3	19.0	9.5
150	27.3	16.4	8.2	38.2	21.9	10.9
200	33.7	20.2	10.1	47.2	27.0	13.5
250	39.4	23.6	11.8	55.2	31.5	15.8
300	44.4	26.6	13.3	62.2	35.5	17.8
350	48.9	29.3	14.7	68.5	39.1	19.6
400	53.0	31.8	15.9	74.2	42.4	21.2
500	60.0	36.0	18.0	84.0	48.0	24.0
600	65.8	39.5	19.7	92.1	52.6	26.3
700	70.8	42.5	21.2	99.1	56.6	28.3
800	75.0	45.0	22.5	105.0	60.0	30.0

From Iowa Eng. Exp. Sta. Bull. 121

Values computed by Ramser Formula, $a = c\left(130 - \frac{77{,}000}{A+600}\right)$

Where a = cross-sectional area of culvert in sq ft.

A = watershed area in acres, c = coefficient depending on nature and type of watershed.

Formula not recommended for areas larger than given in table.

Use above values for vertical drop through culvert up to 5 ft.

Multiply above values by 0.71 for drop through culvert = 10 ft.

Multiply above values by 0.58 for drop through culvert = 15 ft.

For fan or square shaped watersheds multiply above values by 1.25.

If side spillway of appreciable capacity is provided reduction of culvert area may be made accordingly.

Determining Sizes of Drop-Inlet Culverts

A large number of earth soil-saving dams have been built during the past few years as a means of conserving agricultural lands and bringing gullies under control. Many of these dams are provided with drop-inlet culverts to take care of the excess

Fig. 146. Bolting a drop inlet to 66-in. Multi-Plate pipe for soil-saving dam in Atchison County, Missouri.

TABLE 26-5 CROSS-SECTIONAL AREAS FOR VARIOUS PIPE DIAMETERS

Diameter in Inches	*Area in Sq Ft*	*Diameter in Inches*	*Area in Sq Ft*
6	0.196	84	38.5
8	0.349	90	44.2
10	0.545	96	50.3
12	0.785	102	56.7
15	1.23	108	63.6
18	1.77	114	70.9
21	2.41	120	78.5
24	3.14	126	86.6
30	4.91	132	95.0
36	7.07	138	104
42	9.62	144	113
48	12.6	150	123
54	15.9	156	133
60	19.6	162	143
66	23.8	168	154
72	28.3	174	165
78	33.2	180	177

TABLE 26-6 AREAS DRAINED BY PIPE-ARCHES
(Based on Talbot Formula)

Size in Inches		*Areas Drained in Acres*		
Span	*Rise*	*Mountainous Country* $C=1$	*Rolling Country* $C=1/3$	*Level Country* $C=1/5$
18	11	1.0	6.0	11.0
22	13	2.0	9.0	18.0
25	16	3.0	14.0	28.0
29	18	5.0	20.0	39.0
36	22	8.0	36.0	71.0
43	27	14.0	59.0	116.0
50	31	20.0	89.0	175.0
58	36	29.0	126.0	250.0
65	40	40.0	174.0	345.0
72	44	53.0	229.0	453.0

runoff and prevent washout of the dams (see Fig. 146). It also frequently happens that highway and railway culverts are so situated that drop inlets may be placed on them (either new construction or existing culverts) without subjecting the embankment to undue hazard and with great benefit to erosion control. A minimum clearance of at least 4 ft between the top of the embankment and the maximum water elevation at the inlet must be assured before the embankment can be considered adequately protected.

Wherever this condition prevails, the size of pipe to use can be determined from Tables 26-4 and 26-5.

To illustrate the use of these tables, assume that a dam with a culvert having an inlet drop of 12 ft of corrugated pipe is to serve an ordinary watershed of 25 acres of rolling cultivated land. Interpolating between 5.8 sq ft for 20 acres and 7.8 sq ft for 30 acres, 6.8 sq ft is obtained. Interpolating likewise between a multiplying factor of 0.71 for a 10-ft drop and 0.58 for a 15-ft drop, 0.66 times 6.8 gives 4.491 sq ft as the proper cross-sectional area. The nearest commercial size from Table 26-5 is a 30-in. pipe with an area of 4.91 sq ft. Therefore, a 30-in. culvert should be used for the conditions assumed.

Sizes of Pipes, Arches and Pipe-Arches

When the peak flood discharge has been computed or estimated for the desired frequency of once every 10, 25, 50 or 100 years, the design engineer must select the type of drainage opening he wishes to use.

The accompanying tables, Nos. 26-5, 26-6, 26-7 and others in Chapter 8, give the dimensions and end areas of standard size corrugated metal pipes, arches and pipe-arches of riveted and structural plate construction.

Culvert vs. Small Bridge

From the foregoing tables, it is seen that pipe culverts now range up to 15 ft in diameter, pipe-arches in spans up to 16 ft 7 in. and arches up to 30 ft. In single or

TABLE 26-7 DIMENSIONS AND END AREAS OF MULTI-PLATE PIPE-ARCHES

Nominal Dimensions				*Layout Dimensions—in Inches*†				
Span	*Rise*	*End Area in Sq Ft*	*Total Periphery in Pi Inches*	*B*	*Rise*	*½ Span*	*R*	*R′*
6′-1″	4′-7″	22	66	21.0	55.0	36.5	36.8	76.3
6′-4″	4′-9″	24	69	20.5	57.1	38.0	38.1	98.6
6′-9″	4′-11″	26	72	22.0	58.9	40.6	41.0	83.5
7′-0″	5′-1″	28	75	21.4	61.1	42.1	42.3	104.2
7′-3″	5′-3″	31	78	20.8	63.2	43.5	43.5	136.2
7′-8″	5′-5″	33	81	22.4	65.0	46.2	46.5	109.8
7′-11″	5′-7″	35	84	21.7	67.2	47.6	47.7	137.9
8′-2″	5′-9″	38	87	20.9	69.4	48.9	48.9	182.9
8′-7″	5′-11″	40	90	22.7	71.1	51.7	51.9	141.0
8′-10″	6′-1″	43	93	21.9	73.3	53.0	53.0	178.7
9′-4″	6′-3″	46	96	23.8	75.1	55.9	56.2	144.6
9′-6″	6′-5″	49	99	22.9	77.3	57.1	57.3	177.5
9′-9″	6′-7″	52	102	21.9	79.5	58.3	58.3	227.7
10′-3″	6′-9″	55	105	24.0	81.2	61.3	61.5	178.3
10′-8″	6′-11″	58	108	26.1	82.9	64.2	64.9	153.2
10′-11″	7′-1″	61	111	25.1	85.1	65.5	65.9	180.4
11′-5″	7′-3″	64	114	27.4	86.9	68.4	69.4	157.9
11′-7″	7′-5″	67	117	26.3	89.1	69.7	70.2	183.2
11′-10″	7′-7″	71	120	25.2	91.3	70.9	71.1	216.4
12′-4″	7′-9″	74	123	27.5	93.0	73.9	74.7	186.5
12′-6″	7′-11″	78	126	26.4	95.2	75.1	75.5	216.8
12′-8″	8′-1″	81	129	25.2	97.4	76.2	76.4	257.4
12′-10″	8′-4″	85	132	24.0	99.7	77.2	77.3	314.7
13′-5″	8′-5″	89	135	26.4	101.3	80.4	80.7	254.8
13′-11″	8′-7″	93	138	28.9	103.0	83.6	84.4	220.7
14′-1″	8′-9″	97	141	27.6	105.2	84.7	85.1	254.1
14′-3″	8′-11″	101	144	26.3	107.5	85.7	85.9	297.6
14′-10″	9′-1″	105	147	28.9	109.2	88.9	89.6	254.3
15′-4″	9′-3″	109	150	31.6	110.8	92.0	93.4	226.8
15′-6″	9′-5″	113	153	30.2	113.1	93.2	94.0	255.7
15′-8″	9′-7″	118	156	28.8	115.3	94.2	94.7	291.5
15′-10″	9′-10″	122	159	27.5	117.6	95.2	95.5	338.1
16′-5″	9′-11″	126	162	30.1	119.2	98.5	99.2	290.9
16′-7″	10′-1″	131	165	28.7	121.5	99.5	99.9	332.7

Dimensions are to inside crests and are subject to manufacturing tolerances.

*These structures are preferred because they give greatest area for given number of plates and bolts per ring. Each structure of less span than those marked provides correspondingly less area for the same number of plates and bolts.

†See Fig. 66, page 83.

multiple units, these give waterways equivalent to those of small bridges. When should the designer use a culvert and when a bridge?

A culvert is recognized as having advantages such as simple foundations, ease of installation with less interference to traffic, less maintenance, no fire hazard, wider safer roadway at lower cost, and ease of extending to widen the roadway. Furthermore, under normal fill heights it is possible to increase live load, whereas for bridges such is not the case.

Waterway capacity should be a principal factor in choosing between a culvert and a bridge. If the roadway level is sufficiently high and the channel wide enough to permit the use of one or more culvert openings without causing water to back up and to flood valuable property, then a culvert may be the answer. This assumes, too, that if driftwood or floating ice is expected, there will either be sufficient clear waterway to permit it to pass, or some way be found to avert any serious damming up behind the embankment.

Single vs. Multiple Opening

A single culvert opening is in general the most satisfactory. However, in many cases the greater portion of the waterway area should be kept near the invert elevation in order to get the water through quickly without undue ponding or flooding of the land upstream. In such cases, the solution may consist of using either a low wide culvert such as an arch or pipe-arch, or using a battery of two or more openings, or both. Fig. 147.

Bridge Replacements

Because of the lower cost and other advantages of corrugated metal pipe culverts,

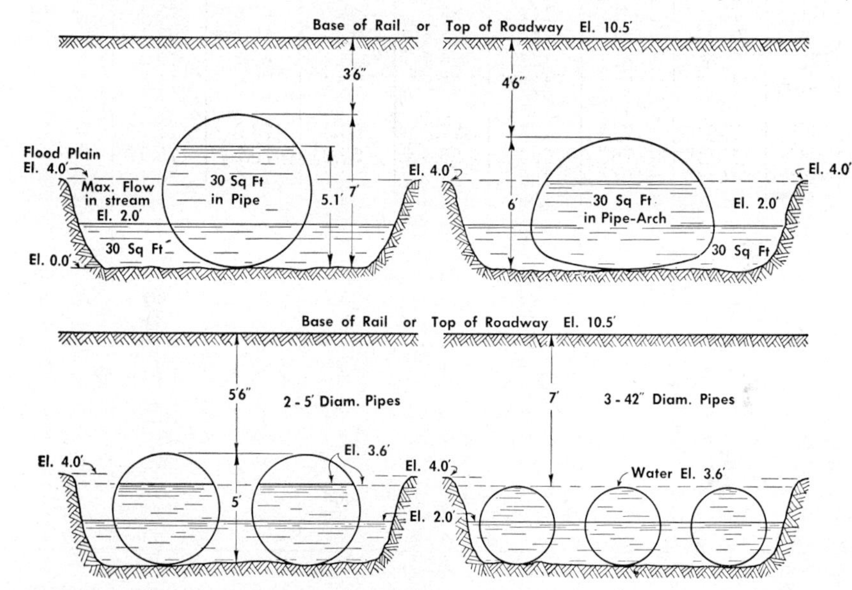

Fig. 147. Diagrams showing four possible choices of a culvert opening. For the assumed conditions, a single large pipe will cause the water to back up and flood the adjacent land. A twin or triple opening, while less efficient hydraulically, offers the best solution.—*From Railway Engineering & Maintenance*, 1952.

Fig. 148. Replacing a timber trestle on a branch of the S. P. & S. Ry. in Oregon with a 130-ft high embankment over an 84-in. Multi-Plate pipe, 456 ft long.

many road departments[5] and railroads[6] are using them to replace inadequate and obsolete bridges. However, before reducing the size of any waterway, a careful survey should be made.[7]

It is well known that some of the earlier bridges were made oversize either because of lack of information or engineering supervision, or because it was cheaper to build a bridge across a ravine or stream than to make a fill. Now it generally costs less to build a culvert and fill (see Fig. 148).

REFERENCES

1. Highway Research Board Report No. 11-B, 1950, Carl F. Izzard.
2. "Hydraulic Treatise," Ohio Dept. of Highways, 1947, p. 9.
3. "Jarvis-Myers Formula Recommended for Bridge Waterway Areas," by F. B. Marsh, in *Civil Engineering*, Feb. 1951, Vol. 97, p. 47.

4. "Hydraulics of the Miami River Flood Control Project (Ohio)," Technical Report, Part 7, p. 147.
5. "Replacement of Old, Long Bridges with Culverts," *Better Roads Magazine Forum*, Chicago, March and April 1952.
6. "SP&S (Spokane, Portland & Seattle Ry.) Rebuilds with Cuts and Fills," *Modern Railroads*, Chicago, March 1952.
7. "Use of Stream-flow Records in Design of Bridge Waterways," by Tate Dalrymple, U. S. Geological Survey, in Proceedings of 26th Annual Meeting of the Highway Research Board, Dec. 1946, pp. 163–179.

CHAPTER TWENTY-SEVEN

Culvert Location and Length

Principles of Culvert Location

Culvert location means alignment and grade with respect to both roadway and stream. Proper location is important because it affects the adequacy of the opening, maintenance of the culvert, and possible washout of the roadway. Although every culvert installation is a separate problem, a few principles are explained here to apply in a majority of cases.

A culvert is an enclosed channel serving as a continuation of and a substitute for an open stream wherever that stream meets an artificial barrier such as a roadway embankment or a levee. It is necessary to give consideration to abutting property both as to ponding upstream and to safe velocities to avoid undue scour or silting downstream.

An open stream is not always stable. It may be changing its channel—straightening itself in some places, and becoming more crooked in others. It may be scouring itself deeper in some places, silting in others. Change of land use upstream by clearing, deforestation or real estate development may change both the stability and the flood flow of a stream.

Because a culvert is a *fixed* line in a stream, judgment is necessary in properly locating the structure. Some principles are discussed here. Fig. 149.

Fig. 149. Locating a culvert in mountainous country requires good judgment. Here a 10-ft diameter Multi-Plate pipe, 266 ft long, is skewed and placed on a steep slope before covering it with 50 ft of fill on California Highway 49.

CULVERT ALIGNMENT

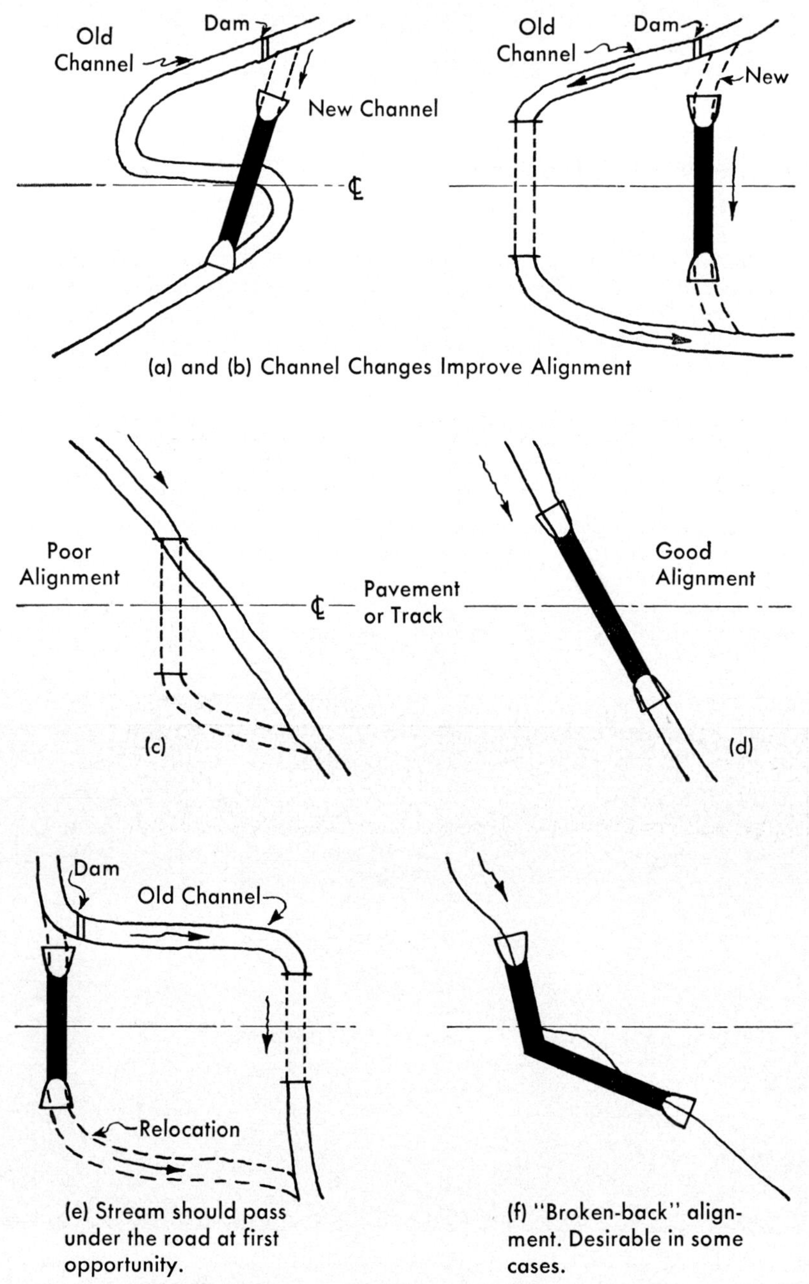

Fig. 150. Various methods of securing correct culvert alignment.

Alignment

The *first* principle of culvert location is to give the stream a direct entrance and a direct exit. Any abrupt change in direction at either end will retard the flow and make a larger structure necessary.

A direct inlet and outlet, if not already existent, can be obtained in one of three ways—by means of a channel change, a skewed alignment, or both. The cost of a channel change may be partly offset by a saving in culvert length or decrease in size. A skewed alignment requires a greater length of culvert but is usually justified by improving the hydraulic condition and the safety of the roadbed.

For correct fabrication of corrugated metal drainage structures with cut ends, it is necessary to specify the *direction* as well as the *angle* of the skew, particularly for Paved-Invert pipe, Multi-Plate pipe with heavier gage bottom plates, and Multi-Plate arches and pipe-arches.

The *second* principle of culvert location is to use reasonable precautions to prevent the stream from changing its course near the ends of the culvert. Otherwise the culvert may become inadequate, cause excessive ponding, and possibly wash out or require expensive maintenance of the roadway. Riprap, sod, paving or metal end sections will help protect the banks from eroding and changing the channel.

Culvert alignment may also be influenced by choice of a grade line. Methods of selecting proper alignment are illustrated in Fig. 150.

Fig. 151. Pipe spillway drops the water safely on a 168-in. Multi-Plate pipe culvert under a railroad in Iowa.

Grade

The ideal grade line for a culvert is one that produces neither silting nor excessive velocities and scour, one that gives the shortest length and one that makes replacement simplest.

Velocities as great as 10 ft per second cause destructive scour downstream and to the culvert structure itself unless protected. Safe streambed velocities are given in Table 24-2, page 210. The silt carrying capacity of a stream varies as the square of the velocity.

The capacity of a culvert with a free outlet (not submerged) (page 231) is not increased by placing on a slope steeper than the "critical slope." (About 1 per cent for a 96-in. pipe.) The capacity is controlled by the amount of water that can get into the inlet. On the other hand, the capacity of a pipe on a very slight gradient and with a *submerged* outlet is influenced by the head (difference in elevation of water surface at both ends). In this case, the roughness of the culvert interior, in addition to the velocity head and entrance loss, is a factor.

A slope of 1 to 2 per cent is advisable to give a gradient equal to or greater than the critical slope, provided the velocity is permissible. In general, a minimum slope of 0.5 ft in 100 ft is recommended to avoid sedimentation.

Ordinary practice is to make the grade line coincide with the existing streambed. However, deviation is permissible if for a good purpose, as follows:

1. In *freshly graded areas*, on relatively flat gradients, expect sedimentation to occur. Set the culvert invert several inches higher than the streambed, but on the same slope (see Fig. 152-b).
2. Where *headroom is limited*, setting a culvert below streambed grade is likely to result in sedimentation and reduced waterway area. Either use a low, wide culvert such as a pipe-arch or raise the road grade.
3. Under *high fills*, anticipate greater settlement of the culvert under the center than at the sides of the fill. Give the culvert *camber* by laying the upstream half nearly level and putting all the fall in the downstream half.
4. Under *high fills*, it may not be necessary to place the culvert at streambed level. If some ponding is permissible, the culvert can sometimes be placed in firm ground at a higher level, thus reducing the length and simplifying replacement, should that ever be necessary.
5. In *steeply sloping areas*, as on hillsides, it is not always necessary to place the culvert on the same steep grade. The culvert can be put on the "critical" slope and then a spillway or cutoff wall provided at the outlet to prevent undermining. This keeps the culvert shorter and under shallower cover.
6. On *steep slopes*, it is also possible to use a broken-back grade line under the fill, although this is less desirable. See Figs. 151, 152-f and 152-g. Or a drop inlet or catchbasin will help give the culvert a suitable slope.

Remember the ideal grade line avoids silting and also avoids high velocities and scour. (See Chapter 45 on Soil Conservation including riprap, end sections, ditch checks, spillways and other means of controlling scour.)

Culvert Length

The required length of a culvert depends on the width of the roadway or roadbed, the height of fill, the slope of the embankment, the slope and skew of the culvert, and the type of end finish such as end section, headwall, beveled end, drop inlet or spillway.

CULVERT GRADES

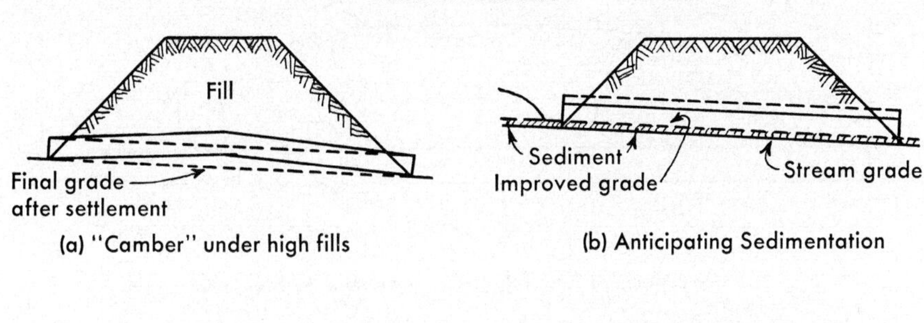

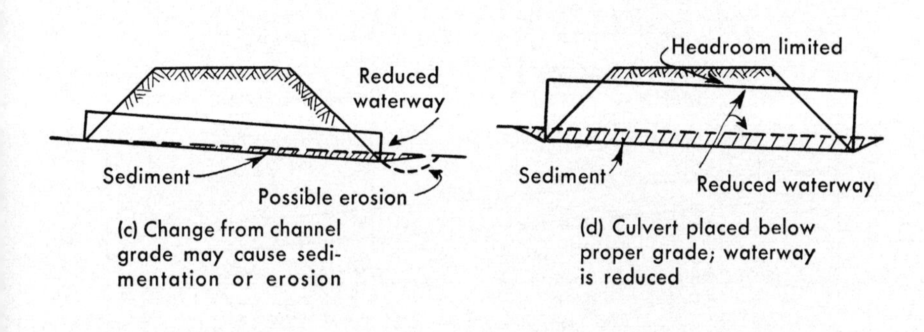

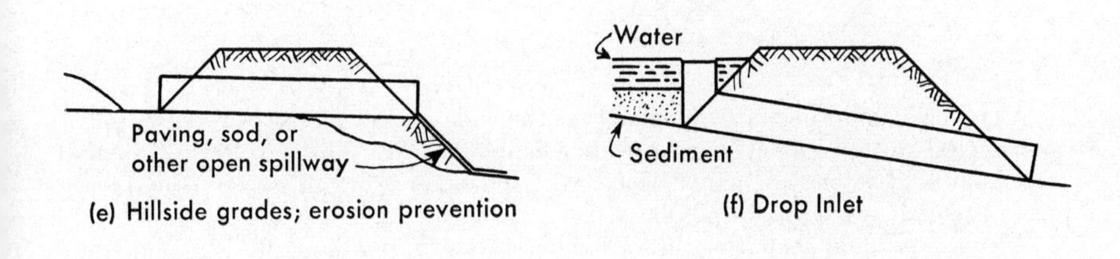

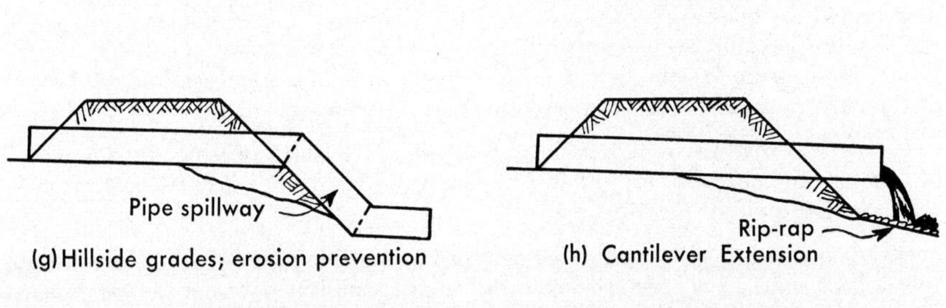

Fig. 152. Proper culvert grades to fit each condition are essential to the safe functioning of any culvert.

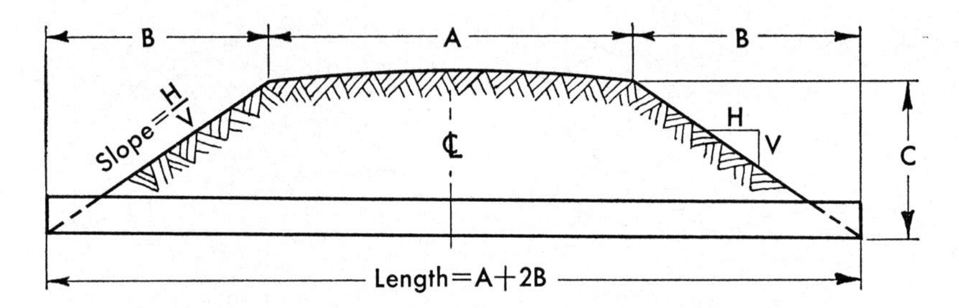

Fig. 153. Computation of culvert length when the flow line is on a *flat* grade.

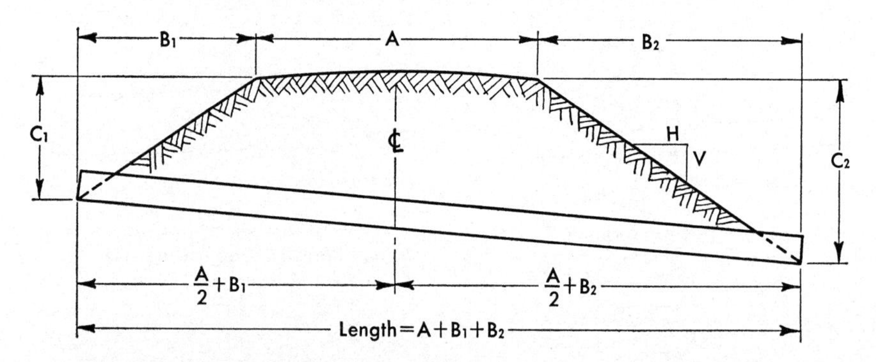

Fig. 154. Computation of culvert length with flow line on a *steep* grade.

A culvert should be amply long so that the ends are not clogged up by sediment or covered over by a settling, spreading embankment. This results in impaired efficiency and increased maintenance. On the other hand, a culvert should not have the ends wastefully exposed.

A cross-sectional sketch of the embankment and a profile of the streambed are perhaps the best means of determining the length of culvert needed. In the absence of such a sketch, the length of a simple culvert under an embankment can be determined as follows: To the width of the roadway (and shoulders), add twice the slope ratio times the height of fill at the center of the road. The height of fill should be measured to the flow line if headwalls are not to be used, and to the top of the culvert if headwalls or end sections are to be installed.

Example: A roadway is 40 ft wide on top, two to one side slopes, and at the center of the road the height of fill to flow line is 7 ft. $40 + (4 \times 7) = 68$ ft length at flow line. See example in Fig. 153.

If the culvert is on a slope of 5 per cent or more, it may be advisable to compute the sloped length. Fig. 154. However, fill slopes usually vary from the established grade stakes so that any refinement in computing culvert length may not be necessary.

Beveled Ends

A common practice on large culverts is to bevel the ends. This may be a full height bevel or a partial bevel. Recommended bevels for Multi-Plate structures may be obtained from the manufacturer. Fig. 155.

When the culvert gradient is more than about 5 per cent, it is advisable to take this into consideration in determining the required bevel for each end. Otherwise the resulting appearance may be unsatisfactory.

Skew Angles

Where a culvert crosses the roadway at other than a right angle, the skewed length should be computed. (Multiply the normal length by the cosecant of the skew angle).

The ends of the structure may be cut to make them parallel to the center line of the road. For correct fabrication of corrugated metal culverts it is essential to specify the *direction* of flow as well as the *angle* of the skew. This is particularly true for pipes and pipe-arches with the invert paved, for structural plate pipe with heavier plates in the invert, for structural plate pipe-arches and for arches.

Where the ends of a culvert are cut for both skew and bevel (known as "skew-bevels"), the manufacturer should be consulted as to strength limitations and for other details so that a satisfactory installation will result. On such skew bevels it is customary to secure the unsupported sections by means of hook bolts imbedded in headwalls or grouted riprap.

Fig. 155. Beveled ends on a quadruple 150-in. diameter Multi-Plate culvert will fit the slope of the fill on New Mexico State Highway 180 at Warm Springs Creek, N. Mex.

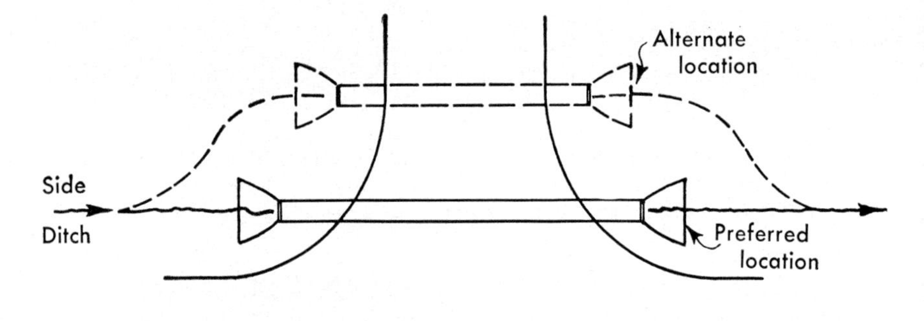

Fig. 156. Entrance culverts should be long enough to allow a good turning radius and preferably continue the straight alignment of the ditch.

Special Problems

Side road culverts and culverts at farm entrances and in residential areas where side ditches serve instead of curb and gutters, should be placed in the nominal ditch line. They should be amply long to permit an easy turn onto or off the main road. In many locations where the quantity and velocity of water is small, the culvert may be set back from the ditch line and a shorter length be used (see Fig. 156).

Where good appearance is essential or where a side ditch is hazardous, enclosing the entire ditch in a pipe may cost but little more and be much more satisfactory than a short culvert or intermittent culverts.

Equalizer culverts are sometimes installed in low places where there is no channel for the water, but where it is desirable to have the backwater at equal elevations

Fig. 157. A paved dry ford with battery of four 36-in. pipes to carry ordinary flow on Scenic Drive, Davis Mountains, Texas.

on both sides of the fill. For this purpose the culvert can be placed at right angles across the road and with a level grade.

Relief culverts. On sidehill roads or wherever a road intercepts surface water, it is well to drain the water to the lower side and, if possible, away from the road before it can cause damage. Such relief culverts should generally be placed obliquely across the roadway to give the water more effective inlet and outlet. On long grades, storm sewers may be necessary to prevent overloading of the ditch.

Siphons (inverted) are used to conduct irrigation water under a road where there is insufficient clearance for a culvert. Siphons must be watertight and can be made so by proper fabrication and joints.

Paved Fords. On light-traffic roads and where overflow is infrequent, it is possible to economize on bridges and large culverts by permitting the flood waters to pass directly over a depression in the road. A single or multiple pipe or pipe-arch culvert will handle all water except occasional flood flows. To prevent washout the embankment must be paved (Fig. 157), or the roadway protected by means of sheeting or buried steel bin-walls.

CHAPTER TWENTY-EIGHT

Highway Surface Drainage

General Considerations. In the construction of a highway, *drainage* is one of the most essential elements to be considered. Three problems are involved: (1) disposal of surface water from the roadway section, (2) spanning of streams or man-made drainage channels and (3) elimination or control of subsurface water.

Surface water on a highway creates a hazard to driving, which is aggravated if freezing occurs. It also causes erosion and expensive maintenance. It may seep into the subgrade, thereby robbing the roadway surface and shoulders of their support.

Location Considerations. Early roads generally followed the ridges, the contours, or the valleys, with stream crossings and mountain passes as the control points. With heavier traffic came the need for straighter alignment, smoother grades and wider roadbeds. This requires deeper cuts, higher fills. This also exposes greater areas where direct precipitation must be handled (see Fig. 158).

Fig. 158. Surface drainage of New York State Thruway near Syracuse, N.Y. Each two-lane roadway measures 25 ft and is flanked by a 10-ft stabilized shoulder. Center mall is depressed.—Fairchild Aerial Photo.

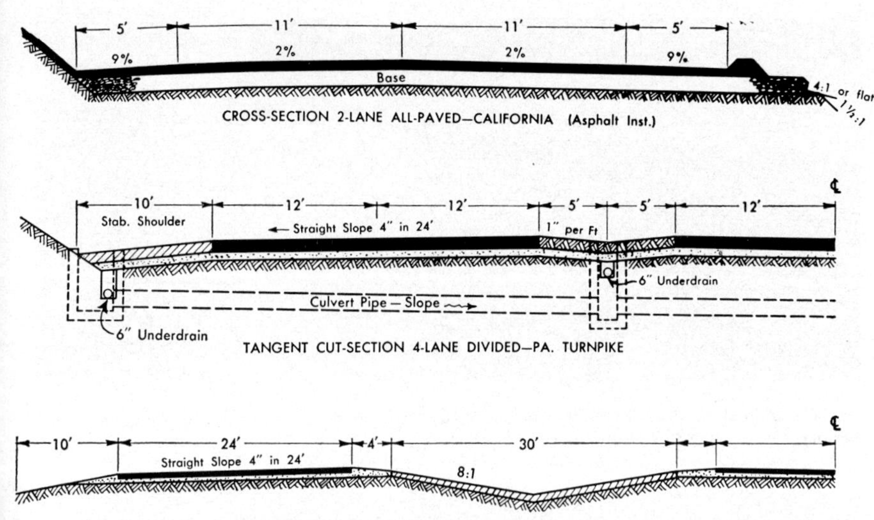

Fig. 159. Typical cross-section of modern primary highways showing how surface drainage is handled by crowning and sloping.

The locating engineer and the designer should know what effect their work has on the adjoining land. Present stream channels cannot be blocked to flood upstream property, nor should runoff erode bordering land. Natural stream courses should be altered as little as possible unless to improve conditions.

Cross-Section of Roadway. A standard roadway cross-section reveals several phases of controlling surface water (see Fig. 159). In a cut section, the road surface is first "insulated" from water that falls on adjacent areas by means of a ditch section. This may be supplemented by an intercepting ditch or subdrain at some point on or behind the backslope, but only if surface runoff is excessive.

For excessive flow against a fill section, an intercepting ditch, sod, revetment, sheeting or a retaining wall will resist direct erosion (see Chapter 45 on Erosion Control).

Crown. Sloping the roadway to the side will shed the water from the path of traffic. For earth and low-type surfaces, the crown recommended is about ½ in. per ft of width of roadway; on high-type pavements, as little as ⅛ in. per ft. Shoulders should generally slope not more than 1 in. per ft. A common mistake is to have the outer edge of the shoulder *higher* than the pavement edge.

A minimum longitudinal grade line of 0.5 per cent is desirable to provide adequate drainage lengthwise of the roadway. Steeper grades may be required in the ditch.

Side Slopes. Rain or melting snow drained to the edge of the road surface will ordinarily flow over the shoulder in a broad sheet or series of rivulets and down the side slope to a side ditch or the natural ground. Side slopes vary from 4 to 1 on shallow fills to as steep as 1½ to 1 on high fills. Vegetation or some form of erosion resistant material is desirable.

Fig. 160. California state highway with bituminous berm to divert water into a corrugated pipe spillway down a long side slope.

Shallow Gutters. Where shoulders or side slopes are easily eroded, an intercepting curb and gutter may be built beyond the edge of the pavement, preferably near the outer edge of the shoulder so as not to restrict traffic. Fig. 160 shows a type of paved gutter used extensively on state highways in California.

Curbs and gutters are also used where side ditches are considered hazardous or undesirable as in built-up areas, along parkways and on express highways. They should be far enough from the traffic lane so vehicles need not travel in a trough of water. Lip curbs built to a height of 2 or 3 in. along the pavement edge to prevent shoulder erosion were once popular but because of the hazard are no longer recommended.

The design of gutters for capacity is the same as for triangular ditches on page 207. Usually the water should be outletted down the embankment or into storm sewers at frequent intervals. Gutters and curbs may both be built of bituminous paving material, concrete, stones set in grout, or other erosion-resistant materials.

Median Strips. On dual-lane or divided highways, the median strip, grassed mall or island, may vary from a few feet to several hundred feet. Thirty to 40 ft is common, depending on whether right angle or U-turns are permitted. The latest practice in most states is to depress the median strip if it exceeds about 20 ft in width. See typical cross-section, Fig. 159.

Depressing the median strip aids surface drainage, serves as a storage space for plowed snow, and tends to keep melting snow and ice off the pavement.

Large Paved Areas. At wide intersections, rotaries, interchange approaches, airport runways and aprons, and large parking areas, surface water should be removed by crowning or warping the surface to conduct the water to low areas or to the edges where various types of inlets or gratings will transfer the water to a storm sewer system. Gratings must be large enough to handle all of the water promptly and to allow the sewer to utilize its full capacity.

Bridge Surfaces. On bridges or overpasses more than 100 ft in length the surface water conducted to the edges of the roadway should pass through grates in the gutter at intervals of 50 ft or at each bent or pier, discharging either into the air or into downspouts. Fig. 161.

Fig. 161. Surface water from high-level bridge between Toronto and Oshawa, Ontario, is removed by downspouts of 6-in. spiral welded steel pipe.

For railroad bridges, see page 342 on Deck Drains.

Side Ditches. Side ditches along a roadway serve to intercept surface water from the roadway—pavement, shoulder and side slope. In a cut section they also intercept flow from the backslope. In snow country, the side ditch provides storage space for snow. Side ditches are of limited value in lowering the water table under a roadway.

Where side ditches are objectionable or unsafe, it may be desirable to use a gutter, a stream enclosure or a storm drain.

Ditches are usually V-shaped or trapezoidal. The V-ditch can be made and maintained with a blade grader, and while this may be satisfactory for secondary or unimportant roads, proper erosion prevention measures and grassing of the ditch bottom should make this blading unnecessary. The trapezoidal ditch is a more natural shape and has greater capacity.

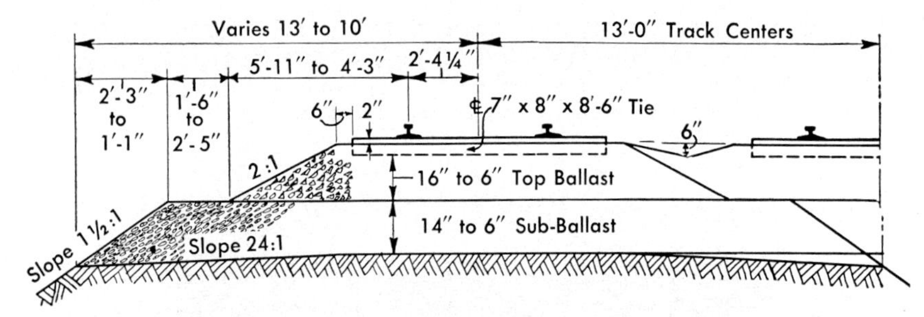

BALLAST SECTION

Fig. 162. Drainage of surface water on a railroad track is accomplished by crowning and sloping the various surfaces. Typical ballast section for single or double track on tangent. After AREA Manual.

CHAPTER TWENTY-NINE

Railway Surface Drainage

General Considerations

Drainage is recognized as a major factor in the economical maintenance and operation of a modern, high speed railroad.* The problem is threefold: (1) prompt removal of surface water from roadway tracks, yards and terminals, (2) diverting water from adjacent areas or crossing property with culverts, stream enclosures and storm drains and (3) removing ground water with subdrains in order to keep roadbed and yards in stable condition for minimum maintenance. (Part 3 is discussed under Railway Subdrainage, page 323.)

"It may be said, therefore, that a fundamental principle of railroad location, construction and maintenance is to keep the roadbed dry."*

Cross-Section of Roadway

The cross-section of a railroad roadbed is designed to give prompt and proper removal of the rain or other precipitation. Fig. 162. Water falling on the ballast is intended to filter through to the *crowned* earth subgrade and then laterally to either side of the roadbed. If the ballast is foul, or if the ballast has been pounded into the subgrade, the water may not escape but remain in the roadbed and make it unstable, as discussed in the section on Subdrainage.

In multiple track areas, including yards and terminals, surface water should be caught in shallow gutters and ditches and led to catchbasins and into culverts or storm drains. Surface water should, insofar as possible, be prevented from soaking into the subgrade. Figs. 163-164.

At least a part of the rain and melting snow which drains to the edge of the roadbed or berm will ordinarily flow down the side slope to the side ditch or natural ground. The remainder may be absorbed by the roadbed.

*AREA Manual, Committee 1, Roadway, Sec. V Roadway Drainage.

Intercepting Ditches

In a cut section, the roadbed is "insulated" or protected from water that falls on adjacent areas by means of a side ditch at the bottom of the cut or by an intercepting or diversion ditch at the top of the slope or by an intermediate berm. A fill section may also need protection from flow against the base by an intercepting ditch. Such ditches should be deflected away from the roadway to prevent erosion.

Ditches in long cut sections should be made wider to reduce both erosion and maintenance. The alternative is to protect the ditch with riprap or paving. Wide ditches require less frequent cleaning, besides serving to store snow removed from the track.

A method of computing required ditch sizes is given on page 206. For erosion control, see pages 361–367.

Much helpful information on drainage and related matters is given in the American Railway Engineering Association Manual, 1953 Edition, Chapter 1: Part 1, roadway cross section, roadway protection, roadway drainage; Part 3, natural waterways, erosion prevention; and Part 4, culverts.

Fig. 163. Well drained railway track (left) in cut flanked by metal retaining walls.
Fig. 164. Risers and catchbasins for interrupting surface water between tracks and in side ditches.

CHAPTER THIRTY

Culverts Under Levees and Dikes

General Considerations

Levees and dikes are built mainly to keep floodwaters and tides from inundating agricultural lands. Floodwalls serve the same purpose in urban areas.

In flood time, levees are like dams in that they are subject to extreme horizontal and vertical pressures, plus erosion due to currents and wind-wave action. However, unlike a dam for which special foundation and seepage cutoff walls are provided, an agricultural levee is usually built without these precautions and often on soils subject to settlement.

The precautions to be taken then in building a culvert under a levee include: (1) providing a reasonably satisfactory foundation, (2) giving the structure "camber," (3) watertight connections, (4) diaphragms or cutoff walls, (4) protection of the ends against erosion and (5) control of surface drainage and backwater through the culvert by means of a valve or gate. (See Chapter 46 on Flood Control).

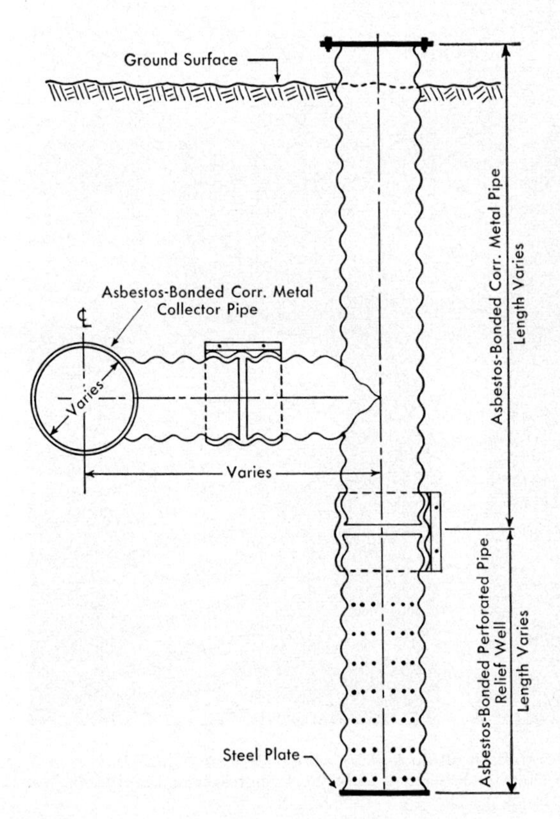

Fig. 165. Vertical section of relief well and collector pipe as used on river levees.

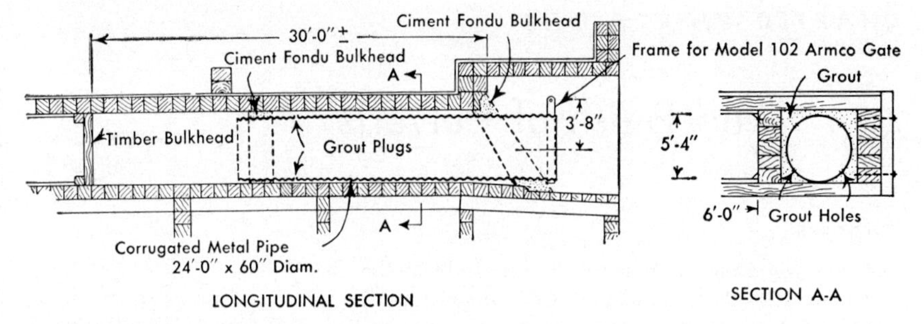

Fig. 166. Lining a triple timber box under a railroad dike in Nova Scotia with 60-in. Asbestos-Bonded corrugated metal pipe, equipped with Armco Model 102 gates. Ciment Fondu is a quick-setting cement—Courtesy *Railway Track & Structures.*

Culvert Design

The *size* of a culvert under a levee is determined just as for any other location, (see pages 224–240) based on peak flood flow for a frequency of once in twenty-five or fifty years. This is based on the assumption that this flow can pass through the culvert unhindered by high water on the outside of the levee.

When the water is higher on the outside than behind the levee, the storm water or natural flow is impounded. For sewage, pumping may have to be resorted to.

Fabrication of pipe for levee purposes generally includes shop strutting, the use of watertight joints, diaphragms, flap and slide headgates, and end sections or headwalls. Fig. 165.

The use of perforated vertical drains and toe drains to relieve ground water pressure back of levees and dams is quite common.

Pipe Under Dams

The capacity of outlet structures on dams depends partly on the purpose of the dam.[1] Many are built for impounding water in reservoirs or small farm ponds. The outlet of a farm pond may consist of only a 1½ to 2-in. galvanized water pipe for stock water purposes. However, a well designed dam should have both a mechanical and auxiliary spillway.[2] See pages 369–370.

The mechanical spillway of farm ponds and on soil conservation dams may be constructed of corrugated metal pipe designed to carry the runoff from the normal inflow of water. The auxiliary or grassed spillway carries the overflow from severe storms.

REFERENCES

1. "Low Dams," Natural Resources Committee, Washington, D. C., U. S. Government Printing Office, 1938.
2. "Build a Farm Pond for Pleasure and Profit," by Armco Drainage & Metal Products, Inc., Middletown, Ohio.

CHAPTER THIRTY-ONE

End Finish of Culverts

Purposes

There is a wide difference of opinion about the need for end finish on culverts and about the design and materials to use for that purpose. As a result the end treatment may vary from an ornate retaining wall to riprapping of the embankment slopes. End treatment may be essential or it may be added for appearances' sake only.

Among the principal needs are: (1) preventing scour and undermining, (2) preventing seepage and burrowing of animals, (3) retaining the fill, (4) anchorage for short-sectional pipe, (5) hydraulic efficiency and (6) appearance.

Preventing Scour and Undermining

Occasionally it is necessary to protect the toe of a fill against an onrush of water. Treatment may consist of a headwall although paving the slope, riprapping or sodding may be effective against erosion over a larger area.

Moreoften, the *outlet* end of a culvert is subject to scour and undermining. On steep grades, a pipe spillway, flume or apron may conduct the water to a point where scour or undermining cannot endanger the culvert or the fill. Fig. 167. See

Fig. 167. Badly eroded side slopes on an eastern turnpike are now protected by corrugated pipe spillways connected with curb inlets and culvert outlets. Flared metal end sections help to retard the velocity of the water.

Fig. 168. Heavy, uneconomical anchorage for a sectional-pipe culvert.

Chapter 27 on Culvert Location. The use of a cutoff wall at the outlet end will give added protection against undermining.

Preventing Seepage and Burrowing

Porous, granular fills around a culvert may encourage seepage unless sealed off at the upstream end by means of clay or other impervious material. A small headwall or curtain wall also helps prevent seepage.

Where small animals burrow along the barrel of a culvert, the chances for a washout can be reduced by the use of a headwall or by diaphragms at intermediate points along the barrel. See Fig. 165.

Retaining the Fill

Ordinarily, lengthening a culvert is more economical than building a big headwall or retaining wall. On the other hand, there are cases where it is impossible to procure sufficient right of way or where physical conditions make it inadvisable to extend the culvert to the toe of the fill.

For these and other special cases, a retaining type of headwall of steel or concrete may be the answer.

Anchorage for Sectional Pipe

Short-sectional pipe does not have positive protection against pulling apart at the joints. As a result, progressive undermining of the end sections may occur as well as honeycombing of the fill at any intermediate joints which have pulled apart. The use of heavy headwalls tends to prevent such disjointing. Fig. 168.

When heavy headwalls are used, they should be on suitable foundations. Otherwise unequal settlement of barrel and headwall may result in damage to either or both.

Improved Hydraulics

The carrying capacity of a culvert can be increased by making it easier for the water to enter (and leave) the culvert. This can be done by improving the channel and/or by providing a flared or funneled end.

Appearance

Where roadsides are kept mowed and the ends of culverts are visible, the use of a simple, standard unobtrusive end finish adds to the general attractiveness of the roadway. While this applies particularly to expressways and parkways, it is generally true of state highways, principal county roads and where railroads parallel highways.

Design Considerations

Besides the foregoing purposes of end finish on culverts, the designer should consider the following before choosing any particular end treatment.

Headwalls should not be chosen either to mark the end of a culvert nor to serve as a safety measure to keep a highway vehicle from running off into a stream. A simple inexpensive marker can serve the first purpose. A protruding culvert headwall is a traffic hazard which is better handled by means of a flexible beam-type guardrail. Fig. 169.

From a maintenance standpoint, a protruding headwall also interferes with machine mowing of weeds or grass, and, at roadway level, with snow removal. If painted, a headwall requires continual maintenance to keep it looking right.

Other, desirable features of end treatment include reasonable first cost, ease of moving in case of changing conditions (salvability), and resistance to damage.

Fig. 169. Safety, improved appearance and ease of mowing are features of this beveled end half headwall pipe-arch culvert and guardrail combination.

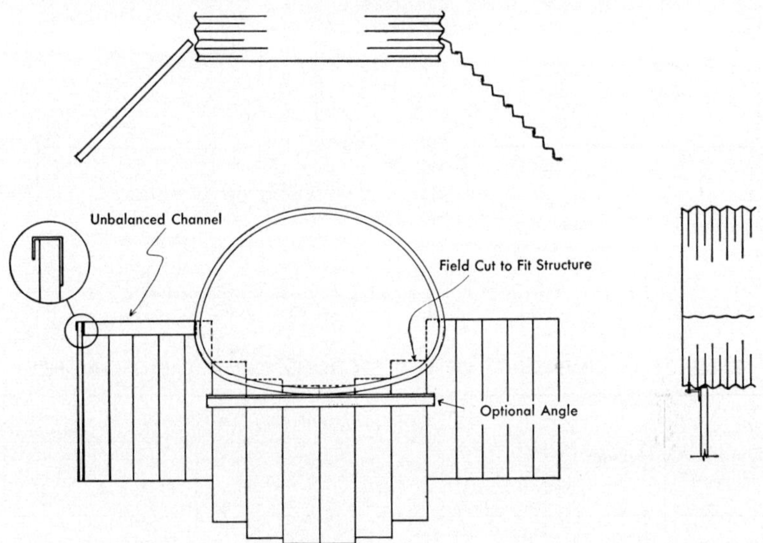

Fig. 170. Low headwall (at top) provided by corrugated steel sheeting at ends of culvert.
Fig. 171. Drawing showing how sheeting headwall is provided on a pipe-arch culvert.

Materials Available

Materials commonly used for end treatment on culverts and pipe spillways include wood, concrete, steel, stone masonry, rubble masonry, riprap and vegetation. Several of these are here described.

Sheeting. One practical form of end protection consists of driving sheeting as a cutoff wall at each end of a culvert, cutting it to receive the last section of the culvert barrel, and capping it at about the mid-diameter of the culvert, as shown in Fig. 170. This type of end finish is particularly suited to large culverts which may have the ends beveled. The length of the sheeting below the flow line should be one-half to one diameter of the culvert, with a minimum of 3 ft. [*Cont'd, p. 264*]

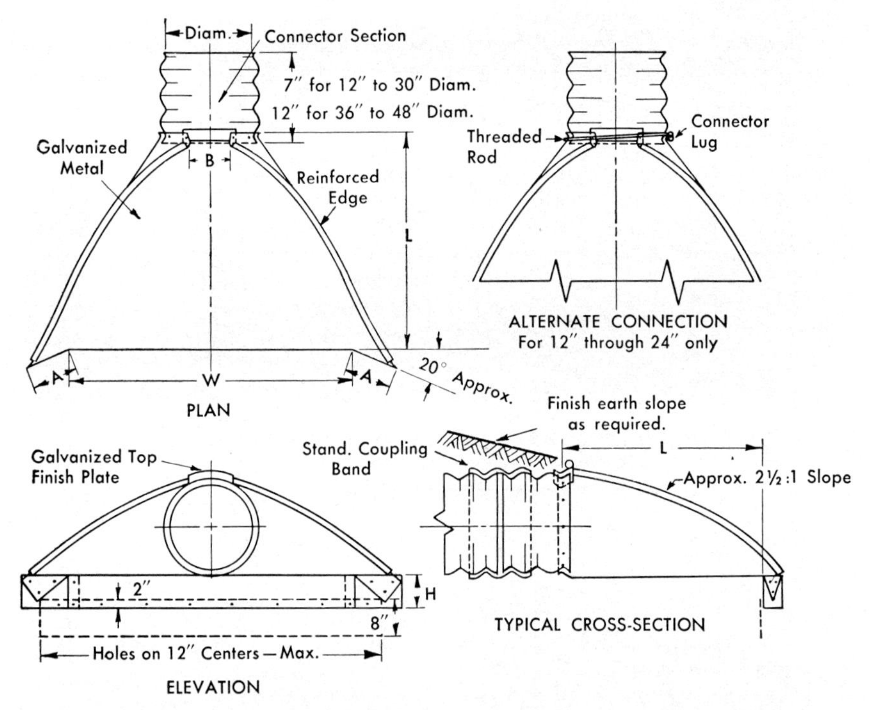

Fig. 172. Details of Armco metal end section for pipe culverts.

TABLE 31-1 DIMENSIONS OF END SECTIONS FOR ROUND METAL PIPE

Pipe Diam. in Inches	*Gage*	*Dimensions in Inches*				
		A *1″ Tol*	*B* *Max.*	*H* *1″ Tol*	*L* *1½″ Tol*	*W* *2″ Tol*
12	16	4¾	6	6	21	24
15	16	6	8	6	26	30
18	16	7	9	6	31	36
21	16	8¼	11	6	36	42
24	14	9½	12	6	42	48
30	14	12	15	7½	52½	60
36	12	14	18	9	63	72
42	12	16	21	10½	73½	84
48	12	18	27	12	84	90

Tolerances in manufacturing dimensions are shown at tops of columns.

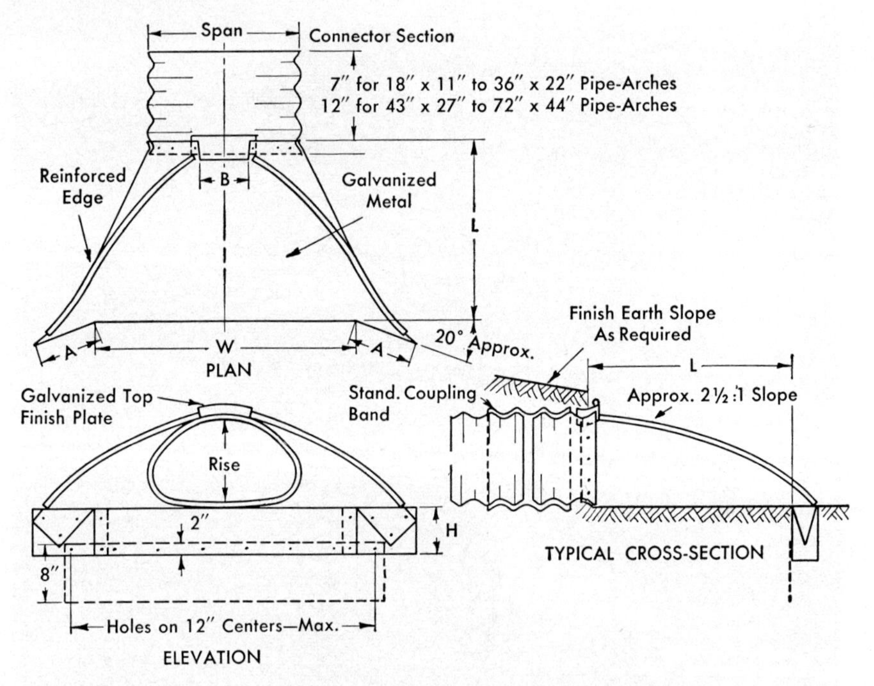

Fig. 173. Details of metal end section for pipe-arches.

TABLE 31-2 DIMENSIONS OF END SECTIONS FOR PIPE-ARCHES

Pipe-Arch Dimensions in Inches		*Gage*	*Dimensions in Inches*				
Span	*Rise*		*A* *1″ Tol*	*B* *Max.*	*H* *1″ Tol*	*L* *1½″ Tol*	*W* *2″ Tol*
18	11	16	4½	9	6	19	30
22	13	16	5¼	10	6	23	36
25	16	16	6¼	11½	6	28	42
29	18	14	7	14	6	31½	48
36	22	14	8¾	16	6	38½	60
43	27	12	10¾	17½	7⅝	47	75
50	31	12	12¼	20	9⅛	54	85
58	36	12	14	26	10⅝	63	96
65	40	12	15¾	23	10⅝	70	112
72	44	10	17¼	24	12⅛	77	128

Figs. 174–175. Attractive appearance and non-interference with mowing and snow removal operations are features of these metal end sections. Top view is on a Minnesota trunk highway.

[*Continued from page 261*]

End Sections. Armco Metal End Sections are shop fabricated for assembling in the field and attaching to corrugated pipe culverts from 12 to 48 in. in diameter and for pipe-arches from 18 x 11 in. to 72 x 44 in. Dimensions and other data are given in Tables 31-1 and 31-2. See also Figs. 174 and 175.

These end sections meet all the requirements for efficient and attractive end finish on culverts, conduits, spillways and sewer outfalls. They are attached to the culvert ends by simple bolted connectors and can be completely salvaged if lengthening or relocation is necessary. They are in the standard specifications of state highway departments, county road departments, railroads and others.

Riprap. The slope at the end of a culvert can be economically protected against erosion by means of riprap. Stone riprap should preferably be sealed by means of portland cement grout or asphaltic concrete.

Sand bags filled with a dry sand-cement mixture (1 part cement to 4 parts sand) make a neat and satisfactory end treatment. This can be vertical or sloped to fit the end of the culvert.

CHAPTER THIRTY-TWO

Design of Sewers for Size

Combined or Separate Systems

A sewer is an underground conduit or channel for carrying storm water or sanitary sewage or both. A storm sewer or storm drain is in effect an elongated culvert or stream enclosure, either in a rural or an urban area. The benefits of an enclosed drain are: greater sanitation, improved appearance, elimination of surface erosion, less interference to free and safe movement of surface traffic, and reclamation of valuable land.

Modern municipal sewer systems may be classified into combined or separate systems. Storm water and sanitary sewage may be carried in the same conduit or in separate conduits. Each system has its advocates and advantages. Considerations include: required depths, obtainable slopes, possible cleanliness, lower first costs, replacements, and operation of sewage treatment plant.

General Size Factor

Change of land use has an important effect on the percentage of rainfall that runs off as storm water. In rural areas, the clearing of land or the changing of crops may cause an increase or decrease in flow. In residential, commercial and industrial areas, the runoff increases as real estate is developed and additional impervious roofs and paved areas are created.

Fig. 176. Flooding of a city street because of inadequacy of a storm sewer. It is expensive to design for the heaviest rainfall ever likely to occur.

Fig. 177. The designer asks, "Will the sewer retain its full carrying capacity during the projected life span of the structure?" View shows interior of 42-in. combined sewer at Columbia City, Ind. after two decades of service.

Changes in types of industrial operations may increase or decrease the amount of waste waters dumped into sewers. Such things as air conditioning, domestic garbage disposal and ground water infiltration can measurably increase the volume of flow in sewers.

The cost of constructing a sewer to handle the largest possible flood should be balanced against one sufficient to handle a maximum flood flow of once in every ten or twenty-five years and paying for possible damages due to flooded basements. Where sanitary sewage backs up, there is always the danger of epidemics of disease. Flooded streets may interfere with traffic and with business, but may not be too serious if infrequent and only for very short periods. Fig. 176.

The designer should provide adequate facilities for handling not only present flow but for the entire projected life of the sewer. Fig. 177. This required capacity generally needs to be greater at the end of the life of the sewer. Such things as possible structural faulting of the sewer, heavy deposits in the bottom and increased ground water flow should be given consideration in the original design.

Rational Method of Design

Rainfall and runoff have been discussed in Chapter 23, pages 195–205. The rational method of computing runoff is used by many cities, the formula being:

$Q = A\ I\ R$

where

Q = rate of runoff in cu ft per sec = **1** acre in. per hour

A = area to be drained, in acres

I = percentage of imperviousness of the area (see Table 23-5, page 201)

R = maximum average rate of rainfall over entire drainage area, in in. per hour, which may occur during the time of concentration (see page 200)

Example: Assume that storm water intercepted by inlets at an intersection is the runoff from half of two city blocks plus the street, the total area being 3 acres. Also that one third of this area is covered with pavements, walks and roofs with a runoff factor of .85, the remaining two-thirds being lawns with a runoff factor of .15. Also assume that the time of concentration is ten minutes.

$$I=\frac{(1\times.85)+(2\times.15)}{3}=.38 \text{ average imperviousness}$$

$$R=\frac{105^*}{t+15}=\frac{105}{10+15}=4.2 \text{ in. per hr}$$

$$Q=3\times.38\times4.2=4.8 \text{ cu ft per sec}$$

Many designers use a maximum of 2 cu ft per sec per acre.

Sewage Flow

Domestic sewage can roughly be determined by the amount of water pumped by the public water supply system. The average water consumption in the United States is about 100 gallons per person per day. This varies considerably for different communities. Topography determines the drainage area served by each

*By Talbot for eastern United States; there are many variations of this formula.

Fig. 178. Asbestos-Bonded corrugated metal pipe in sewage treatment plant at Dallas, Texas.

TABLE 32-1 SEWAGE FLOW FROM DIFFERENT CLASSES OF DISTRICTS

District	*Gallons per Capita per Day*	*Gallons per Acre per Day*
Buffalo, N. Y. From Report of International Joint Commission on the Pollution of Boundary Waters:		
Industrial: Metal and automobile plants. Maximum	.....	13,000
Industrial: Meat packing, chemical and soap	.....	16,000
Commercial: Hotels, stores and office buildings	.....	60,000
Domestic: Average	80	.....
Domestic: Apartment houses	147	.....
Domestic: First-class dwellings	129	.....
Domestic: Middle-class dwellings	81	.....
Domestic: Lowest-class dwellings	35.5	.....
Cincinnati, Ohio. 1913 Report on Sewerage Plan:		
Industrial, in addition to residential and ground water	.....	9,000
Commercial, in addition to residential and ground water	.....	40,000
Domestic	135	.....
Detroit, Mich.:		
Domestic	228	.....

Arranged from data by Kenneth Allen in Municipal Engineer's Journal, Feb. 1918. From "Sewerage and Sewage Treatment," H. E. Babbitt.

sewer line, so that the average daily flow of domestic sewage in gallons per day is obtained by multiplying the number of people living in the area by the daily water consumption per capita. The *maximum* flow for which the sewer must be designed occurs during peak hours which may be determined by weir measurements.

Allowance should be made for population increase. Ground water infiltration is also a factor, the amount of which varies with the depth of the sewer below water level, perviousness of the soil, tightness of joints, cracks and other factors. "Under favorable conditions, infiltration may be as low as 5,000 gallons per day per mile of sewer. However, under other conditions, it may be more than five times that amount. Instances have occurred where the entire sewer has been filled by ground water."[1] It is becoming the practice to base infiltration on area served—a nominal figure being 1,000 gallons per acre per day.

Commercial and industrial sewage flow can usually be measured or approximated and allowance be made for expansion of industry. Table 32-1 shows typical flow rates from different classes of districts.

1. "Sewerage and Sewage Treatment," by Wm. A. Hardenbergh, 1950.

CHAPTER THIRTY-THREE

Hydraulics of Sewers

Factors That Affect Flow

Having computed the amount of flood and sewage flow, it next becomes necessary to determine the size of sewer required to handle that flow. Factors that affect the flow of water by gravity through sewers are: (1) entrance loss, (2) velocity head of approach, (3) outlet condition, (4) disturbances such as infiltration, inlets, contractions, enlargements and bends and (5) internal friction.

1, 2. Entrance loss and velocity head of approach, both of which are small as compared with friction losses in long lines, are here considered as being of compensating effect and of practically no importance in determining sewer sizes.

3. Outlet Condition

The outlet condition, whether "free" or "submerged," influences the capacity of sewers. (See pages 218, 231 on culvert outlets.) Sewers discharging into manholes or open streams where there is no backwater, are said to have "free outlets." The capacity of the sewer is controlled by the amount that can enter the pipe at the intake. Under these conditions the pipe cannot flow full. See Table 33-2, page 278, for determining capacity of various sizes of pipe.

On the other hand, where sewers are laid on relatively flat slopes or are subject to backwater, the "submerged" outlet condition prevails and the conduit can run full (see Table 33-3).

Figs. 179–180. Capacity of any sewer depends on tightness of joints and exclusion of sediment. Theoretical values of flow coefficient are meaningless in cases such as those shown here.

4. Disturbance Factors

Most sewers are not installed under ideal conditions and therefore are subject to some or all of the following "disturbance factors" (see Figs. 179–180) which vary in magnitude with the different types of construction:

1. Rough, opened or offset joints.
2. Poor alignment and grade, due to settlement, or lateral soil movements.
3. Sewage, sediment or other solids carried in suspension which may become lodged in the pipe.
4. Contraction in size due to sediment or other deposits in the bottom due to carelessness in laying pipe which permits mortar to form a dam at each joint.
5. Enlargement at manholes and junction chambers causing eddying and deposit of solids due to decreased velocity.
6. Retarding effect of bends or sharp turns at manholes.
7. Retarding effect of tree roots, joint compound and other protrusions.
8. Flow from laterals and infiltration at joints and cracks.

Proper selection of materials, adequate design, and careful installation help to minimize these factors although service and age usually aggravate them. Regular and frequent sewer inspections will show up any of the above conditions that may be classed as disturbance factors.

5. Internal Friction

In the basic hydraulic formula

$$Q = AV$$

Q = discharge or required capacity
A = end area of the sewer
V = velocity of flow

The velocity of flow varies with the friction of the fluid against the wetted interior of the sewer as well as with the disturbance factors listed above.

As the size of a sewer increases the wetted perimeter increases directly with the diameter whereas the cross-sectional area increases as the square of the diameter. Consequently the effect of friction probably becomes less as the diameter increases.

The coefficient of friction, known as n, is used in either Kutter's or Manning's formula. It varies for different materials as well as for the disturbance factors under different service conditions and length of service. Values of n have been determined experimentally for a few diameters for a limited number of ideal laboratory conditions such as with clear water in long, straight lines with controlled velocities.

Selecting a Value of *n*

Should the designer use a value of n based on the new and ideal condition of a sewer, or should he use a more realistic value based on the anticipated condition of the sewer at a later date? Should he, as in other design work, allow a factor of safety to provide for the uncertainties and variables on which the factor n is based? For example, sedimentation (Fig. 180) and infiltration, described on page 268, can easily rob a sewer of a considerable portion of its capacity.

Laboratory and field tests indicate that for galvanized corrugated metal pipe (riveted construction) a fair or average value of $n = .021$. (Test values have ranged from .019 to .024). For a smooth asphaltic surface, the value of $n = .009$ to $.011$. If the interior of a conduit consists of two different kinds of materials, the accepted practice is to use a direct weighted value of n based on the percentage of the periphery covered by each material. Table 33-1.

TABLE 33-1 COEFFICIENT OF ROUGHNESS *n* FOR LONG PIPE LINES

Straight Uniform Pipe (No Disturbances)		*Usual Design Cases*	
n	*Material*	*Modified n*	*Material and Service Condition*
.009-.011	Smooth asphaltic lining	.009-.011	Smooth asphaltic lining
.012	Unplaned lumber and ordinary iron pipe	.015 Min.*	Concrete and vitrified clay pipe for *sewers* with manholes, inlets, etc. (good alignment)
.013	Concrete and vitrified clay pipe with good alignment and smooth joints	more than .015	Vitrified clay *subdrains* with open joints
.015	Ordinary brick work	.019 or less	Paved–Invert pipe *sewers* (smooth bottom)
.021	Corrugated metal		
.025	(Canals and rivers in good condition)	.019	Corrugated metal *subdrains*
.030	(Canals and rivers in average condition)	.021	Corrugated metal *storm drains* (plain galvanized)

*From article by Chas. W. Sherman of Metcalf and Eddy published in *Engineering News-Record*, Vol. 95, pp. 434–6, Sept. 10, 1925:

"When allowance for deposits and for resistances to flow resulting from enlargements at manholes, changes of direction, entrances of branches, etc., must be considered, a value of *n* not less than .015 should be used in design. Since these factors are rarely absent, this value should generally be used."

Fig. 181. A smooth bituminous pavement in the bottom segment of the pipe aids the flow materially.

For Armco sewer pipe, the smooth bituminous pavement covers 25 per cent or more of the pipe periphery. See Fig. 181. By calculating a weighted value of n for various percentages of pavement, a combined value of n can be determined or selected. This is demonstrated in the following example.

Example: A galvanized corrugated pipe is paved for 25 per cent of its periphery. The value of n is computed:

$$.75 \times .021 = 0.016$$
$$.25 \times .011 = 0.003$$
$$\text{Adding, } n = 0.019$$

Example: A value of $n = .017$ is sought

$$y = \text{per cent galvanized}$$
$$100 - y = \text{per cent of periphery paved}$$
$$\frac{y \times .021}{100} + \frac{100 - y}{100} \times .011 = .017$$
$$.021y - .011y = 1.7 - 1.1$$
$$.010y = 0.6$$
$$y = 60\% \text{ galvanized}$$
$$1.0 - y = .4 = 40\% \text{ paved}$$

Because corrugated metal pipe resists disjointing and remains more watertight against infiltration of ground water, there is greater likelihood that the value of n will remain nearly constant throughout the life of the pipe. Many engineers experienced in the use of corrugated metal pipe sewers use equal values of n in designing corrugated metal and other types of pipe. The reason is that they consider the many other important factors which affect pipe capacity and therefore require no size differential which might result by considering the value of n as the only criterion.

The designer who realizes the shortcomings of flow formulas and who attempts to get a satisfactory installation through enforcement of practical specifications, is likely to end up with a more serviceable sewer than one who splits hairs on formulas and overlooks the numerous other factors.

Determining Storm Sewer Sizes

The following diagrams and tables are for convenience in designing storm sewer sizes:

Fig. 182 (p. 273). Chart for solution of Kutter's formula, for circular sewers flowing full on various slopes (for various values of n). Kutter's formula has been extensively used in the past, but has been largely superseded by Manning's formula because of greater simplicity.

Figs. 183–186 (pp. 274–277). Charts based on Manning's formula showing discharge for circular pipe sewers flowing full on various slopes, for value of $n = .015$, .017, .019 and .021.

Table 33–3, p. 279. Solution of Manning's formula to obtain discharge of circular pipe sewers flowing full, for value of $n = .013$ to .021. It is necessary to multiply the values in the table by the square root of the slope to obtain the discharge.

Charts and table apply only when the flow has reached a constant velocity.

Example 1: Assume a 48-in. pipe sewer with a value of n of 0.015 on a slope of .006 ft per ft. (Submerged outlet condition.) What is the discharge capacity?

[*Text continued on page 280*]

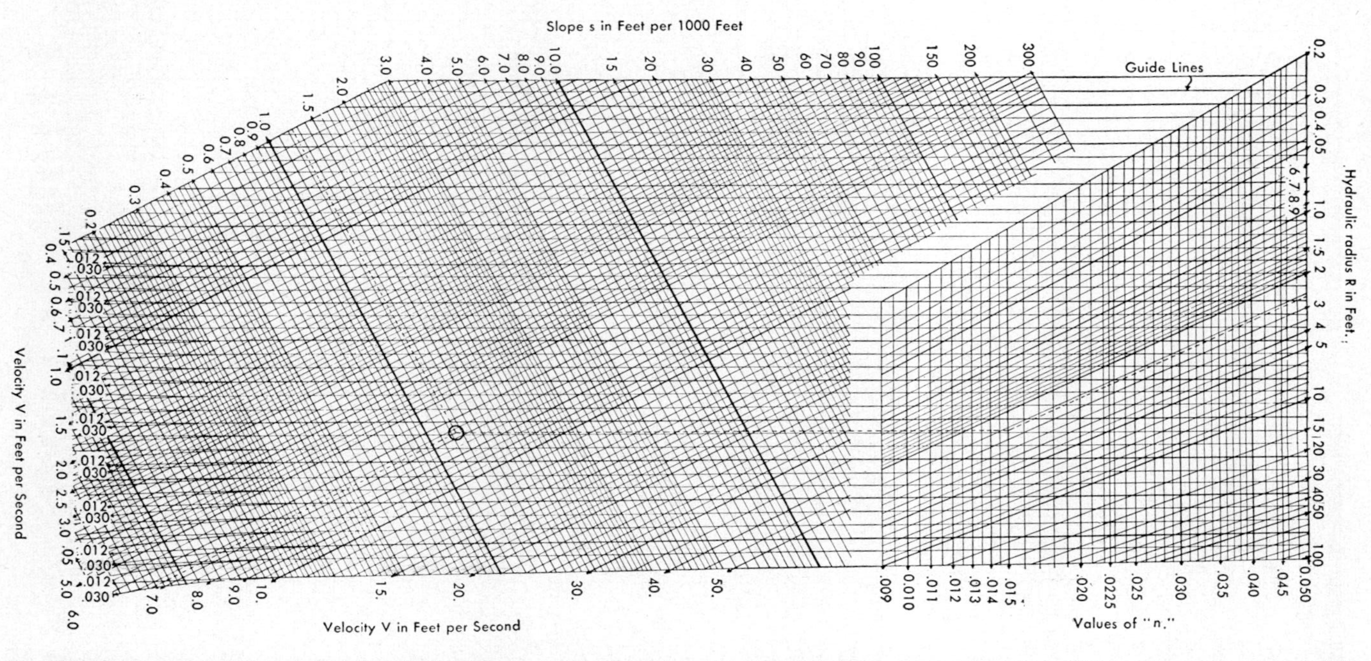

Fig. 182. Solution of Kutter's formula. From the intersection of *R* and *n* follow the guide lines to the intersection of *s* and *V*; or vice versa.—Prepared by F. C. Scobey, senior irrigation engineer, U.S. Dept. of Agriculture.

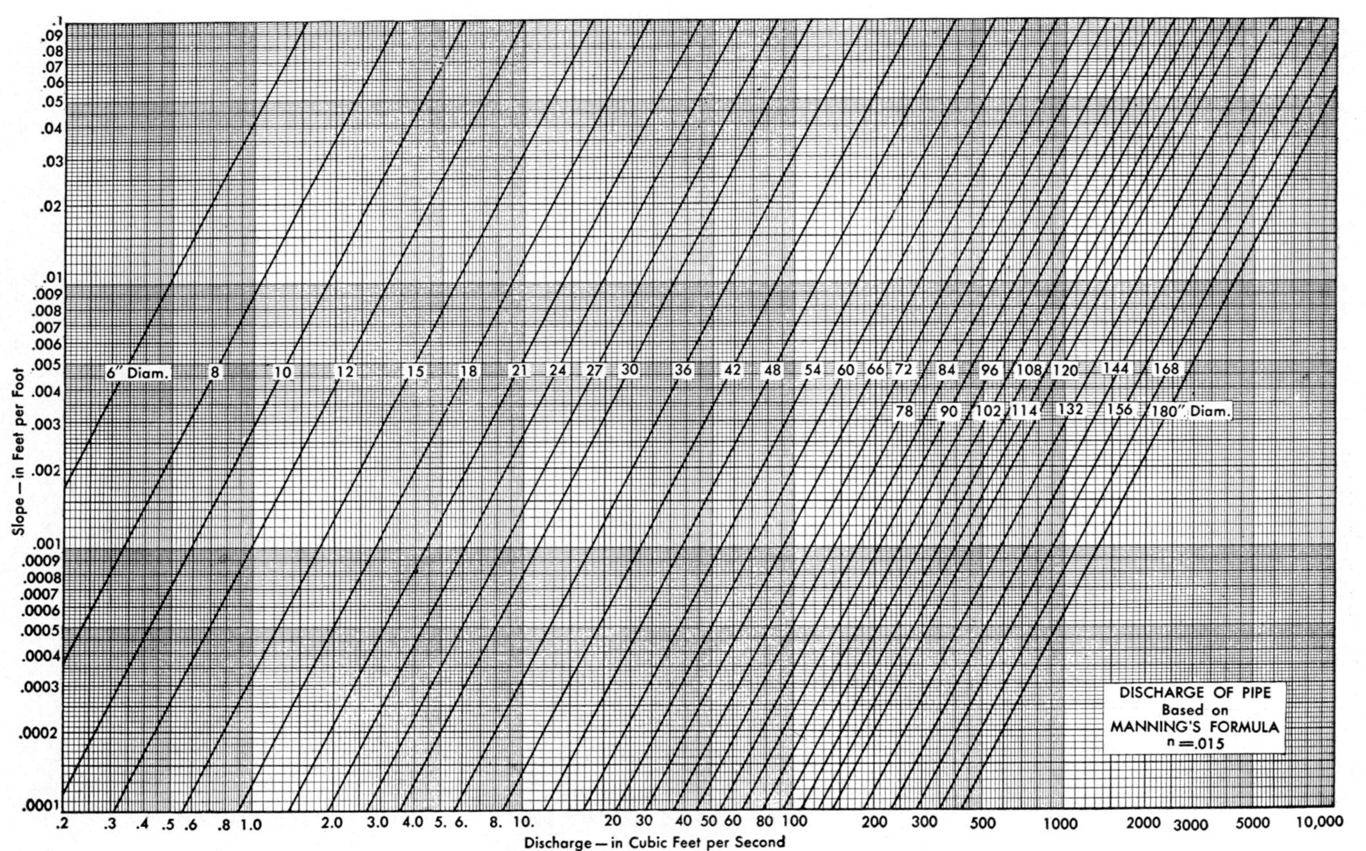

Fig. 183. Discharge for circular pipe sewers flowing full, based on Manning's formula, for $n = .015$.

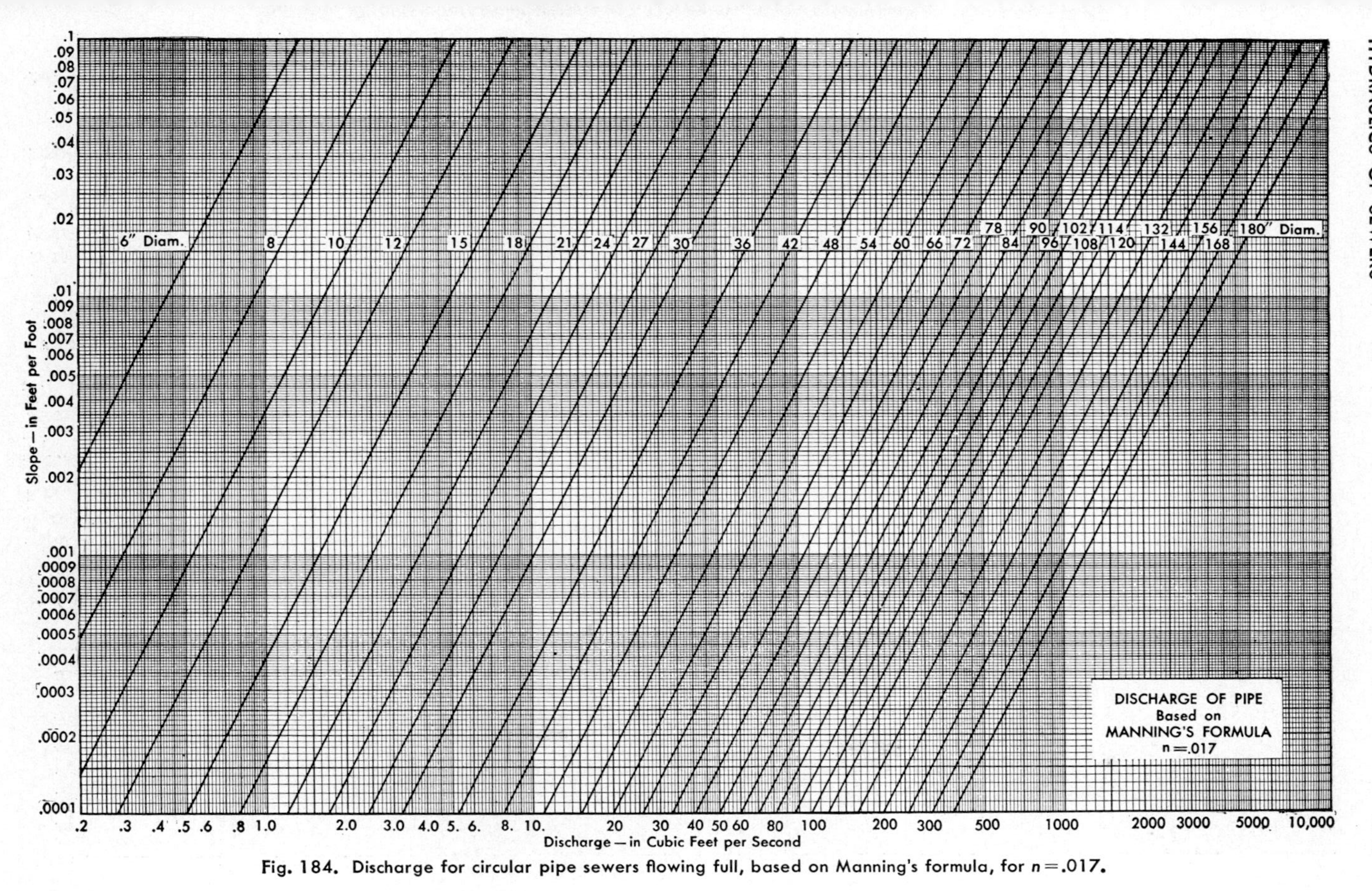

Fig. 184. Discharge for circular pipe sewers flowing full, based on Manning's formula, for $n = .017$.

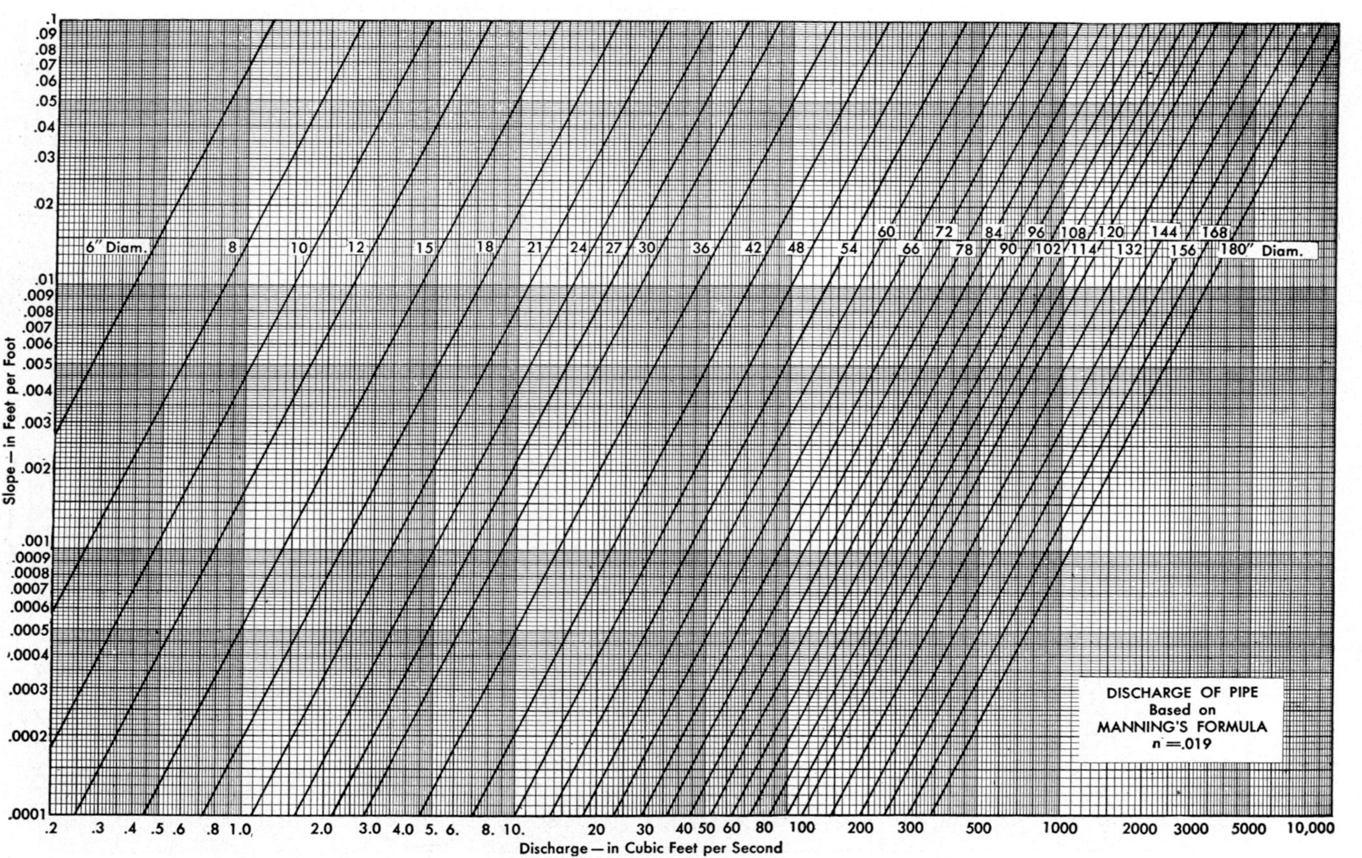

Fig. 185. Discharge for circular pipe sewers flowing full, based on Manning's formula, for $n = .019$.

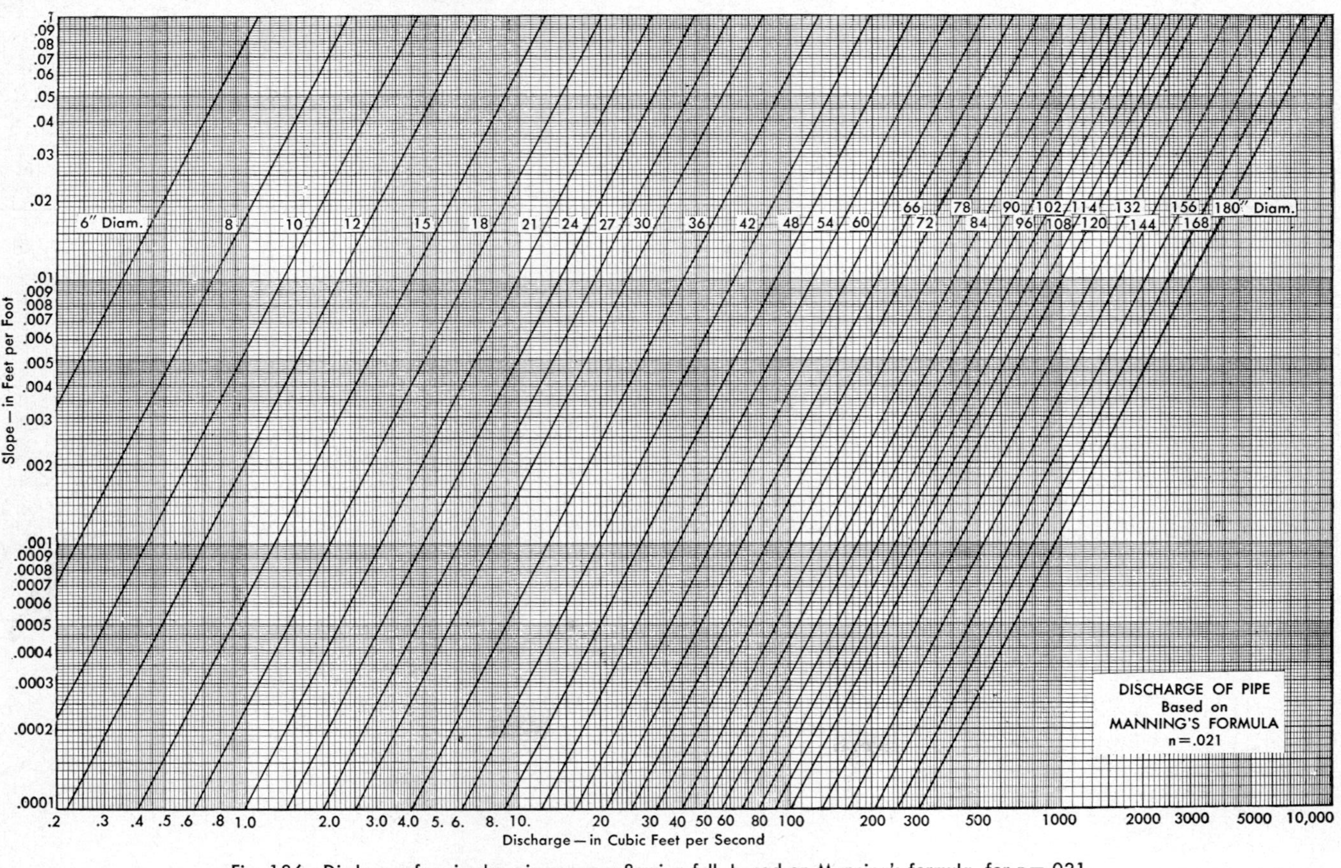

Fig. 186. Discharge for circular pipe sewers flowing full, based on Manning's formula, for $n = .021$.

TABLE 33-2 CAPACITY OF CONDUITS HAVING *FREE OUTLET* WITH WATER SURFACE AT INLET SAME ELEVATION AS TOP OF PIPE AND OUTLET UNSUBMERGED

Values are in cubic feet per second

Slope in Per Cent	*Diameter of Pipe in Inches*																				
	8	*10*	*12*	*15*	*18*	*21*	*24*	*30*	*36*	*42*	*48*	*54*	*60*	*66*	*72*	*78*	*84*	*90*	*96*	*108*	*120*
0.1	0.3	0.6	1.0	1.8	2.9	4.4	6.6	12	19	30	42	57	75	100	125	155	190	230	270	375	490
.2	0.5	0.9	1.6	2.7	4.3	6.6	9.4	17	26	42	60	83	110	140	175	215	260	315	370	505	670
.3	0.6	1.0	1.9	3.3	5.2	8.0	11.0	20	32	50	70	95	125	160	205	250	300	360	430	580	760
.4	0.7	1.2	2.1	3.7	5.9	8.9	13.0	23	35	55	75	100	135	175	220	270	320	385	455	615	810
.5	0.8	1.4	2.3	4.0	6.4	9.6	13.5	24	38	57	80	110	140	180	230	280	330	400	470	630	810
.6	0.8	1.4	2.4	4.2	6.8	10.0	14.0	25	40	59	82	110	150	190	230	280	330	400	470	630	810
.7	0.9	1.6	2.5	4.4	6.9	10.0	15.0	25	40	59	83	110	150	190	230	280	330	400	470	630	810
.8	0.9	1.6	2.6	4.5	7.1	10.5	15	26	40	59	83	110	150	190	230	280	330	400	470	630	810
.9	0.9	1.6	2.6	4.6	7.1	11	15	26	40	59	83	110	150	190	230	280	330	400	470	630	810
1.0	0.9	1.6	2.6	4.6	7.1	11	15	26	40	59	83	110	150	190	230	280	330	400	470	630	810

Note: The underlined values indicate discharge at the approximate "critical slope" when $n = .015$. Steeper slopes than "critical" do not result in increased discharge.

Approximate velocities are indicated on Figures 128 and 129.

TABLE 33-3 SOLUTION OF MANNING'S FORMULA—PIPE RUNNING FULL

$Q = AV$

$Q = A \times \frac{1.486}{n} \times R^{2/3} \times S^{1/2}$ $V = \frac{1.486}{n} \times R^{2/3} \times S^{1/2}$

V = Velocity in ft per sec
Q = Capacity in cu ft per sec
R = Hydraulic Radius.
A = Area of pipe in square ft.
S = Hydraulic slope = fall in ft divided by length in feet.
n = Kutter's Coefficient of Roughness.

Note: To obtain Q for any diameter pipe, multiply the figure shown in the column under the proper value of n by the sq root of the slope.

Diam. in. Inches	*Area in Square Feet*	*Hydraulic Radius*	$R^{2/3}$	$AR^{2/3}$	*Values of* $\frac{1.486}{n} \times R^{2/3} \times A$ *for various values of n*				
					n=.013	*n=.015*	*n=.017*	*n=.019*	*n=.021*
6	.196	.125	.250	.049	5.601	4.854	4.283	3.832	3.467
8	.349	.167	.303	.106	12.12	10.50	9.266	8.290	7.501
10	.545	.208	.351	.191	21.83	18.92	16.70	14.94	13.52
12	.785	.250	.397	.312	35.66	30.91	27.27	24.40	22.08
14	1.069	.292	.440	.470	53.73	46.56	41.08	36.76	33.26
15	1.227	.3125	.461	.566	64.70	56.07	49.48	44.27	40.05
16	1.396	.333	.480	.670	76.59	66.38	58.57	52.40	47.41
18	1.767	.375	.520	.919	105.1	91.04	80.33	71.88	65.03
20	2.182	.417	.558	1.218	139.2	120.7	106.5	95.26	86.19
21	2.405	.437	.576	1.385	158.3	137.2	121.1	108.3	98.01
24	3,142	.50	.630	1.979	226.2	196.1	173.0	154.8	140.0
27	3.976	.5625	.681	2.708	309.6	268.3	236.7	211.8	191.6
30	4.909	.625	.731	3.588	410.1	355.5	313.6	280.6	253.9
36	7.069	.75	.825	5.832	666.6	577.8	509.8	456.1	412.7
42	9.621	.875	.915	8.803	1006	872.1	769.5	688.5	622.9
48	12.566	1.00	1.00	12.566	1436	1245	1098	982.8	889.2
54	15.904	1.125	1.082	17.208	1967	1705	1504	1346	1218
60	19.635	1.25	1.16	22.777	2604	2256	1991	1781	1612
66	23.758	1.375	1.236	29.365	3357	2909	2567	2297	2078
72	28.274	1.50	1.310	37.039	4234	3669	3238	2897	2621
78	33.183	1.625	1.382	45.859	5242	4543	4009	3587	3245
84	38.485	1.75	1.452	55.880	6388	5536	4885	4370	3954
90	44.179	1.875	1.521	67.196	7681	6657	5874	5255	4755
96	50.266	2.00	1.587	79.772	9119	7903	6973	6239	5645
102	56.745	2.125	1.653	93.799	10720	9292	8199	7336	6637
108	63.617	2.25	1.717	109.230	12490	10820	9548	8543	7729
114	70.882	2.375	1.780	126.170	14420	12500	11030	9868	8928
120	78.54	2.5	1.842	144.671	16540	14330	12650	11320	10240

[*Cont'd from page 272*]

Solution: Entering the left hand column of Table 33–3 at the 48-in. diameter and reading horizontally to the value of $n = .015$, we get a value of 1245. Multiplying this value by the square root of the slope—.006 (Table 65-19, p. 506), we get $1245 \times .07746 = 96$ cu ft per sec.

Example 2: For the same conditions as in the foregoing example, but with a free outlet, what will be the discharge capacity of this sewer?

Solution: Entering Table 33-2 with a value of 0.6 per cent slope and reading to the right to a pipe size of 48-in. diameter, we obtain a discharge value of 82 cu ft per sec.

Example 3: Assume that a storm runoff of 250 cu ft per sec. has been computed by the use of the rational formula. Free outlet conditions and a maximum slope of 0.3 ft per 100 ft are obtainable. What size circular sewer can handle this flow?

Solution: Entering Table 33-2 with a value of 0.3 per cent slope, a 78-in. pipe is required to handle this flow.

Determining Sanitary Sewer Sizes

Although the specific gravity of sewage is undoubtedly heavier than that of water, no distinction is made in the hydraulic design of sanitary or combined sewers as compared with storm sewers. The methods of design described on the preceding pages apply equally well to sanitary, combined or storm sewers.

In regard to refinement in design, the following statement is made by A. P. Folwell in his book on "Sewerage":

"The uncertainties necessarily existing in the estimates of the amount of sewage to be provided for and the difficulty of selecting just the proper value of n, owing to the non-uniform character of the interior surface of the sewer, make a refinement of calculations out of keeping with the data used."

TABLE 33-4 RELATIVE VELOCITY AND DISCHARGE FOR VARIOUS DEPTHS OF FLOW
Circular Conduits (Folwell)

					By Kutter's Formula	
d *Depth*	*p* *Wetted Perimeter*	*a* *Area of Flow*	*R* *Hydraulic Radius*	$2\sqrt{R}$	*Corrected Proportional Velocities*	*Corrected Proportional Discharge*
Full 1.0	3.142	0.7854	0.25	1.00	1.00	1.000
0.95	2.691	0.7708	0.286	1.07	1.11	1.068
0.9	2.498	0.7445	0.298	1.09	1.15	1.073
0.8	2.214	0.6735	0.304	1.10	1.16	0.98
0.7	1.983	0.5874	0.296	1.08	1.14	0.84
0.6	1.772	0.4920	0.278	1.05	1.08	0.67
Half 0.5	1.571	0.3927	0.250	1.00	1.00	0.50
0.4	1.369	0.2934	0.214	0.93	0.88	0.33
0.3	1.159	0.1981	0.171	0.83	0.72	0.19
0.25	1.047	0.1536	0.146	0.76	0.65	0.14
0.2	0.927	0.1118	0.121	0.69	0.56	0.09
0.1	0.643	0.0408	0.0635	0.50	0.36	0.03
Empty 0.0	0.0	0.0	0.0	0.0	0.0	0.0

CHAPTER THIRTY-FOUR

Sewer Appurtenances

Storm Sewer Inlets

An inlet is an opening for admitting storm water runoff from a street gutter, on/or adjacent to an airport runway or taxistrip, or at a low point in a highway ditch or railroad yard.

Street gutter or curb openings are usually located at street intersections to intercept the water before it reaches pedestrian crossings. Gratings or bars prevent large objects from entering the inlet, but may be clogged by leaves or trash during a storm. Considerable research has been done in recent years as to length, width and height of opening, deflection ribs in gutter, kind of grating and location. Fig. 187.

On airport runways and taxiways, surface water is drained off either (1) through a previous backfill along the edges and picked up by subdrainage pipe (see page 348), (2) through a continuous grate along the edges or (3) through grates located at sumps in the runway or in the grassed areas at the sides.

At the ends of highway bridges and overpasses, and at low places in paved ditches or curb and gutter sections, various types of inlets are used, generally attached to a pipe spillway.

Large areas such as railroad yards, and single or multiple tracks in long cuts may require grate inlets at intervals to remove storm water from the surface. These fre-

Fig. 187. Deflecting vanes in a gutter are helpful in getting water to flow into a side inlet. However, they are usually not as effective in removing water as a grate with ribs parallel to the curb.

Figs. 188–189. Two types of corrugated manholes. One at left, along Bronx-Whitestone Expressway in New York City has stub connections at various levels. One at right is joined to the top and side of an industrial sewer at Dayton, Ohio.

quently consist of corrugated metal "risers" varying in diameter from 8 to 36 in. See Fig. 164, page 255. Where catchbasins are desired to trap solids, these may be supplied as shown in Fig. 191. The base may be of concrete or may be of metal welded to the bottom.

Standard and Special Fittings

Standard fittings such as tees, saddle branches, wyes, elbows and reducers are available for all types of corrugated metal sewers. Typical T and Y-branches and other fittings are shown in Fig. 190. Special fittings with various outlets and connections can readily be fabricated from corrugated metal.

Saddle branches for house connections on sanitary sewers, or as junctions to larger sewers, may be either welded on at the plant or may be prefabricated and attached in the field. See Fig. 194.

Manholes

Manholes provided with cast iron frames and covers are primarily for the purpose of giving access to the sewer from the street to provide for easier inspection and cleaning. They are usually located at street intersections, at changes in alignment or grade and at intermediate points of 300 to 500 ft.

Twenty-four inches is the usual top diameter, enlarging rapidly to about 4 ft in diameter, although 3 and 5-ft diameters are not uncommon. Larger sizes of monolithic construction may be used as junction chambers where two or more large sewers merge, or where gates, flush tanks and other regulating devices are required.

If the sewer is carried through the manhole, this is done with a half circle pipe with a floor at the springing line to serve as a platform for workmen. The manhole is generally centered on the sewer. However, on large sewers, the manhole may be

[*Continued on page 286*]

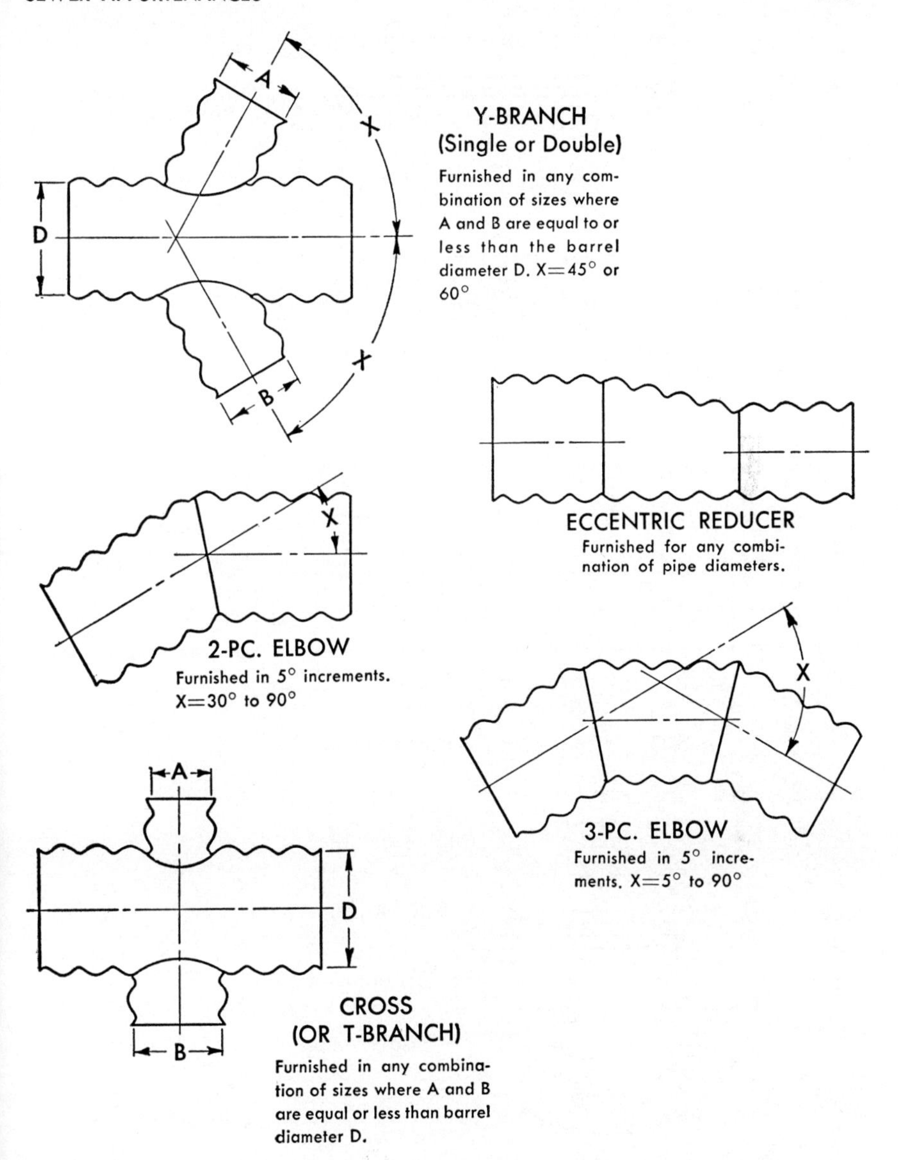

Fig. 190. Standard fittings for standard corrugated pipe and Hel-Cor perforated pipe.

NOTES: All fittings are furnished in as short lengths as possible but with sufficient length for attaching standard connecting bands.

Bends up to 5° can be made in one or two standard connecting bands due to their flexibility.

Connecting bands are corrugated to match corrugations in the pipe and insure strong joints.

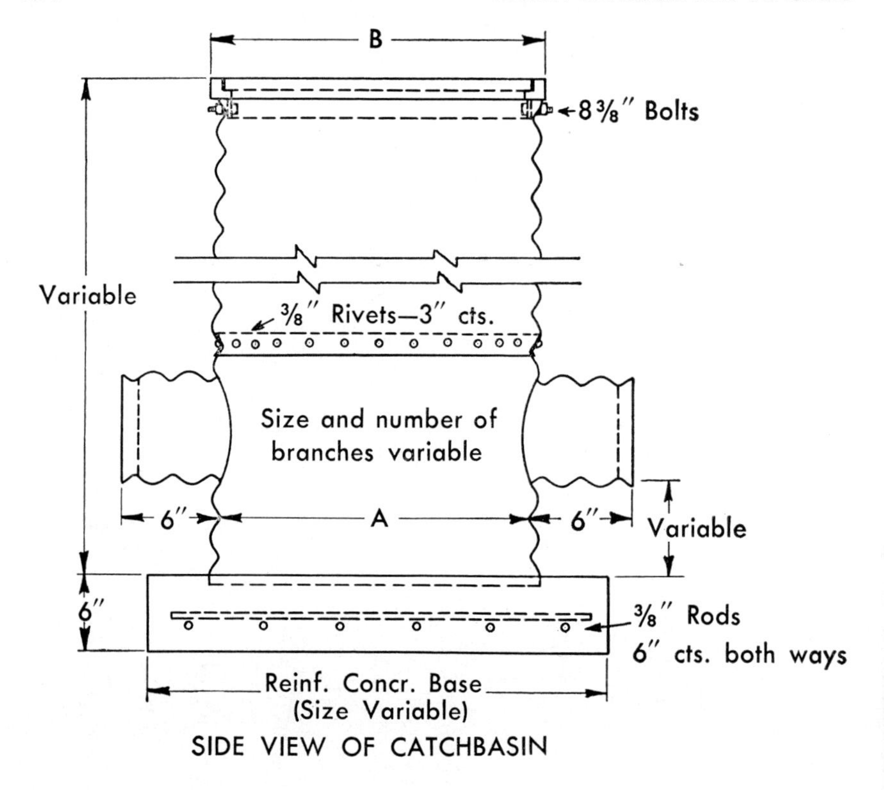

SIDE VIEW OF CATCHBASIN

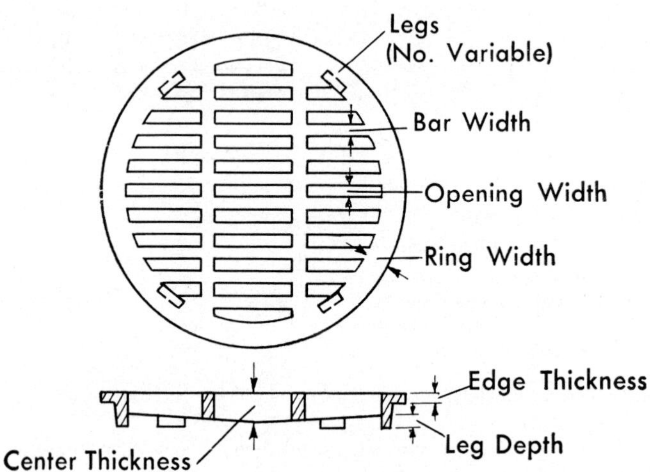

PLAN AND CROSS SECTION OF GRATE

Fig. 191. Design for corrugated metal catchbasin, with details for cast iron grate.

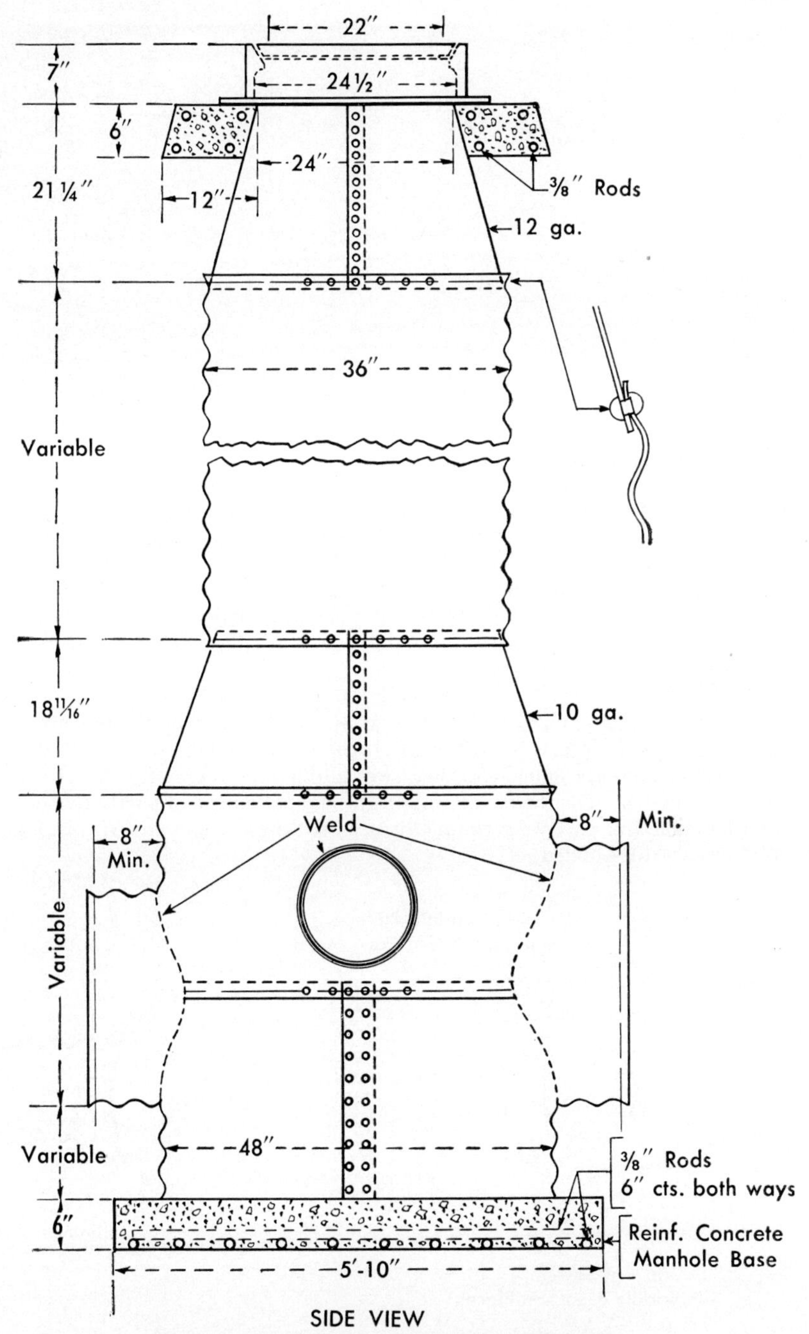

SIDE VIEW

Fig. 192. Design for corrugated metal manhole. This is subject to many variables to meet local conditions.

Fig. 193. Watertight coupling on corrugated pipe, using rods and lugs. This type is used on aerial sewers, levee culverts and wherever "bottle-tightness" is required.

[*Continued from page 282*]
at one side to permit workmen to reach the bottom without a special ladder. See Fig. 189, page 282.

Manholes are commonly constructed of corrugated metal, brick or concrete, or combinations of these materials. Metal manholes are usually prefabricated and can quickly be set in place by means of a light crane. See Figs. 188 and 192.

Sewer Joints

Standard corrugated pipe, usually in lengths of 20 ft, has shop riveted circumferential seams at 2-ft intervals, and longitudinal seams. Where pipe sections or fittings in sewer lines are joined together, several different types of joints or connections are available. The degree of watertightness is controlled partly by the type of construction and partly by the material as to whether galvanized, bituminous coated or asbestos-bonded.

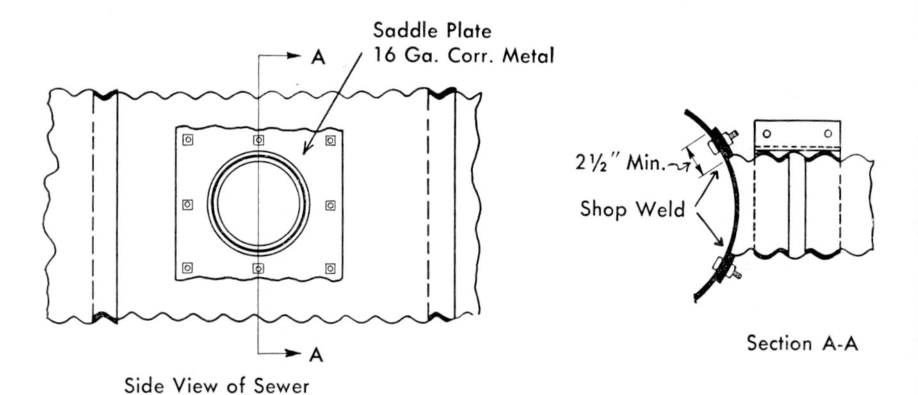

Fig. 194. Saddle branch, bolted to main sewer, enables laterals and house connections to join the sewer.

Fig. 195. Repairs to existing sewers may consist of complete relining or just half-soling. Workman is tightening an internal expanding coupling band.

1. *One-piece, Bolted.* Usually 3 to 5 corrugations wide (7½ to 13 in.), this type of coupling is satisfactory for storm drains where only moderate watertightness is essential. (Inexpensive gaskets may be added for additional watertightness.) For diameters larger than 48 in., the coupling may be in two parts to enable drawing it up for a tighter fit. See page 73.

2. *Two-Piece, Half Riveted.* By shop-riveting half of a two-piece coupling band to the lower half of one end of the pipe section, it is easier to join pipe in a trench or a wet area. The top half is bolted at the sides.

3. *Two-Piece, Both Riveted.* The half riveted is usually preferable to the joint where both halves are shop riveted to the pipe.

4. *Watertight.* See Fig. 193. This joint is made with a coupling band without the usual angle flange. Rods with threaded ends are put through special "silo" lugs and tightened by means of nuts. This type of construction has been found satisfactory for levee culverts, dam and farm pond outlets, aerial sewers and wherever watertightness is a consideration.

5. *Inside Expanding or Outside Contracting.* For relining existing sewers, an inside expanding or an outside contracting band, with angle flanges riveted to the inside are used to join the pipe from the inside. See Fig. 195.

Fig. 196. Subaqueous outfall sewer being lowered into tidal river at Jacksonville, Florida. The seams were close-riveted for watertightness.

6. *Field Riveted or Bolted.* This type of connection is made on jacking jobs and on some large threading jobs where it is necessary to apply great pressure to the end of the pipe to move it into place.

7. *Close-Riveted, Soldered and Bituminous Coated.* Used only on siphons and irrigation lines to assure watertightness.

8. *Multi-Plate.* These joints are lapped and bolted together. Where watertightness is required, a bituminous gasket can be inserted. On siphons, the seams can be welded.

Joints on metal sewers are generally as strong as the remainder of the pipe, and they minimize or eliminate infiltration of ground water and suction of sandy or silty backfill which could result in undermining and failure.

Sewer Outfalls

Storm sewers and outlets from sewage treatment plants generally discharge into streams, lakes or bays. If the line extends across swampy, unstable soils or is subject to the direct impact of flooded streams, some special construction may be necessary to avoid disastrous settlement or lateral movement of the outfall end of the sewer. Cradling is not used except in unusual cases. An aerial sewer as described elsewhere, or the use of pile bents to support the sewer may be needed. Steel sheeting helps prevent undermining.

Protection against floating debris, drifting beach sands and ice may be provided by sheeting, retards or other devices. Heavy monolithic headwall structures are not usually needed or desired because they may settle and thereby damage the sewer.

Subaqueous sewers may have to be weighted with heavy concrete blocks to keep them from moving. Fig. 196.

Sewers passing through wet, unstable subsoils can sometimes be stabilized by means of a line of subdrain pipe under or at one side to lower the ground water level.

Sewage Treatment Plants

The modern sewage treatment plant requires several thousand feet of sewer pipe and pressure pipe as well as many control gates. Asbestos-Bonded corrugated metal pipe is gaining in favor for the first use. See Fig. 178, page 267. Welded steel pipe serves for the force mains.

Oxidation of sewage is generally obtained by passing the effluent from primary treatment through a trickling filter bed. Such filters consist of a bed of broken stone, slag or other coarse material 3 to 10 ft deep, and from 40 to 60 ft and larger in diameter, partly buried. Both standard riveted corrugated sheets and corrugated structural plates have been used satisfactorily in the building of such filters. Fig. 197.

Perforated corrugated metal pipe is used in connection with some of the subsurface filtration processes.

Septic Tanks

For dwellings not served by public sewerage systems, the septic tank is still considered "an efficient, economical and wholly satisfactory method of sewage disposal."* Septic tanks of sheet steel have been used for decades and found satisfactory and economical. However, the use of Asbestos-Bonded steel gives greatly improved corrosion resistance, based on tests at the University of Illinois from June 1947 to July 1950. "It may be concluded from these observations that the use of Asbestos-Bonded steel will result in a long life for a septic tank."*

House connections may be of Asbestos-Bonded pipe. For the drain field assembly, perforated corrugated metal pipe may be used.

*"An Investigation of the Performance of Small Septic Tanks," by E. R. Baumann and H. E. Babbitt, Univ. of Ill. Eng. Experi. Station Bull. Series No. 409, Feb. 1953.

Fig. 197. Large tanks of standard corrugated sheets or structural plates are used for trickling filters at sewage disposal plants. One shown here is 35 ft in diameter.

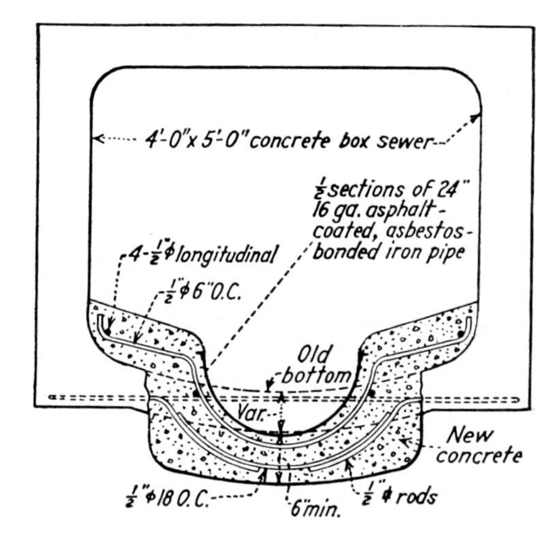

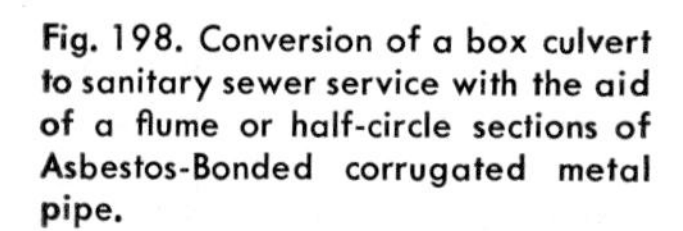
Fig. 198. Conversion of a box culvert to sanitary sewer service with the aid of a flume or half-circle sections of Asbestos-Bonded corrugated metal pipe.

Sewer Maintenance and Repairs

Sanitary sewers are a relatively modern development. Many were built around the beginning of the Twentieth Century, as were also storm sewers. These have deteriorated to such an extent that numerous repairs and replacements are becoming the problem of many communities.

A cleaning of all sewers, followed by a thorough inspection, especially of the sizes 30-in. and larger would be valuable. Such inspection would reveal bad joints, cracks, erosion, poor connections and bad settlement or misalignment. Many sewers could be repaired or salvaged before failure requires complete replacement.

Deterioration of the sides and top of large arch and pipe sewers can be repaired in several ways. One method frequently used is to reline the structure with a corrugated metal arch or pipe and then fill the voids between the two structures by pumping in a weak cement grout. (1:4). See Fig. 195.

Where just the invert has worn through and the remainder of the structure is in good condition, it may be possible to "half-sole" the invert by using half circle plates with a bituminous paved invert. Attaching the old to the new may be done by drilling holes in concrete and inserting expansion bolts through the metal invert and grouting them in the holes. Fig. 198.

Damage due to explosions in concrete or masonry sewers may sometimes be repaired and not require a complete replacement. If the invert is sound, crown plates of corrugated metal can replace the arch of the sewer or reinforce it sufficiently.

SUPPLEMENTARY READING

"Review of Storm Drain Inlet Design Material," by G. S. Tapley, Bureau of Eng. City of Los Angeles, Calif., Dec. 1946. Mimeographed, illustrated report.

"Design and Capacity of Gutter Inlets," by N. W. Connor, Prof. of Fluid Mechanics, North Carolina State College, Engineering Exp. Sta. Bull. No. 30, July 1945.

Unpublished report on studies of grating inlets by University of Illinois and Bureau of Public Roads.

CHAPTER THIRTY-FIVE

Part Circle Culverts

STORM water in the larger towns and cities is cared for mostly by curbs and gutters from which the water is discharged into storm sewers. In the smaller towns and boroughs and in outlying districts of larger cities, street water is carried away in surface ditches and may not be connected to a sewer system. The sizes of these ditches can be determined as for highways.

Drainage at Paved Intersections

In some cases, the practice still is to carry surface water across intersections in a dip or valley. These dips are a hazard to traffic at all times and unpopular with pedestrians in wet weather. There is a definite danger where fast traffic such as emergency vehicles cannot be expected to slow down.

A popular and economical solution to the problem, where excessive amounts of water are not encountered, consists of corrugated metal part circle culverts built in the depression and covered with a pavement. Fig. 199. These part circles have their edges resting on small angle irons set in a concrete or masonry base, or on a corrugated or flat metal base. The intake and outlet may be in the gutter, or the construction may be such that it does not restrict the width of the street.

With as little as 2 in. of cover over them, they develop strength to withstand traffic loads and impact satisfactorily. However, if rigid type pavement is used, a thickness of 3 or 4 in. is desirable to minimize the pavement cracking.

Fig. 199. Part circle culverts provide surface drainage at street intersections with minimum interference to traffic and pedestrians. This installation is in Glendale, Calif.

TABLE 35-1 GAGES OF PART CIRCLE CORRUGATED CULVERTS

Gage	*Weight Per Foot, in Pounds*																														
12	5.4	5.7	6.0	6.4	6.7	7.1	7.4	8.1	8.5	9.2	9.9	10.7	10.8	11.3	11.6	11.9	12.5	12.7	13.4	13.8	14.2	14.5	14.9	15.4	16.2	17.0	18.9	19.9	21.3	21.9	22.6	25.4
10	6.9	7.2	7.6	8.1	8.5	9.1	9.5	10.3	10.8	11.8	12.7	13.6	13.8	14.4	14.8	15.2	16.0	16.2	17.1	17.6	18.1	18.4	19.0	19.6	20.7	21.6	24.2	25.3	27.2	27.9	28.8	32.4
8	8.4	8.8	9.2	9.9	10.3	11.0	11.6	12.5	13.2	14.3	15.4	16.5	16.8	17.5	18.0	18.5	19.4	19.7	20.8	21.4	22.0	22.4	23.1	23.9	25.2	26.3	29.4	30.8	33.1	34.0	35.1	39.5
Base in In.	*Rise, in Inches*																														
12	2	2¾	3½	4⅛	4⅝	5⅛	5⅝																								
14				2¼	3¼	4⅛	4¾	5¾	6¼	7																						
16							3⅛	4¾	5⅜	6½	7⅜								*12 Ga. Min.*													
18								2½	3¾	5½	6⅝	7½	7¾	8¼	8¾																	
20										2⅝	5½	6¾	7	7⅝	8	8⅜	9⅛	9⅜														
22											3¼	5⅜	5⅞	6⅝	7⅛	7⅝	8⅜	8¾	9½	10	10½	10¾										
24													3⅝	5	5¾	6⅜	7⅜	7¾	8¾	9¼	9¾	10⅛	10⅝	11¼								
26															3¼	4¼	6	6½	7⅝	8¼	9	9¼	9⅞	10½	11⅝	12⅜						
28																	3½	4¼	6⅛	7	7⅞	8¼	9	9⅝	10⅞	11¾				*10 Ga. Min.*		
30																			3⅝	5	6¼	6⅞	7¾	8½	10	11	13½	14⅝				
32																				*8 Ga. Min.*		4½	5⅞	7⅛	8⅞	10	12¾	13⅞				
34																								5	7½	8¾	11⅞	13⅛	15	15¼		
36																									5	7⅛	10⅞	12¼	14⅜	15⅜	16⅝	
42																											5⅝	8½	11¼	12¼	13¼	17⅝
48																														6⅝	9⅝	14½

Note: Minimum gages shown on chart are for traffic conditions. 12 gage corrugated may be used under sidewalk areas for all sizes.

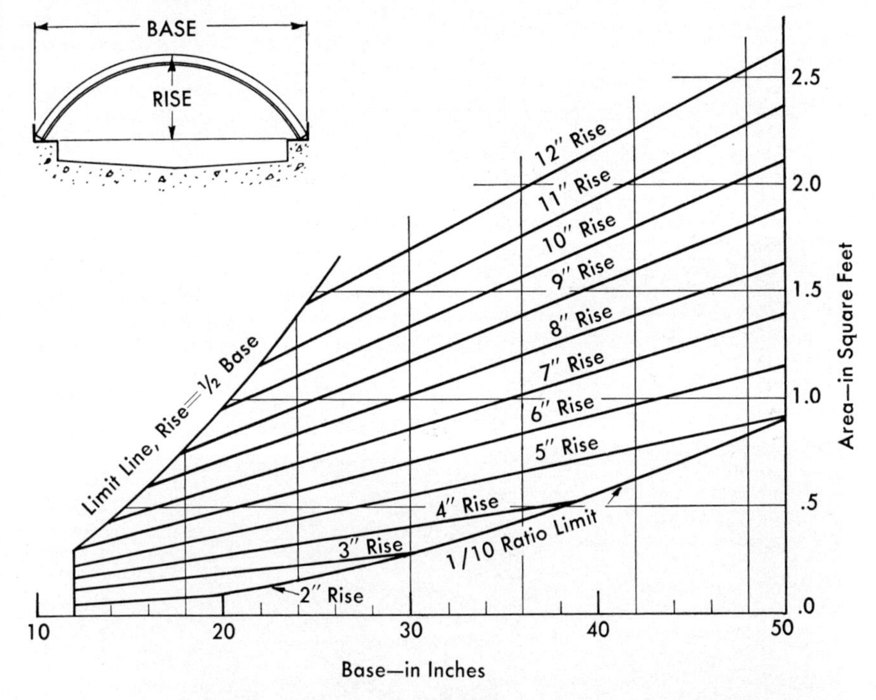

Example: Find the area for a part circle section with base 24 in., rise 10 in.

Solution: Where the 24-in. base line intersects the 10-in. rise line, follow to right and read 1.12 sq ft.

Fig. 200. Areas of part circle arches.

Part Circle Culvert Sizes

Part circles are made up in standard lengths of 25½ in., which when lapped, make a length of 2 ft even. The lengths are not bolted; the pavement holds them in place. See Table 35-1 and Fig. 200 for sizes and areas.

How Installed

Installation of part circle culverts is as follows: In a properly prepared trench, a concrete or metal base is placed. If a concrete base is used, a pair of angle irons is set or grooves are formed to take the thrust. A metal base is provided either with turned up edges or with angle irons riveted at the edges. Between these the curved corrugated sheets are placed and the angle irons are blocked out from the shoulders so as to press against the edges of the corrugated arches. The whole structure is then grouted in and the street constructed over it.

Fig. 201. Soils play an important part in engineering construction. Here a bulldozer is moving thawed slush on the Alaska Highway.

SECTION SEVEN

SUBSURFACE DRAINAGE

CHAPTER THIRTY-SIX

Soil Studies

PART ONE

SOILS

SOILS, even though the most abundant of all materials to be used in engineering works, have until recently received little consideration in comparison to their importance. Since they are made up of natural materials varying both in physical and chemical characteristics, and with no control possible in their creation, knowledge of their proper use was very limited until the modern concept of soil mechanics was introduced in the United States some 30 years ago. Since that time, great strides have been made in the use of soils for actual structures such as dams and levees. Methods have been developed for improving soils by various treatments so that they will sustain greater loads and better resist the ravages of time.

As roadbeds and foundations for modern transportation facilities and structures, soils must be strong. Strength can be increased and controlled by (1) regulation of water content, (2) chemical additives (3) proper gradation of natural soils and (4) compaction. Regardless of the treatment chosen, the intrusion of excessive water after construction will weaken or even destroy the desired foundation. Therefore, it is particularly important that there should be a clear understanding as to the effect of water in its relation to soils. Fig. 201.

Origin of Soils

Soils are primarily of mineral origin, being formed by the disintegration of rocks through the agency of wind, water, ice, frost, temperature changes, chemical action, plant growth and animal life. In addition to the rock or mineral constituent, soils contain organic matter extracted from the air and from the vegetation which has grown in the soil. Also there are many forms of minute animal life in the soil which influence drainage and plant growth. Whether the soil be sedentary or transported, its principal constituents are silicates, with varying amounts of aluminum, iron, lime, magnesia and the alkalis, together with small amounts of organic matter.

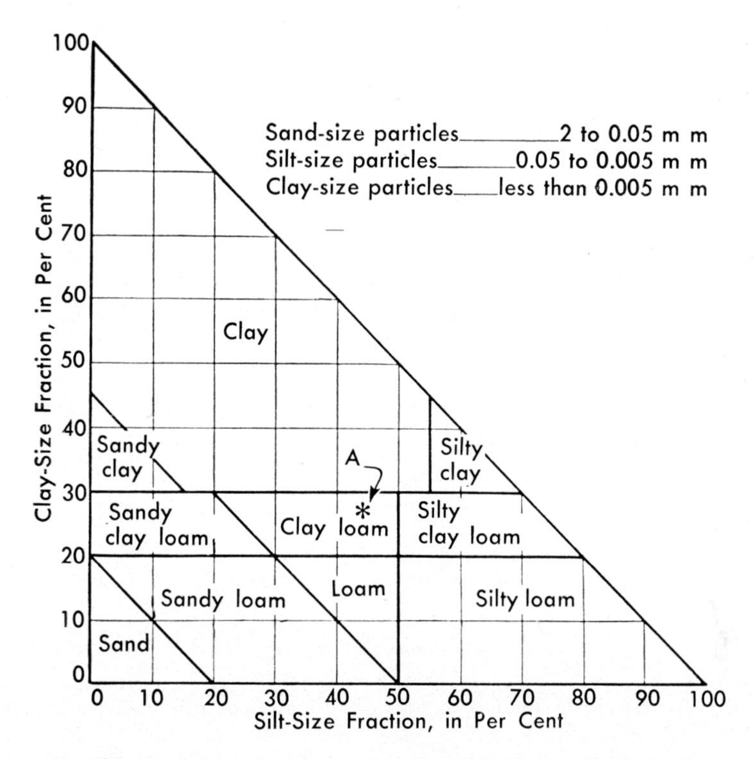

Fig. 202. Textural classification chart for soils.—U. S. Bureau of Public Roads.

Textural Soil Classifications

Soils are generally classified in three groups according to grain size—sands and gravels, silts, and clays. Various agencies have established limiting grain sizes to identify these soils. That adopted by the U. S. Bureau of Public Roads is shown in Table 36-1.

In pure form, these soils can be identified visually and by feel. Sand and gravel are loose and granular. Silt is fine grained like flour, not usually distinguishable by looks or by feel; however, it powders easily when dry. Clay is plastic when moist but when dry, is hard and does not powder readily.

Although these three soils may occur in pure form, especially the sand and gravel, they usually exist in combination. A method of identifying soils by name in terms of the percentage of gravel, sand, silt and clay has been devised by the U. S. Bureau of Soils and Chemistry in the form of a triangular chart, shown in Fig. 202.

Example: A soil contains
28 per cent clay
45 per cent silt
27 per cent sand (by difference)

This is located as point A in Fig. 202 and its classification is found to be "clay loam." Translating the chart into tabular form, the values are given in Table 36-2.

TABLE 36-1 GRAIN SIZE OF SOIL CONSTITUENTS

Classification	*Diameter of Particles in Millimeters*	*U. S. Standard Sieve*	
		Passing	*Retained on*
Gravel	Larger than 2.0		No. 10
Coarse sand	2.0 to 0.42	No. 10	No. 40
Fine sand	0.42 to 0.05	No. 40	No. 270
Silt-size	0.05 to 0.005		
Clay-size	Smaller than 0.005	Cannot be separated by sieving. Size is determined by settling velocity in a soil-water suspension.	
Colloidal size	Smaller than 0.001		

From "Soil Engineering," by M. G. Spangler.

While the triangular chart reveals the grain-size distribution and gives a textural name, it has its limitations in that it does not reveal the other physical properties of the soil.

Any textural system of classifying soils is based on the properties of the grains themselves or of remolded material, and not of the material intact as found in nature. Hence, these systems need to be supplemented by engineering experience and by information as obtained in other fields such as geology and pedology.

Further classification of soils, as adopted by the Corps of Engineers and the Bureau of Reclamation in 1952, is given in Table 36-3. This describes the soils and is followed by field identification procedures for the fine-grained soils.

The relationship of soil classifications to subgrades, embankments and foundations is given in Tables 36-4 and 36-5. Tables 36-3 and 36-5 are from Technical Memorandum No. 3-357, Vol. 1, Corps of Engineers, Vicksburg, Miss., March 1953.

[*Continued on page 301*]

TABLE 36-2 TEXTURAL CLASSIFICATION OF SOILS

Textural Class	*Composition in Per Cent*		
	Sand	*Silt-size*	*Clay-size*
Sand	80–100	0–20	0–20
Sandy Loam	50–80	0–50	0–20
Loam	30–50	30–50	0–20
Silt Loam	0–50	50–100	0–20
Sandy Clay Loam	50–80	0–30	20–30
Clay Loam	20–50	20–50	20–30
Silty Clay Loam	0–30	50–80	20–30
Sandy Clay	55–70	0–15	30–45
Silty Clay	0–15	55–70	30–45
Clay	0–55	0–55	30–100

From "Soil Engineering," by M. G. Spangler.

TABLE 36-3 UNIFIED SOIL CLASSIFICATION

Major Divisions			*Group Symbols*	*Typical Names*	*Field Identification Procedures (Excluding particles larger than 3 inches and basing fractions on estimated weights)*	*Information Required for Describing Soils*
1	2		3	4	5	6
Coarse-grained Soils *More than half of material is larger than No. 200 sieve size.* *The No. 200 sieve size is about the smallest particle visible to the naked eye.*	*Gravels* *More than half of coarse fraction is larger than No. 4 sieve size.* *(For visual classification, the ¼-in. size may be used as equivalent to the No. 4 sieve size)*	*Clean Gravels (Little or no fines)*	GW	Well-graded gravels, gravel-sand mixtures, little or no fines.	Wide range in grain sizes and substantial amounts of all intermediate particle sizes.	For undisturbed soils add information on stratification, degree of compactness, cementation, moisture conditions and drainage characteristics.
			GP	Poorly-graded gravels, gravel-sand mixtures, little or no fines.	Predominantly one size or a range of sizes with some intermediate sizes missing.	
		Gravels with Fines (Appreciable amount of fines)	GM	Silty gravels, gravel-sand-silt mixtures.	Nonplastic fines or fines with low plasticity (for identification procedures see ML below).	Give typical name; indicate approximate percentages of sand and gravel, max. size; angularity, surface condition and hardness of the coarse grains; local or geologic name and other pertinent descriptive information; and symbol in parentheses.
			GC	Clayey gravels, gravel-sand-clay mixtures.	Plastic fines (for identification procedures see CL below).	
	Sands *More than half of coarse fraction is smaller than No. 4 sieve size.*	*Clean Sands (Little or no fines)*	SW	Well-graded sands, gravelly sands, little or no fines.	Wide range in grain size and substantial amounts of all intermediate particle sizes.	
			SP	Poorly-graded sands, gravelly sands, little or no fines.	Predominantly one size or a range of sizes with some intermediate sizes missing.	Example: *Silty sand*, gravelly; about 20% hard, angular gravel particles ½-in. maximum size; rounded and subangular sand grains coarse to fine; about 15% nonplastic fines with low dry strength; well compacted and moist in place; alluvial sand; (SM).
		Sands with Fines (Appreciable amount of fines)	SM	Silty sands, sand-silt mixtures.	Nonplastic fines or fines with low plasticity (for identification procedures see ML below).	
			SC	Clayey sands, sand-clay mixtures.	Plastic fines (for identification procedures see CL below).	

Table continued below

Major Divisions		Group Symbols	Typical Names	Dry Strength (Crushing characteristics)	Dilatancy (Reaction to shaking)	Toughness (Consistency near PL)	
				Identification Procedures on Fraction Smaller than No. 40 Sieve			
Fine-grained Soils *More than half of material is smaller than No. 200 sieve size.*	*Silts and Clays* *Liquid limit less than 50*	ML	Inorganic silts and very fine sands, rock flour, silty or clayey fine sands or clayey silts with slight plasticity.	None to slight	Quick to slow	None	Give typical name, indicate degree and character of plasticity, amount and maximum size of coarse grains, color in wet condition, odor if any, local or geologic name and other pertinent descriptive information; and symbol in parentheses.
		CL	Inorganic clays of low to medium plasticity, gravelly clays, sandy clays, silty clays, lean clays.	Medium to high	None to very slow	Medium	
		OL	Organic silts and organic silty clays of low plasticity.	Slight to medium	Slow	Slight	
	Silts and Clays *Liquid limit greater than 50*	MH	Inorganic silts, micaceous or diatomaceous fine sandy or silty soils, elastic silts.	Slight to medium	Slow to none	Slight to medium	For undisturbed soils add information on structure, stratification, consistency in undisturbed and remolded states, moisture and drainage conditions.
		CH	Inorganic clays of high plasticity, fat clays.	High to very high	None	High	
		OH	Organic clays of medium to high plasticity, organic silts.	Medium to high	None to very slow	Slight to medium	Example: *Clayey silt*, brown, slightly plastic, small percentage of fine sand, numerous vertical root holes, firm and dry in place, loess, (ML).
Highly Organic Soils		Pt	Peat and other highly organic soils.	Readily identified by color, odor, spongy feel and frequently by fibrous texture.			

(1) *Boundary classifications:* Soils possessing characteristics of two groups are designated by combinations of group symbols. For example GW-GC, well-graded gravel-sand mixture with clay binder. (2) All sieve sizes on this chart are U. S. standard.

Field identification procedures for fine-grained soils or fractions. These procedures are to be performed on the minus No. 40 sieve size particles, approximately 1/64 in. For field classification purposes, screening is not intended, simply remove by hand the coarse particles that interfere with the tests.

Dilatancy (Reaction to shaking).

After removing particles larger than No. 40 sieve size, prepare a pat of moist soil with a volume of about one-half cubic inch. Add enough water if necessary to make the soil soft but not sticky.

Place the pat in the open palm of one hand and shake horizontally, striking vigorously against the other hand several times. A positive reaction consists of the appearance of water on the surface of the pat which changes to a livery consistency and becomes glossy. When the sample is squeezed between the fingers, the water and gloss disappear from the surface, the pat stiffens, and finally it cracks or crumbles. The rapidity of appearance of water during shaking and of its disappearance during squeezing assist in identifying the character of the fines in a soil.

Very fine clean sands give the quickest and most distinct reaction whereas a plastic clay has no reaction. Inorganic silts, such as a typical rock flour, show a moderately quick reaction.

Dry Strength (Crushing characteristics).

After removing particles larger than No. 40 sieve size, mold a pat of soil to the consistency of putty, adding water if necessary. Allow the pat to dry completely by oven, sun or air drying, and then test its strength by breaking and crumbling between the fingers. This strength is a measure of the character and quantity of the colloidal fraction contained in the soil. The dry strength increases with increasing plasticity.

High dry strength is characteristic for clays of the CH group. A typical inorganic silt possesses only very slight dry strength. Silty fine sands and silts have about the same slight dry strength, but can be distinguished by the feel when powdering the dried specimen. Fine sand feels gritty whereas a typical silt has the smooth feel of flour.

Toughness (Consistency near plastic limit).

After removing particles larger than the No. 40 sieve size, a specimen of soil about one-half inch cube in size, is molded to the consistency of putty. If too dry, water must be added and if sticky, the specimen should be spread out in a thin layer and allowed to lose some moisture by evaporation. Then the specimen is rolled out by hand on a smooth surface or between the palms into a thread about one-eighth inch in diameter. The thread is then folded and rerolled repeatedly. During this manipulation the moisture content is gradually reduced and the specimen stiffens, finally loses its plasticity, and crumbles when the plastic limit is reached.

After the thread crumbles, the pieces should be lumped together and a slight kneading action continued until the lump crumbles.

The tougher the thread near the plastic limit and the stiffer the lump when it finally crumbles, the more potent is the colloidal clay fraction in the soil. Weakness of the thread at the plastic limit and quick loss of coherence of the lump below the plastic limit indicate either inorganic clay of low plasticity, or materials such as kaolin-type clays and organic clays which occur below the A-line.

Highly organic clays have a very weak and spongy feel at the plastic limit.

TABLE 36-4 CLASSIFICATION OF HIGHWAY SUBGRADE MATERIALS
U. S. Bureau of Public Roads with 1945 Highway Research Board Modification

General Classification	*Granular Materials (35 Per Cent or Less Passing No. 200)*							*Silt-Clay Materials (More Than 35 Per Cent Passing No. 200)*			
Group Classification	*A-1*		*A-3*	*A-2*				*A-4*	*A-5*	*A-6*	*A-7*
	A-1-a	*A-1-b*		*A-2-4*	*A-2-5*	*A-2-6*	*A-2-7*				*A-7-5*, *A-7-6*
Sieve analysis per cent passing:											
No. 10	50 max										
No. 40	30 max	50 max	51 min								
No. 200	15 max	25 max	10 max	35 max	35 max	35 max	35 max	36 min	36 min	36 min	36 min
Characteristics of fraction passing No. 40:											
Liquid limit				40 max	41 min	40 max	41 min	40 max	41 min	40 max	41 min
Plasticity index	6 max		N.P.	10 max	10 max	11 min	11 min	10 max	10 max	11 min	11 min
Group index	0		0	0		4 max		8 max	12 max	16 max	20 max
Usual types of significant constituent materials	Stone fragments—gravel and sand		Fine sand	Silty or clayey gravel and sand				Silty soils		Clayey soils	
General rating as subgrade	Excellent to good					Fair to poor					

Classification procedure: With required test data in mind, proceed from left to right in chart; correct group will be found by process of elimination. The first group from the left consistent with the test data is the correct classification. The *A-7* group is subdivided into *A-7-5* or *A-7-6* depending on the plastic limit. For $P_w < 30$, the classification is *A-7-6*; for $P_w \geqq 30$, *A-7-5*.

N.P. denotes nonplastic.

Soil Characteristics

Because of their effect on the stability of structures, the following physical characteristics of soils are of interest to the engineer:

1. *Internal Friction* is the resistance of a soil to motion and it varies with size, shape and roughness of individual grains and with applied pressure. Sands have a high internal friction value, clay a low value.

2. *Cohesion* is the resistance to force tending to separate soil particles held together by moisture films, possibly supplemented by natural stickiness of colloids. Sands have a low value, clay a high value.

3. *Compressibility* is the change in volume that can be produced by pressure. Sands have a low value, whereas clays can have the capillary moisture squeezed out and therefore have a much higher value.

4. *Elasticity* is a characteristic of clays and some soils containing organic matter and is evidenced by rebound of the soil after removal of the load. Plasticity, on the other hand, is a property of clayey soils which at certain moisture contents can be deformed in the hand without disintegration. The liquid limits (Atterberg) and the plasticity index together constitute a measure of the plasticity of a soil.

5. *Permeability* is a measure of the rate or volume of flow of water through a soil. The coefficient of permeability depends largely on the void space and therefore on the size, shape and state of compaction of the soil grains. Permeability affects the spacing and depth of underdrains, and also the rate of settlement or compaction of soils under load. Clayey soils because of their finer grains and smaller pores are less permeable than sandy soils and therefore require longer to consolidate.

According to Eno[1], "It appears that soils having a clay content lower than 40 per cent, a volumetric change below 30, and a lower liquid limit[2] under 40 per cent, may be effectively drained. Soils containing more than 70 per cent clay are practically non-percolating."

6. *Capillarity* is the movement or absorption of water in a soil through the capillaries or hair-fine openings between the grains of soil. It takes place in all directions and is affected only in a minor way by gravity. Sands with their larger void spaces show little capillarity. Clays, by contrast, possess high capillarity which contributes to the properties of cohesion, compressibility, elasticity and permeability.

7. *Shrinkage and Bulking* of soils can be detrimental to engineering structures due to the change in volume, especially in cases of non-uniformity. The smaller the shrinkage limit as compared with the liquid limit, the greater is the tendency for the soil to undergo detrimental changes in volume with changes in moisture content.

Of considerable importance is the fact that the behavior of certain soils in their natural state and after they have been handled or reworked may be considerably different. This is explained by the repositioning of particles during the handling process which may cause them either to bulk up into a looser state or become more compacted than they were in nature. As a result, the performance of a given soil in nature having the same water content as dead soil after being reworked may not agree as predicted. Sand will bulk when slightly moist when poured into a container whereas the same amount of sand may contain the same moisture content in a natural state but occupy less volume. In finer grained soils, reworking will frequently show up as a change in the cohesive properties and bearing power of the material.

TABLE 36-5 SOIL CHARACTERISTICS PERTINENT TO EMBANKMENTS AND FOUNDATIONS (Corps of Engineers)

Coarse Grained Soils

Major Divisions (2)	*Name* (3)	*Value for Embankments* (4)	*Compaction Characteristics* (5)	*Std AASHO Max Unit Dry Weight Lb Per Cu Ft* (6)	*Value for Foundations* (7)	*Requirements for Seepage Control* (8)
Gravel and gravelly soils	Well-graded gravels or gravel-sand mixtures, little or no fines	Very stable, pervious shells of dikes and dams	Good, tractor, rubber-tired, steel-wheeled roller	125–135	Good bearing value	Positive cutoff
	Poorly-graded gravels or gravel-sand mixtures, little or no fines	Reasonably stable, pervious shells of dikes and dams	Good, tractor, rubber-tired, steel-wheeled roller	115–125	Good bearing value	Positive cutoff
	Silty gravels, gravel-sand-silt mixtures	Reasonably stable, not particularly suited to shells, but may be used for impervious cores or blankets	Good, with close control, rubber-tired, sheepsfoot roller	120–135	Good bearing value	Toe trench to none
	Clayey gravels, gravel-sand-clay mixtures	Fairly stable, may be used for impervious core	Fair, rubber-tired, sheepsfoot roller	115–130	Good bearing value	None
Sand and sandy soils	Well-graded sands or gravelly sands, little or no fines	Very stable, pervious sections, slope protection required	Good, tractor	110–130	Good bearing value	Upstream blanket and toe drainage or wells
	Poorly-graded sands or gravelly sands, little or no fines	Reasonably stable, may be used in dike section with flat slopes	Good, tractor	100–120	Good to poor bearing value depending on density	Upstream blanket and toe drainage or wells
	Silty sands, sand-silt mixtures	Fairly stable, not particularly suited to shells, but may be used for impervious cores or dikes	Good, with close control, rubber-tired, sheepsfoot roller	110–125	Good to poor bearing value depending on density	Upstream blanket and toe drainage or wells
	Clayey sands, sand-silt mixtures	Fairly stable, use for impervious core for flood control structures	Fair, sheepsfoot roller, rubber-tired	105–125	Good to poor bearing value	None

TABLE 36-5 (Cont'd) SOIL CHARACTERISTICS PERTINENT TO EMBANKMENTS AND FOUNDATIONS

Fine Grained Soils

Major Divisions (2)	*Name* (3)	*Value for Enbankments* (4)	*Compaction Characteristics* (5)	*Std AASHO Max Unit Dry Weight Lb Per Cu Ft* (6)	*Value for Foundations* (7)	*Requirements for Seepage Control* (8)
Silts and clays LL < 50	Inorganic silts and very fine sands, rock flour, silty or clayey fine sands or clayey silts with slight plasticity	Poor stability, may be used for embankments with proper control	Good to poor, close control essential, rubber-tired roller, sheepsfoot roller	95–120	Very poor, susceptible to liquefaction	Toe trench to none
	Inorganic clays of low to medium plasticity, gravelly clays, sandy clays, silty clays, lean clays	Stable, impervious cores and blankets	Fair to good, sheepsfoot roller, rubber-tired	95–120	Good to poor bearing	None
	Organic silts and organic silt-clays of low plasticity	Not suitable for embankments	Fair to poor, sheepsfoot roller	80–100	Fair to poor bearing, may have excessive settlements	None
Silts and clays LL > 50	Inorganic silts, micaceous or diatomaceous fine sandy or silty soils, elastic silts	Poor stability, core of hydraulic fill dam, not desirable in rolled fill construction	Poor to very poor, sheepsfoot roller	70–95	Poor bearing	None
	Inorganic clays of high plasticity, fat clays	Fair stability with flat slopes, thin cores, blankets and dike sections	Fair to poor, sheepsfoot roller	75–105	Fair to poor bearing	None
	Organic clays of medium to high plasticity, organic silts	Not suitable for embankments	Poor to very poor, sheepsfoot roller	65–100	Very poor bearing	None
Highly organic soils	Peat and other highly organic soils	Not used for construction	Compaction not practical		Remove from foundations	

Notes:

1. Values in columns 4 and 7 are for guidance only. Design should be based on test results.
2. In column 5, the equipment listed will usually produce the desired densities with a reasonable number of passes when moisture conditions and thickness of lift are properly controlled.
3. Column 6, unit dry weights are for compacted soil at optimum moisture content for Standard AASHO (Standard Proctor) compactive effort.

Fig. 203. Granular base material spread for the second lane of a divided highway in northern Ohio.

Subgrade Soil Classifications

Some of the earliest subgrade soil tests were made in 1914. Today most state highway departments make a regular practice of conducting soil surveys. Various colleges and universities, the U. S. Bureau of Public Roads, the Corps of Engineers and the Civil Aeronautics Administration and other organizations and individuals have contributed towards a more complete understanding of the properties affecting subgrade soil behavior.

The Bureau of Public Roads in 1928 set up a subgrade soil classification system, dividing soils into eight groups from A-1 to A-8. This system was extensively modified for the Highway Research Board in 1945 as shown in Table 36-4.

Another system of soil classification, developed by A. Casagrande for the U. S. Corps of Engineers, is known as the Airfield Classification (AC) system. It is used in the construction of military airfields. The system has many classifications but is relatively simple.

A third soil classification system, employed by the Civil Aeronautics Administration, is based on mechanical analysis, liquid limit and plasticity index. It also takes into account the drainage qualities and the degree of frost susceptibility.

Supplementing the unified soil classification, Table 36-3, of the Corps of Engineers and the Bureau of Reclamation is a further one, Table 36-5, from the Corps of Engineers, which relates these classifications to embankments and foundations.

Subgrade Soils

Subgrade or roadbed soils should be such that in combination with a pavement or ballast and track, they will support the loads without displacement. It usually is impractical to exclude all precipitation and surface water from passing down through cracks, shoulders or open ballast. The importance of removing such free water from the subgrade is discussed in Chapters 38-40 on Subdrainage.

The use of desirable subgrade soils is an aid to subdrainage as well as a means of intercepting capillary water, and avoiding frost damage, mud pumping and the formation of water pockets under the loads and impact of railroad traffic. Granular soils (such as the A-1, A-2 and A-3 groups of the Bureau of Public Roads) have relatively high values of internal friction and permeability and in general are satisfactory as subgrades for moderate combined thickness of base and surface courses[4].

According to Rockwell Smith[5], sands with high frictional qualities when compact are not subject to water pocket development under present conditions of railroad loading. A measure of the ability of sandy soils to maintain stability as railroad subgrades is the plasticity factor. Plasticity indices below 8 in sandy soils are generally indicative of very good subgrade support under present loadings. Silts when loosely compacted can be unstable. Good densification is difficult to obtain, which along with high capillary water holding properties make silts generally unsuitable for roadbed materials, particularly near the top of the subgrade. Pockets will develop in silt soils, although slowly. Frost heaving is prevalent and fills, unless well compacted under close control, continue to subside for long periods.

Silts may be non-plastic in the coarser materials and usually show plasticity indices under 10. Low plasticity in a predominantly silty soil is not a good measure of its stability in the subgrade. In addition, silts are subject to underground erosion and piping around leaking culverts, drains, etc.

Clays and clayey soils are most subject to loss of strength with increase in moisture content. Their permeability is relatively low and after once started, a pocket can develop quickly in the presence of water. The treatment for clays, where used, varies but should include provisions for drainage and for a granular cap or blanket sufficient to reduce stresses below the strength of the soils under unfavorable conditions. Fig. 203.

Making Soil Studies

Soil studies or surveys may vary in purpose and extent. They may be made in advance of new construction and thus assist in finding the best location and soils for

Fig. 204. Making soil borings along edge of highway pavement to locate water-bearing strata.

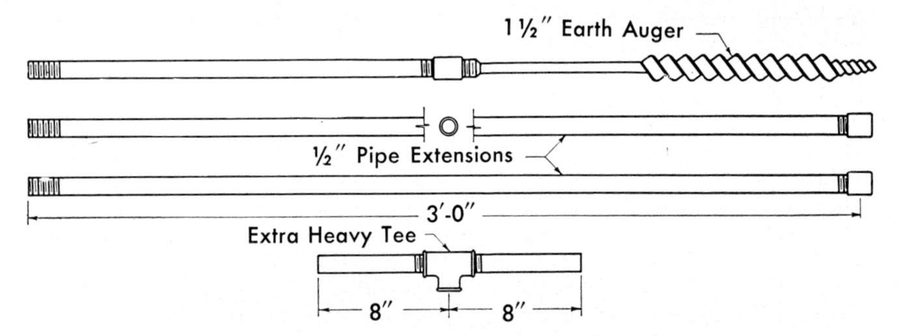

Fig. 205. An adequate soil survey can be made quickly and economically with this simple auger.

a road. Or they may be made on existing roads where trouble is being experienced due to heaving, unequal settlement or premature destruction of the road surface. Fig. 206.

The method of making these soil studies, both in the field and in the laboratory, varies with almost every state, but the following observations will be helpful.

1. Because ground water is the principal cause of the instability in subgrade soils, surveys should preferably be made in the spring or whenever ground-water conditions are at their worst.

2. Free ground water can often be detected as springs, as seepage flowing from the face of a slope or cut bank, or as seepage through the surface or shoulder of the road.

3. In the case of landslides and other conditions where a distant source of water is suspected of being the cause of the trouble, the use of fluorescein as a "tracer" sometimes enables the verification of the source of trouble[3]. This material is more stable and hence is used in preference to either potassium permanganate or common table salt. If salt is used, tests should first be made on the seepage water to make sure that there is no salt present.

4. A simple soil auger is generally sufficient for locating the free water-table or the impervious stratum. See Figs. 204 and 205.

5. Ledge rock and other conditions complicate the problem of locating free water, but regardless of the difficulty or expense of the investigation, the location of the water should not be guessed at if there has been trouble or trouble is anticipated.

6. Make observations in advance of construction, during construction and afterwards. More than one engineer gets first-hand information for his soil studies by "following behind the construction in rubber boots."

7. A road is no better than its foundation, so the study of the foundation should be commensurate with the importance of the road.

PART TWO

SOIL MOISTURE

Subgrade research has emphasized the fact that excess moisture in subgrade soils is in most cases the cause of unsatisfactory or varying support and the subsequent failure of the road surface, or the cause of rough track.

Water reaches the subgrade through percolation, seepage, springs, interception of water-bearing strata, capillarity, etc.

Kinds of Soil Moisture

Soil moisture is of three kinds: gravitational, capillary and hygroscopic.

1. Gravitational water is free to move under the influence of gravity. It is the only kind which can be removed by drainage.

2. Capillary moisture clings to the soil particles by surface tension and reaches the particles either when the free water passes through the soil, or by capillary attraction from a wetter to a drier stratum. It is not affected by gravity, being able to move upward as well as in any other direction, and cannot be removed by drainage but can be controlled by lowering the water-table. Capillary water can only be removed by heating, evaporation, freezing or subjecting it to great pressure.

The freezing of capillary water is explained under the heading "Theory of Frost Heaving," page 309. Thawing of the ice layers creates free water which can be removed by drainage.

3. Hygroscopic moisture (adsorbed water) is that which condenses from the

Fig. 206. Free water is often in plain sight and evident as the cause of poor foundations.

atmosphere upon the surface of the soil particles and combines with the soil. It cannot all be driven off, except by excessive heat, and it fails to freeze at −78 degrees C. It is of little or no importance to the engineer.

Capillary Water

When the grains of a soil are sufficiently fine, the capillary tubes are so small that capillarity (movement in any direction) is more powerful than gravity. Subdrainage will not remove capillary water directly, but it will control the height to which it can rise.

The presence of capillary moisture in a subgrade soil without the added presence of free water may not be distinctly harmful if it serves to bind the soil particles rather than lubricate them. However, the capillary moisture in any soil is generally about one-half more than the lower plastic limit, so that soils saturated to their capillary limit are in a condition to be dangerous.—(Eno.) Its greatest harmfulness generally occurs in connection with frost action, where, as explained on page 309, the formation of ice lenses causes heaving and subsequent liberation of free water which creates a mushy, unstable subgrade.

The rate of capillary action is more rapid for coarse-grained soils than for fine-grained ones. However, the maximum height to which the capillary water will rise in coarse-grained soils is much less than for the fine-grained. In a medium sand (0.3 mm. diameter soil particles) the water will rise about 18 inches above the water table (free water) level. In a silt (upper limit, 0.05 mm.), the rise may be about 9 feet, and in a clay the rise may be a little greater.

Subgrade soils vary all the way from coarse-grained to fine-grained, with perhaps a very large percentage falling in the middle group. The coarse-grained ones respond readily to drainage and the majority of the others do also. But the fine-grained clays are less susceptible to drainage.

Free Water

Free water enters or leaves the subgrade by the action of gravity. Such water percolates through the pores of various soils, through cracks, and through holes or channels formed by insects, worms, decayed plant roots and frost action. The porosity of the soils controls to a large extent the rate of flow.

Gravels and sands over impervious subsoils afford excellent underground channels, provided there is any slope to the top of the impervious underlying soil and provided they are not hemmed in by impervious soils. These same underground channels which will carry away ground water may also serve to bring unwanted water to the subgrade. This is quite evident where water-bearing strata or the underlying impervious strata are intercepted in cuts and sidehill excavation—perhaps most frequently just below the crest of a hill or where the road section changes from cut to fill. Fig. 214, p. 317.

While especially noticeable in the springtime, this seepage is often visible shortly after rains when the remainder of the road surface has dried off. Passing traffic also serves to "pump" some of this water through the cracks and joints or directly through the surface.

This water is harmful not only in that it lowers the bearing power and stability of the subgrade, but because it may freeze on the surface and create a hazard to traffic coming unawares upon these icy areas. Such water can and should be removed before it does harm.

Free water or gravitational moisture then is not only of greatest importance but fortunately is most susceptible to control.

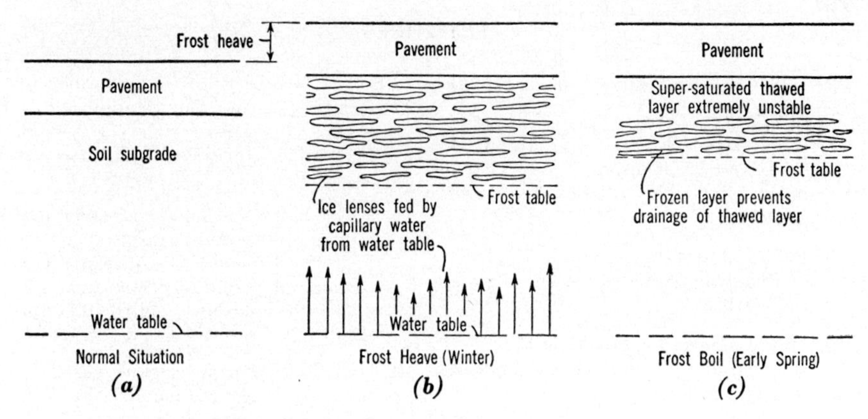

Fig. 207. Frost heave and frost boil in soil.—Spangler

Theory of Frost Heaving

It is well known that freezing of water in the subgrade can cause dangerous and destructive heaving, cracking and premature failure of road surfaces and pavements. If the heaving and later settlement were uniform there would perhaps not be much trouble, but it is the differential heaving, that causes the damage.

Considerable research has been done in the last 20 years on the theory of frost heaving among which are several informative studies made in the Scandinavian countries. Copies of these are available from the Highway Research Board on loan as well as many university studies in this country such as those carried on at the joint highway research project at Purdue University, Lafayette, Indiana.

A concise statement of the theory of frost heaving is given by F. H. Eno, as follows:

"In freezing weather with some fine silty-clay soils, where the rate of freezing and the movement of water in the capillaries appear to correlate, freezing seems to withdraw the water from the larger capillaries and to freeze it into lenticular masses of free ice, which continue to grow as more water is attracted until the excess supply of water through the capillaries has been exhausted, or until the rate of freezing increases beyond the rate at which the water is supplied. Then the soil and water are frozen as they stand until the correlation is again established and ice layers formed. (See Fig. 207.)

"It is quite evident, therefore, that when this situation arises, the pavement may be raised many times as much as it would normally be raised if the soils with the water it held was frozen without additional water entering. In fact, in northern Michigan, Wisconsin and Minnesota there may be 2 or more feet of heaving by this method. Of course, this is sufficient displacement to cause serious failure in the pavement."

1. "Soil Surveys for Highways—a Review of Present Practices and a Brief History," Ohio State Engineering Experiment Station Circular No. 33, F. H. Eno, July 1936.

2. The "lower liquid limit" is measured by the proportion of water to dry weight of soil that is required to bring the mixture just to the verge of flowing when slightly jarred. Eno.

REFERENCES

3. U. S. Geological Survey, Water Supply Paper No. 160.

4. "Foundation Engineering," by R. B. Peck, W. E. Hanson, T. H. Thornburn, John Wiley & Sons, Inc., New York, 1953.

5. Rockwell Smith, Research Engineer of Roadway, American Assn. of Railroads, 1953.

*6. "Soil Engineering," by M. G. Spangler, International Textbook Co., Scranton, Pa., 1951.

*7. "The Application of Aerial Strip Photography to Highway and Airport Engineering," by J. E. Hittle, Proceedings of Highway Research Board, Vol. 26, 1946.

*8. "New Glacial Features indentified by Airport Photos Soil Mapping Program," by R. E. Frost and J. B. Mollard, Proceedings of Highway Research Board, Vol. 26, 1946.

*9. "Landslides, a selective annotated bibliography," Bibliography No. 10, Highway Research Board, 1951. This bibliography contains some 290 references to landslides and the relationship to water and soil types.

*10. "Soil Mechanics in Engineering Practice," by K. Terzaghi and R. B. Peck, John Wiley & Sons, Inc., New York, 1948.

*11. "Theoretical Soil Mechanics," by K. Terzaghi, John Wiley & Sons, Inc., New York, 1942.

*Additional references or bibliographies—not specifically referred to in the text.

CHAPTER THIRTY-SEVEN

Design of Subdrains

Summary

There are two important kinds of soil moisture—free and capillary. A little moisture may help to bind soils together and make them more compact. However, excess moisture is detrimental in that it reduces the capacity of soils to support loads, and, if it freezes, it usually results in detrimental heaving. Embankments, pavements, runways and tracks are robbed of adequate support, so that they fail prematurely or require excessive maintenance. Slopes become unstable, landslides occur.

Subsurface drainage continues to be a mystery to many design, construction and maintenance engineers. Consequently in too many cases the tendency is to treat the effect without eliminating the cause.

The solution is simple. Choose the best soils. Drain the water out and keep it out. A dry soil makes the best foundation.

Soil Studies

Recognizing that soils are a raw construction material, many engineering departments have made soil studies a required part of their survey and investigational work. It is known that some soils make better foundations and backfill materials than do others (see Chapter 36, Soil Studies).

Also well known but less understood is the important relationship of the moisture content of soils to their stability. Soil *moisture* studies are needed—the location, source and direction of flow and fluctuation of ground water table. These are best made in spring or during the wet season.

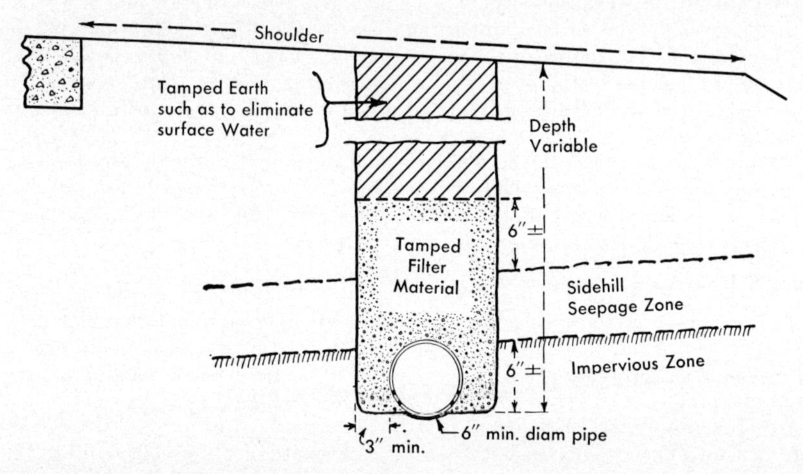

Fig. 208. An intercepting drain placed in the impervious zone is effective for preventing poor foundation for a roadway.

TABLE 37-1 REQUIRED CAPACITY OF A SUBDRAIN TO REMOVE VARIOUS DEPTHS OF WATER IN 24 HOURS

Depth in Inches		*Capacity in Cu Ft per Sec*	
Fraction	*Decimal*	*Per Acre*	*Per Sq Mile*
1	1.000	.0420	26.88
15/16	.938	.0394	25.20
7/8	.875	.0367	23.52
13/16	.812	.0341	21.84
3/4	.750	.0315	20.16
11/16	.688	.0289	18.48
5/8	.625	.0262	16.80
9/16	.562	.0236	15.12
1/2	.500	.0210	13.44
7/16	.438	.0184	11.76
3/8	.375	.0157	10.08
5/16	.312	.0131	8.40
1/4	.250	.0105	6.72
3/16	.188	.0079	5.04
1/8	.125	.0052	3.36
1/16	.062	.0026	1.68

Subsurface Runoff and Drainage

Ground water may consist of an underground "reservoir" or it may be flowing through a thin seam between impervious strata, or through a thick seam of pervious material. It may be concentrated in the form of a spring.

The amount of subsurface runoff is in general equal to the amount that soaks into the ground from surface application, less that lost by evaporation and that used by plants. The nature of the terrain, its size, shape and slopes, as well as the character and slopes of the substrata are contributing factors. Rate of subsurface flow depends on the permeability of the soil, the slope of the substrata and the tributary area.

It is difficult to calculate the flow or runoff of ground water by any formulas. The more practical way may be to observe the flow into a trench or test pit. This is especially helpful where an *intercepting* drain (Fig. 208) is to be placed across a seepage zone in order to intercept or divert the flow.

Runoff from Large Areas

In the case of landing fields, athletic fields and other large flat or rolling areas, including farm land, the subsurface runoff has by experiment been determined as equivalent to a certain uniform depth of water to be drained away within a period of 24 hours.

Experiments by the Engineering Experiment Station of Iowa State College and the Agricultural Experiment Station of the University of Minnesota indicate that 5/16 to 3/8 inch of water in 24 hours is a satisfactory rate of runoff for average soils. This factor may be increased to 3/4 or even 1 inch in 24 hours in regions of excep-

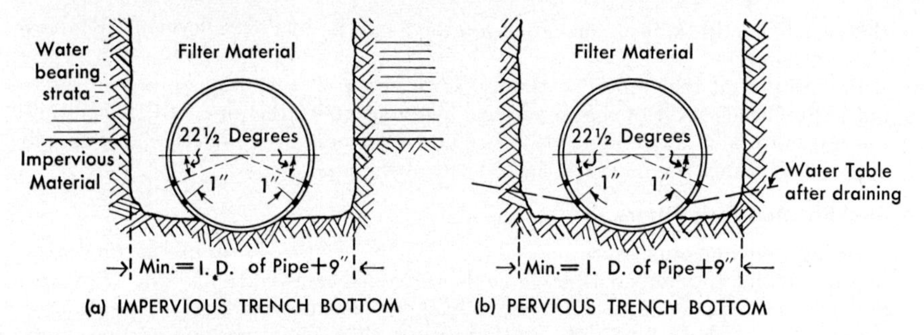

Fig. 209. The bottom of a subdrain pipe should be deep enough in an impervious material (a) to effect complete removal of the water. In a pervious soil (b) the water table is lowered to the bottom row of perforations. Space in the bottom of the pipe between the rows of perforations is sufficient to carry normal flow.

tionally heavy rainfall and where more pervious soils are encountered. The exact factor should be determined by a study of local conditions.

While it is customary to refer to subsurface runoff as inches of depth over the watershed or drainage area to be removed in 24 hours, this unit, called "drainage coefficient," must be converted to cubic feet per second per acre before runoff requirements can be compared with subdrain capacity. See conversion table (Table 37-1) for this purpose.

Example of Runoff Computation

The following simple formula is given:

$$Q = Az$$

in which

Q = discharge or required capacity, in cu ft per sec
A = area to be subdrained, in acres
z = subsurface runoff factor, converted to cu ft per sec per acre

Assuming a drainage coefficient of ⅜ inch in 24 hours ($z = .0157$), and laterals 600 ft long, spaced on 50-ft centers, the following result is obtained:

$$Q = .0157 \times \frac{600 \times 50}{43{,}560} = .0108 \text{ cu ft per sec}$$

This result is for the area served by each main or submain (for the area A in the formula), and is not the sum of the discharges from all contributing laterals.

Kinds of Subdrains

Subdrainage (or underdrainage) is defined as the control of ground water. Early subdrains consisted of a trench filled with brush or large rocks which quickly silted up. French drains, which are trenches filled with coarse rock, are not satisfactory for long periods of time. They are inefficient and require excessive maintenance.

The modern subdrain has these important features: a trench filled with a finely graded pervious material (known as a filter), and with a subdrain pipe for controlling the water and quickly conducting it away. The top of the trench is sealed to keep out surface water and silt. To insure complete interception and collection the trench should be deep enough so the pipe can be in the impervious zone (see Fig. 208, p. 311).

Preparation of the trench bottom is shown in Fig. 209. Former practice was to put a 2 to 4-inch layer of coarse pervious material under the pipe, but this permits the water to flow under the pipe. In muddy bottoms, use only enough granular material to stiffen the mud and keep it out of the pipe.

Backfill Material; Filters

Silting and plugging up is one of the principal causes of failure of subdrains. Coarse backfill materials with large voids were once believed to be best. However, research and experience show that such backfills encourage silting.

Extensive research by the U. S. Waterways Experiment Station at Vicksburg, Miss., shows that a graded material roughly equivalent to concrete sand (AASHO Specs.) has been found most suitable. See Table 37-2 and Fig. 210, for a typical analysis. Such material gives better support to the side wall of the trench and thereby reduces erosion and silting.

Sealed Trench

Use of a sealed trench top keeps out surface water which may carry silt and clog the backfill. The material used to obtain imperviousness may be clay or an artificial mixture employing asphalt or other binder.

On ordinary construction it is advisable to remove surface water by means of gutters and catchbasins or drop inlets rather than through the trench backfill.

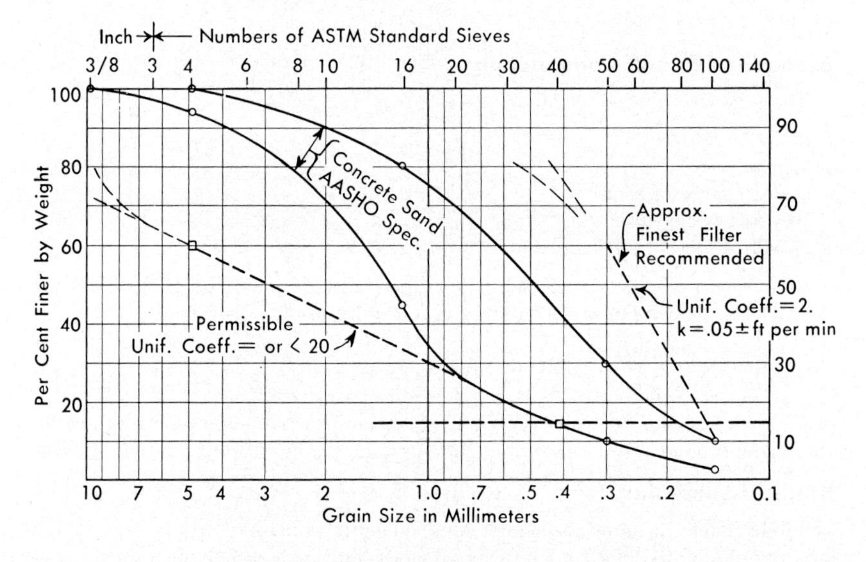

Fig. 210. Chart showing range and gradation of granular material to give most suitable backfill for a subdrain pipe. AASHO concrete sand falls within the recommended limits. Maximum size is ⅜-in. gravel.

TABLE 37-2 SIZE OF FILTER MATERIAL FOR SUBDRAINS

Standard ASTM Sieve	*Per Cent*
Passing a 3/8-in. sieve	100
Passing a No. 4 sieve	95–100
Passing a No. 16 sieve	45–80
Passing a No. 50 sieve	10–30
Passing a No. 100 sieve	2–10

AASHO Spec. M6-51, Gradation limits of concrete sand.

However, if the subdrain is adequate in size, and can be cleaned out when necessary, surface water can safely be admitted through the backfill.

Subdrain Pipe

Any subdrainage system to be economically sound must continue to function efficiently year after year. When a subdrain stops functioning, it can usually be traced to crushing and breaking of the pipe or to mal-alignment and clogging. To replace failed pipe often costs more than the original installation.

Perforated corrugated metal pipe is used widely as a means of controlling ground water. Fig. 211. Advantages given are long lengths, light weight, strength, positive coupled joints, ample infiltration area but with exclusion of solids. Diameters for Hel-Cor pipe range from 6 to 21 in. Standard perforated corrugated pipe ranges from 8 in. up. (AASHO Spec. M-136, and AREA Manual, 1953, page 1-4-11).

The Vicksburg tests showed least clogging occurs with porous or perforated walls rather than through open joints. Other experiments showed that with the use of finely graded backfill, least clogging takes place when the perforations are in the bottom half of the pipe and at least 22½ degrees below the horizontal axis. Also,

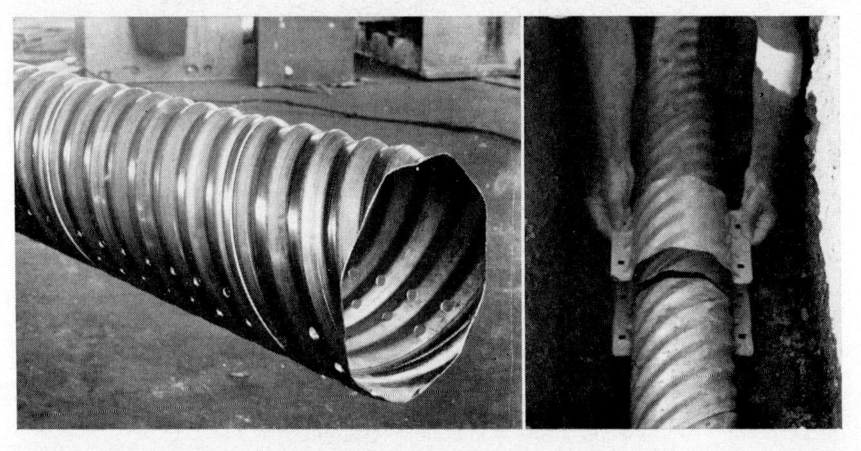

Figs. 211–212. Section of helically corrugated (Hel-Cor) perforated pipe (left). Method of joining lengths of pipe with two-piece bolted coupling.

a minimum of 16 perforations, ⅜ in. in diameter, per linear foot of pipe is desirable for all pipe sizes.

Where portions of the line are used as a water conductor rather than interceptor, the perforations may be turned up or may be omitted. The pervious backfill should be eliminated beyond the point where seepage occurs.

Pipe Size and Slope

For normal subdrainage, approximately 500 ft of 6-in. pipe may be used as an interceptor before any increase in diameter is needed. In other cases, larger sizes may be desirable.

Where possible, a minimum slope of 0.15 ft per 100 ft should be employed for all subdrainage lines. It is sometimes permissible to use an even flatter slope where necessary to obtain a free outlet.

Fig. 213. It is important that a subdrain outlet be high enough to prevent clogging. Corrugated metal pipe cantilevered over a channel is commonly used for this purpose.

Pipe Outlets

Free outlets are important; and the failure of subdrains to function properly can often be attributed to plugged, damaged or improper outlets.

Outlet pipes should be built high enough so they cannot clog from silt or snow. Fig. 213. Otherwise the maintenance man must keep them open and be sure not to damage them with his maintenance equipment. A suitable screen should be used to keep out rodents whose nests would cause clogging.

If it is difficult to obtain a suitable outlet for the subdrainage system, it may be necessary to carry the water to a sump and then pump it out.

CHAPTER THIRTY-EIGHT

Highway Subdrainage

"A good road requires a tight roof and a dry cellar."—*Anonymous*

Symptoms of Trouble

Spring is known to be the bad time of the year for roads—the time when breakups occur. That is when the frost goes out. At other seasons, especially after rains, water flows freely from joints and cracks in the road surface. Mud pumping occurs. Fig. 214.

Results are rough, broken, dangerous pavements. Maintenance and repair costs are high. Next year the trouble is repeated.

A rapid increase in the amount of traffic, traveling at higher speeds and a greater proportion of heavy truck and bus traffic has made the situation worse.

The cause of the trouble is almost always the same—"too much water and not enough drainage."*

*"New York Reduces Frost Damage," by Earl I. Fuller, Senior Soils Engr., N. Y. State Dept. of Public Works, in *Better Roads*, Chicago, March 1951.

Fig. 214. Cut sections or where the roadway changes from cut to fill are frequently locations of poor drainage and bad pavement. Water flowing out from cracks and joints is an obvious signal of the source of trouble.

Dry Foundation Important

Although water is easily recognized as the cause of the trouble, the method of overcoming it is not universally understood. Instead of removing the cause, the tendency too often is to treat the symptoms—namely by adding gravel, patching the surface or resurfacing the whole pavement.

"If a sufficiently firm roadbed could be obtained, any thin surface which would not shatter under traffic and which would withstand abrasive wear, should be sufficient," says F. C. Lang, Engineer of Materials and Tests, Minnesota Dept. of Highways.

"All highway surfaces depend upon the underlying earth for their support," reads a booklet published by the Michigan State Highway Department. "If that support is weak, or if it lacks uniformity, it may fail to fulfill its function. Further, if improved surfaces are built upon soils which at certain seasons are subject to extreme changes in volume, not only is support lacking, but destructive counter stresses may be developed which will result in serious heaves, frost boils, excessive pavement cracking and similar troubles. No type or design of surface is capable of successfully resisting these forces. It becomes evident, therefore, that the design of the road should begin with the subgrade, and that effective preventive measures taken in the initial stages of construction will be reflected by ultimate economy in maintenance."

Surface vs. Base

There are several ways of providing a road surface strong enough to carry traffic. If the native soil has good natural drainage, all that may be required is a waterproofing of the surface and stabilizing or strengthening of the top few inches of soil.

Heavier traffic requires a stronger surface or pavement. Under this may be a compacted impervious base or a pervious base. This in turn is supported by the native subgrade (in cut) or by a fill built on the native soil or foundation (see Fig. 203, p. 304).

The drier each one of these strata is within limits, the less thickness is required. There is a direct relationship between drainage and economy of construction.

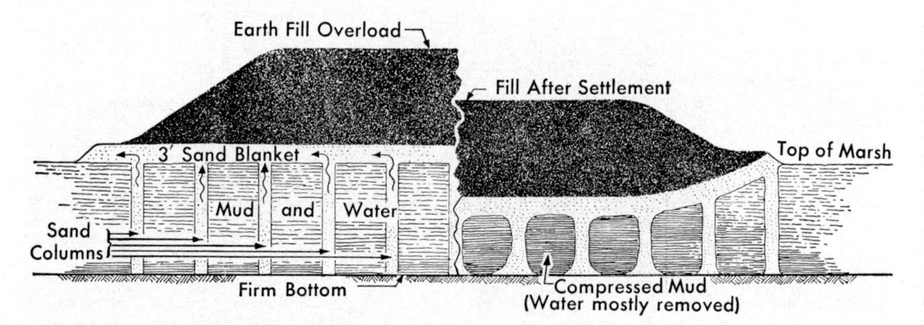

Fig. 215. Modern method of squeezing the water from swampy ground and removing it through vertical sand drains. Pipe outlets are recommended when practicable.—Drawing from Garden State (N. J.) Parkway bulletin.

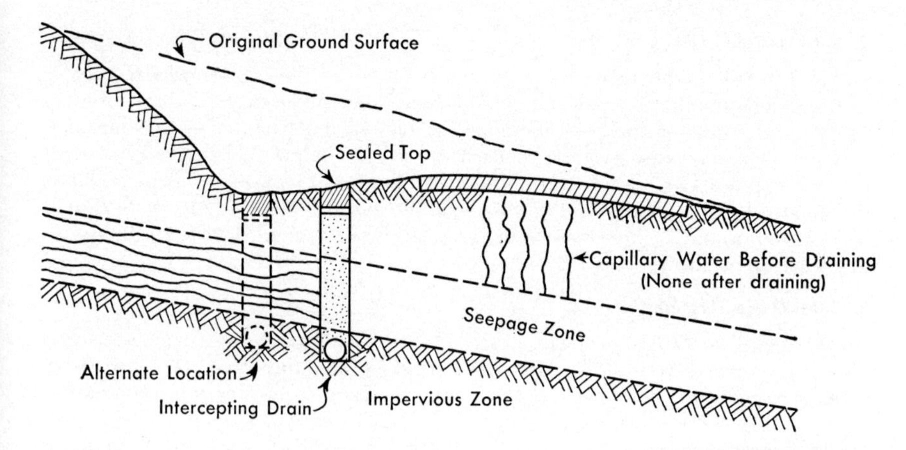

Fig. 216. How intercepting drain cuts off the source of supply of harmful capillary water—and free water—under a road surface. Note that the top of the trench is sealed to prevent silting.

Three General Conditions

Soil surveys to locate free ground water will usually indicate one of the following conditions:

Sidehill seepage
Level water table
Surface leakage

Depending on the kind of soil, capillary water may rise from the first two conditions to aggravate subgrade troubles.

Sidehill seepage should be intercepted, preferably before the water enters the roadway area (see Fig. 216). For level water table conditions, it may be possible to lower the water table below the effective capillary limit by means of subdrainage pipe in a pervious backfilled trench (page 311), or to greater depths by loading with an embankment and removing the water by vertical sand drains (Fig. 215). New road locations should avoid large swampy areas when possible.

Where surface leakage occurs, base drainage is advisable (Figs. 203 and 217).

1. Fill Foundation Drainage

An embankment exerts a load or pressure on its foundation. If that foundation soil is wet or compressible, settlement occurs, depending on the fill height. Where seepage strata or springs exist, a subdrain trench and pipe should be placed low enough to intercept the ground water and conduct it to an outlet.

Where a fill is to be built across swampy ground, it may be possible to place a thick blanket of sand over the area, drilling or driving holes into the subsoil, and backfilling with sand. The fill is built over the sand blanket to an extra height for load purposes, and later reduced to finished grade. Fig. 215.

Weight of the fill compresses the foundation soil and squeezes the water up through the "sand piles," then laterally through the sand blanket to an outlet. Perforated metal pipe subdrains are used to direct such water to a suitable outlet.

2. Soft, Unstable Fills

Where fills have not been properly made, based on present knowledge of soils and drainage, mudholes, mud-pumping and soft spots may develop. Such fills may subside or "go out" entirely at some time. See Fig. 247 and Chapter 44 on Landslides.

A more common case even on modern roads is for fills to be supplied with free water through underground strata from an adjacent cut section. If at all possible, the source of water should be located and intercepted. Where the trouble cannot be localized, it may be necessary to use cross drains at various depths and intervals to effectively drain the mass.

3. Sidehill and Through Cuts

For sidehill or lateral seepage conditions, two conditions are considered—one where the seepage zone falls within the cut slope and the other where it passes under the roadway. The zone may be a narrow seam or a deep, pervious (laminated) zone (see Fig. 216).

Cut slopes eroded by seepage are unsightly. Very often they result in mud, water and ice on the traveled roadway. For a relatively low bank, the remedy may consist of an intercepting drain on the top of the bank to prevent the water reaching the face of the cut. The slope becomes stable and can be maintained as desired.

Where the seepage zone is under the road, two cases are considered. In the first case, the top of the seepage zone is 2 to 4 ft below the road surface, and the bottom 7 ft or less. There can be free water in the subgrade, pumped up by traffic. On the other hand, the damaging agent can be capillary water which causes an unstable subgrade or frost heave.

The suggested solution is to place an intercepting drain either in the shoulder or in the ditch line to shut off the free water before it enters the roadway area.

In the second case, with a wide (deep) seepage zone, the problem is to lower the water table sufficiently to reduce the effective height reached by capillary water. The drain will probably be at least 6 ft deep.

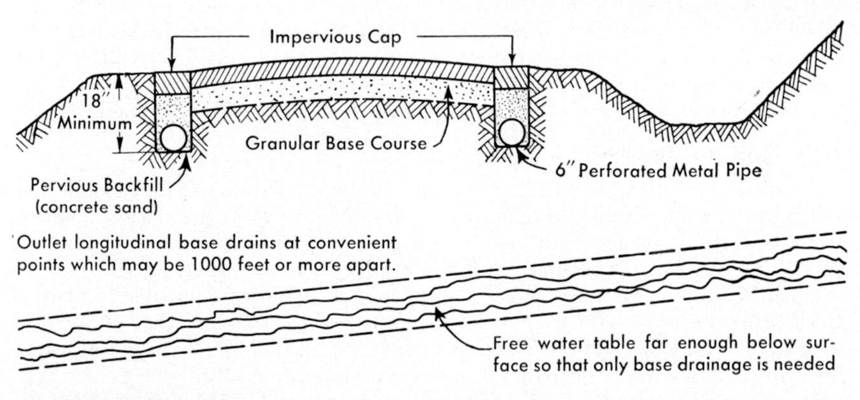

Fig. 217. Base drainage is needed to remove surface water that may be trapped when a pervious base is laid over a relatively impervious subgrade. On steep slopes, laterals may be added under the pavement.

Fig. 218. Placing subdrains in a cut section along the West Virginia Turnpike. Base drains are usually shallower than intercepting drains.

4. Rock Cuts

Ledge rock under the side ditches or under the roadway may hold pockets of water and cause the road foundation to become saturated. Frost heaving aggravates the trouble. The remedy consists of making original rock cuts deeper (1 to 4 ft) and backfilling with pervious material drained with a subdrain pipe. One state highway district in New York specifies that undrainable pockets be filled with a fine-grained bituminous mix.

On old construction the ditch can be deepened, but it may be necessary to blast a trench under or along both sides of the road surface.

Where boulders exist under the pavement area, they are likely to work their way to the surface and give trouble unless they are removed below frost penetration depth. However, if the base is drained, this heaving should not occur.

5. Transition from Cut to Fill

Although previously mentioned under Soft, Unstable Fills, the transition from cut to fill section is such a frequent location of pavement break-ups that special attention is deserved. The ground water usually follows or flows on top of an impervious stratum or is retained in undrainable soil or rock pockets.

The remedy consists of placing a subdrain across the roadway in the cut to intercept the seepage and to using a pervious base to a depth of several feet under the finished grade line in the transition area.

6. High Water Table Conditions

There are further ways in which water can get into the subgrade under the road surface to make the subgrade spongy and unable to properly support the pavement, namely:

Capillary water through clays or silty subsoils.
Percolation through cracks, pavement joints, porous surfaces.
Surface water resulting from rutted or improperly crowned shoulders; snow banks on high shoulders; farm entrance and side road culverts too small; shallow, clogged side ditches; culverts across the road plugged up.
Water trapped in a pervious base trench without adequate outlet.

Capillary water can be kept from reaching the pavement subgrade or the frost zone in two ways. One is to lower the water table by means of a subdrain as shown in Fig. 216, p. 319. The other is to place a blanket of sand or a base of finely graded pervious material under the pavement (see Fig. 203, p. 304). Even though the pervious layer may extend to the side slopes, the use of an underdrain pipe assures positive drainage at all times.

Percolation through cracks, pavement joints and porous surfaces can largely but not entirely be prevented by proper sealing and other maintenance measures. More positive assurance against such "roof leakage" and subsequent pumping joints can be obtained by the use of a pervious base, properly drained.

Where surface water reaches the subgrade because of rutted or high shoulders, clogged ditches and culverts and the like, proper maintenance is the best cure.

CHAPTER THIRTY-NINE

Railway Subdrainage

Effects of Soil Moisture

Some soils are recognized as making a more stable railroad roadbed and foundations than others, namely granular soils high in internal friction and cohesion, and low in compressibility, capillarity and elasticity. A large clay content is usually adverse. New construction should use only the best available soils. Water is the principal enemy of soil stability.

"Excess soil moisture in the roadbed is detrimental in four respects: (a) it greatly reduces the bearing power of soils of all kinds, some more than others, resulting in 'soft spots'; (b) in case of freezing it causes 'heaving'; (c) in case of increase or decrease of amount of excess moisture, unequal swelling or shrinkage results in unequal displacement of the track and (d) it leads often to subsidence and slides."*

Control of Ground Water

Adequate surface drainage is the first step towards providing a dry, stable roadbed. This is achieved by proper crown, slopes, intercepting and side ditches, culverts and other means described elsewhere in this handbook.

---

*AREA Manual, Committee 1, Roadway, Sec. V Roadway Drainage.

Fig. 219. Sandy backfill being placed around perforated pipe subdrain under a track in a new railroad yard at Roseville, California.

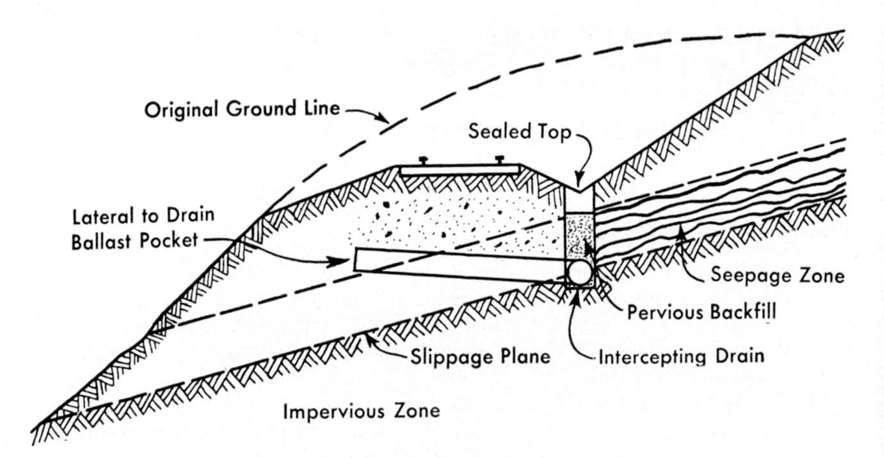

Fig. 220. Typical intercepting drain under railroad track with laterals to drain wet ballast pockets.

Soil moisture, passing through or retained by the roadbed, foundation or side slopes, is of two principal kinds—gravitational and capillary. Gravitational or free water can be controlled by pervious subdrain trenches, subdrainage pipe and other channels. Capillary water moves less freely. It cannot be removed directly by drainage, although by lowering the water table it can be controlled to some extent. Also it can be prevented from rising by a thick layer of pervious material.

Long experience has shown that simple drainage measures are effective in intercepting or removing harmful ground water. Such drainage is long lasting and generally more economical than other measures which treat the symptoms rather than the cause of the trouble. A dry soil is a strong, stable soil.

Fill Foundation

Either a high fill or a relatively low fill may overload the foundation soil if it is not dry and stable. Soil studies and borings made in advance may reveal a high water table in swampy ground, springs or water-bearing strata near the surface. One solution is to place a subdrain trench and pipe and conduct the water to an outlet.

On swampy ground it may be possible to place a thick blanket of sand over the area, drilling or driving holes into the subsoil and backfilling them with sand. The use of such sand piles is described on p. 319. Perforated metal pipe subdrains carry the water to a suitable outlet.

Water Pockets

Water pockets (according to the 1953 AREA Manual, 1-1-52) result from ballast being driven by increasingly heavy loads into unstable subgrade soils in cut or on fill, causing it to hold water.

Water pockets can sometimes be prevented during construction by choosing stable materials, compacted and crowned before ballasting. Proper kind and depth of sub-ballast is also important.

Placing subdrains at the time the roadbed is constructed, especially in cut sections, is good insurance against the formation of water pockets. A typical example is shown in Fig. 220, with perforated metal side drains and laterals.

Where water pockets already exist, the following procedure is recommended. Test holes should be dug or drilled at frequent intervals to determine the extent and depth of the pockets. Subdrains to tap the low spots are usually placed at right angles to the track, spaced from 15 to 30 ft or more, depending on conditions. Perforated metal pipe 6 or 8 in. in diameter should be placed 6 to 12 in. below the bottom of the pocket on a minimum grade of 0.3 per cent and backfilled with a finely graded filter material.

In cut sections it will usually be necessary to provide an outlet for the laterals by means of mains in one or both ditches. Such mains should be at least 6 in. below the bottom of the deepest pocket, on a minimum grade of 0.15 per cent.

Wet Cuts

Water pockets and unstable track in cut sections are likely to be aggravated by lateral seepage. Deep side ditches may be of some help, but the more satisfactory way of remedying the situation is to place an intercepting drain in the ditch of a sidehill cut, or in both ditches of a long cut, on a minimum grade of 0.15 per cent (see Fig. 221). Laterals should extend under the track at intervals of 25 to 30 ft.

Multiple Tracks

There is practically no difference between draining a roadbed carrying two or more tracks and one carrying a single track, except that surface water must be accommodated. For a double track it may not be necessary to use a longitudinal main between the tracks in addition to the subdrain laterals and mains on both sides of the roadbed. However, for other cases, a longitudinal drain of perforated metal pipe is recommended between tracks or each pair of tracks. Such drain should be of 8-in. diameter or larger, on a grade of 0.15 per cent or more, backfilled with a finely graded pervious material.

Lateral outlets of unperforated corrugated pipe should be provided at intervals of 200 to 500 ft to discharge into the side mains or ditches, or the right of way on fill sections.

Fig. 221. Subdrainage with Hel-Cor perforated pipe in a low cut along the C&NW RR in Iowa.

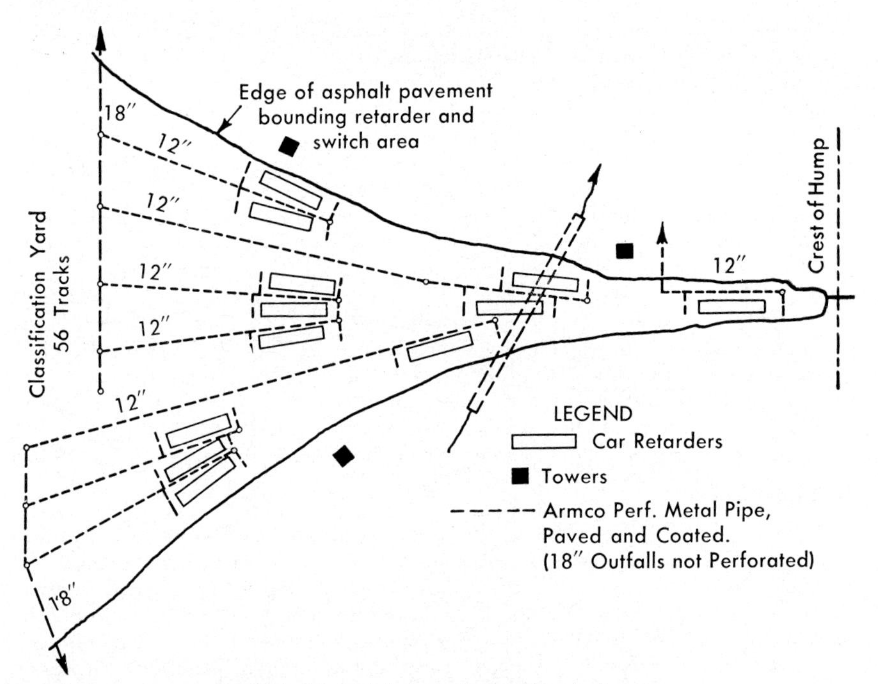

Fig. 222. Principal drainage features in retarder section of Santa Fe Railway yard at Kansas City, Kansas.

Yards and Stations

For the large, wide flat areas occupied by railroad yards and terminals, special drainage problems present themselves. (AREA Manual, 1-53, 505, E). Tracks in such congested areas should be kept in first class condition with a minimum of maintenance (see Fig. 219).

Unless the subgrade soil is an open, well-drained one, a combined storm drain and subsurface drainage system is required (see Fig. 222). Proper design at the time a yard is constructed or reconstructed will help much in the control of surface water for quick runoff at right angles to the tracks. Surface water reaching the yard from adjacent areas should cross the yard preferably in a closed conduit or storm sewer.

Water falling on the yard area should be handled by a storm sewer system which may also serve for subdrainage if sufficiently deep. In general, a series of longitudinal drains of perforated pipe between pairs of tracks with cross drains at intervals of 200 to 300 ft and an intercepting drain across the ends of these cross drains will be satisfactory.

Risers with iron gratings should be provided at junction points to catch the surface water. All subdrainage pipe should be backfilled with fine pervious material. Sizes of pipe will depend on the areas drained. Depth and spacing of pipe depend on soil and ground water conditions but in general should be 3 to 6 ft below the ties.

The drainage system should outlet into surface ditches, or in the case of passenger car yards and stations into storm sewers. If these outlets are not deep enough, a sump and automatic pump should be provided.

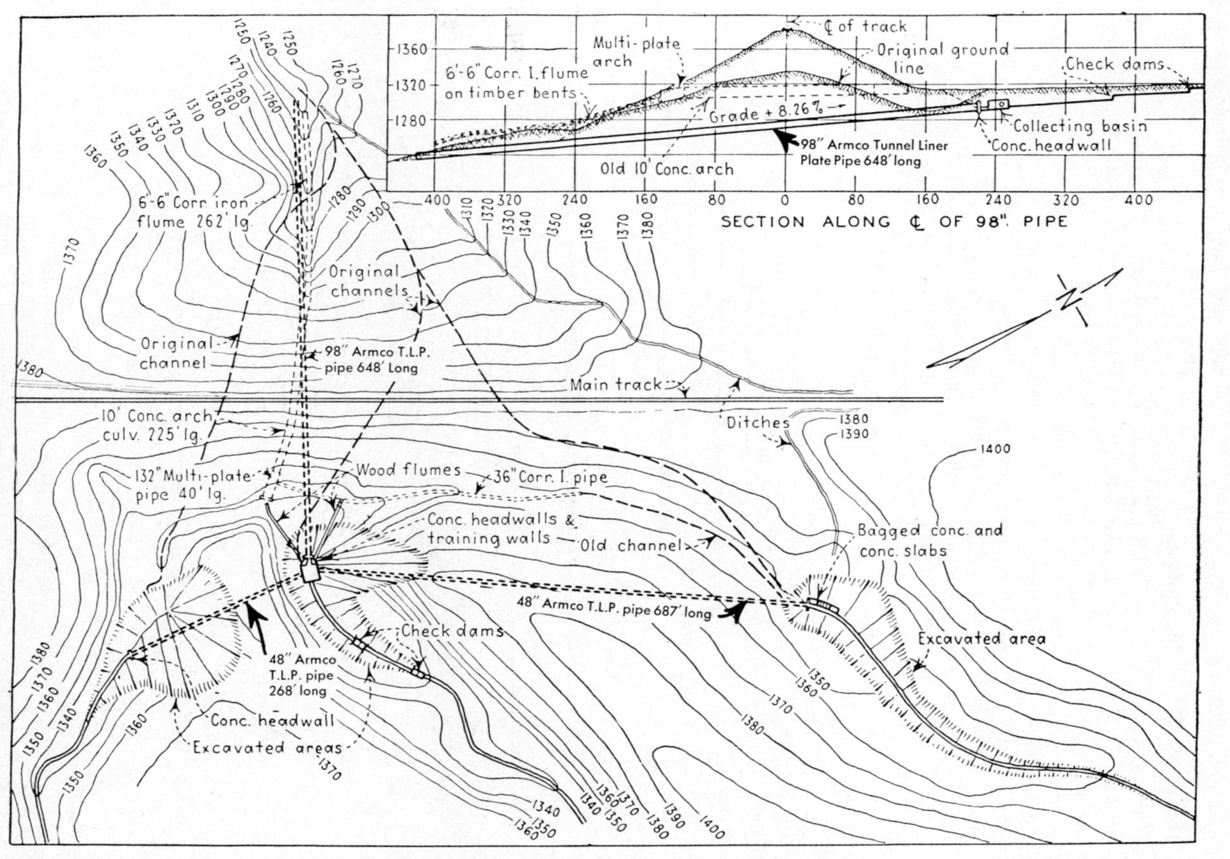

Fig. 223. System of large drains for surface and subsurface water installed by tunneling which aided in stabilizing a particularly wet high fill on the Erie RR in western New York State.—From *Railway Track and Structures*, Chicago.

Passenger Terminals and station platforms should have a line of subdrain pipe in a trench between the ends of the ties and the edge of the platform, with catchbasins and laterals at intervals of 200 to 300 ft. Backfill with fine pervious material.

Highway Grade Crossings

Wherever railroad tracks cross each other at grade or where railroad tracks cross a highway at grade, the problem is to keep a smooth-riding crossing with minimum maintenance.

Drainage should consist of perforated metal pipe placed in a trench at the ends of the ties on single and double tracks and between pairs of multiple tracks. On two or more tracks, perforated metal cross drains should also be placed at the uphill side of crossings in order to drain the intertrack spaces. Otherwise such spaces may act as subsurface channels and conduct storm water to crossings. Pipe should be on at least a 0.3 per cent grade and at a depth of 3 to 4 ft below the ties if on embankment, or, if in cut, as controlled by the bottom of the side ditches (see Fig. 224). All trenches should be filled with fine material (similar to AREA concrete sand).

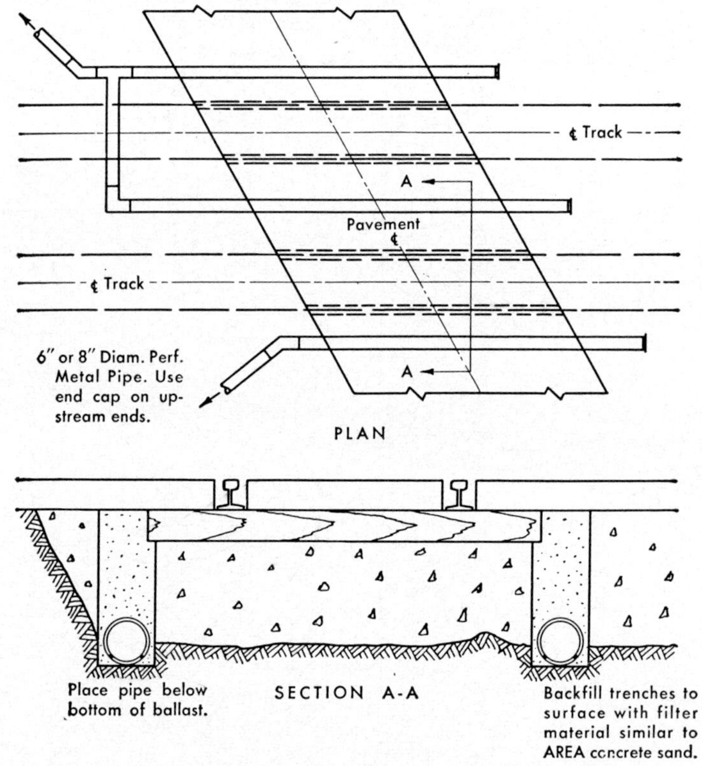

Fig. 224. Subdrainage of railway—highway grade crossing under normal conditions. A dry, stable foundation improves the riding surfaces and reduces maintenance.

Fig. 225. The city of Baltimore, Maryland, uses perforated pipe subdrains to maintain smoother riding surfaces and for less frequent pavement repairs of its thoroughfares.

CHAPTER FORTY

Municipal Subdrainage

Street Subdrains

City streets differ but little from many rural highways when it comes to loads and foundations. The problem of adequate drainage is common to both.

Where free water exists in the subgrade, it is advisable to determine the source, direction and depth. Ground water flow should be intercepted by placing a pipe subdrain in the grass plot behind the curb in residential districts and wherever most convenient in business and industrial districts. Generally such subdrains are parallel to the curb. However, in case of wide streets, laterals may be needed at right angles to or diagonally with the curb. Figs. 225, 226.

It is important to get the subdrain into the impervious zone so that all water will be intercepted. The outlet can generally be a storm sewer manhole. Where a pervious base is needed under a pavement, that base should be provided with a pipe interceptor and outlet.

Golf Courses, Parks, Cemeteries

Soft, spongy areas interfere with play and with maintenance operations. On golf courses they may reduce the income from greens fees, or may make a golf course or park unpopular. They also increase maintenance costs and make it

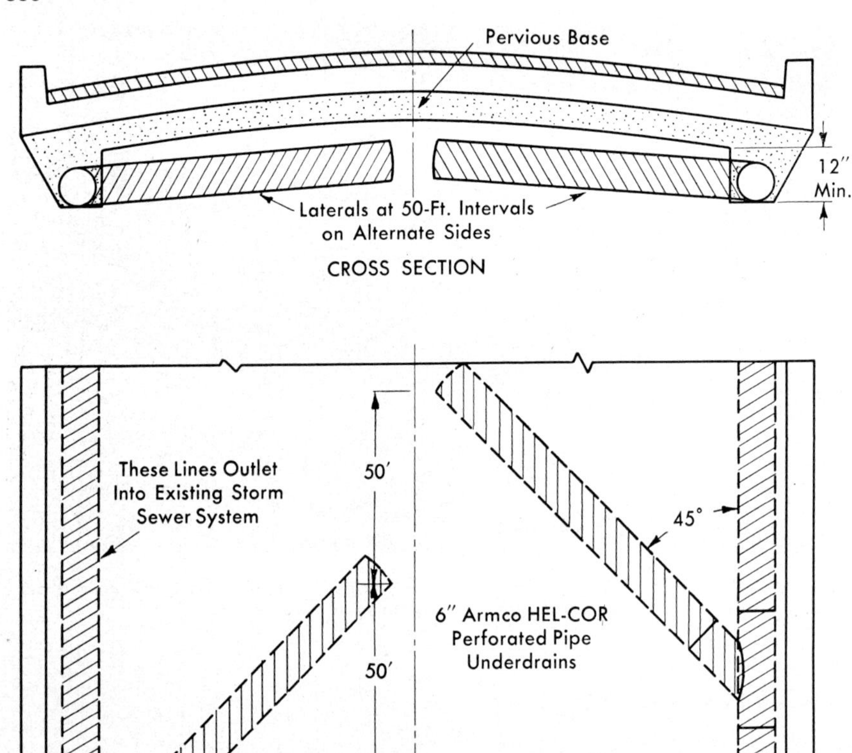

Fig. 226. Details of underdrainage of streets in Baltimore, Maryland.

difficult to grow good turf. Usually such wet areas indicate a high water table or seepage above an impervious stratum.

Drainage should preferably be installed when the golf course, park or cemetery is constructed, although it can be done later as needed. A survey of ground water conditions during the rainy season is necessary to determine where to locate the drains. In some cases these may combine surface drainage with subdrainage. See Fig. 209, p. 313, for illustration of a subdrain suitable for most requirements.

Playgrounds, Tennis Courts

Areas such as playgrounds and tennis courts may be affected by ground water during the spring or wet season. If caused by seepage, an intercepting subdrain along one end of the area will generally suffice to keep the area dry and playable. Depth of the subdrain will vary with the location of the impervious stratum, but 3 to 5 ft will ordinarily be adequate.

Usually a gravel or stone base will not be needed under the court surface.

Baseball Diamonds

A well-drained baseball field usually has a healthier growth of turf and the infield soil is not baked hard. Besides being easier on the players, such a field may mean more playing days and fewer postponed or cancelled games.

Drainage layouts will vary with the depth and direction of the ground water. One typical successful job of infield drainage served to catch surface water as well as to intercept ground water. Spacing of 8-in. perforated metal pipe was on 15-ft centers. The pipe was covered with pervious material to within 6 in. of the surface.

Stadiums and Athletic Fields

Actual playing days on athletic fields are usually limited. Every precaution should be taken to keep the field dry and in good playing condition—and to grow a stronger, tougher sod for the protection of the players.

Tarpaulins are frequently used to cover the playing field between games and rolled up on corrugated metal pipe during the game. Removal of surface water alone is not sufficient, but should be supplemented by subdrainage. Particularly is this true in the case of the playing field lower than its surroundings, where ground water is almost sure to be encountered.

The field should be well-crowned and good topsoil be used for the upper 12 in. or more. A system of subdrains placed at a depth of about 4 ft below the surface will generally keep the ground water level low and make the soil receptive so that rainfall will be quickly absorbed and carried away from the field.

A system of surface and subsurface drains, as illustrated in Fig. 233, p. 336 and Fig. 227, is effective for most playing fields.

Fig. 227. Playing field of the Rice Institute stadium in Houston, Texas is well below the original ground surface. Crew here is placing corrugated pipe mains and perforated pipe laterals to control the ground water.

Running Tracks

Drainage of cinder running tracks is usually simple. On a base of crushed rock or gravel, a layer of 4 to 6 in. of compacted cinders is placed. If the track is on well drained soil, no further drainage is necessary. If on an impervious soil that holds the surface water, drainage of the base is likely to be needed.

A single line of 6-in. diameter perforated pipe under the center or one edge of the track is sufficient. By giving the subgrade an inverted crown or sloping it towards one side of the track and placing the pipe in a trench backfilled with a finely graded pervious material, surface water can be quickly removed. The depth of the pipe can vary from about 12 in. below the base to whatever depth is necessary to attain a slope of about 0.2 per cent.

Race Tracks

So-called "dirt tracks" should be provided with one or two lines of subdrain pipe under or at the edges of the straightaway, and with one line on the inside of the curve. On wide tracks, a parallel line under the center or the outer edge may be needed. Figs. 228-229.

A depth of 3 to 5 ft is usually sufficient, depending on the source of the water. A pervious backfill to within a foot of the surface is desirable. A minimum slope of 0.2 per cent is recommended.

Surfaced or paved race tracks can be drained similarly except that the pipe should be kept beyond the edges of the pavement instead of under them.

Figs. 228–229. Garden State race track near Camden, N. J. is kept in good running condition with the aid of a subdrainage system of perforated metal pipe. Upper view shows surface inlet in gutter at inside rail. Lower view shows pipe outlet.

CHAPTER FORTY-ONE

Agricultural Subdrainage

SOILS inadequately drained are detrimental to land development and plant growth. Agricultural land, golf courses and parks, airports, cemeteries and residential districts are often greatly benefited by adequate subdrainage.

Moisture Requirements

The ideal soil for crops and other vegetation is one containing a balanced supply of water, air and plant food.[1] The proper combination is found in a medium open soil which permits rapid percolation of surface water, yet retains a large amount of capillary water. Free water is injurious if it excludes the air from the root horizon too long. But capillary water is beneficial to plant growth, and in combination with air, liberates plant food from the soil. An open soil promotes deeper root growth which enables crops to withstand droughts for longer periods. Further advantages of an open soil are:

Friability and ease of cultivation.

Greater plant food supply.

Resistance to heaving by alternate freezing and thawing.

More air and more warmth.

Soils approaching a pure sand or gravel generally do not retain moisture nor are they capable of raising sufficient water by capillary action for plant growth. The addition of humus, clay or various binders is necessary to increase their water-holding capacity, and to supply plant food. Heavy clay or loam soils which afford imperfect natural drainage should be modified by means of artificial drainage so that they more nearly approach the ideal condition.

A well-drained soil with all free water passing through to the water-table, retains about the right amount of capillary moisture for plant growth.

Increased cultivation and fertilizer usually are not economical substitutes for drainage in the production of crops.

Movement of Gravitational or Free Water

Upon entering the ground, water sinks vertically until it reaches the water-table or some impervious stratum (Fig. 230). Later it may again rise to the surface as capillary moisture and evaporate. After this water enters the ground, it remains there as a residual supply or begins flowing laterally to some lower supply or outlet. Such outlet may consist of crevices, an open channel or a natural or artificial underground channel. The water may also appear as a spring on the side of a hill where the impervious stratum ends.

Control of Free and Capillary Moisture

As is evident from Table 41-1, the coarser textured soils are more permeable, retain less capillary moisture and therefore respond readily to drainage. Such soils, however, may contain considerable free water if surrounded by or underlaid with an

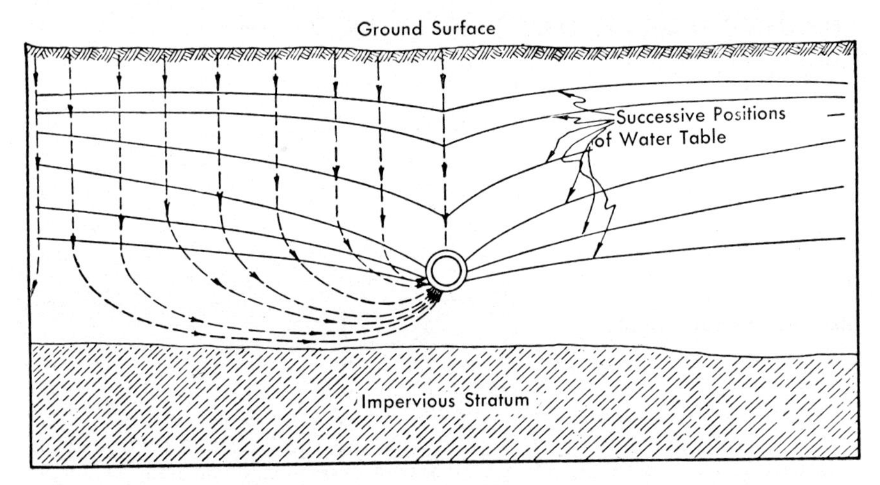

Fig. 230. How water moves to reach an underdrain pipe.

impervious subsoil. There are several possible solutions for a high water-table in an open soil. If there is a pervious stratum at a lower level, it may be possible to puncture the impervious layer and drain the water out. In case of a bowl shaped area, the rim can be cut and drainage outlets be provided. In other cases, a drainage system can be installed with an outlet in a sump and pumped out.

Where there is seepage from higher areas, the source and direction of the water should be ascertained and this water intercepted before it can reach the surface and have an adverse effect.

For the tighter, less pervious soils, it is preferable to keep out as much water in the first place as possible. Subdrain pipes are of great benefit in this type of soil by removing free water and creating more favorable growing conditions. Drain pipes at regular intervals serve as outlets for free ground water and facilitate its removal by shortening the distance it would otherwise have to travel to a natural outlet.

Preliminary Surveys

Wherever the proper location for the drains is not obvious (as frequently is the case on undulating or gently rolling lands), surveys should be made of the areas to be drained. And, if available, maps of adjacent areas should be obtained either locally or from the U. S. Geological Survey, for determining the extent of the watershed. Depending upon the nature of the land, either a complete contour map should be made, or a boundary line survey with cross profiles at intervals.

Such a survey is intended to show possible location of the outlet or outlets, the natural surface drainage available and the slopes obtainable. In addition, borings should be taken or test pits dug at a number of typical places to locate the water-table, determine the nature of the soil and obtain soil samples which can be sent to a laboratory for soil analysis. Observation by one experienced in soils can also be made in the field to determine perviousness of the soil. Aerial surveys also are helpful in determining soil classifications as well as the area of watersheds.[2]

TABLE 41-1 HYGROSCOPIC WATER IN SOILS[3] AND FIELD CAPACITY FOR CAPILLARY MOISTURE[4]
Expressed in Per Cent by Weight

Kind of Soil	*Hygroscopic Moisture*	*Capillary Moisture*
Sandy	1 to 3	14
Sandy Loam	3 to 5	14½
Loam	5	16–17
Clay Loam	5 to 7	18
Clay	7 to 10	19

Selecting the Outlet

The number of outlets is governed by topographic and other conditions, but in any event the selection should be carefully made. Such outlets are usually an open ditch or stream. The use of a screen to prevent rodents from entering and building nests in the drain is advisable. Better yet is the use of a flap-type drainage gate, page 375, which serves not only the purpose of preventing a flooded outlet stream from backing into the pipes, but keeps animals out as well. The outlet should be protected against undermining and should be deflected so that it enters the stream at an angle (see Figs. 231-232).

Figs. 231–232. Two types of outlets for farmland drains. Upper view shows that a concrete headwall did not prevent a short-sectional pipe outfall from failing before the contractor left the job. Lower view shows how metal pipe outlets can be cantilevered and deflected to enter the stream at an angle.

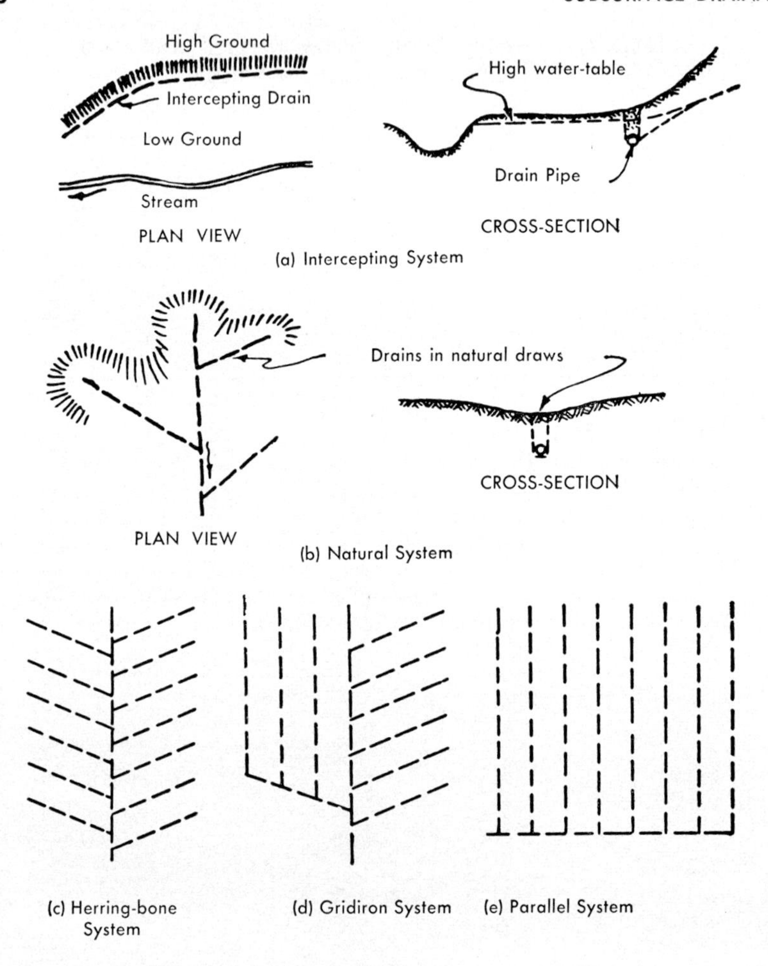

Fig. 233. Various types of subdrainage systems commonly used.

Locating the System; Spacing, Depth, Slope

The main should, so far as possible, follow the line of natural drainage. Drains should be in straight lines, or in long easy curves.

Submains should also follow the line of natural drainage. Laterals should be laid in the line of greatest slope. Intercepting drains are an exception, generally being placed across the slope.

Design of Lateral System

Three principal types of lateral subdrainage systems are in common use, the herring-bone, gridiron and parallel systems. (Fig. 233). The parallel system is the most economical type because it involves the least duplication of drainage by laterals and mains. The preferable arrangement is short mains and long laterals rather than the reverse.

TABLE 41-2 SUBDRAIN SPACINGS
For depths of 3, 4 and 5 ft

Permeability Class	*Permeability Rate In. per Hour*	*Spacing for Various Depths*		
		3 Ft	*4 Ft*	*5 Ft*
Very slow	0.0 to 0.05	0 to 15	0 to 20	0 to 25
Slow	0.05 to 0.2	15 to 30	20 to 40	25 to 50
Moderately slow	0.2 to 0.8	30 to 60	40 to 80	50 to 100
Moderate	0.8 to 2.5	60 to 110	80 to 145	100 to 180
Moderately rapid	2.5 to 5.0	110 to 155	145 to 205	180 to 255
Rapid	5.0 to 10.0	155 to 220	205 to 290	255 to 360

C. S. Slater, *Agricultural Engineering*, Sept. 1950, p. 450.[5]

TABLE 41-3 RECOMMENDED DEPTH AND SPACING OF SUBDRAINS FOR VARIOUS SOIL CLASSES

Soil Classes	*Percentage of Soil Separates*			*Depth of Bottom of Drain in Feet*	*Distance Between Subdrains in Feet*
	Sand	*Silt*	*Clay*		
Sand	80–100	0–20	0–20	3–4	150–300
				2–3	100–150
Sandy Loam	50–80	0–50	0–20	3–4	100–150
				2–3	85–100
Loam	30–50	30–50	0–20	3–4	85–100
				2–3	75–85
Silt Loam	0–50	50–100	0–20	3–4	75–85
				2–3	65–75
Sandy Clay Loam	50–80	0–30	20–30	3–4	65–75
				2–3	55–65
Clay Loam	20–50	20–50	20–30	3–4	55–65
				2–3	45–55
Silty Clay Loam	0–30	50–80	20–30	3–4	45–55
				2–3	40–45
Sandy Clay	50–70	0–20	30–50	3–4	40–45
				2–3	35–40
Silty Clay	0–20	50–70	30–50	3–4	35–40
				2–3	30–35
Clay	0–50	0–50	30–100	3–4	30–35
				2–3	25–30

The spacing of laterals depends on the physical composition and texture of the soils. Having classified the soil according to Table 36-2, p. 297, the spacings given in Table 41-2 or Table 41-3 are recommended. They cannot be strictly followed in every case, but they serve as a general guide.

The *depths* given in these tables may be safely followed in placing laterals. It should be remembered that soils loosen up after they have been subjected to subdrainage for several years. If laterals are placed higher, they should be spaced at closer intervals to compensate for the loss of head so obtained. Deep drainage is preferable to shallow drainage, provided, of course, that the water-table is left sufficiently high to supply capillary water for vegetation and that the subsoil at the greater depth is sufficiently pervious to permit infiltration into the drains at a reasonable rate.

A minimum *slope* of 0.1 per cent (0.1 ft in 100 ft) is recommended. Steeper slopes are better.

Design of Mains and Submains; Depth and Sizes

The depth of mains and submains is controlled by the available outlet and a minimum recommended slope of 0.1 of 1 per cent. Large pipes have not infrequently been installed on grades of 0.05 ft per 100 ft or even less in extreme cases but, almost without exception, trouble with silting has followed. Mains and submains may be much deeper than laterals if necessary.

The design of a subdrainage system is similar to that of surface drains, except that the runoff to be handled is slower. Character of the surface, soil and subsoil, spacing and depth of drains and other factors all affect the rate of runoff and consequently the size of pipe required.

A runoff of ¼ to ½ in. per acre in 24 hours is commonly accepted for agricultural underdrainage. "In average Iowa soils (fine sandy loam) systems with laterals 4 ft deep and 100 ft apart and not provided with surface inlets, should be designed to care for runoff at a rate of at least 5/16 to ⅜ in. per twenty-four hours."[6]

A runoff of ¼ in. per acre in 24 hours is equal to .0105 cu ft per second from each acre drained. A runoff of ½ in. is equal to .0210 cu ft per second per acre (see Table 37-1, p. 312).

With the rate of runoff or discharge known, the proper size of laterals and mains can be calculated by the use of Manning's formula. See page 272.

Selection of Subdrain Pipe

Common clay tile is used extensively for agricultural subdrainage. It is low in first cost. The short lengths with open, butt joints to admit the ground water need to be laid carefully on a uniform foundation. Otherwise mal-alignment results, the pipe silts up and becomes ineffective.

There are many locations, particularly under very shallow cover or in deep trenches, where perforated corrugated metal pipe is advantageous, longer lasting and less costly in the end. Among its advantages are: strength to resist crushing and disjointing; positive couplings; perforations spaced uniformly to admit the water fully[7] and yet exclude the surrounding soil; resistance to the entrance of tree roots in border areas.

Although higher in price, perforated metal pipe costs less to install, goes together quickly, remains effective longer and generally costs less per year. In many locations it is indispensable.

French Drains

A French drain consists of a trench loosely backfilled with stones, the largest stones being placed in the bottom, and the size decreasing towards the top. The interstices between the stones serve as a passageway for the water.

Pipe drainage is preferable in all cases, but for temporary use where the subsoil is especially silty and the amount of water is small, French drains have a limited application. They need to be dug up frequently and cleaned out if they are to remain effective.

REFERENCES

1. "Tile Drainage," by J. A. King and W. S. Lynes, Mason City Brick & Tile Co., Mason City, Iowa, 129 pp.
2. "Engineering Soil Survey Mapping," Highway Research Board, Bull. No. 46, 1951.
3. Report of Agri. Experiment Station of Univ. of Calif., 1897–1898.
4. "Dry Farming," J. A. Widtsoe, 1911.
5. "Depth and Spacing of Tile Drains," by C. S. Slater, Soil Cons. Research, U. S. Dept. of Agri., Beltsville, Md., in *Agricultural Engineering*, Sept. 1950, p. 450.
6. Iowa Eng. Experiment Station Bulletin 52, p. 9.
7. "The Effect of Circular Perforations on Flow into Subsurface Drain Tubes," by Don Kirkham and G. O. Schwab, Iowa Agricultural Experiment Sta., in *Agricultural Engineering*, April, May 1951, pp. 211 and 270.

Fig. 234. Inlet from reservoir to canal, controlled by an Armco gate beyond the levee. Corrugated sheeting helps protect against erosion. Texas.

Fig. 235. Hel-Cor pipe for roof drainage on a large parking garage in Chicago, Ill.

SECTION EIGHT

SPECIAL DRAINAGE PROBLEMS

CHAPTER FORTY-TWO

Drainage of Bridges and Grade Separations

MAJOR structures such as bridges, underpasses, overpasses and grade elevations should be protected and stabilized by drainage.

An undrained fill behind an abutment or retaining wall tends to hasten the disintegration of the wall. Also, lateral pressures tending to overturn the wall are greater. If freezing occurs, the lateral thrust may cause failure.

Fig. 236. Abutment on this grade separation structure on the Oklahoma Turnpike is provided with two vertical pipe drain outlets, at right center, leading to outlet at toe of slope, lower left.

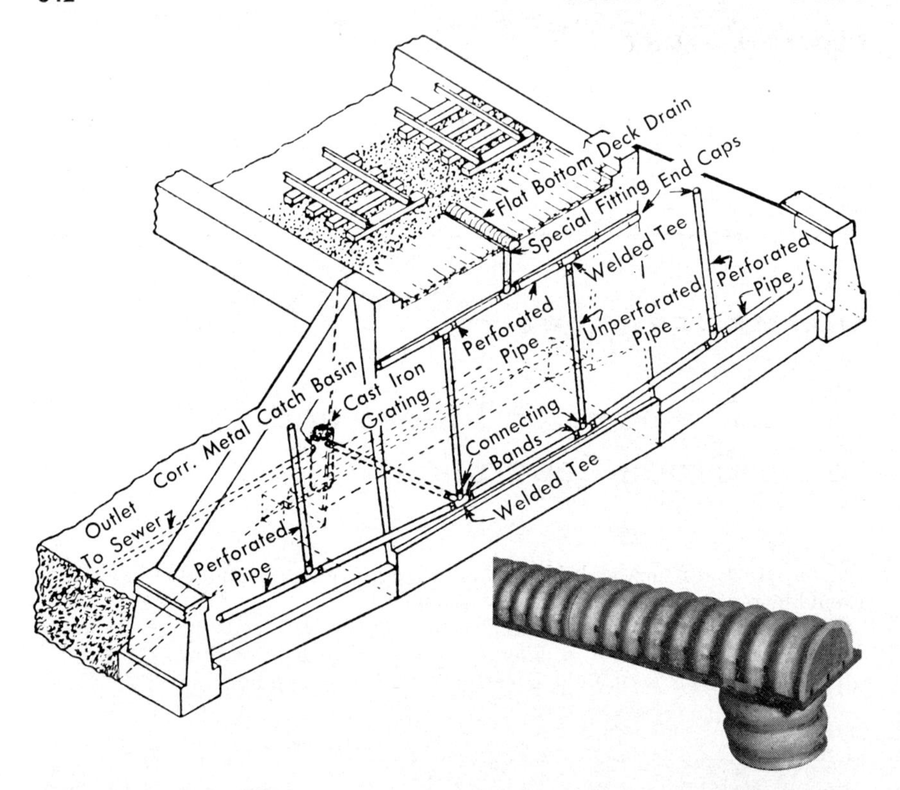

Fig. 237. Drawing of typical drainage and subdrainage system on railroad overpass. Surface water from the bridge floor is conducted in a corrugated perforated deck drain to the corrugated pipe drains behind the abutment.

Fig. 238. Photo showing details of flat-bottom deck drain and stub for downspout.

Surface Water

Water falling on the surface of a long highway bridge should be discharged through downspouts at the piers in such a way as not to stain or disintegrate the piers. In the case of a long overpass, the water should be downspouted into sewer inlets or a drainage ditch.

At the end of a highway bridge or overpass the water should be caught in an inlet and discharged through a spillway to the toe of the slope or into a sewer manhole. See Fig. 236.

In the case of a railway bridge or overpass, the water generally seeps through the ballast towards a depression in the center or sides of the deck where a perforated corrugated half-circle deck drain is installed to collect and conduct the water to an outlet at the abutment, as shown in Figs. 237, 238 and 239.

In railroad grade separation work through built-up areas, surface water is intercepted near the top of the retaining walls by placing perforated metal pipe on a ledge or layer of impervious material and backfilling with concrete sand or graded filter material. The water is downspouted at convenient intervals.

Subdrainage

Ground water from the fill or backfill against the abutment or retaining wall should lead to an "intercepting drain" which consists of a trench or blanket of pervious filter material 1 ft or more in width or thickness placed directly against the wall. Then, at the lowest point for which a suitable outlet can be obtained, a line of perforated metal pipe is placed with the perforations up and with an impervious material underneath the pipe and up to the lowest row of perforations to insure that all of the water gets into the pipe.

The use of weepholes for discharging drainage water behind retaining walls and abutments is not the best practice. This is true because the weepholes are generally inadequate and because the accompanying discoloration of the concrete or masonry is unsightly. Weepholes may discharge part of the water, if the pervious backfill has not unduly shifted or settled, or they may be entirely ineffective.

The cut approaches to an underpass in wet soil should be thoroughly subdrained, either by means of an intercepting drain in each ditch or gutter line or surrounding the entire project.

Outlets

The drainage system of a bridge, underpass or retaining wall should be provided with a definitely designed outlet system. If possible, the water should be discharged directly into the stream or into a sewer; otherwise into an adequate surface ditch. The outlet should be as low as practicable to insure complete drainage. In the case of underpasses, this may require a sump and an automatic pumping system.

Fig. 239. Partly completed subdrain system for abutment of grade separation structure.

CHAPTER FORTY-THREE

Airport Drainage

AIRPORTS may range from an emergency landing strip to a major airport covering several square miles. The subsoil may be favorable to natural drainage, but often the location will involve swampy or unstable foundation soils.

In any case, the interception and disposal of both surface and ground water on these areas is an important problem. The use of thick pavements and stabilized mats or bases is not an economical substitute for adequate drainage.

Good drainage increases the earning power of a commercial airport, and the efficiency of a private or a military field, by extending the service period. It makes for greater safety by providing a dry, firm subgrade. A well-drained soil offers a more uniform support for runways and direct wheel loads; it encourages a healthier, more drought-resistant growth of grass, thus keeping the surface in prime condition.

Characteristics of Airport Drainage

Airport drainage is different insofar as the landing areas and taxiing strips are concerned. Ditches and deep gutters are objectionable. Therefore, some other method of uniform interception of surface water is needed, both to prevent loss of stability of the ground surface and to prevent soil erosion.

Airport drains can and often must carry ground water as well as surface water. The drainage system must be strong and durable. Being subject to the weight of heavy planes landing on or passing over the drains, they must resist crushing, vibration and disjointing. A strong, positively connected drainage system is vital.

Drainage Surveys

Before an efficient drainage system can be designed, certain preliminary information must be available, including:

1. Topographical map of entire site and surrounding area.
2. Map showing contours of graded site on 1- or 2-ft intervals, along with profiles and cross sections along axis of runways, taxiways and aprons.
3. Profiles of proposed drains.
4. Rainfall and other climatological data.
5. Drainage from tributary areas.
6. Soil and moisture studies.

Rainfall Data

It is possible, but not economically sound, to design an airport drainage system with capacity to remove the heaviest rainfall within a few minutes after it ends. A more practical way is to determine the maximum intensity for a one-hour rainfall on a one, two or five-year frequency and provide for its removal in a reasonable period of time.

For rainfall intensity-frequency curves, see pages 200–201. There is considerable difference in the amount of water to be handled when computed by various accepted formulas. This being the case, local experience and judgment should count most in any designs. Further information on runoff formulas for airports is given on page 349.

Fig. 240. Enlargement of the Philadelphia International Airport required diverting and enclosing a stream in three parallel lines of 78 and 84-in. Multi-Plate pipe. Special welded bends were provided in the line.

Drainage from Roofs and Aprons

Water draining from the roofs of hangars and other buildings, or from aprons and similar surfaces, should be conducted underground into a sewer or into the outlet mains of the field drainage system.

Tributary Watersheds

Unless located on a plateau or other high ground, an airport may be subject to water flowing over the surface from tributary watersheds. This surface water should be intercepted at the immediate foot of slopes by drain pipe connected to catch-basins or drop inlets.

Ditches or streams crossing the field should be diverted around the edge, or enclosed in a conduit of suitable size and strength. See Fig. 240.

Soil Data

The soil underlying an airport site should be studied to determine (1) the drainage characteristics of the soil, (2) the location of the water table, impervious strata and seepage areas. Samples can be obtained with a simple soil auger (see page 306), post-hole digger or from test pits.

Identification of soil types can be made visually but soil samples should be checked in the laboratory. See classification of soils in Table 36-2, page 297. The group between sandy loam and silt are the soils most affected by excess moisture.*

---

*"Any soil that is wet can be drained if the climate and topography are favorable. —If ground water is present in the soil then the soil is not impervious and the water can seep out as well as it entered, if the proper facilities for outlet are provided." —"Subsurface Drainage for Airfields," by Capt. Ira P. Griffin, U.S.N., (Retired), in *Military Engineer*, May-June 1952.

At the time of taking soil borings, the level of the water table and the seepage zones should be noted. It may be advisable to repeat this after the grading is completed.

Airport Drainage Design

Two Basic Types of Fields

The two basic types of fields are the "all-over-sod" and the runway-type. Although the more important fields use paved runways, the all-over-sod field is suitable for private airports, emergency landing fields, auxiliary fields for training purposes and small town airports.

Drainage of a sod field is much the same as for farm land. See Chapter on Agricultural Subdrainage, pages 333–339. The methods used include the natural, herringbone, gridiron and parallel systems as illustrated on page 336.

Drainage of runway-type fields generally includes interceptor lines along the paved areas. Fig. 241. For the unpaved areas, the drainage may be as for sod fields.

Drainage Methods

One or more of the following methods are used for removing unwanted water from airports:

Storm drains
Base drains
Subdrains
Combined drains

Storm Drains

A storm drain is generally considered as a conduit discharging surface water only. The water may reach the pipe through catchbasins, inlet grates or by draining into a pervious backfilled trench in a turf valley to enter the pipe through perforations or open joints.

Many engineers favor a storm drain based on municipal practice which depends entirely on gutters and catchbasins to collect surface water, with the catchbasins placed in sod areas away from the runways (usually about 175 ft). An alternative is to place catchbasins at the edge of the runways with a shallow gutter to collect and conduct the water to the catchbasins. The first method may result in erosion at the edges of the runway; the second creates a landing hazard especially when cross-runway landings are attempted.

Another method is to use an open grill over a concrete box. This presents no hazard but is more expensive.

Still another method, commonly used, is to place an intercepting trench and drain pipe with pervious backfill at the edge of the runway. See Fig. 242, page 348. This eliminates any ponding on the runway and is not subject to clogging.

For surface drainage of the sod areas, catchbasins are recommended.

For larger streams which cannot be diverted around an airfield, enclosure in a large single or multiple storm sewer is described elsewhere. Interception of surface water from tributary areas and from building roofs has been discussed.

Base Drains

Paved areas are subject to cracking, so that water seeps through these cracks and also through construction joints. If the base is relatively impervious, such water becomes trapped and results in lowered base stability, weakened subgrade, loss of

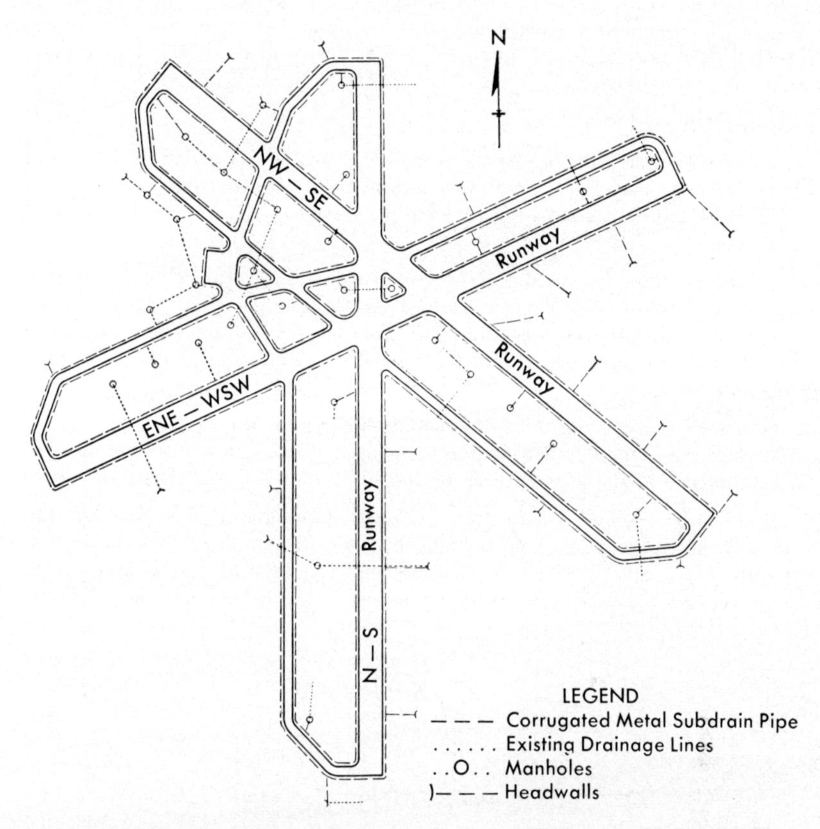

Fig. 241. Drainage layout for the Rome, Georgia airport. Base drains of perforated metal pipe border both sides of the runways and taxiways. Surface and ground water is conducted away by a storm sewer system.

bond between surfacing and base materials and possible damage from frost.

Further results may be mud pumping, cracking of the pavement, increased maintenance and early failure.

Design of pavements should include a pervious granular base crowned to drain to the edges of the paved area and into the interceptor drains. See Fig. 242.

Subdrains

Removal of free ground water by subdrainage is often necessary in order to lower the water table sufficiently to prevent loss of stability of pavement subgrades and turfed field areas due to saturation.

In northern climates, destructive frost heaving is prevented by lowering the water table. Although capillary water cannot be removed directly by subdrains, it can often be removed indirectly by lowering the water table. A study of the subsoil and the fill material as previously recommended will determine whether or not subdrainage is needed or can be effective.

The location of subdrains is generally at the edges of the runways and taxiways. These, however, may be supplemented by other lines under the paved areas and by lines in the grassed areas.

Combined Drains

A combined drain functions both as a surface water drain and as a subdrain. Where soil and ground water conditions permit, the combined drain is used because it is generally more economical than separate systems. Several combinations are possible:

1. *Combined Base Drain and Subdrain*—In this case, storm water from the runways and grassed areas is carried in a separate pipe line. This combined drain can be of small capacity, because the water from the pervious base and any ground water will not be of any great volume or reach the subdrain rapidly. The trench has an impervious top to exclude surface water.

2. *Combined Outlet Drain*—Under certain conditions, the designer may economize by utilizing a single pipe for subdrainage and storm water. Storm water is led from catchbasins in the grassed area to the subdrain alongside the runway.

3. *Runway Interceptor Drain*—A variation of combination (2) is to use a pervious intercepting drain along the edge of the runway and to dispense with any storm drain in the grassed area. In this case, the same pipe also serves as a subdrain for removing groundwater, and possibly also the base drainage. Fig. 242.

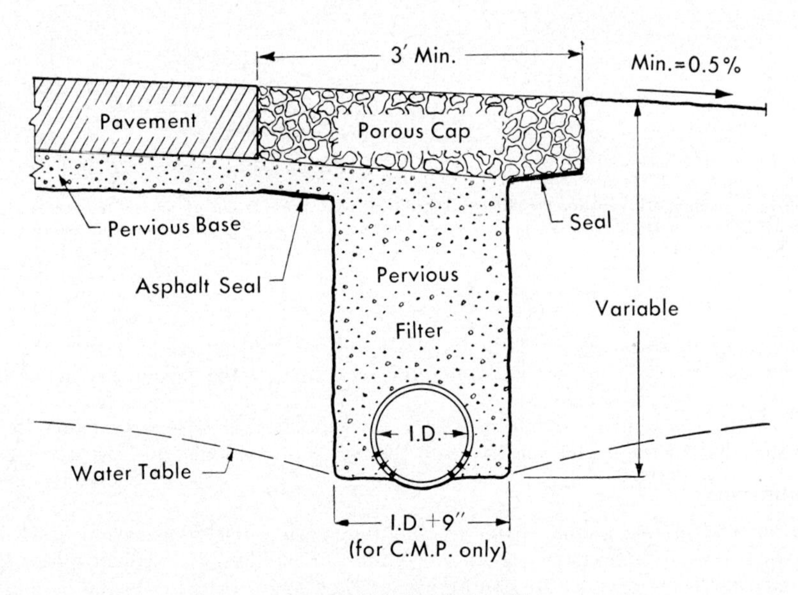

Fig. 242. Combination drain at edge of runway for intercepting surface and seepage water through a porous cap and filter and for lowering the ground water level.

Fig. 243. Sewer outfall for storm drainage system at Philadelphia International Airport. Note the three corrugated metal pipe risers or manholes on the lines of Multi-Plate pipe.

Where conditions permit its use, this type of system has several advantages over other methods. It removes the surface water from the edge of the runway pavement, thus preventing erosion and soft shoulders. Operational hazards are eliminated, since there is no need for curbs, gutters or other obstructions. A smooth, safe surface is assured for cross traffic as well as for planes that may stray from the runway limits on take-offs or landings.

In accordance with approved runway design, all unpaved surfaces should slope away from the pavement. This prevents silt from clogging the pervious cap over the drain.

Spacing of Catchbasins

Catchbasins and manholes serve not only to collect surface runoff but as openings for inspection and possible cleaning out of the drainage system.

In sod areas, catchbasins should be about 175 ft from the edge of the runway or apron and spaced approximately 300 ft apart. Wherever ice is a problem the catchbasins can be on closer centers to aid in steaming open. Some designs include lamp holes (small diameter risers) at intervals along the line for inspection purposes. These can be 6-in. corrugated metal pipe with solid cover.

Catchbasins and manholes can be of corrugated metal construction. Fig. 243. This design speeds up construction and also resists impact.

Determining Size of Pipe—Surface Runoff

Several methods of computing surface runoff from airports are in common usage. Any one of these will give satisfactory results when proper weight is given to the various factors involved.

1. *U. S. Engineers*—A procedure developed by the U.S. Engineers is probably the most highly refined method of computing runoff available today. It is described in the Engineering Manual, Chapter XXI, Part 1, published by the War Department, Office of the Chief of Engineers. A series of curves on all the variables affect-

ing runoff has been built up to aid in the solution of the problem. By choosing or assuming the values for each of the variables, and applying them properly, the engineer may calculate the quantity of runoff for each drainage area. However, the process is long and somewhat complex.

2. *CAA Method*—The Civil Aeronautics Administration uses an adaptation of the Rational Method where:

$$Q=CIA$$

Q = runoff in cfs
C = a coefficient representing the ratio of runoff to rainfall (See Table 23-4)
I = intensity of rainfall in inches per hour for the time of concentration. (A complete set of rainfall intensity-frequency maps is provided on pages 202–205)
A = drainage area in acres

Here again a group of curves for determining time of concentration with respect to lengths, slope and texture of the areas are provided to aid in calculations. Details of this method may be obtained from the CAA Airport Drainage Manual printed in 1946.

3. *Armco Rational Method*—The rational method as used by Armco has been modified by the introduction of the factor "*f*." It has been used satisfactorily in the drainage design of many airports during the past 15 years in the following form:

$$Q=\frac{AIR}{f}$$

Q = volume of runoff from area A in cfs
A = drainage area in acres
I = surface runoff factor or imperviousness from Table 23–5, page 201
R = rainfall in inches per hour. (See rainfall maps, pages 202–205)

Fig. 244. Installing system of Hel-Cor perforated subdrains to permit widening of runways at Cleveland, Ohio, airport.

f = a factor to compensate for surface slope which in turn affects the time of concentration
For slopes 0.5 per cent or less, $f=3.0$
For slopes between 0.5 and 1.0 per cent, $f=2.5$
For slopes greater than 1.0 per cent, $f=2.0$

This procedure eliminates all charts and graphs. In general, the small individual drainage areas into which an airport can be divided are of roughly the same slope, shape and area. Therefore, it is possible within certain limits to choose a constant value of "f" which eliminates the necessity of recomputing time of concentration, slope and length of overland flow for each area considered.

Example 1: Assume a rainfall of 1.5 inches per hour lasting for one hour, to be removed in one to three hours after end of storm, a surface runoff factor of 20 per cent from a sodded area of 6 acres, an average ground slope of 0.4 per cent and a pipe grade of 0.005 ft per foot.

$$A=6 \quad I=.20 \quad R=1.5 \quad f=3 \quad S=0.005$$

$$Q=\frac{6\times.20\times1.5}{3}=0.600 \text{ cfs}$$

The size of drain necessary to carry either surface or subsurface discharge may be computed by means of the Manning Formula:

$$Q=\frac{A\times1.486}{n}\times R^{\frac{2}{3}}\times S^{\frac{1}{2}}$$

Q = the quantity of water a given size drain will carry in cfs
S = the hydraulic slope = the fall of the pipe in ft per ft
A = cross-sectional area of the drain in sq ft
R = mean hydraulic radius in ft $=\dfrac{\text{area of section}}{\text{wetted perimeter}}$
n = the coefficient of roughness for the pipe material

Using the value $S=0.005$ and $Q=0.600$ cfs from above, we find from Fig. 183, page 275, that a pipe between 6 and 8 in. in diameter is required. In this case, the 8-in. size would be selected.

Example 2: In calculating pipe sizes for the combination runway drain, let us assume a pavement with a transverse slope of 0.05 per cent having a width of 75 ft and length of 800 ft, a rate of rainfall of 1.5 in. per hour for 1 hour, a runoff factor of 90 per cent, and a pipe grade of 0.5 per cent.

$$A=\frac{75\times800}{43560}=1.377$$

$$I=0.90 \quad R=1.5 \quad f=3 \quad S=0.5 \text{ per cent}$$

$$Q=\frac{1.377\times0.90\times1.5}{3}=0.620 \text{ cfs}$$

$$\text{Runoff per lin ft of runway}=\frac{0.620}{800}=0.000775 \text{ cfs}$$

From Fig. 183 it is determined that for a slope of 0.5 per cent that a 6-in. pipe will carry 0.34 cfs and an 8-in. pipe will carry 0.73 cfs. Then the total lineal feet of

6-in. pipe to be used at the beginning of this run will be X when:

$$0.000775 \times (X) = 0.34 \text{ cfs}$$

$$X = \frac{0.34}{0.000775} = 439 \text{ ft}$$

The remainder of the 800-ft line will be of 8-in. pipe, since it will carry 0.73 cfs while the total amount to be received is only 0.62 cfs.

Subsurface Runoff

The primary purpose of an airport subdrain is to lower and hold the water table to the proper depth for soil stability and vegetation.

Experience indicates that the maximum discharge from a subdrainage system generally occurs from 4 to 6 hours after a heavy rain of short duration. Rainfall records show that the heaviest rains are usually of less than one hour duration. Thus, the surface drainage system should be running at a maximum concentration in less than 45 minutes following the beginning of a rain. Since the drainage system is normally designed to remove surface water in from one to three hours following a storm, it is generally unnecessary to increase the capacity of the surface drainage system to handle the subsurface water when they are combined.

The amount of subsurface runoff within the boundaries of the airport, and discounting that from tributary watersheds, is equivalent to the rainfall less the surface runoff, less the water lost through evaporation and that used by plant life. The nature of the terrain, its size, shape and slopes, as well as the character and slopes of the substrata, are contributing factors. The rate of subsurface flow depends largely upon the permeability of the soil, the slope of the substrata and the tributary area.

Subsurface runoff has, by experiment, been determined as equivalent to a certain depth of water to be drained away within a period of 24 hours. Tests by the Engineering Experiment Station of the University of Minnesota indicate that 5⁄16 in. to 3⁄8 in. of water per acre in 24 hours is a satisfactory rate of runoff for average soils. This factor may be increased to 3⁄4 in. or even 1 in. for regions of exceptionally heavy rainfall, or where more pervious soils are encountered.

While it is customary to refer to subsurface runoff as "inches of depth that must be removed in 24 hours from the watershed or drainage area," this unit called "drainage coefficient" must be converted to cubic feet per second per acre before runoff requirements can be compared with subdrain capacity. Table No. 37–1 may be used as a conversion table for this purpose. The size of pipe can be computed by the method shown on page 349, exactly the same as for surface intercepting drains.

Spacing and Depth of Subdrains

Spacing of subdrains depends upon the type of drainage system used and the depth at which it is installed. This depth in turn depends largely upon the character of the soil to be drained. Table 41–2 will serve as a rough guide. In no case should the data given in this table be considered more than an approximate guide.

Requirements of Airport Drains

Selection of the airport drain is of prime importance not only from the standpoint of safety but for economic reasons. Since airport drainage requirements are more stringent than almost any other type of service, it is wise to consider all the factors involved and to profit by the experience gained in farm, railway and highway drainage.

Fig. 245. Installing Hel-Cor perforated pipe on an airport. Long lengths with tight, bolted joints help to bridge any inequalities in the trench bottom.

If the need for drainage is present when the airport is built, it generally continues as long as the field is in operation. This means that to be economically sound the drainage system must function efficiently both as a conduit and as a structure for a long period of time. To replace pipe that has failed is often much more expensive than the original installation. This is especially true where costly surfacing materials and interference with ground equipment are involved.

Failure of airport drains can generally be traced to either structural failure, caused by crushing and breaking, or loss of efficiency as a conduit by reason of mal-alignment or clogging.

Structural Strength

Airport drains must be considered for their resistance to intensified vibration, live and dead loads, as well as impact stresses along and under the runway. Continued drainage efficiency and the maintenance of safe flying facilities are based on the ability of the drain pipe to withstand the excessive pounding of airport traffic.

Furthermore, the very nature of subdrains—lowering the water table or intercepting ground water—implies that they will be placed on a wet, unstable foundation. Obviously, then, the subdrain must be able to bridge inequalities in the subgrade. This requires a continuous line with tight joints—a line of uniform strength throughout its entire length. Fig. 245.

Mal-alignment

Mal-alignment is a common cause of drainage system failures where short sectional pipe is used. Plain or unglazed tile has long been a favorite for draining farm lands, not so much for its drainage efficiency as for its relatively low first cost. Even though farm drainage systems are not subject to heavy loads or excessive impact, they frequently fail, especially where frost action is severe. Such failures in an airport system could have serious and expensive results.

One of the greatest disadvantages to short sectional pipe is the lack of positive connection between sections, and the inability of the pipe to adapt itself to uneven or yielding foundations. When such lines are subjected to loading, and especially vibration, the pipe often loses both grade and alignment. It up-ends or is otherwise disturbed to such an extent that silting and stoppage of flow destroys the effectiveness of the subdrainage system.

Drainage Efficiency

Structural strength is important but of little value if the drainage system fails to function as a conduit for other reasons. Openings in subdrainage pipe should be of balanced design. In the interception of surface water, for example, rapid infiltration is desirable, yet for continued efficiency the openings should be designed to exclude backfill material.

Where a pervious backfill enables large quantities of water to quickly reach the drain pipe, perforations in the wall of the pipe, because of their greater efficiency, are preferable to large open joints. They permit the water to enter along the entire length of the drain. There is less horizontal flow to disturb the backfill material and the perforations are less likely to admit solids that would clog the line. Then, too, closed joints, tightly connected, help to prevent disjointing, loss of alignment and clogging of the pipe.

Determining Safe Depths of Cover

Methods of determining the safe minimum cover over corrugated metal pipe and Multi-Plate Pipe of various gages are given on pages 134–139. These apply to airport loading conditions.

REFERENCES

"Airport Engineering," by Sharp, Shaw and Dunlop. John Wiley & Sons, Inc., New York, 1944.

"The Planning and Design of Airports," by Horonjeff and Jones. The University of California Syllabus Series—No. 316.

"Roads and Airfields," by the Engineer School, Corps of Engineers, U. S. Army, Fort Belvoir, Virginia. Publication ST-5-250-1, 1951.

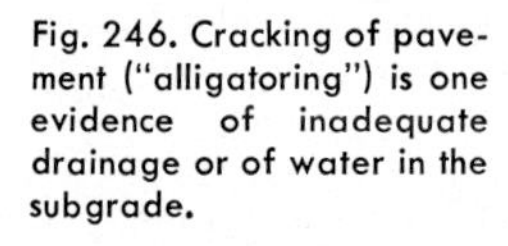

Fig. 246. Cracking of pavement ("alligatoring") is one evidence of inadequate drainage or of water in the subgrade.

Fig. 247. Landslide has destroyed a portion of this mountain highway. One of the basic causes is the presence of excess moisture which made the mass unstable.

CHAPTER FORTY-FOUR

Landslides

LANDSLIDES have been defined by Terzaghi as follows: "The term landslide refers to a rapid displacement of a mass of rock, residual soil or settlement adjoining a slope in which the center of gravity of the moving mass advances in a downward and outward direction."

Landslides are a major phenomenon. They involve not only hillsides and mountainsides but cuts and fills for roadways, channels and other engineering works. Fig. 247.

The change from equilibrium and stability to the movement of vast volumes of earth or rock may require only a slight change in the balance of forces. These include the addition of water to masses of earth or to lubricating planes. Other disturbing factors could be undermining, cave-ins due to underground settlement and explosions or earthquakes.

Corrective Measures

The analysis of landslides and a recommendation of the corrective measures to apply requires the skill of geologists and soils engineers. An excellent reference and

Fig. 248. Slide area along a state highway in southeastern Ohio where control is obtained by low metal retaining walls, left, backed by a subdrainage system.

bibliography on this subject, particularly as applied to highways, is to be found in Highway Research Board Bulletin 49, "Analysis of Landslides," 1952, by R. F. Baker* and H. Gordon Larew.†

Five control methods or retaining devices on highways are described:

1. Buttresses
   a. Rock.
   b. Cementation of loose material at toe.
   c. Chemical treatment—flocculation—at toe.
   d. Excavate, drain and backfill—at toe.
   e. Relocation—raise grade at toe.
   f. Drainage of the toe.
2. Cribbing—concrete, steel (Fig. 248) or timber.
3. Retaining wall—masonry or concrete.
4. Piling—steel, concrete or timber.
   a. Floating.
   b. Fixed.
5. Tie-rodding slopes.

Each of the methods has its advantages and disadvantages, which are described in the above bulletin.

Drainage

Since one of the basic causes of landslides is excess moisture, one of the fundamental ways of preventing or curing them is by drainage. This requires intercepting both surface water and ground water before they can reach the mass that is subject to slides; also, it requires draining the mass to stabilize it. Drainage reduces the soil

---

*Engineer of Soil Mechanics, State Road Commission of West Virginia.
†Instructor of Civil Engineering, Purdue University.

shearing forces by reducing the weight of the moving mass and by eliminating hydrostatic pressures. Drainage also increases the shear strength of the soil. Fig. 249.

Corrective measures by means of drainage are subdivided as follows in Bulletin 49:

a. Surface.
   (1) Reshaping landslide surface.
   (2) Slope treatment.
b. Sub-surface (French drain type).
c. Jacked-in-place or drilled-in-place pipe.
d. Tunneling.
e. Blasting.
f. Sealing joint planes and open fissures.

Drainage may not be simple nor inexpensive. The geologist who has thoroughly examined the site or who has available the results of the survey and borings can best advise the remedy. He can tell where to apply the drainage so that it will be effective and cost least.

Interception of surface water may be done by a ditch or impervious gutter. Intercepting all of the ground water before it reaches the mass is more difficult. It may be necessary to go very deep with a pipe subdrain in a pervious-backfilled trench. It may be necessary to jack a subdrain pipe (see Fig. 250) or to tunnel.

Draining the mass is often of the greatest importance. It requires much skill if it is to be done effectively and economically. Because of continued soil movements and shrinkage during drying, only strongly connected pipe can be effective. Long

Fig. 249. Locating the source of ground water is usually not easy. Here in northwestern Illinois a subdrain pipe will be backfilled with a pervious filter to trap the water and stabilize a slide.

Fig. 250. A crew is here drilling a hole along the new West Virginia Turnpike to tap suspected water pockets. After the drill is removed, long sections of 2 or 2½-in. perforated galvanized smooth tubing are inserted into the hole. Note the one tube beyond the drill with a small flow of water.

lengths of perforated corrugated metal pipe, tightly joined, are most satisfactory for this service.

Culverts and sewers in areas subject to sliding should also have positive joints. Otherwise they will pull apart and discharge their contents into the mass, thereby aggravating the slide.

To repeat, landslides are expensive and their cure may be, too. Various control methods are available but a specialist should determine which, if any, is economical. Because drainage eliminates one of the basic causes of slides, it deserves prime consideration.

CHAPTER FORTY-FIVE

Soil Conservation

PART ONE

ROADWAY EROSION PREVENTION

ONE of the most destructive forces that the engineer is called on to combat is that of soil erosion. Erosion makes gullies on the shoulders and slopes of embankments; gouges out side ditches and endangers the road foundation as well as traffic; undermines fills and backslopes, causing landslides; undermines bridge foundations; washes out drainage structures and other engineering works; fills and clogs ditches, culverts and other waterways with sediment.

Proper design at the time of construction will eliminate much of the burdensome problem of maintenance.

Erosion of Slopes

The erosion of the side slopes of cuts and fills becomes a serious problem if any considerable amount of water flows over them. The effect of the water that falls directly on the slope may be minimized by sodding, strip-sodding or by terracing so

Fig. 251. A bituminous berm and metal shoulder drain ("embankment protector") along a highway in Minnesota. This is an effective way of preventing erosion of slopes.

Fig. 252. Storm water from a mountain highway in California (upper right) is conducted in a corrugated pipe spillway to protect the embankment slope and the roadway below.

as to reduce the velocity. It is often possible to divert the water from adjacent areas by means of a ditch along the top of the slope. Water thus diverted or collected in terraces can be concentrated and led down the slope in a pipe or flume. The water that falls on the roadway of a fill section can be confined by a berm along the shoulder and then disposed of in a similar manner. See Fig. 251.

Transverse Gullies

The most common form of erosion and one which frequently threatens a roadbed is transverse gullies. Such gullying may result from scour at the inlet end or from a turbulent discharge at the outlet end of a short culvert, and can be prevented by extending the culvert beyond the affected area. If the culvert pierces the roadbed near the top of a high embankment, transverse gullying can be prevented by the installation of a corrugated metal culvert extension equipped with elbows at top and bottom to fit the extension to the slope of the embankment. See Fig. 252. A slight tendency toward erosion at the ends of a culvert, likely to lead to gullying, may be corrected by means of a flared or drop-type inlet, or by the use of riprap or paved gutter at the outlet.

As a rule, every effort should be made to install the culvert so that the discharge will be beyond the toe of slope. In cases where this cannot be done, it will probably be advisable to extend the structure with a corrugated metal pipe having sufficient strength to act as a cantilever and still function properly. If the structure is not extended, an apron or spillway of suitable material is necessary to protect the embankment.

Use of Vegetation

Erosion of slopes can be retarded if a rank growth of grass or other vegetation can be maintained. Native vines and grasses are preferred especially those that grow rapidly and have spreading root systems. Honeysuckle, Bermuda grass, lespedeza, sweetclover, red top, kudzu and other ground covers are effective for this purpose.

TABLE 45-1 SPACING OF DITCH CHECKS

Formula: $\frac{100h}{A-B}$ = Spacing Between Checks, in Feet

*Diff. in Slope Between Road and Proposed Ditch, A—B Per Cent**	*Values of h, in Feet*				
	1	*1½*	*2*	*2½*	*3*
½	200	300	400	500	600
1	100	150	200	250	300
1½	67	100	133	167	200
2	50	75	100	125	150
2½	40	60	80	100	120
3	33	50	67	83	100
3½	29	43	57	71	86
4	25	38	50	63	75
4½	...	33	44	56	67
5	...	30	40	50	60
5½	...	27	36	45	55
6	...	25	33	42	50

Notes on construction of Ditch Checks:

1. For ordinary soil, allow a 2 per cent flow grade between spillways.
2. Generally allow a 2-ft drop for the water.
3. It is usually advisable to turn the wings back and raise the outer ends to fit the shoulder and backslope.
4. Extend wings far enough back into the slopes to make effective cut-offs.
5. Insofar as possible, use the natural undisturbed ground as a form. When wood forms are necessary, use every precaution to tamp the backfill solid.

*See Fig. 253, page 362.

Willow, locust, sumac, roses and native trees or shrubs can be used to stabilize the slopes where they will not interfere with the flow in the drain or present an objectionable appearance. Modern highway practice favors the preservation of existing trees and shrubs that do not interfere with the sight distance and the planting of additional material in order to help prevent erosion.

Ditch Erosion

Aside from the use of vegetation, several systems for controlling ditch erosion are available, employed separately or in combination. Open drainage channels may be lined with rubble or be paved, the ditch may be replaced with a pipe or conduit or check dams can be installed to slow down the velocity of the water. See Table 45-1.

When open ditches are called upon to care for velocities of flow exceeding 2 ft per second, erosion is a hazard that cannot be disregarded. The simplest method of controlling erosion is to provide a succession of ditch checks or weirs across the ditch, thereby slowing down the velocity of flow so that suspended solid matter will be deposited behind the checks and stop the erosion. The difference in elevations of the tops of successive checks should not exceed 3 ft in order that the ditch will

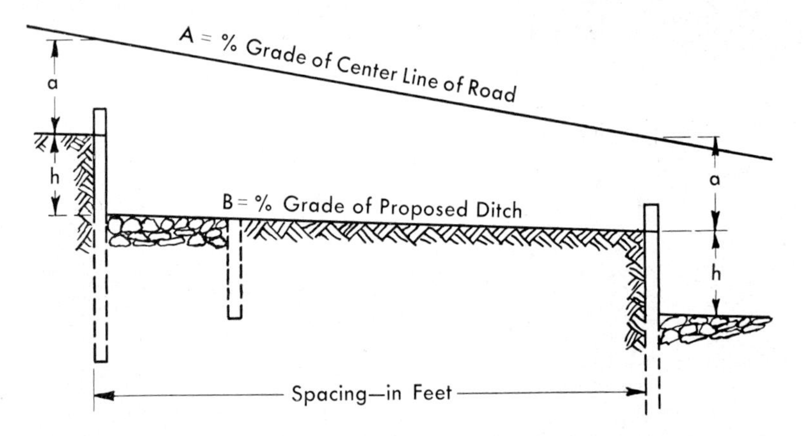

Fig. 253. Ditch checks of metal or concrete reduce the slope of the ditch bottom and thus retard or prevent erosion. The method of computing the spacing can be determined from Table 45-1, page 361.

Figs. 254-255. Large metal ditch checks installed by U. S. Forest Service in California. Above is a bin-type retaining wall with a weir or notch. At right is one constructed of Multi-Plate plates.

not be too deep. (Fig. 253, Table 45-1). Ditch checks are a possible hazard to traffic and they interfere with mowing and other maintenance operations.

The checks may be constructed of many materials: sod, brush, logs, woven wire, wood planks; or loose rock can be used for temporary checks. Corrugated metal, steel sheeting, bin-wall sections, rubble masonry, concrete or earth dams with drop-inlet pipe culverts have all been used for permanent installations. Figs. 254 through 257, and Fig. 259, page 366.

Ditch Enclosure in Storm Sewer

When the grade of the ditch is in excess of 5 per cent, the cost of placing ditch checks will be such that it will usually be cheaper and more satisfactory to provide a paved gutter or conduit for the entire length of the hill.

Erosion of a side ditch may not only undermine the roadway but may deprive the backslopes of support and cause landslides.

As an effective means of preventing pavement undercutting due to ditch erosion, a parallel drain of corrugated metal pipe can be laid in the ditch bottom and then covered over. Its continuous, flexible construction enables the pipe to resist any disjointing effect of a high velocity of flow through the pipe and to conform to a shifting or subsiding foundation soil.

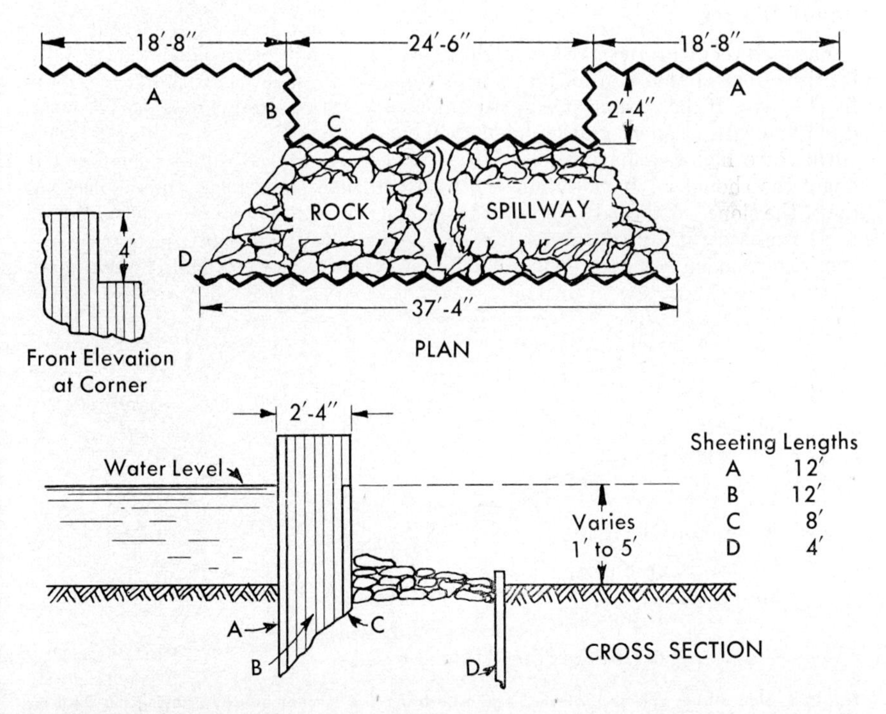

Fig. 256. Ditch check of Armco corrugated steel sheeting in a reclamation district in central Washington with rock spillway and sheeting cut-off wall.

Fig. 257. A series of corrugated steel sheeting ditch checks in an irrigation ditch in Utah.

Paved Ditches

Paved ditches are used when high velocities cannot be avoided. They may consist of portland cement or bituminous concrete, or of rubble with dry or grout-filled joints. If the volume of water is sufficient, a storm sewer can be placed in the ditch line with frequent grating inlets as shown in Fig. 258.

On some highway and railroad fills, a paved or surfaced ditch is constructed along the shoulder. Inlets admit the water to pipe spillways or flumes leading down the slope. A specially designed metal inlet or "embankment protector" that has been used with much success is shown in Fig. 251, page 359. Inlets may also consist of wooden boxes for temporary use, or of concrete or corrugated metal pipe.

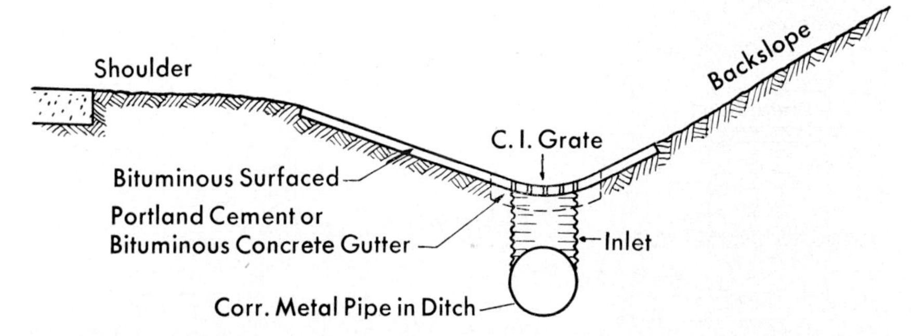

Fig. 258. Side ditches can be protected against erosion in a number of ways. Paving the ditch or providing a pipe storm sewer are effective ways. In other cases, sodding or riprapping may be adequate.

Spillway Capacity

So far as capacity is concerned, embankment spillways may be considered in the same category as culverts or long pipe lines with free outlets. The spillway gradient will invariably be greater than the "critical slope" so that the capacity is limited by the amount of water which can get in at the entrance or inlet. If the inlet is of the "sharp-crested weir" type, the values in Table 45-2 will give its capacity when the inlet dimensions are known. The size of the spillway flume or pipe can be approximated from the "free outlet" table in Table 26–2, page 230, when the inlet discharge is known. If a flume is used it should have sufficient freeboard to prevent overtopping by wave splashing.

TABLE 45-2 DISCHARGE FOR WEIR NOTCHES IN EROSION CHECK DAMS*

Computed by formula $Q=3.39LH^{3/2}$†
Where Q = discharge in cubic feet per second.
L = length of weir notch in feet.
H = depth of weir notch in feet.

Note: The Wisconsin model tests indicate that for weir notch dams of special design and operating under a maximum head of 1.5 feet under ideal conditions, the coefficient in this formula may be increased to 3.60.

Depth of Weir Notch, in Feet	*Length of Weir Notch in Feet*								*Depth of Weir Notch, in Feet*
	1	2	3	4	5	6	7	8	
0.5	1.2	2.4	3.6	4.8	6.0	7.2	8.4	9.6	0.5
1.0	3.4	6.8	10.2	13.6	17.0	20.3	23.7	27.1	1.0
1.5	6.2	12.5	18.7	24.9	31.1	37.4	43.6	49.8	1.5
2.0	9.6	19.2	28.8	38.3	47.9	57.5	67.1	76.7	2.0
2.5	13.4	26.8	40.2	53.6	67.0	80.4	93.8	107.2	2.5
3.0	17.6	35.2	52.8	70.5	88.1	105.7	123.3	140.9	3.0
3.5	22.2	44.4	66.6	88.8	111.0	133.2	155.4	177.6	3.5
4.0	27.1	54.2	81.4	108.5	135.6	162.7	189.8	217.0	4.0
4.5	32.4	64.7	97.1	129.4	161.8	194.2	226.5	258.9	4.5
5.0	37.9	75.8	113.7	151.6	189.5	227.4	265.3	303.2	5.0
	9	*10*	*11*	*12*	*13*	*14*	*15*	*16*	
0.5	10.8	12.0	13.2	14.4	15.6	16.8	18.0	19.2	0.5
1.0	30.5	33.9	37.3	40.7	44.1	47.5	50.9	54.3	1.0
1.5	56.0	62.3	68.5	74.7	81.0	87.2	93.4	99.6	1.5
2.0	86.3	95.9	105.5	115.0	124.6	134.2	143.8	153.4	2.0
2.5	120.6	134.0	147.4	160.8	174.2	187.6	201.0	214.4	2.5
3.0	158.5	176.1	193.8	211.4	229.0	246.6	264.2	281.8	3.0
3.5	199.8	222.0	244.2	266.4	288.6	310.8	333.0	355.2	3.5
4.0	244.1	271.2	298.3	325.4	352.6	379.7	406.8	433.9	4.0
4.5	291.2	323.6	356.0	388.3	420.7	453.1	485.4	517.8	4.5
5.0	341.1	379.0	416.9	454.8	492.7	530.6	568.5	606.4	5.0

*From Iowa Eng. Exp. Sta. Bull. 121.
†King's Handbook of Hydraulics.

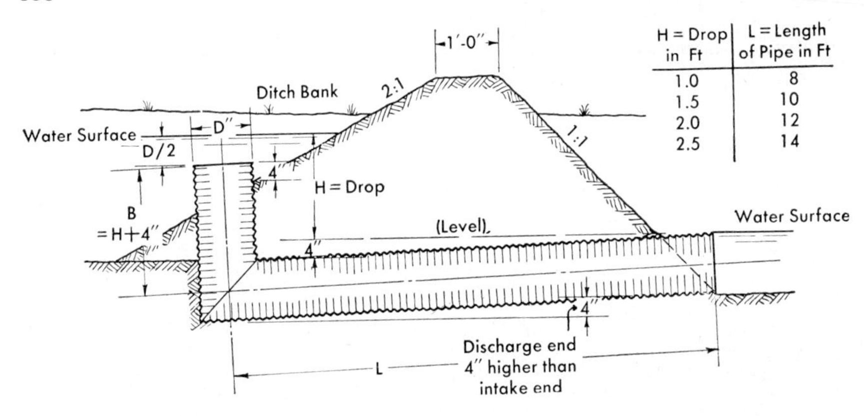

Fig. 259. Small ditches with steep slopes can sometimes be protected from erosion by means of "pipe drops" as illustrated above.

Encroachment of Parallel Streams

The tendency of a stream is to erode on the outside of a curve and build up a bank on the inside. This is particularly undesirable where a roadway parallels the stream along the outside of the curve, inasmuch as the roadway is continually being robbed of its support.

Relief from this condition is usually by means of slope protection, stream diversion, channel relocation or an installation of a large diameter pipe parallel to the road to carry the stream, provided the volume of flow is not too great. If a large diameter pipe is used to prevent encroachment on a roadway by a parallel stream, care should be taken to provide sufficient waterway under flood conditions.

Fig. 260. Shores of lakes and streams are protected from wave action by bulkheads of corrugated sheeting. Here at the Cleveland (Ohio) Yacht Club is one of a series of docks inside the breakwater along Lake Erie.

Protection of the slope against stream erosion may be achieved by the use of riprap; paved revetment; flexible mats of brush, willow saplings, concrete and other materials; wooden or steel sheet piling (Fig. 260); retaining walls of metal or concrete (Fig. 261); or by a system of retards. Often the slopes are planted with willows or similar trees as an additional protection when retards, jetties, riprap or mats are used to prevent cutting below the low water line.

Fig. 261. Future erosion by flash floods along a mountain stream in Tennessee will be prevented by an installation of Armco bin-type retaining wall.

PART TWO

SOIL-SAVING DAMS

During the past few decades there has developed a better understanding of the magnitude of the soil erosion problem and the economic value of taking the necessary steps to prevent the loss of valuable top soil. "Sheet erosion" and "gullying" are being counteracted by terracing, contour plowing, strip cropping, ditch checks, soil-saving dams, vegetative coverings, reforestation and other soil conservation measures. The principles and practices discussed in the first portion of this chapter can be applied, with certain modifications, to farmland.

A soil-saving dam may vary from a few inches in height up to 10 ft or more. Its purpose is primarily to reduce the velocity and scouring action of a stream by forming a partial barrier across the channel. Depending on the present and future amount of erosion upstream, the channel above the dam may ultimately be built up by sedimentation to the level of the spillway.

The dams may be built of earth, timber, masonry, steel sheeting, metal bin-wall or concrete. Except for the very low dam where the erosion can be controlled by

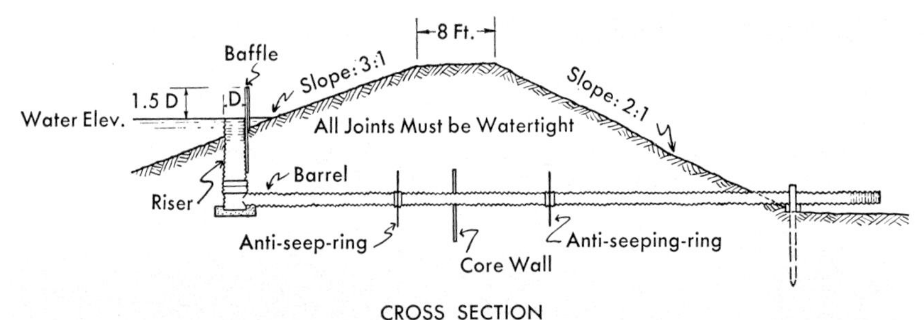

Fig. 262. Overflow of surplus water from a small "farm pond" or reservoir is provided by a "mechanical spillway" of corrugated metal pipe. (From "Build a Farm Pond for Pleasure and Profit," Armco Bulletin No. PO 3749.)

vegetation, a spillway or drain must be provided for an earth dam. Open flumes or apron spillways are suitable in most cases. In others, a culvert pipe drop-inlet or sluiceway through the dam will be found most satisfactory. Typical installations using corrugated metal pipe are shown in Figs. 262, 263 and 264.

Drain Pipe for Dam

The drain pipe through soil-saving dams should be watertight under a head equal to the approximate height of the dam and should be strong enough to carry the load from the earth in the dam without disjointing, regardless of settlement. Furthermore, the pipe should resist the erosion of water flowing at high velocity.

Depending on the location of the intake with respect to the axis of the dam, the pipe must be built up to its full height at once or can be built up successively as

Fig. 263. Pipe spillway for large pond during construction. Note square diaphragms and corrugated pipe riser. The pipe at right is a toe drain for the dam.

the sediment behind the dam increases in depth. A straight or a flared inlet may be used. For dams of some height a baffle may be desirable to screen out floating debris.

A 3-in. spacing of rivets along circumferential seams is advisable for pipe to be placed through soil-saving dams. For further assurance of watertightness the pipe should be coated inside and out, to a thickness of 1/16-in., with the correct grade of bituminous material, and for high dams, soldering at the intersection of circumferential and longitudinal seams may be advisable, and, since such pipe lines may be subjected to severe erosion, a pipe having a bituminous pavement in the invert should be used.

A watertight field joint is made by using a corrugated collar and 1/2-in. rods and nuts with cast lugs shaped to fit the corrugations. See Fig. 59, page 75.

Diaphragms or anti-seep rings are desirable on large dams in order to intercept possible seepage along the pipe.

Artificial Lakes

Dams for small artificial lakes or farm ponds are generally larger than soil-saving dams and require more care in the design. The dam must be of adequate size and shape to hold the water, adequate spillways must be provided and seepage under or through the dams must be prevented.

When impervious clay or clayey soils are available, seepage can be prevented by building a well compacted core of impervious material through the longitudinal axis of the dam. The core should extend from well below the base of the dam to a height above the normal surface of the water. When the material used to construct the dam is not sufficiently impervious or when the base is pervious for too great a depth to handle with a core wall trenched in, a core wall can be provided by the use of

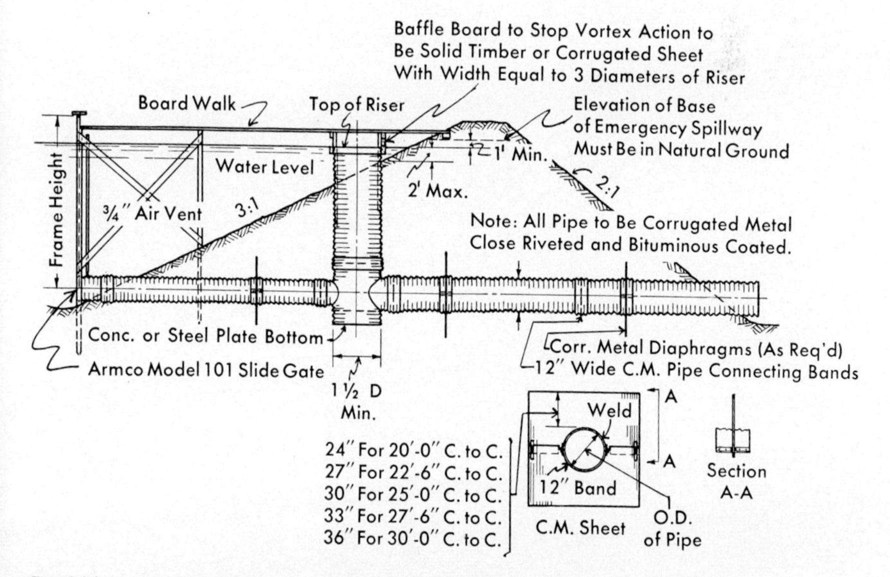

Fig. 264. Larger pipe spillway for artificial lake or pond, showing slide headgate for draining all the water from the lake. Size of diaphragms is shown for various spacings between diaphragms.

interlocking steel sheeting. The sheeting should be driven into the foundation soil deep enough to prevent the possibility of water flowing under it and should extend up to an elevation above the normal surface level of the pond. The metal core wall will also serve as a block to rodents.

Two spillways should be used, a mechanical spillway through the axis of the dam to carry normal runoff and an auxiliary spillway built around one end to handle possible flood flows.

A drop inlet spillway, made of corrugated metal pipe is generally the most satisfactory type of mechanical spillway for use in a small pond. It should be fabricated so as to be watertight, installed with watertight bands and diaphragms, properly baffled at the inlet and protected against erosion at the outlet. When it is desired to provide for complete or partial draining of the pond, the corrugated pipe can be extended into the pond and a slide headgate attached to the inlet end; see Fig. 264.

A more complete treatise on the design and construction of dams for small ponds will be found in Armco Bulletin No. PO 3749 "Build a Farm Pond for Pleasure and Profit."

CHAPTER FORTY-SIX

Flood Control and Land Reclamation

ANY broadly conceived and carefully-thought-out planning program, looking toward that use of land for which each parcel is naturally best suited, will show the advisability of permanently retiring large areas of "marginal" and "submarginal" land from cultivation. It will also show that much land can advantageously be reclaimed for such purposes as agriculture, reforestation, residential sites and industrial sites. Land already under cultivation or in use can frequently be made more productive and valuable.

Many of the areas available for reclamation by drainage are located along the sea coast, gulf coast, inland lakes or streams and may consist of fertile soil deposited from the uplands. The increased value of the land after reclamation should ordinarily be greater than the cost of reclamation. There may be other considerations from a health standpoint such as the elimination of mosquito breeding places.

General Methods

In some instances, marshes, sloughs or swamps need only to be provided with outlet ditches to drain them by gravity. More often, however, the land available for reclamation is low land subject to flood flow or backwater. The need then is to provide a levee or dike which will protect the land from being flooded.

While a levee serves to protect land from flood and backwater, it also serves to prevent natural drainage from taking place during low water periods unless a culvert or sluiceway is provided, or pumping is resorted to. The most common

Fig. 265. Series of twenty-eight Armco flap gates Model 100 attached to corrugated pipe culverts through low levee in Texas.

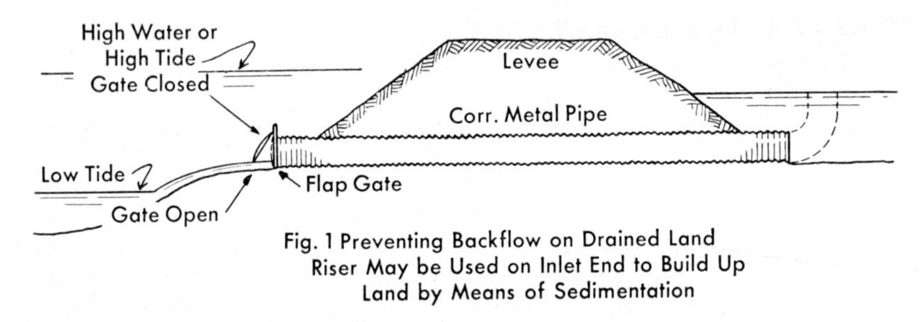

Fig. 1 Preventing Backflow on Drained Land
Riser May be Used on Inlet End to Build Up
Land by Means of Sedimentation

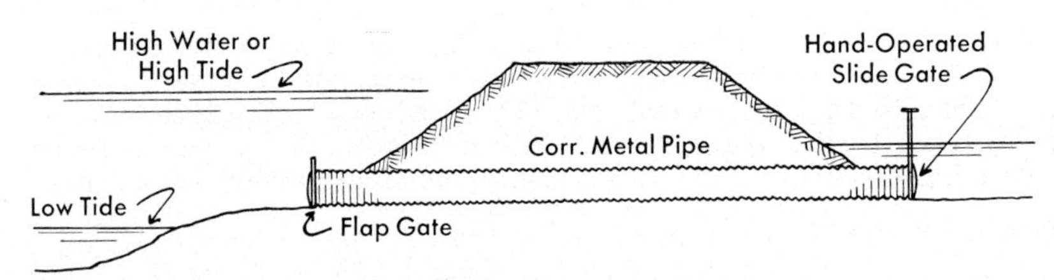

Fig. 2 Controlling Water on Land Side by
Means of Hand-Operated Gate

Fig. 266. Two suggested ways of preventing backflow and of controlling the water level on the land side of the levee or dike.

and satisfactory way is to lay an outlet pipe under the levee and provide it with a valve or gate for controlling backwater and allowing natural drainage from behind the levee.

Culverts or Sluiceways

The type of sluiceway to be used depends upon the size of opening required, being either rectangular or circular. Standard corrugated metal pipe has been used extensively for sluiceways in diameters up to 84 in., either singly or in multiple. See Figs. 265 and 266.

Due to saturated and unstable soil conditions, corrugated pipe for levee culverts is fabricated somewhat differently than ordinary culverts, including the use of heavier gages for some sizes. Rivets in circumferential seams on all diameters should be on a maximum of 3-in. centers to insure watertightness when bituminous coated. Watertight field joints are often specified, as illustrated in Fig. 59, page 75.

Pipe 60 in. in diameter and larger is often vertically elongated. Where headwalls are to be used, the inlet and outlet ends should be left round with a gradual increase in vertical elongation to a maximum of 5 per cent under the main load. Details on strutting are given on pages 443–445.

Diaphragms are usually required as cut-off walls to retard any possible leakage alongside the pipe. Such diaphragms or bulkheads should project a minimum of 2 ft beyond the outside of the pipe, regardless of pipe size, when the diaphragms are spaced 20 ft apart. Greater spacing requires larger diaphragms so the distance the

Fig. 267. Installing an Asbestos-Bonded corrugated pipe culvert under a levee along the Missouri River in southwestern Iowa. Note the bottom half of diaphragm in place.

water must travel is at least 20 per cent more than without diaphragms. See Fig. 264.

Diaphragms should be located midway between circumferential riveted seams and at least 4 ft from a field joint. In multiple lines, diaphragms should be spaced so as to provide a minimum of 12 in. clearance between the faces of diaphragms on adjacent pipes. This permits proper placing and tamping of backfill.

Metal end sections in diameters up to and including 48 in. can be used on the ends of the pipe as shown on pages 262–264.

The service record of corrugated metal pipe culverts and sewers under flood conditions along the Mississippi, the Missouri and many other rivers indicates that they particularly resist disjointing, settlement and infiltration of the surrounding soil. They retain their watertightness under these severe conditions. Under levees on the lower river, the U. S. Engineers specify and use only corrugated metal pipe.

Drainage Gates

Two general types of drainage gates are available, the flap and the screw lift-operated types. Lift-operated gates are used where special control is desired, but they require a caretaker for their timely opening and closing. Should the gates become inaccessible because of impassable roads during a flood, the manually operated gates may be rendered useless.

Wooden flap gates have been employed to some extent in the past, but their disadvantages are warping, tardy response to change in water level, leakage and fire hazard.

A flap gate of cast iron (Model No. 100) has been found suitable for pipe openings of 8 to 90 in., where the head of water does not exceed 10 ft above the center of the gate. See Fig. 268 and Table 46-1, for dimensions of Model No. 100 gate.

For rectangular openings 24 to 60 in. square, for heads of water not exceeding 20 ft, Model No. 103 automatic gate is available. This gate must be fastened to concrete or wooden headwalls and therefore is not as easily installed as the Model No. 100 gates. Model No. 103 can also be made in sizes to fit the end of Armco pipe-arches.

For heads over 20 ft and up to 50 ft, cast steel and structural steel gates are available.

The above gates consist of a double-hinged flap valve which seats against a flange which is riveted to the end of a corrugated pipe or bolted to the headwall. The gate and seat are accurately machined to insure practical watertightness. The gate offers but little obstruction to outflow and it responds quickly to slight changes in water level.

TABLE 46-1 DIMENSIONS OF ARMCO FLAP GATE MODEL 100

(All dimensions in inches)

Diam.	*A*	*B*	*C*	*D*	*E*	*F*	*G*	*H*	*J*	*T*
4	6	3/4	2 7/8	5 1/4	5/16	7/8	1 7/8	1	1/4	1/4
6	8 1/8	7/8	4 1/4	7 1/4	3/8	7/8	2 9/16	1	1/4	1/4
8	10 3/4	1 3/8	5 11/16	10	1/2	1 1/8	3 9/16	1 1/4	3/8	3/8
10	12 3/4	1 3/8	7 1/8	12 1/4	1/2	1 1/8	4 3/8	1 1/2	1/2	7/16
12	14 3/4	1 3/8	8 1/2	14 1/2	1/2	1 1/8	5 1/8	1 1/2	1/2	1/2
14	17 1/4	1 3/8	9 7/8	16 3/4	1/2	1 1/4	5 15/16	1 1/2	1/2	9/16
15	17 3/4	1 3/8	10 5/8	17 3/4	1/2	1 1/4	6 1/4	1 1/2	1/2	9/16
16	19 1/4	1 3/8	11 1/4	18 3/4	1/2	1 1/4	6 5/8	1 1/2	1/2	9/16
18	22 1/4	2	12 5/8	21	3/4	1 9/16	7 7/16	1 3/4	9/16	9/16
20	24 3/4	2	14 1/8	23 3/4	3/4	1 3/8	8 1/4	1 3/4	5/8	5/8
21	25 1/4	2	14 7/8	24 1/4	3/4	1 3/8	8 9/16	1 3/4	5/8	5/8
24	28 1/4	2	17	27 1/2	3/4	1 1/2	9 3/4	1 3/4	5/8	5/8
30	35 1/4	2 1/2	20 1/2	34	1	1 9/16	12	2	1 1/16	5/8
36	41 1/2	2 1/2	25	40 7/8	1	2 1/16	14 7/16	2 1/4	1 1/8	11/16
42	47 1/2	2 1/2	29 3/4	47	1	2 5/16	16 5/8	2 1/4	1 1/8	3/4
48	53 1/2	2 1/2	34	54	1	2 3/4	19 1/16	2 1/4	1 3/8	3/4
54	60 3/4	2 1/2	38	62 1/4	1 1/4	2 3/4	22	3	1 1/2	7/8
60	67	2 1/2	42	68 1/2	1 1/4	2 3/4	24 1/4	3	1 1/2	15/16
66	73 3/8	2 1/2	47	75	1 1/4	2 7/8	26 1/2	3	1 1/2	1
72	79	2 1/2	51	82	1 1/4	3	29	3	1 1/2	1
78	86	2 1/2	55 1/4	88 3/4	1 1/4	3 1/2	31 3/8	3	1 5/8	1 1/8
84	92 1/2	3 1/2	59 1/2	95 1/2	1 1/2	3 1/2	33 3/4	3	1 3/4	1 1/4
90	99	3 1/2	64	102 1/4	1 3/4	4	36 3/16	3 1/4	1 7/8	1 1/4

From "Armco Water Control Gates" Catalog G-3253.

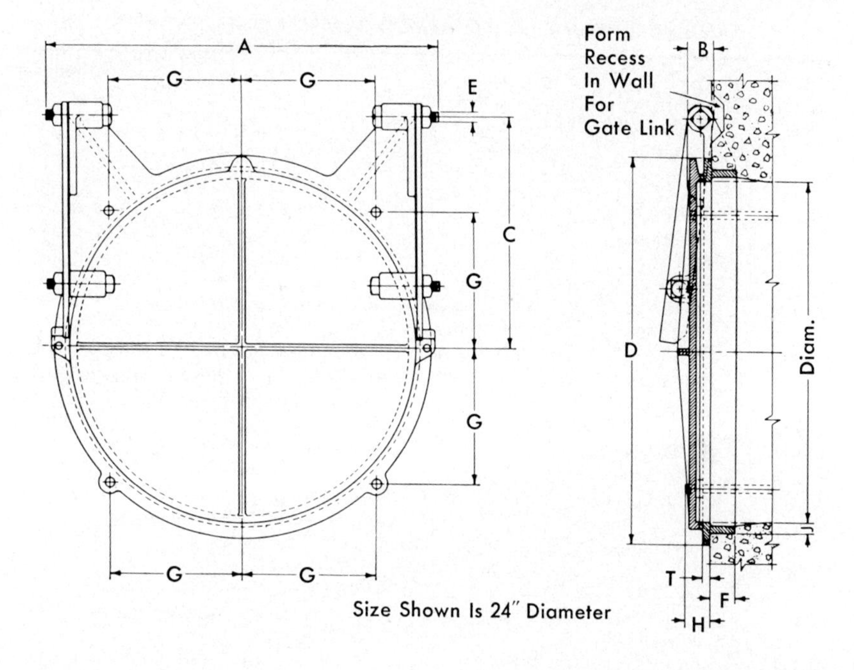

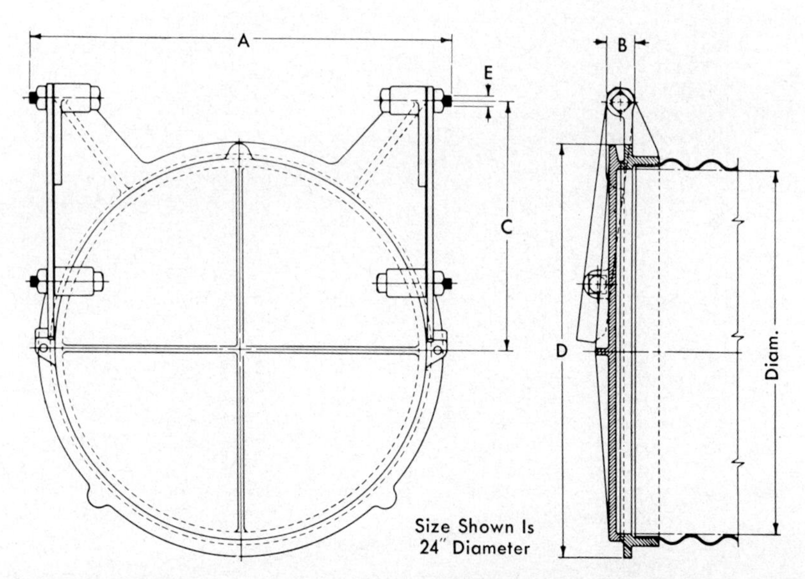

Fig. 268. Top: Details of Armco flap gate Model No. 100 for attaching to a concrete headwall.
Bottom: Details of the same flap gate but for attaching directly to corrugated metal pipe without a headwall.

TABLE 46-2 SUMMARY OF ARMCO WATER CONTROL GATES

Model No.	*Description*	*Maximum Permissible Head (Face Pressure)*	*Range of Usual Sizes*	*General Use*
50-10	SLIDE GATE Rectangular	50 ft	8″x8″ to 96″x96″	Flood control, detention and irrigation storage dams, hydroelectric developments. Will stand back pressure.
50-10C	SLIDE GATE Circular	50 ft	8″ to 96″	Same as Model 50-10.
30-05	SLIDE GATE Rectangular	30 ft	18″x18″ to 96″x96″	Flood control. Under-levee structures. Outlets for irrigation storage dams. Will stand back pressure.
30-05C	SLIDE GATE Circular	30 ft	18″ to 96″	Same as 30-05.
Levee Gate	SLIDE GATE Circular and Rectangular	50 ft	Cir. 18″ to 96″ diam. Rect. 18″ x 18″ to 96″ x 96″	Flood control and drainage. Will stand back pressure.
101	SLIDE GATE Circular	4 to 20 ft	8″ to 72″	Irrigation turnout gates. Sluice gates.
20-10C	SLIDE GATE Circular	20 ft	8″ to 36″	Sewage disposal plants and irrigation districts. Will stand back pressure.
10-00	STRUCTURAL STEEL SLIDE GATE Rectangular	10 ft	24″ x 24″ to 72″ x 72″	Waterway gate.
5-00	STRUCTURAL STEEL SLIDE GATE Rectangular	5 ft	24″x24″ to 72″x72″	Waterway gate.
101M	METER GATE Circular	Same as 101. Limited by height of wells	8″ to 48″	A turnout gate for measurement of diverted or delivered water.
140	FLAP GATE Circular	50 ft	54″ to 120″	Flood control and general drainage.
102	FLAP GATE Circular	50 ft	8″ to 78″	Flood control or swamp drainage.
103	FLAP GATE Rectangular	20 ft	24″x24″ to 60″x60″	Drainage of low areas. Prevention against backflow.
100	FLAP GATE Circular	10 ft	8″ to 90″	Marsh or tidal drainage and flood control.
1001	COMBINATION SLIDE AND FLAP GATE Circular	10 ft	18″ to 60″	Equalize water level. Draining or filling ponds. Flood control.
299	MUD DRAIN VALVE OR PLUG	20 ft	4″ to 18″	Sewage treatment plants. Will stand back pressure.

Fig. 269. Waters of the Montezuma Slough where the New York State Thruway crosses it are controlled by batteries of Armco slide headgates, Model 30-05.

Slide Gates: Lift-Operated

Lift-operated slide headgates are used not only on flood control and drainage reclamation projects but also for irrigation, water supply and recreational reservoirs. Circular and rectangular gates are available for heads varying from 10 ft up to 50 ft. The general limitations of the Armco gates of various models are given in Table 46-2.

A typical low-head installation is shown in Fig. 269.

For further data on the selection of gates and gate lifts, see gate catalog G-3253 of Armco Drainage & Metal Products, Inc., Middletown, Ohio.

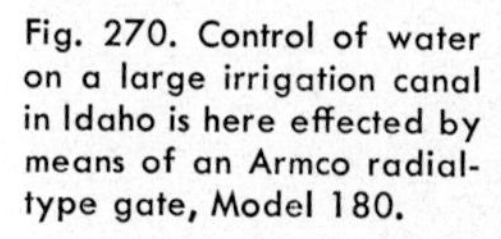

Fig. 270. Control of water on a large irrigation canal in Idaho is here effected by means of an Armco radial-type gate, Model 180.

Fig. 271. Note the Hel-Cor pipe subdrain installed under a bin-type metal retaining wall along a Connecticut state highway near Naugatuck.

SECTION NINE

MISCELLANEOUS PROBLEMS

CHAPTER FORTY-SEVEN

Earth Control

SOILS and other materials have their own "angle of repose." To maintain a steeper slope, some type of wall or support is necessary to prevent sloughing. Retaining walls are commonly used for this purpose. For low walls, and for trenches and cofferdams, sheeting is the answer. The design and use of these two products is here described.

Earth Pressures

For low walls or shallow trenches, up to 20 ft, the usual practice is to use empirical methods of determining the earth pressures. Such methods have been found conservative. On high walls or deep trenches that are the major item of a construction project, a complete soil survey and a more thorough analysis of loads may be justified by possible savings.

Regardless of how the pressures are calculated, the kind of soil and the moisture conditions are the principal factors and should be given careful attention.

PART ONE

RETAINING WALLS

RETAINING walls are commonly used on highways, railways and other public and private property for the following purposes: (1) to solve problems of limited right of way and to confine slopes within practical limits, (2) on road-widening and grade-separation projects, (see Fig. 271), (3) to stabilize steep cut and embankment slopes, (4) to repair breaks in roadway, (5) to prevent bank erosion, (6) as wing-walls for abutments and headwalls, (7) as loading platforms, (8) for parking areas and (9) as aircraft splinter protection walls and barricades or explosion walls in chemical plants.

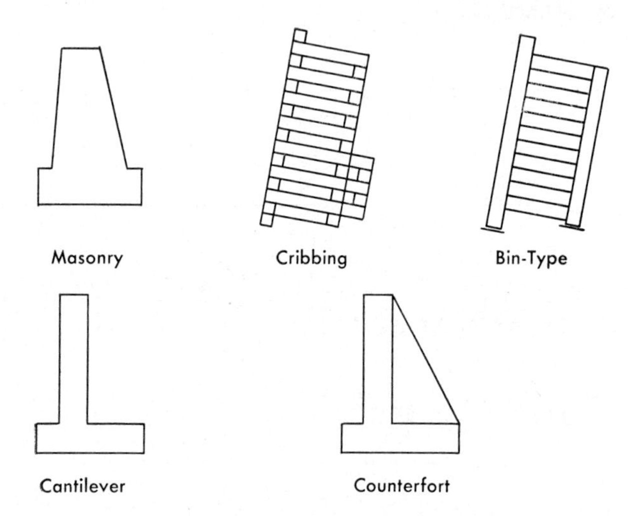

Fig. 272. Various gravity-type retaining walls (top row), and cantilever and counterfort.

The pressures acting upon a retaining wall tend to slide it forward, make it settle or overturn it. The bearing power of the foundation soil is important as is the character of the backfill which may vary from well drained gravel to very plastic clay. Determination of the magnitude, direction and point of application of pressure is a lengthy and involved procedure and the reader is directed to standard reference works on this subject.

An adequate foundation is necessary for satisfactory performance of a retaining wall. Most failures have occurred when the walls were built on clay foundations. On the other hand, coarse-grained soils provide stable foundations and backfill.

Clay soils or soils having a high percentage of clay should be avoided in backfills, particularly if seepage water is present in the slopes. Stiff clay placed in chunks should not be used for backfill unless seepage and surface waters can be prevented from entering the backfill material. Adequate drainage, always important, will improve the stability of all backfills. Drainage is essential whenever water bearing strata are present in the slopes.

Types of Walls

Retaining walls are of three types: gravity, cantilever and counterfort. See Fig. 272. Cantilever and counterfort types depend partly on the weight of the soil over the footings to give stability. The gravity type consists of heavy solid masonry or concrete, or a cellular, cribbing or bin-type wall. This latter type is discussed here.

Stability of a gravity wall is obtained through weight. In a cellular or bin-type wall this weight comes largely from the confined filling material, the bin or crib serving as a form or container.

A cellular wall should be set deep enough to resist sliding forward along the plane of the base. It should be of sufficient base width to resist overturning and resist settlement at the toe caused by overloading or crushing of the soil. The units of a cellular wall should have sufficient strength to resist flexure or shear, and the connections between units should be such as to resist bulging or other movement.

It is apparent that the wetter soils exert greater pressure and hence the necessity or advantage of employing drainage in connection with retaining walls. See Fig. 271.

The metal bin-type wall, because of its flexibility, adaptability and strength with light weight, has found general acceptance among engineers.

Recommended Base Width

In general, the base width or thickness of a bin-type wall filled with earth should be about one-half the height of the wall. Where there is a limited or level surcharge, however, it is conservative practice to specify the base width equal to about 45 per cent of the height. In case of a heavily surcharged wall, the base width should be increased to at least 55 per cent of the height. For recommended designs, see Figs. 274 and 275.

In order to increase the stability of the wall, a batter or inclination of 1 to 6, or 2 in. per ft of height, has been adopted in the computations of the accompanying design charts. If the wall is to be installed without batter, the additional stability can be obtained by selecting a design with greater base width.

Corner Columns and Base Plates

One of the important features of a metal bin-type wall is the U-shaped corner column to which all of the other units are bolted. This is in contrast to "cribbing" in which the longitudinal and transverse units overlap at the corners. See Figs. 272 and 277.

Base plates serve primarily to aid in building a bin-wall to proper line, grade and batter. They are not intended to carry the load of the wall or its contents. If the

Fig. 273. The need for a retaining wall along this mountain road in California is quite evident.

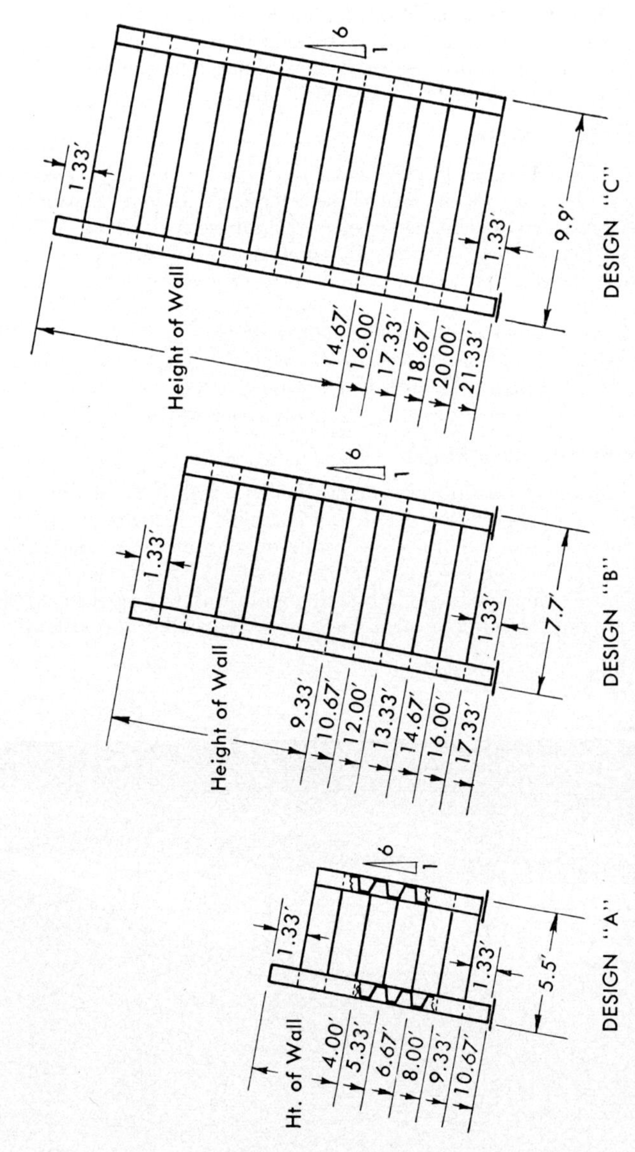

Fig. 274. Cross-sections of Armco bin-type retaining walls, Designs A, B and C, showing some of the standard sizes available.

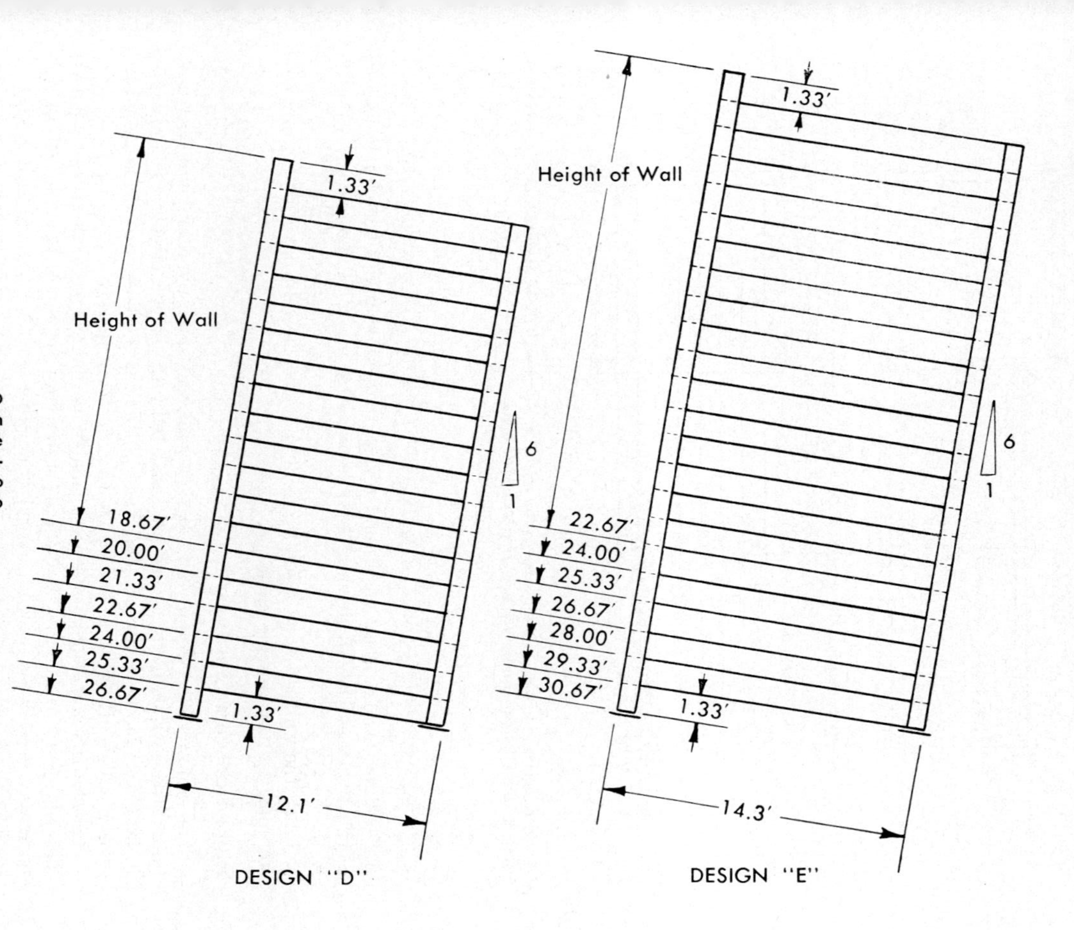

Fig. 275. Dimensions of Designs D and E. The ratio between width and height is a function of the surcharge and the type of material behind the walls. This ratio also changes if the batter of 6 to 1 is deviated from.

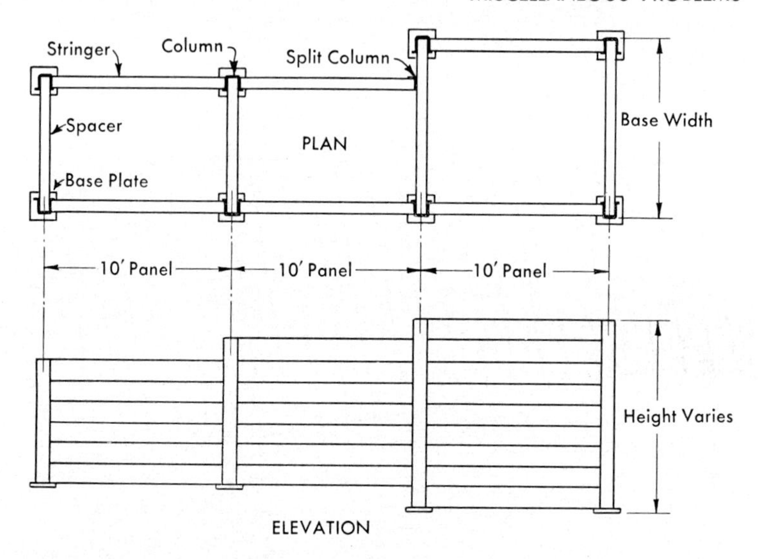

Fig. 276. Foundation plan and elevation of bin-type retaining wall showing details and how the base width and the height can be varied, using standard units.

soil within a wall settles, it is intended that the wall should settle equally instead of resisting that settlement with possible overstressing of the units comprising the wall.

When the wall is set on a solid rock foundation, an 8-in. layer of compressible soil must be placed under each base plate.

Rigid Transverse Sections

The transverse section of the bin-type wall consists of overlapping spacer units bolted together along the flanges and inserted into the corner columns and bolted to both legs of the columns. See Figs. 277 and 279. This provides a transverse section sufficiently rigid to prevent bulging in the wall.

The stringer and spacer units are available in different metal thicknesses (gages). This makes it possible to design a wall with a uniform bin or panel length of 10 ft regardless of wall height, and at the same time to effect economies in design by varying the gage of material as required by the pressures at various points. The stringer and spacer units have been shaped to eliminate voids in the fill material and to prevent retention of water on the exterior faces of the units.

Changes in Elevation and Curves

The stringer or panel units are generally erected on a horizontal plane. However, the top or base of the wall can be varied to meet changes in grade. This is accomplished by constructing "steps" of 16 in., or multiples of 16 in., every 10 ft or multiples of 10 ft (see Fig. 276).

Where a change in the height of a wall requires a change in the base width, a "split" column is attached to the transverse spacers at an intermediate point. Walls

Unit Number	Name	Description
1.	Column	Vertical member connecting all other units
2.	Column Cap	Cover for front column
3.	Stringer stiffener	Top flange protector
4.	Stringer	Horizontal longitudinal members in front and rear walls
5.	Connecting channel	Connector for attaching stringers to columns
6.	Spacer	Transverse members that separate the front and rear columns
7.	Bottom spacer	Special bottom transverse member
8.	Base plate	Installation plate on which the column rests
9.	1 ¼″ x ⅝″ bolts	
10.	⅝″ nuts	
11.	⅝″ spring nuts	

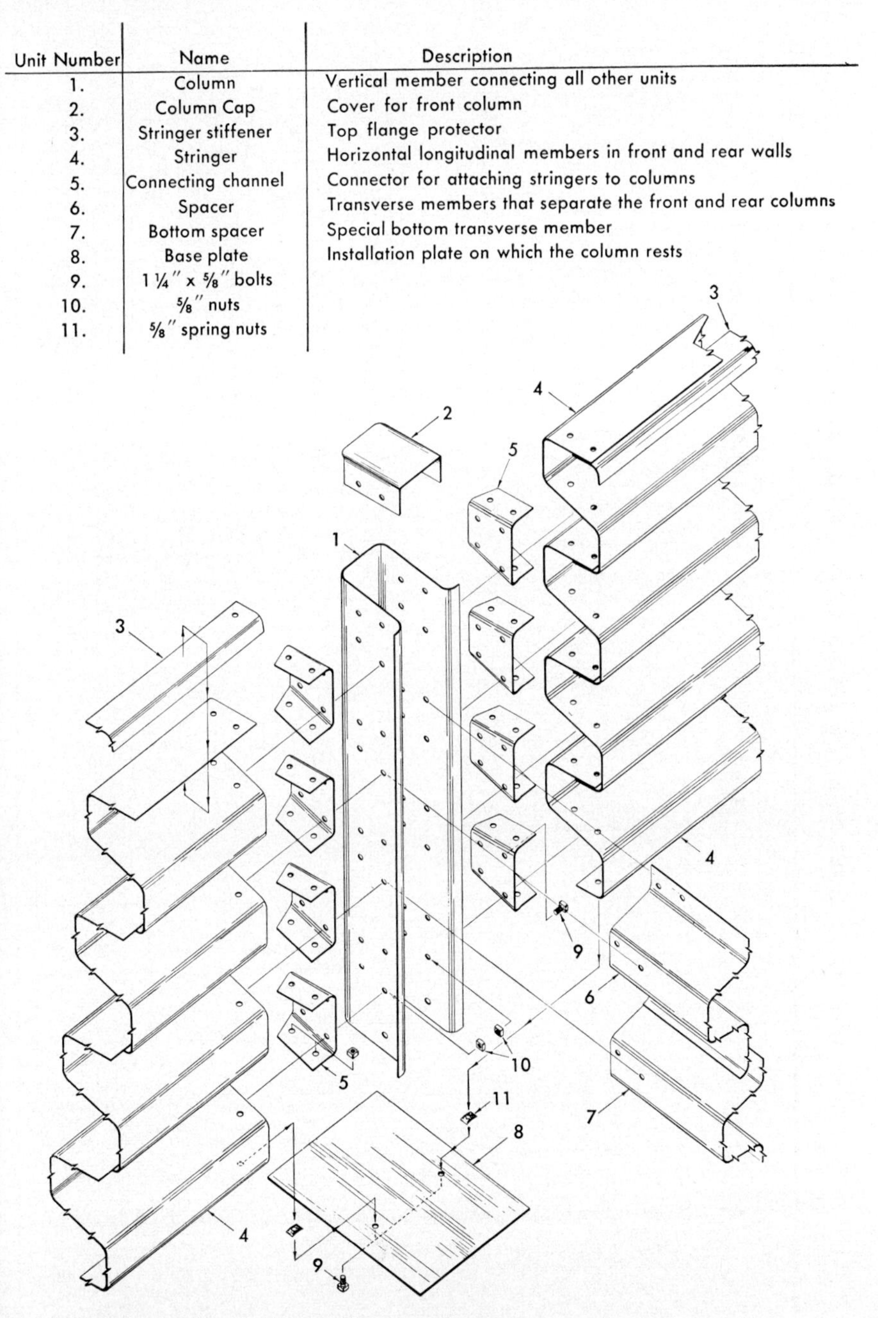

Fig. 277. "Exploded" view of Armco bin-type retaining wall at a front panel joint. View is from rear.

TABLE 47-1 CURVE DATA FOR ARMCO BIN-TYPE RETAINING WALLS

Design	Wall Height in Feet	Degree of Curve: 1	2	3	4	5	6	7	8	9	10	11	12	13	14	15	16	17	18	19	20	21	22	23	24	25	26	27	28	29	30	31	32	33	34	35
	Radius of Curve in Feet	5730	2865	1910	1432	1146	955	819	716	637	573	521	477	441	409	382	358	337	318	302	286	273	260	249	238	229	220	212	205	198	191	185	179	174	169	164
A	4.00	61	31	20	15	12	10	9	8	7	6	6	5	5	4	4	4	4	3	3	3	3	3	3	3	2	2	2	2	2	2	2	2	2	2	2
	5.33	61	31	20	15	12	10	9	8	7	6	6	5	5	4	4	4	4	3	3	3	3	3	3	3	2	2	2	2	2	2	2	2	2	2	2
	6.67	61	31	20	15	12	10	9	8	7	6	6	5	5	4	4	4	4	3	3	3	3	3	3	3	2	2	2								
	8.00	61	31	20	15	12	10	9	8	7	6	6	5	5	4	4	4	4	3	3	3	3	3													
	9.33	61	31	20	15	12	10	9	8	7	6	6	5	5	4	4	4	4	3	3	3															
	10.67	61	31	20	15	12	10	9	8	7	6	6	5	5	4	4	4	4																		
B	9.33	42	21	14	10	8	7	6	5	5	4	4	3	3	3	3	3	2	2	2																
	10.67	42	21	14	10	8	7	6	5	5	4	4	3	3	3	3	2	2																		
	12.00	42	21	14	10	8	7	6	5	5	4	4	3	3	3	3																				
	13.33	42	21	14	10	8	7	6	5	5	4	4	3	3																						
	14.67	42	21	14	10	8	7	6	5	5	4	4	3																							
	16.00	42	21	14	10	8	7	6	5	5	4	4																								
	17.33	42	21	14	10	8	7	6	5	5	4																									
C	14.67	32	16	10	8	6	5	5	4	4	3	3	3																							
	16.00	32	16	10	8	6	5	5	4	4	3	3																								
	17.33	32	16	10	8	6	5	5	4	4	3																									
	18.67	32	16	10	8	6	5	5	4	4																										
	20.00	32	16	10	8	6	5	5	4	4																										
	21.33	32	16	10	8	6	5	5	4																											
D	18.67	25	13	9	6	5	4	4	3	3																										
	20.00	25	13	9	6	5	4	4	3	3																										
	21.33	25	13	9	6	5	4	4	3																											
	22.67	25	13	9	6	5	4	4	3																											
	24.00	25	13	9	6	5	4	4																												
	25.33	25	13	9	6	5	4	4																												
	26.67	25	13	9	6	5	4																													
E	22.67	21	10	7	5	4	3	3	3																											
	24.00	21	10	7	5	4	3	3																												
	25.33	21	10	7	5	4	3	3																												
	26.67	21	10	7	5	4	3																													
	28.00	21	10	7	5	4	3																													
	29.33	21	10	7	5	4	3																													
	30.67	21	10	7	5	4																														

Use of Table—Figures in table indicate number of bins in which one set of short stringers must be included in the front or rear of one bin to produce curves.

Example: A wall 10.67 ft in height, Design "B," must have 1 set of short stringer units included in every 3 bins in order to build wall on 15° curve.

STANDARD STRINGER UNITS
SHORT STRINGER UNITS
STD. STRINGERS
9.5′ 10.0′ 10.0′ 120′

Note: Curvature limits are established by the variation in center to center spacing between the top and bottom of columns resulting from slight play at the joints. The difference in the chord lengths at the top and bottom of each panel varies with the batter in the wall because of different radii at the top and bottom of the wall. Data set forth in this table apply only to walls on batter of 2 in. per foot.

can be erected on curves as a series of short straight sections or the shape of the bins can be changed to fit the curve by using short stringers on the inside of the curve. See Fig. 278 and Tables 47–1 and 47–2.

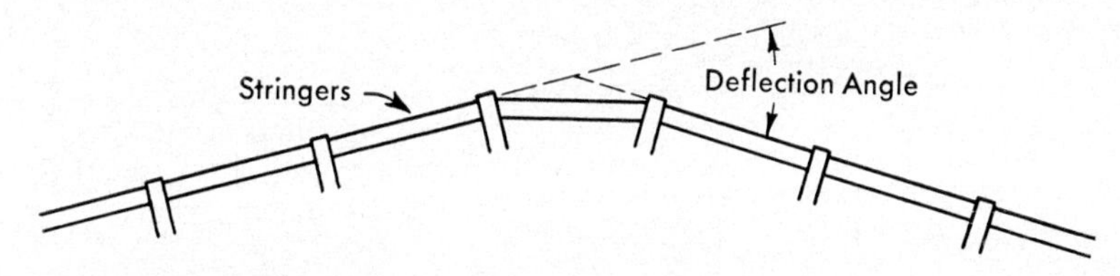

Fig. 278. Deflection angles on bin-type retaining walls can be small or large as shown in Table 47-2

TABLE 47-2 DEFLECTION ANGLES FOR BIN-TYPE RETAINING WALLS

Design of Wall	*Deflection Angle*	
	Standard Stringers in Both Faces	*Short Stringers in One Face*
A	0°-51′	4°-46′ to 5°-37′
B	0°-47′	3°-24′ to 4°-01′
C	0°-29′	2°-39′ to 3°-08′
D	0°-24′	2°-10′ to 2°-34′
E	0°-20′	1°-50′ to 2°-10′

These deflections between the faces of adjacent bins can be made in one bin for any height of wall by use of the parts indicated. When more deflection angle is needed in the face of the wall, bins using short stringers (6 in. shorter than standard) must be separated by standard bins. The minimum spacing of short stringer bins for each height and design of wall is shown by the last figure on each line in Table 47-1.

Fig. 279. Method of providing a large deflection angle between two independent tangential sections of bin-wall.

Fig. 280. Reverse curves in a metal retaining wall can be made as shown on this job along a river in Minnesota.

Installation Considerations

Retaining walls are frequently used in connection with unstable cut and embankment slopes, and sometimes mistakenly used to stop landslides. Minor slides may be stopped but large slides require more fundamental treatment.

Experience has shown that retaining walls are more effective and less susceptible to failure if used near the top of a slope rather than at the bottom. Soundings or borings should be made to determine the subsoil, ground water and foundation conditions. Unless a retaining wall can be placed on a uniform, stable foundation, it is likely to become distorted.

Good drainage back of the wall and the use of pervious material with a subdrain to intercept water and prevent lubrication of the base is important.

A bin-type wall is advantageous in that excavation may be reduced to a minimum by trenching for the bin outlines. Also, by scheduling the assembly, the earth excavated for one bin may be used directly to backfill the adjacent bin if the material is suitable. It is not necessary to leave an unstable slope exposed for long distances nor for a very long time. For details of installation, see pages 470–472.

PART TWO

SHEETING

WHERE bank erosion is to be prevented or where earth must be retained, as in the case of trenches, cofferdams, bulkheads and cut-off walls, the use of steel sheeting is quite common. Comparatively light-weight corrugated steel sheets are now being used for these purposes where the loads do not exceed the strength limitations of the section.

The points to be considered in selecting sheeting for a job are: (1) proper type of unit for various service conditions, (2) units of such size and weight as to be easily handled, (3) ease and speed of driving, (4) ample strength, (5) resistance to damage of the driving and leading edges, (6) ability to be salvaged readily and re-used frequently, (7) ease of storing the units and (8) nestability for compactness in shipping.

Types Available

Because of the many uses to which steel sheeting is put, several types are needed to best meet the individual conditions. Two widely used are: interlocking and flange. See Figs. 281 and 282. The interlocking type is used primarily where practical watertightness is desired such as cut-off walls. Flange type sheeting is commonly used for sheeting trenches, particularly where watertightness is not essential. The flanges can butt against each other or alternate sections can be reversed so that the flanges overlap. Flange type sheeting can be more easily driven to full penetration before excavation is started.

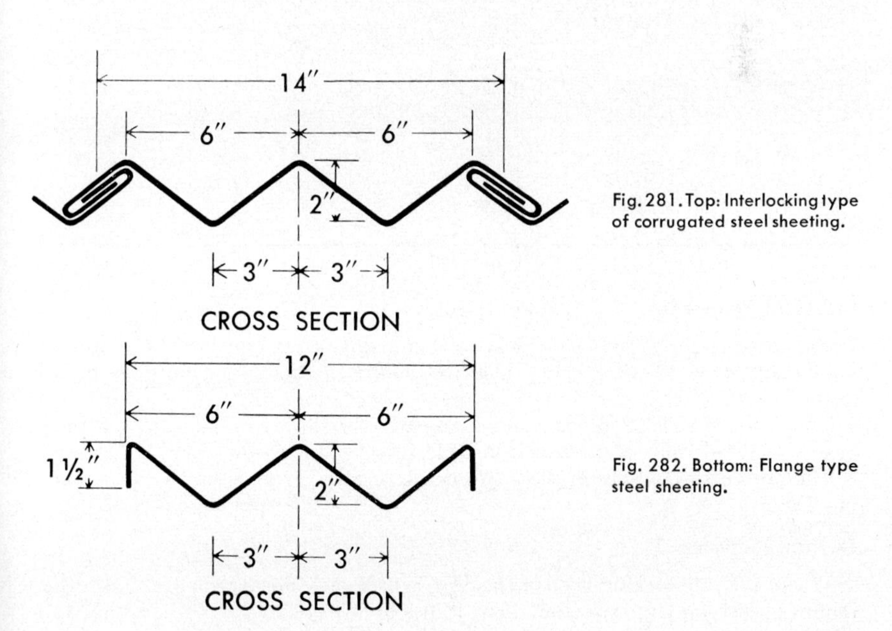

Fig. 281. Top: Interlocking type of corrugated steel sheeting.

Fig. 282. Bottom: Flange type steel sheeting.

Fig. 283. Driving steel sheeting to serve as a cut-off wall and half-height headwall on a railroad culvert in Iowa.

TABLE 47-3 PHYSICAL PROPERTIES OF ARMCO CORRUGATED SHEETING

Gage	*Decimal Thickness in Inches*	*Section Modulus per Unit in Inches Cubed*		*Weight per Lineal Foot of Sheeting Unit—in Pounds*	
		Flange	*Interlocking*	*Flange*	*Interlocking*
12	.1046	0.620	0.763	6.22	8.75
10	.1345	0.790	0.983	8.00	11.25
8	.1644	0.955	1.200	9.78	13.75
7	.1793	1.032	1.300	10.67	15.00
5	.2092	1.185	.....	12.45	.....
3	.2391	1.325	.....	14.22	.....

Physical Properties

The interlocking type of units have a nominal covering width of 14 in. and are manufactured in 12, 10, 8 and 7 gage. Standard lengths are in multiples of 2 ft from 6 to 20 ft.

The flange type is 12 in. wide and comes in 12, 10, 8, 7, 5 and 3 gage wall thickness. Standard lengths are from 6 to 20 ft.

The physical properties of these two types of units are given in the accompanying Table No. 47-3.

Corner Sections

Where the interlocking type of sheeting is used, any abrupt change in direction requires a special corner section. Two types are shown in Fig. 284. Either type

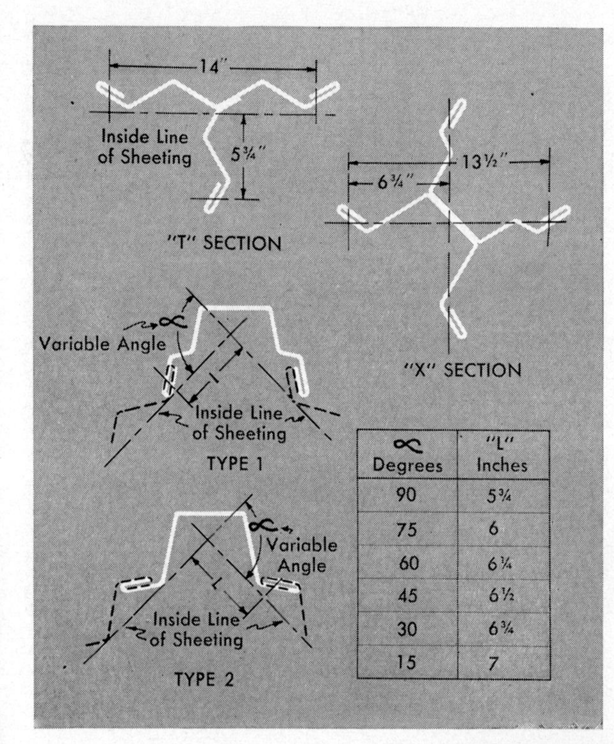

∝ Degrees	"L" Inches
90	5¾
75	6
60	6¼
45	6½
30	6¾
15	7

Fig. 284. "T" and "X" sections of steel sheeting for junction points and intermediate bulkheads. Also two types of corner sections set at variable angles.

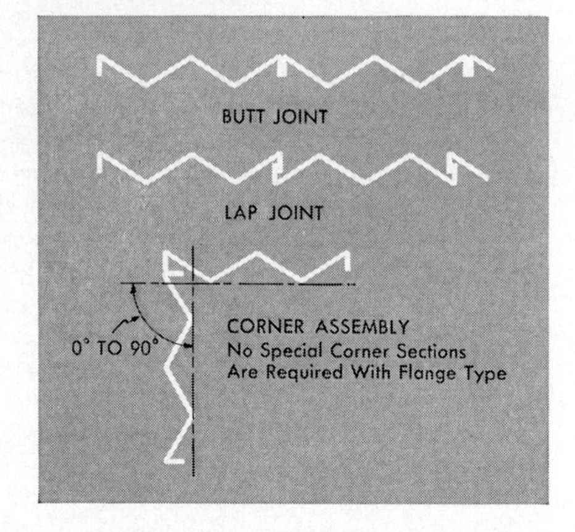

Fig. 285. Two types of joints for flange type steel sheeting, and corner assembly.

may be used where the wall consists of an *odd number* of sheeting units. Where an *even number* of units is used, both Type 1 and 2 corner sections are needed, as shown in the sketch. In beginning a wall, it is advisable to first set the corner section in place so that the sheeting units will face in the proper direction for making the turn.

The use of "X" and "T" sections for intermediate bulkheads is illustrated also. For corner assembly of flange type sheeting see Fig. 285.

Fig. 286. Steel sheeting makes an effective headwall on culverts and sewer outfalls. An angle or channel gives a smooth top line.

Fig. 287. This steel sheeting check dam protects a coaxial television cable across a creek in Nebraska.

Driving

A hand maul or a light pneumatic hammer is satisfactory for pushing metal sheeting or wood sheeting in a trench where the bottom can be excavated ahead of driving, and when the earth loads on the sheeting are light.

If the sheeting is to be driven in advance of excavation, or the side pressures are heavy, then heavier equipment such as a drop hammer or a pneumatic or steam pile-driver will be needed. Under these conditions the use of heavy driving equipment will make for faster driving with less injury to the sheeting for any given condition. Light equipment for this type of driving tends to batter the top edge of the sheeting and slow down the driving.

The driving equipment must be capable of supplying ample foot-pounds of energy to move the sheeting easily. A driver that strikes a heavy blow with a low velocity at impact will do the most work with the least damage to the sheeting. A long, heavy sheet pile requires more energy to start it moving than does a light, short section.

Friction of soil on the sheeting surfaces and force required for penetration are factors hard to evaluate. Knowledge of local conditions and experience with various types of equipment in driving in the soil formations that will be encountered are required to select the proper driving equipment.

Driving heads are used when driving with hand tools or the light pneumatic or gasoline drivers with a narrow driving base. They are generally unnecessary with gravity hammers or the larger air or steam hammers having a wide, flat base that will spread the blow over one or more widths of sheeting.

Wales and Struts for Armco Steel Sheeting

Sheeting, without bracing, will support the earth loads if it is driven to sufficient penetration and if it has the required strength. Generally, it will be found economical to use a lighter sheeting and support it with a system of wales and struts or anchors. When sheeting is used as a retaining wall, the wales are placed on the face of the wall and supported by ties extending through the wall to anchors placed in solid earth. In trenches, the wales are placed on the trench side of the sheeting and are supported by struts extending across the trench from wale to wale. The selection of the strength of sheeting and the design of the wales and supporting members are essentially the same problem in either a trench or wall condition.

Soil pressures vary with types of earth, moisture content and depth. Equivalent fluid pressures are commonly used for computing sheeting loads. Tables are available in many engineering handbooks.

Starting with the equivalent fluid pressure, the wale spacing for various gages of sheeting can be determined from the chart on pages 394–395. With the wale spacing known, the loads on the wales and the size of the wales and their supports can be determined by the approximate method outlined below.

Often wale and strut material will be available on the job and the problem then becomes one of determining maximum spacing allowable for this material.

Load Distribution on Wales

The load per foot of wale (W) is computed as follows:

Let:

p = Equivalent Fluid Pressure

d = Depth below surface to wale (in ft)

Then:

(1st Wale) $W_1 = p/8(d_1+d_2)^2$

(2nd Wale) $W_2 = p/4(d_3+d_1)\ (d_3-d_1)$

Succeeding wales are figured similar to W_2 substituting d_4 for d_3, d_2 for d_1 and so

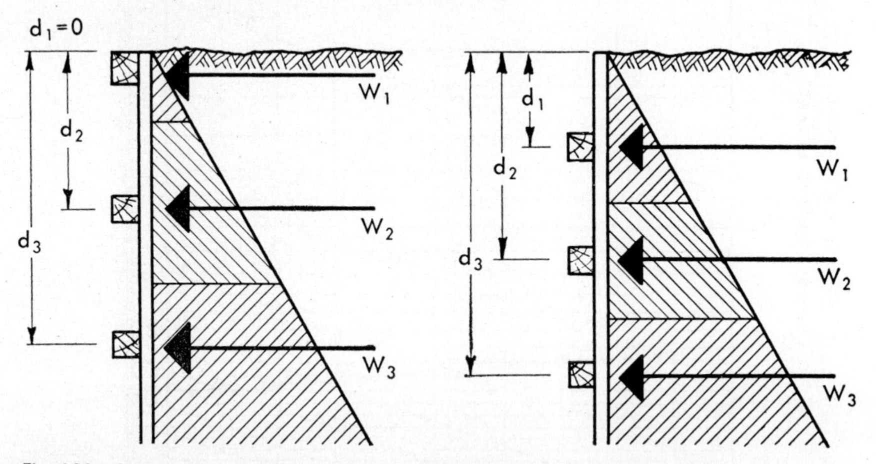

Fig. 288. Cross-sections of trench sheeting. Left, first wale at ground line. Right, first wale below ground line.

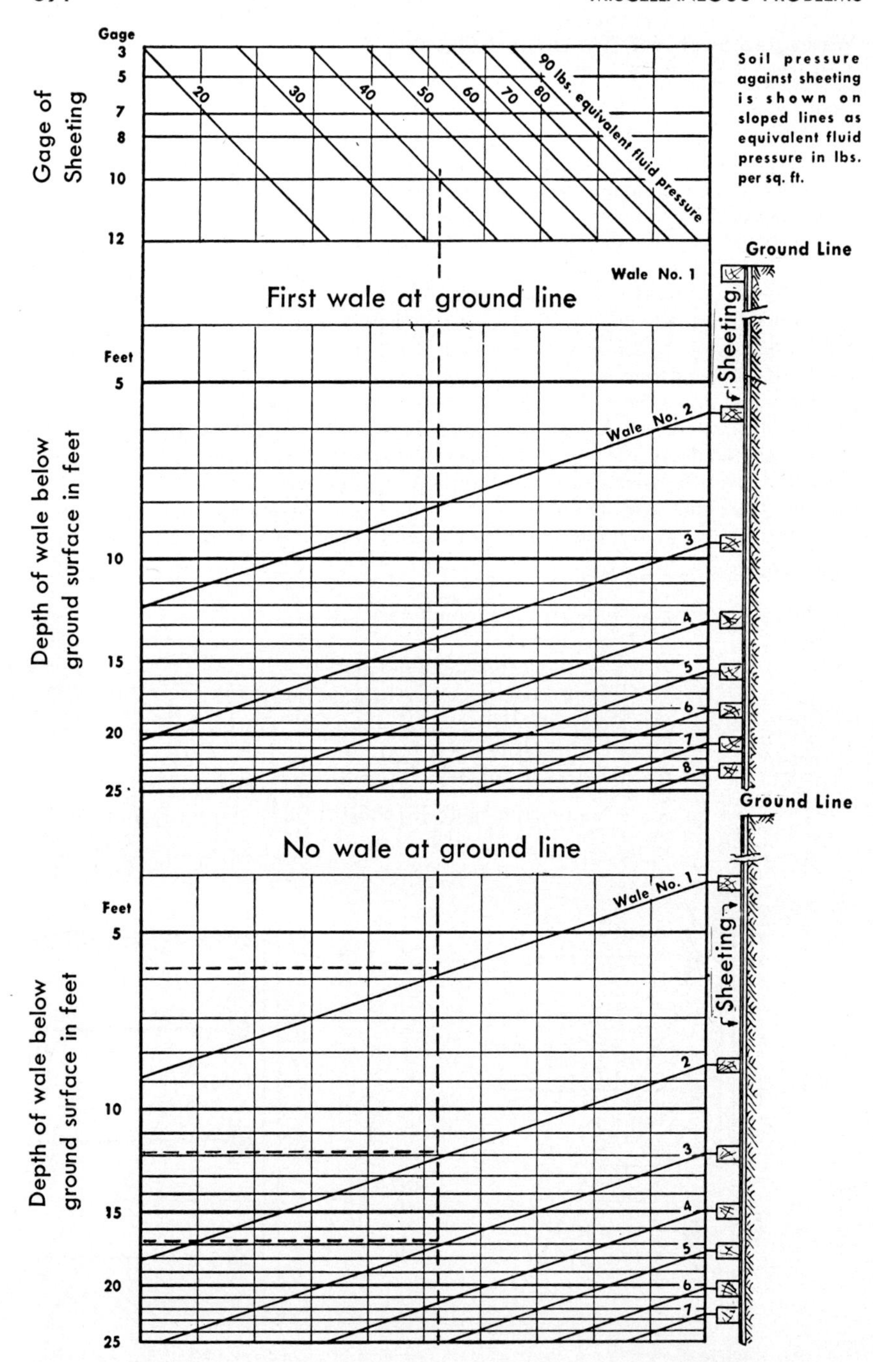

Fig. 289. Case 1: Wale spacing designed for EQUAL STRESS IN SHEETING.

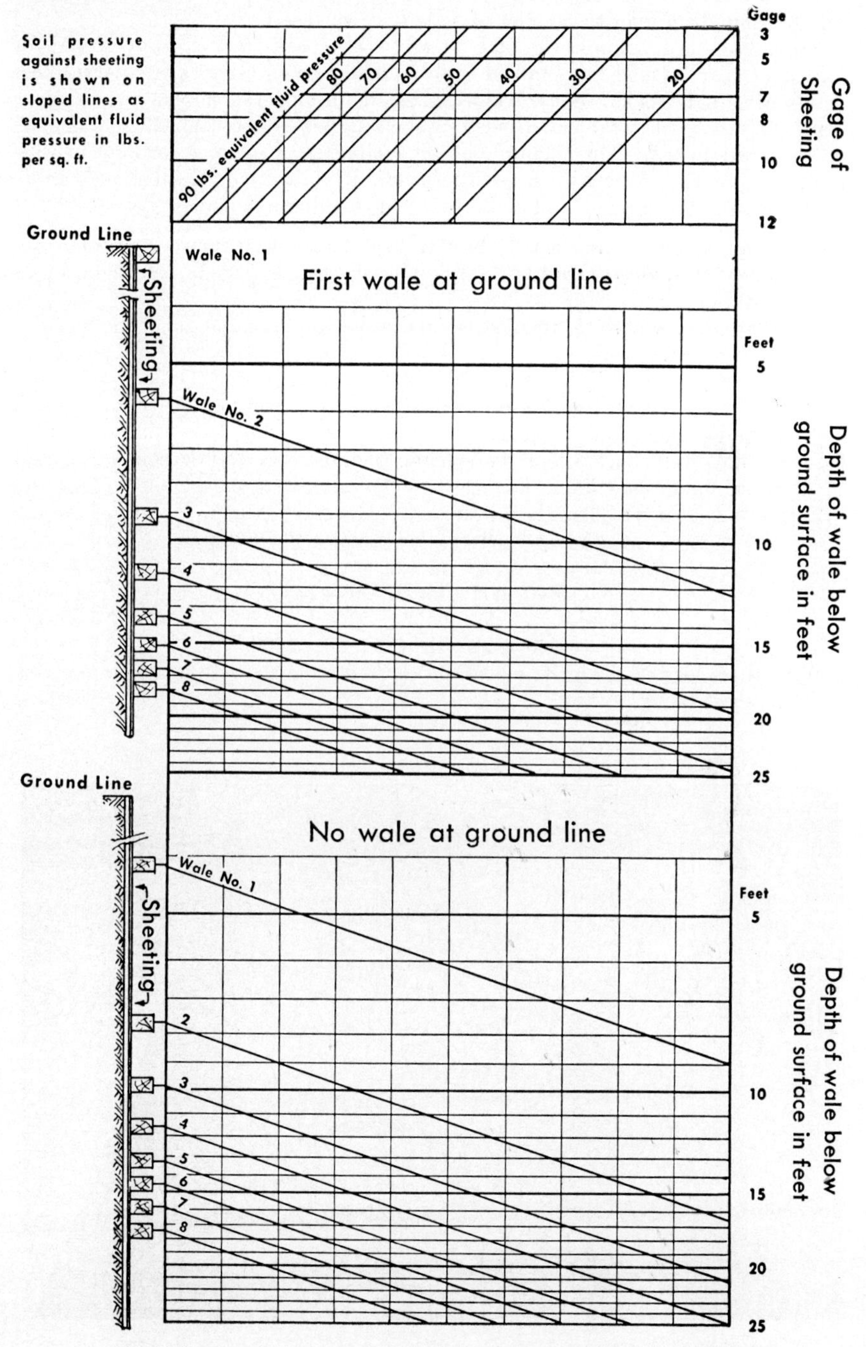

Fig. 290. Case 2: Wale spacing designed for EQUAL STRESS IN WALES.

on. (Subnumbers refer to number of wale from surface.)

The allowable total uniform load for any size of wale (wood or steel) and for any strut spacing may be obtained from standard beam tables available in most engineering handbooks. Shear values often determine the maximum allowable load. The allowable total load divided by the load per foot of wale will give spacing of the struts in feet. The column load on each strut is the load per foot of wale multiplied by the spacing of the struts (in ft). The required size of struts can be obtained from the column loading tables in engineering handbooks.

Example: Assume a trench is to be dug to a depth of 20 ft in a wet earth soil —equivalent fluid pressure is 40 psf. Available sheeting is 10 gage, timber for wales 10 in. x 10 in.

Wales are to be spaced for equal stress in the sheeting with the top of the sheeting loaded as a cantilever.

Then:

In the chart on page 394, Case 1, Equal Stress in Sheeting, locate intersection of 40-lb fluid pressure and 10 gage line. Drop a vertical line from this point down through the lower chart where the spacing of the wales is shown as 6, 12 and 17 ft below the ground line.

Compute load per foot on each wale:

$$(1)\ W_1 = p/8\ (d_1 + d_2)^2 = 40/8(6+12)^2 = 1625$$

$$(2)\ W_2 = p/4\ (d_3 + d_1)\ (d_3 - d_1)$$
$$= 40/4(17+6)\ (17-6) = 2530$$

$$(3)\ W_3 = p/4(d_4 + d_2)\ (d_4 - d_2)$$
$$= 40/4(22+12)\ (22-12) = 3400$$

With these loads known, it is possible to determine the required size of wales and size and spacing of struts.

Fig. 291. Steel sheeting used in trench to repair sewer line break in Indiana.

Fig. 292. This Multi-Plate underpass gives school children a danger-free crossing of this busy U. S. Highway at Fort Knox, Kentucky.

CHAPTER FORTY-EIGHT

Tunnels, Underpasses, Conduits

General Considerations

Underground conduits serve many practical purposes besides drainage, sewerage and water supply. As underpasses they assure safe movement of people and livestock that must cross busy highways, streets or railroads. In industry, conveyance tunnels mean a smooth flow of merchandise, materials or equipment, with weather protection and freedom from surface interference. Service tunnels and conduits protect and provide access to vital utility lines.

Underpasses for Pedestrians and Livestock

Pedestrian underpasses find their principal use where people, including school children, would otherwise be forced to cross dangerous railway tracks, streets or highways. See Fig. 292. Industrial organizations also can include underpasses from parking lots to the plant as a part of their safety program.

Safety is not the only advantage. Where a business, industry or institution is divided by a busy street or railroad, an underpass is the most convenient means of access from one part of the property to another. Lost time is avoided.

Fig. 293. Fifteen of these large Multi-Plate underpasses permit stock and vehicles to cross a new main line railroad in Wyoming.

Farms and ranches, too, are frequently divided by a highway or railroad, requiring livestock to make dangerous crossings. An opening or stock pass under the roadbed is the most satisfactory solution. See Fig. 293.

Conveyance Tunnels

When a plant property is divided by a roadway or other barrier to efficient ma-

Fig. 294. This liner plate tunnel permits uninterrupted flow of material between sections of an industrial plant bisected by an important railroad.

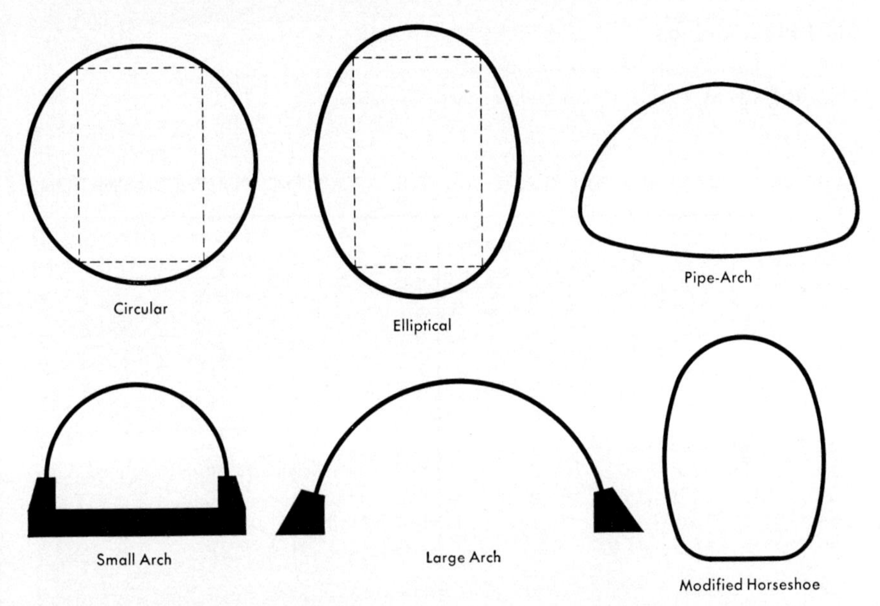

Fig. 295. A few typical shapes of corrugated metal tunnels, underpasses and conduits. They may be circular, elliptical, arched or horseshoe, in spans up to 20 ft or more.

terials handling, a tunnel is an economical means of joining the property. Fig. 294. Examples include a warehouse on the opposite side of a track from the plant; opening a new raw material pit beyond a roadway.

Contractors and aggregate companies are making use of tunnels and belt conveyors under aggregate storage piles. Fig. 297, page 404.

Mining companies use metal tunnel linings for entries, escapeways, shafts, haulageways, overcasts and other locations.

Service Tunnels and Conduits

Where water, steam and gas lines, sewers or power cables pass between buildings or under embankments or other surface obstacles, the trend is to place them inside a conduit. This protects them against direct loading, impact, or corrosion, and against temperature extremes, bombings or sabotage. Fig. 298.

Where used to encase sewers or high pressure lines, they help protect the fill and surface installations from damage in case of sudden breaks.

Circumstances will dictate whether to make the tunnel or conduit large enough to walk through. This gives better access for inspection and repairs.

Brackets, hangers or cushioning bases are easily installed.

Materials for Construction

Tunnels, underpasses and conduits can be built of steel, wood, concrete, vitrified clay or other materials. Of these, corrugated steel is perhaps most widely accepted because of high strength-to-weight ratio, ease of installation and salvability on temporary installations.

The three basic types of corrugated metal structures are steel plate linings, structural plates and standard corrugated pipe.

Steel Plate Linings

Steel plate tunnel structures are available in several shapes: (1) circular, (2) elliptical, (3) arch and (4) horseshoe. See Fig. 295.

TABLE 48-1 STANDARD FULL CIRCLE TUNNELS, AREAS AND PLATE COMBINATIONS

Neutral Axis Diameter—Inches	*Approx. Inside Diameter—Inches*	*Approx. Outside Diameter—Inches*	*Approx. Outside Area—Sq Ft*	*No. Required*				*Neutral Axis Diameter—Inches*	*Approx. Inside Diameter—Inches*	*Approx. Outside Diameter—Inches*	*Approx. Outside Area—Sq Ft*	*No. Required*			
				12 Pi Plate	*14 Pi Plate*	*16 Pi Plate*	*Total Plates*					*12 Pi Plate*	*14 Pi Plate*	*16 Pi Plate*	*Total Plates*
48	45¼	49¼	13.2	4			4	108	105¼	109¼	65.0		2	5	7
50	47¼	51¼	14.3	3	1		4	110	107¼	111¼	67.5		1	6	7
52	49¼	53¼	15.5	2	2		4	112	109¼	113¼	70.0			7	7
54	51¼	55¼	16.6	1	3		4	114	111¼	115¼	72.5		7	1	8
56	53¼	57¼	17.9		4		4	116	113¼	117¼	75.0		6	2	8
58	55¼	59¼	19.1		3	1	4	118	115¼	119¼	77.5		5	3	8
60	57¼	61¼	20.4		2	2	4	120	117¼	121¼	80.1		4	4	8
62	59¼	63¼	21.8		1	3	4	122	119¼	123¼	82.9		3	5	8
64	61¼	65¼	23.2			4	4	124	121¼	125¼	85.8		2	6	8
66	63¼	67¼	24.6	2	3		5	126	123¼	127¼	88.5		1	7	8
68	65¼	69¼	26.1	1	4		5	128	125¼	129¼	90.5			8	8
70	67¼	71¼	27.7		5		5	130	127¼	131¼	93.9		7	2	9
72	69¼	73¼	29.2		4	1	5	132	129¼	133¼	96.8		6	3	9
74	71¼	75¼	30.8		3	2	5	134	131¼	135¼	99.8		5	4	9
76	73¼	77¼	32.5		2	3	5	136	133¼	137¼	102.8		4	5	9
78	75¼	79¼	34.2		1	4	5	138	135¼	139¼	105.8		3	6	9
80	77¼	81¼	36.0			5	5	140	137¼	141¼	108.8		2	7	9
82	79¼	83¼	37.8	1	5		6	142	139¼	143¼	111.9		1	8	9
84	81¼	85¼	39.7		6		6	144	141¼	145¼	115.0			9	9
86	83¼	87¼	41.6		5	1	6	146	143¼	147¼	118.1		7	3	10
88	85¼	89¼	43.5		4	2	6	148	145¼	149¼	121.3		6	4	10
90	87¼	91¼	45.4		3	3	6	150	147¼	151¼	124.5		5	5	10
92	89¼	93¼	47.4		2	4	6	152	149¼	153¼	128.0		4	6	10
94	91¼	95¼	49.4		1	5	6	154	151¼	155¼	131.5		3	7	10
96	93¼	97¼	51.5			6	6	156	153¼	157¼	135.0		2	8	10
98	95¼	99¼	53.6		7		7	158	155¼	159¼	138.5		1	9	10
100	97¼	101¼	55.8		6	1	7	160	157¼	161¼	141.9			10	10
102	99¼	103¼	58.1		5	2	7	162	159¼	163¼	145.5		7	4	11
104	101¼	105¼	60.3		4	3	7	164	161¼	165¼	149.0		6	5	11
106	103¼	107¼	62.6		3	4	7	166	163¼	167¼	152.6		5	6	11

Diameters are available above those shown in the same pattern.
All circular sections can be made elliptical with any ratio of major and minor axes.
Specify on order whether circumferential bolt spacing is to be 6¼″ c. to c. or 12½″ c. to c.

TABLE 48-2 DATA ON ARMCO LINER PLATE ELLIPTICAL UNDERPASSES

No.	*Neutral Axis Periphery, in Pi Inches*	*Inside*		*Neutral Axis*		*No. Plates Required*		
		Height	*Width*	*R.*	*R.*	*12 Pi*	*14 Pi*	*16 Pi*
1	80	87¼″	65¼″	30″	60″	2	4	
2	84	91¼″	69¼″	32″	62″		6	
3	88	95¼″	73¼″	34″	64″		4	2
4	92	99¼″	77¼″	36″	66″		2	4
5	96	103¼″	81¼″	38″	68″			6
6	100	107¼″	85¼″	40″	70″	6	2	
7	104	111¼″	89¼″	42″	72″	4	4	
8	112	119¼″	97¼″	46″	76″	4		4
9	120	127¼″	105¼″	50″	80″		4	4
10	128	135¼″	113¼″	54″	84″			8

No.	*Rectangular Clearance*				
1	4′0″x5′0″				
2	4′0″x5′6″	4′6″x5′0″			
3	4′0″x6′0″	4′6″x5′6″			
4	4′0″x6′6″	4′6″x6′0″	5′0″x5′6″		
5	4′0″x7′0″	4′6″x6′6″	5′0″x6′0″		
6		4′6″x7′0″	5′0″x6′6″	5′0″x6′0″	
7		4′6″x7′6″	5′0″x7′0″	5′6″x6′5″	
8			5′0″x8′0″	5′6″x7′5″	6′0″x6′9″
9			5′0″x8′10″	5′6″x8′4″	6′0″x7′10″
10				5′6″x9′4″	6′0″x8′11″

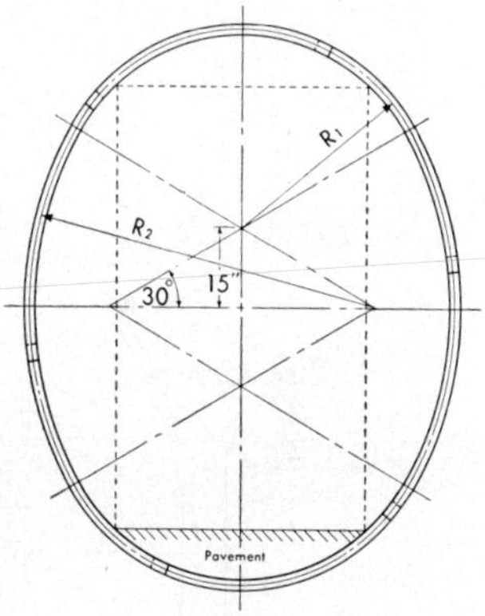

Notes:

1. For elliptical underpasses use gage as shown in Tables 14-4 and 14-5 for structures having the same periphery.
2. Additional sizes of elliptical Armco Liner Plate formed 10 per cent elliptical or less, are available if required.

Experience is the best guide for determining proper gages. However, gage tables have been prepared (Tables 14-1 to 14-5, pages 140–143) which serve as a guide where no better information exists. Where the liner plate is to serve as the permanent finished opening, the gage and protection of the metal must be determined accordingly. For details of plates, see Fig. 299, page 406.

The circular shape ranges from 48 in. to 15 ft or more in diameter in increments of 2 in. and gages from 14 to 3. Table 48-1 gives basic information on the sizes and Table 48-3 the physical properties of this type.

The *elliptical* opening is widely used for its high strength in relation to the vertical diameter. The most common sizes for underpasses are shown in Table 48-2. They range from 4 x 5 ft (rectangular clearance) to 6 x 9 ft, in [*Continued on page 404*]

TABLE 48-3 PROPERTIES AND DIMENSIONS OF ARMCO TUNNEL LINER PLATES

Strength and Weight Data

Gage	*Decimal Thickness in Inches*	*Area in Sq In*	*Section Modulus in Inches Cubed*		*Radius of Gyration*	*X*	*Approx. Plate Weights Including Bolts, in Pounds*		
			Per Inch	*Per Section*			*12 Pi Plate*	*14 Pi Plate*	*16 Pi Plate*
14	.0747	1.744	.0341	0.613	.615	.766	25	28	31
12	.1046	2.440	.0478	0.859	.614	.785	33	37	42
10	.1345	3.130	.0608	1.093	.614	.799	41	47	52
8	.1644	3.837	.0736	1.323	.614	.818	49	56	63
7	.1793	4.185	.0797	1.435	.614	.828	53	61	68
5	.2092	4.881	.0918	1.654	.614	.846	61	70	79
3	.2391	5.581	.1035	1.863	.614	.858	70	80	90

X = Distance from outer face to neutral axis, in inches.

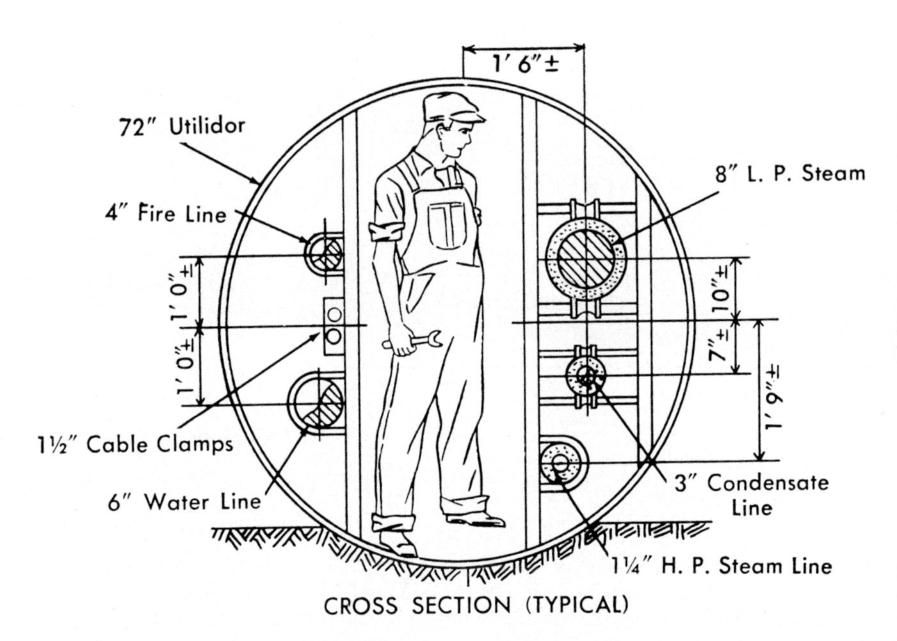

Fig. 296. Cross-section of a 72-in. corrugated metal "utilidor" or service tunnel equipped with brackets and clamps for supporting various utility lines.—Courtesy The Ric-Wil Company.

TABLE 48-4 PLATE ARRANGEMENT FOR ARMCO LINER PLATE ARCHES —to Obtain 4 pi Minimum Stagger of Longitudinal Seams

Plates Required							*Plates Required*						
First Ring				*Second Ring (When different from first ring)*			*First Ring*				*Second Ring (When different from first ring)*		
Arc Length (Pi Inches)	*12 Pi Plate*	*14 Pi Plate*	*16 Pi Plate*	*12 Pi Plate*	*14 Pi Plate*	*16 Pi Plate*	*Arc Length (Pi Inches)*	*12 Pi Plate*	*14 Pi Plate*	*16 Pi Plate*	*12 Pi Plate*	*14 Pi Plate*	*16 Pi Plate*
48	4					3	110	2	5	1			
50							112			7	4		4
52	3		1				114	3	1	4			
54	2	1	1				116	3		5			
56	2		2				118	2	1	5			
58	1	1	2				120	2		6			
60	1		3				122	1	1	6			
62		1	3	4	1		124	1		7			
64			4	4		1	126		1	7	4	1	4
66	3	1	1				128			8	4		5
68	2	2	1				130	3	1	5			
70	1	3	1				132	2	2	5			
72	1	2	2				134	1	3	5			
74	1	1	3				136	2		7			
76	1		4				138	1	1	7			
78	4	1	1				140	1		8			
80	3	2	1				142		1	8	4	1	5
82	2	3	1				144			9	4		6
84	1	4	1				146	4		6			
86	1	3	2				148	3	1	6			
88	1	2	3				150	2	2	6			
90	1	1	4				152	2		8			
92	1		5				154						
94	3	3	1				156						
96	3	2	2				158						
98	3	1	3				160			10	4		7
100	3		4				162						
102	2	1	4				164						
104	1	2	4				166						
106	1	1	5				168	2		9			
108	1		6										

[*Continued from page 401*]

half-foot increments. Larger sizes are also available. Tables 14–1 and 14–2 give data on minimum gages to be used under heaviest railroad and legal highway loads.

Large *arch* openings of steel plate tunnel lining are often used for sloped mine entries. Spans usually range from 12 to 18 ft for mine use, but both larger and smaller spans are available. Arches are also used for stock passes.

Steel plate lining is generally installed by tunneling but can also be placed in open trench. It is also used for relining old structures in conditions where it is unsafe or uneconomical to use structural plate. It is supplied either black or galvanized and can in addition be asphalt coated.

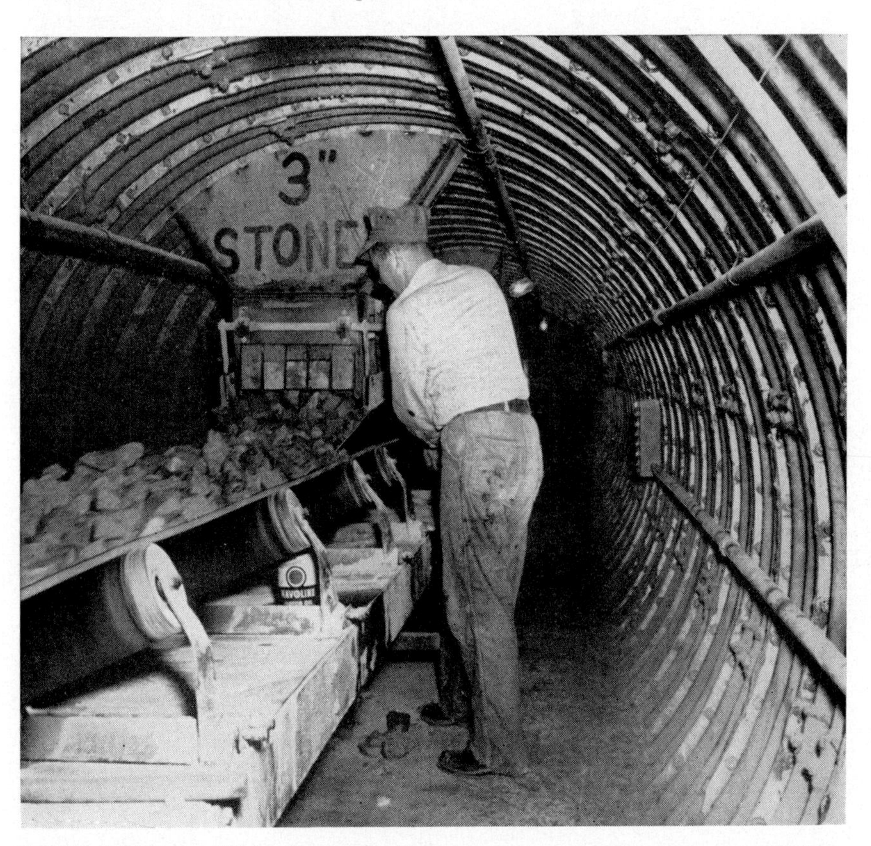

Fig. 297. Difficult materials handling problems are frequently solved with underpasses of this type.

Structural Plate

Structural plate or Multi-Plate installations may be circular, elliptical, arch, horseshoe or pipe-arch in shape. They are available for openings from 5 to 20 ft or more. See pages 78 to 93 and 110 to 130 for various sizes and gages.

Because of its bolted construction and size of the individual plates, structural plate is installed in open trench. It is shipped to the job site knocked down, ready for quick assembly.

Fig. 298. Service lines, mounted on a variety of easily attached brackets, are protected and made available for repair by this tunnel.

Standard Corrugated Pipe

Corrugated metal pipe and pipe-arches are frequently used for conduits, service tunnels and underpasses. Sizes range from 8 to 96 in. for full-round pipe, (Fig. 296) and from 18 x 11 to 72 x 44 in. for pipe-arches. See pages 72 to 77, 107 to 109, 118–119, and 125. Elliptical pipe can also be supplied in the same size range.

Nestable pipe and pipe-arches, as well as part circle corrugated structures are especially useful where a sewer or water line is already in place and a conduit is needed around the line.

Installation Methods

Four different construction methods are available for installing tunnels, underpasses and conduits.

Open trenching is the most practical where the cover is shallow, where it is practical to disrupt surface activities, and on new construction where the need is anticipated before the fill is made.

Jacking. Where soil and other conditions permit, the jacking method of installing corrugated pipe and pipe-arches is practical and economical. This method avoids danger and delays to surface traffic, and does not destroy pavements, or disturb tracks or other surface installations. See Chapter 54, page 455, for general instructions. The most suitable sizes range from 36 to 72 in. in diameter.

Boring. This method permits installing small pipe, in diameters up to 30 in.

Tunneling. Where the above methods are not practical because of size, length or soil conditions, tunneling is the answer. It avoids open trenches which tie up traffic, inconvenience merchants or interfere with business in general.

The introduction of light-weight but strong pressed steel tunnel liner plates has probably done more to expand the tunneling method of installation than any other one factor. These plates plus modern excavating and material handling equipment, coupled with ingenuity and experience, have resulted in thousands of feet of small tunnel jobs being completed each year.

Besides new tunnels, these pressed steel plates are used for renewal of existing or failing tunnels and culverts. Bolting operations are all carried on from the inside. Threaded couplings welded into the plates at intervals, make it possible to pump grout between the two structures to fill the voids when that is required.

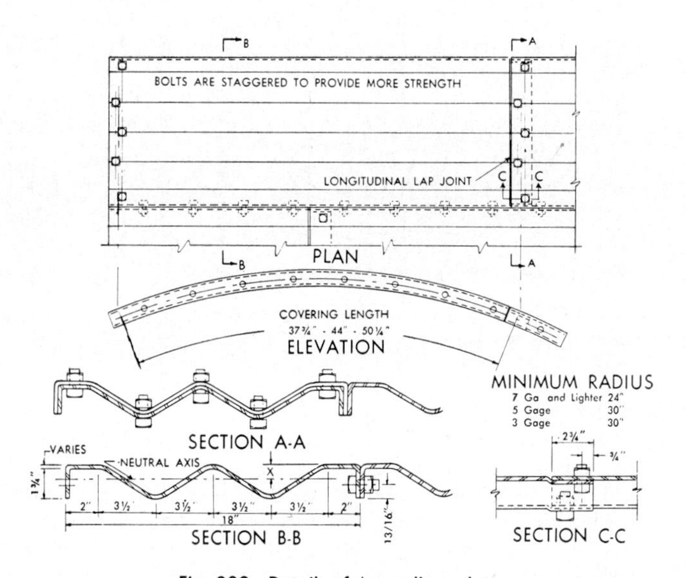

Fig. 299. Details of Armco liner plate.

End and Interior Finish

Appearance and cost are the factors that usually govern the type of end treatment on an underpass or tunnel. The ends may be square or beveled,* and the slope may be sodded, riprapped or landscaped. Simple or elaborate masonry or concrete headwalls of any design can be added. It is also possible to supply a building or shelter over each entrance.

*Beveling applies only to corrugated metal pipe and structural plate—not steel plate linings.

Fig. 300. Beam-type guardrail is standard on many modern highways and expressways. The above installation is on Clear Creek Canyon highway in Colorado.

CHAPTER FORTY-NINE

Guardrail and Bridge Rail

EFFICIENT guardrail must perform two functions of almost equal importance. One is to mark the limit of safe travel and warn of danger beyond. To do this it should have high visibility, especially in fog or at night, and it should create driver confidence—an intangible but exceedingly important factor. Crowding of the center line is reduced and often eliminated by the sight of a sturdy guardrail between the vehicle and the hazard.

The other main function of guardrail is to restrain and guide an out-of-control vehicle in a manner that will cause the least damage and not create undue hazard to other traffic. Its value is in preventing minor accidents from becoming major ones. Three qualities are highly desirable. (1) Beam strength with some flexibility—for primary re-direction and guidance of out-of-control vehicles; (2) coordinated joint strength—to enable adjoining sections to absorb heavy impact beyond the beam strength of individual rail units and (3) in case of impact, to hold the vehicle away from the posts to prevent pocketing, and to minimize damage to rail and car.

Most guardrails are never required to actively resist impact from out-of-control vehicles—yet the ability to do this must always be there when needed.

The ideal guardrail, then, is one that has high visibility and the right proportion of strength to flexibility. It should be simple to install and repair and keep in service despite accidents or lack of proper maintenance.

Various forms of guardrail that have been used in times past, ranging from saplings, wood planks, cable and woven wire to tension plate rail as the speed of vehicles increased. Beam type guardrail—as originated in Flex-Beam—is considered as today's standard and is manufactured in slightly varying forms by several manufacturers. Since all of the manufacturers use the same standard post spacing and essentially the same width and depth of beam, the principles of design for these rails are the same for all.

Fig. 301. Full utilization of marginal property for this municipal parking lot was facilitated by the use of Flex-Beam Guardrail and vertical bin-type retaining walls at Niles, Mich.

Where Required

There is one basic principle for determining where guardrail is required: wherever its use will prevent minor accidents from becoming major. This principle, if carefully followed, will result in well placed guardrail installations on high fills, steep drop-offs, watercourses, sharp curves, junctions and parking lots. Fig. 301. Quite often guardrail will be found useful on divided highways to separate opposing streams of traffic where the median strip may not be wide enough. Bridge approaches generally require guardrail. Protection of property, such as buildings and lawns may require guardrail. Fig. 306. In all cases the principle is the same; to reduce damage and possible loss of life from minor accidents or errors of human judgment.

Height of Installations

Since the average height of car bumpers is about 18 in. and since this dimension is well related to the center of gravity of cars, the usual height for guardrail installations is 18 in. from the ground surface at the posts to the horizontal centerline of the rail elements.

This dimension should be adjusted properly for installations on bridges or at points involving curbs and walks. The rail elements should generally be set with respect to the bridge floor when the rail is close to the floor. However, if a walk or other raised surface is between the guardrail and the roadway, it will probably be

Fig. 302. Proper height for installing guardrail depends upon the particular location. What serves for this industrial use might not be appropriate on a mountain highway.

better to set the rail height with respect to the intervening surface.

It may often be advisable to use guardrails in double lines on truss bridges, one line vertically above the other and in the same plane. The higher line should be placed to provide protection for the bridge members against the contact of high truck bodies or loads. Figs. 304 and 305.

Lateral Placement

Guardrail should be located as far from the edge of the roadway as feasible. Preferably there should be ample space between the roadway and the guardrail to permit parking a car free of the roadway. Consideration should be given, however, to allow sufficient distance from the embankment slope to permit solid post support from the material between the post and slope.

The distance between edge of roadway and guardrail may be variable. On runs protecting high fills or curves it may be desirable to introduce "flares" on each end of the run to increase visibility and reduce possibility of striking the installation directly on the end. These flares can be accomplished with a single length of shop-curved rail or by field bending of the last three or four rails to form a neat curve.

At bridge approaches it will almost always be necessary to effect rather rapidly flaring lines for the guardrail—particularly where the structure is narrower than full roadway width. This can be accomplished with reversed curves or shop-curved sections in a pleasing manner and with resulting increased visibility of the rail and approaches.

Intersections are special problems each requiring special study. Guardrail may often be used rather close to the traveled roadway to separate traffic streams or to prevent parking or encroachment on landscaped islands.

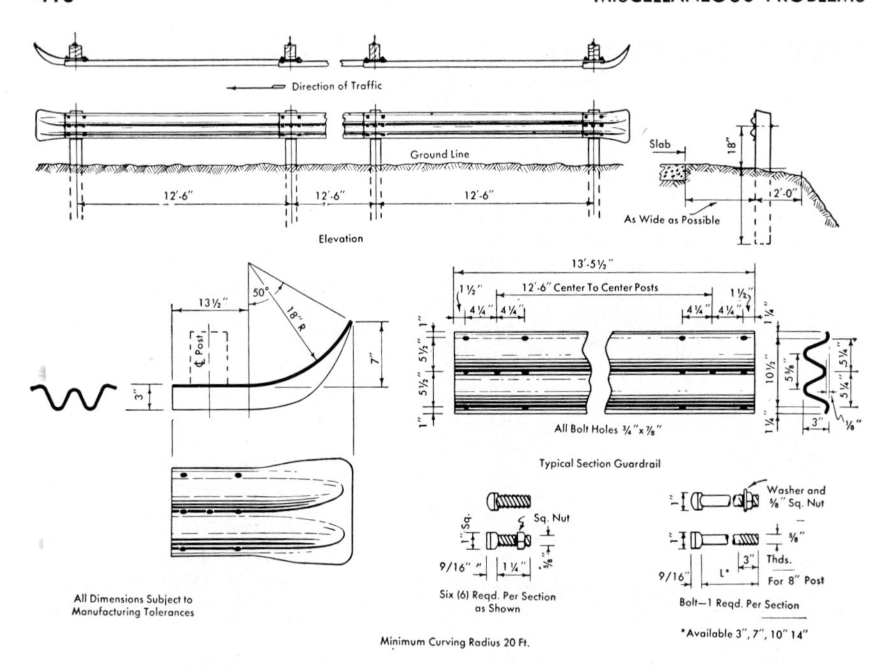

Fig. 303. Diagram of Flex-Beam Guardrail showing simplicity of design and construction.

Fig. 304. A double or triple line of guardrail is sometimes used to protect bridge members. Spacing of posts for guardrail on bridges varies with the spacing of the bridge members.

Post Spacing—Highways

Usage over a period of years is a better indicator of safe post spacing than is either theory or computations. In standard practice for highway use this spacing has evolved as 12½ ft for beam type guardrails. Fig. 303. Consequently the standard panel length of the rails is also 12½ ft. This furnishes just about the right amount of flexibility to avoid undue damage to the vehicle.

Sometimes for a particularly hazardous location it is desirable to stiffen up the installation by using one half or one third of the standard spacing which still permits the economy of standard panel lengths of rail. By selecting either the standard weight of rail (12 gage) or heavy duty (10 gage) and post spacings of 4 ft-1 in., 6 ft-3 in. or 12 ft-6 in., six variations in strength of installation can be made without special panels other than punching holes for post holes. It should be noted that the strength of an installation is determined by post strength and post spacing.

Post Spacing—Bridges

Guardrail post spacing on bridges may be governed by the spacing of bridge members. Fig. 305.

A good criterion for computing the maximum allowable post spacing for bridge rail can be found in the AASHO "Standard Specifications for Highway Bridges" and is quoted below.

"For curbs 10 in. or greater in height, railings shall be designed to carry a lateral force of 150 lb per lineal foot simultaneously with a vertical force of 150 lb per lineal foot. For curbs less than 10 in. high the horizontal force is 300 lb per lineal foot."

Applying this criterion, Table 49–1, page 412 is obtained for Flex-Beam.

Unless specially ordered in mild steel (for welding purposes) Flex-Beam is furnished in high carbon semi-spring steel and 30,000 psi in bending stress is the usual working stress.

Fig. 305. A single line of guardrail protects this bridge over the Susquehanna River at Harrisburg, Pennsylvania. The rail is independent of the truss members.

TABLE 49-1 GUARDRAIL POST SPACING ON BRIDGES

Steel	*Gage*	*Maximum Stress in Lb per Sq In.*	*Allowable Post Spacing, in Feet*	
			Curbs over 10-In.	*Curbs under 10-In.*
Mild.	10	20,000	12.2	9.0
High Carbon.	10	30,000	14.9	11.0
Mild.	12	20,000	11.0	8.2
High Carbon.	12	30,000	13.5	10.1

For practical reasons, the above spacings should be used only as a guide and practical spacings of 6 ft-3 in. and 12 ft-6 in. should be used whenever possible. Especially should these practical spacings be used on new type construction concrete bridges where the guardrail posts are fastened by anchor bolts to the floor for they permit the use of standard length guardrail elements.

For existing structures or for new structures where posts must be fastened to either truss members or floor system members, special length sections (shorter than 12 ft-6 in. only) can be fabricated for the cost of shearing and punching.

Expansion joints should be provided in bridge rail installations as required by the structure itself, since the posts are subject to movement by expansion of the truss. Air gap expansion joints are provided by using two posts as close together as possible, one on each bridge span. If this can be done so that the overhang of the guardrail element beyond each post is small, no end wings are required. As an

Fig. 306. A wide variety of types of posts are used in guardrail construction.

alternate, the guardrail elements can be overlapped and bolted together with double nutted bolts through holes elongated sufficiently to permit the necessary movement.

Posts—Highway and Miscellaneous

Since only a single hole is required for the attachment of deep-beam guardrail, posts are fabricated from all types of materials.

Wood posts are quite commonly used; in the soft woods 8 in.x8 in. and 6 in.x8 in. are good sizes; the hardwoods are employed in 6 in.x6 in. and in 6 in. round. The rounds are usually peeled pole sections. Preservative treatments are used to extend post life.

Portland cement concrete posts are used in 6 in.x6 in., 6 in.x8 in. and 8 in.x8 in. reinforced sections.

Steel posts in several types of section have been in satisfactory service for many years. A distinct advantage is that they can be driven without digging a hole except when the embankment material is too rocky. For satisfactory service, the strength of such posts should be designed as beams equivalent to a hardwood 6-in. round post.

Post imbedment in good soil is satisfactory at 3½ ft. Since the horizontal center line of rail is placed 18 in. above the ground and 6 in. of post is required above the bolt hole to support the rail, post lengths are 5½ ft for posts with tops flush at the rail top. Posts should be longer if it is desired to have the post project above the rail. Where the soil is poor, or where stronger soil resistance is desired, imbedment of 4½ to 5½ ft will produce stronger post resistance than the use of battens.

Posts used in parking lots or for building-wall protection should be more solidly imbedded than posts for highway use. Some "give" is desirable in highway installations and practice over the years has found the 3½ ft imbedment best suited to provide the best balance of strength with some relief under heavy contact. However, parking lot guardrails are struck continuously with rather light contacts which have the effect of gradually pushing the rail out of line. Deeper imbedment of the posts will aid in preventing this.

Posts for Bridges

Posts for bridges are generally structural steel and should be designed to carry the design loading from the rail. A good criterion for this is found in the AASHO "Standard Specifications for Highway Bridges." This has been quoted above under "Post Spacing—Bridges."

Bridge posts are sometimes attached by means of suitable spacers and bolts or welding to the outside stringers of the floor system on steel bridges. They may be attached to the vertical and diagonal members of the trusses where these are considered strong enough for the loading. In these cases the posts may be reduced to some form of offset blocking, either steel or wood, or omitted completely by fastening the rail directly to the member. Welding may be used for this purpose but bolts allow of easier replacement of damaged sections.

For concrete bridges of slab construction, posts can be attached by means of cast-in-place anchor bolts. Alternately the anchor bolts may be set by drilling holes and grouting in; this method is employed when beam type guardrails are used to replace bulky masonry rails on older structures to gain deck width.

When bridge rails are terminated just off the end of the structure the terminal post is generally set in soil. This post should have a deeper imbedment than the usual 3½ ft to provide stronger post resistance. It should be located so as to use

Fig. 307. Curves with a radius greater than 150 ft can be accomplished with Flex-Beam Guardrail in the field. Sharper curves are shop formed. Above installation is on the famed Gaspe Peninsula of Quebec.

the terminal section or sections of rail in standard lengths, properly curved to provide flares.

Curved Installations

No special problems are involved in the design of beam type guardrail for curved installations as no tensioning is required.

For radii greater than 150 ft, shop curving of the sections is not required because a smooth curve results from the slight springing of the straight sections when the bolts are tightened.

For radii from 150 ft down to 20 ft the sections are easier erected if shop curved. Because of the depth of the section, radii less than 20 ft are more difficult to curve and may involve a special shop order.

Better economy will result if curved installations are arranged so as to use standard lengths. Although it is desirable, from simplicity of installation, to have all sections curved their entire length, sections can be curved partially in length and the remainder left straight. Curved lengths shorter than standard may be obtained at additional cost when required.

It should be noted that curved sections become "rights" and "lefts" and must be specified as "traffic face convex" or "traffic face concave."

Vertical Curves

Vertical curves as found on highways require no special treatment. There is sufficient assembly tolerance at post splices to permit deep beam guardrail to nicely adjust to such vertical curves. Grade transitions between a highway and steeply sloped private drive may require special consideration when the guardrail is curved horizontally and vertically to provide guarded drive entrances. Since such situations are not general, inquiry to the guardrail manufacturer should be made for possible special fabrication.

Fig. 308. Liner plates are widely used for mine entries. This one is in West Virginia.

CHAPTER FIFTY

Ventilation

IN MINING, in industry and in construction, ventilation is necessary to protect against health hazards from toxic gases, excessive heat, moisture and dust. Ventilation codes and minimum standards are usually set and policed by state agencies and the U. S. Bureau of Mines.

The use of corrugated metal and other sheet metal products as important components of ventilating systems have been commonplace for many years.

Entries and Air Shafts

Steel liner plates for supporting the roofs of slope entries and the walls of vertical air shafts are commonly used in the proper ventilation of mining operations. In both applications the liner plate may serve as the permanent structure or it may be used as a construction tool prior to placing another type of lining. Such applications are reviewed in Chapter 48, Tunnels, Underpasses, Conduits. Fig. 308.

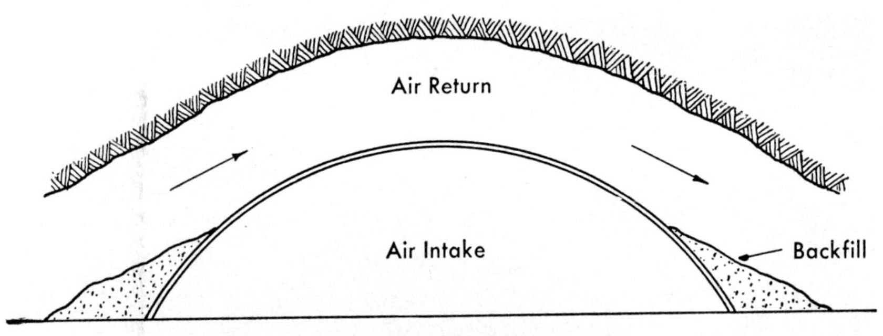

Fig. 309. Typical liner plate overcast.

Overcasts

Underground mining operations often require some method of directing the flow of ventilating air within the mine when the main air passageway is intersected or crossed by other passageways or drifts. It is generally neither necessary nor desirable that the air crossovers or "overcasts" be permanent structures, because of ever-changing conditions as the mining progresses. To meet the need for an economical and fully salvable overcast structure, low-ratio rise/span liner plate arches are being used very successfully. Corrugated metal pipe and pipe-arches are used for some of the smaller size installations. Fig. 309.

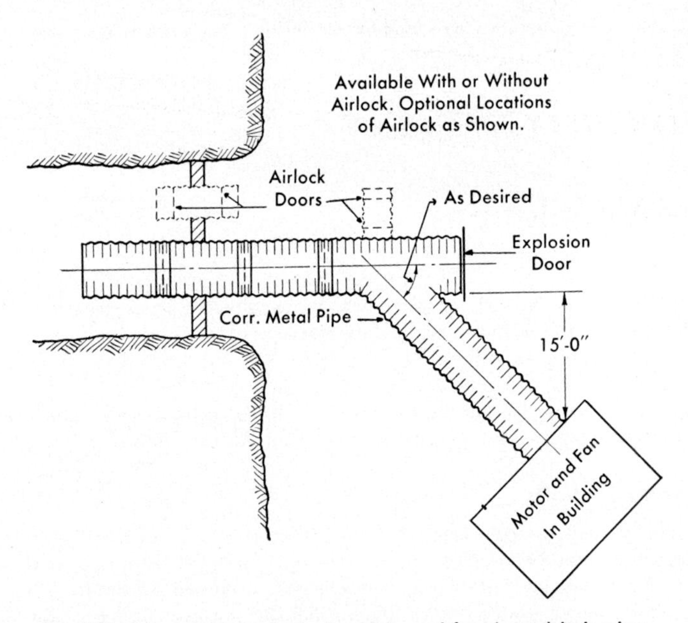

Fig. 310. Corrugated metal pipe is widely used for air conduits in mines.

Fan Ducts

Another phase of mine ventilation where corrugated metal products have found ready acceptance is for conduits extending from the ventilating fan to the mouth of the fresh air tunnel or air shaft. Corrugated metal ducts have a high strength-to-weight ratio, are fully salvable in the event that a change of operations is necessary, resist destruction due to explosive forces and are very fire resistant. They may range in diameter from 36 to 84 in., with 48, 60 and 72 in. being common. Fig. 310.

The ducts are normally fabricated so that the fan opening is placed off the centerline of the main conduit to prevent damage to the fan in the event of an explosion. Spring-loaded doors installed on the outward end of the main duct relieve pressures other than normal fan pressures, minimizing damage to the ventilating equipment. It is also possible to install air lock chambers on the side of the main conduit as a part of the prefabricated duct system to facilitate entry into the air tunnel if desired.

Fig. 311. Providing air for tunneling operations in construction work is often done with corrugated metal pipe. Job shown is part of 15 and 18-in. Hel-Cor pipe for a mine in Utah.

Ventilation During Tunneling or Mining

During tunnel construction, it is often desirable or necessary to provide adequate forced ventilation to the working area to make it safe and comfortable. This is normally accomplished by pumping fresh air to a point near the heading, using the excavated tunnel as the air return.

During tunneling operations which require blasting to loosen the material in the heading, the concussion of the blast often causes considerable damage to smooth-wall sheet metal and cloth ducts. As a result, several sections nearest the heading

TABLE 50-1 COEFFICIENTS OF FRICTION FOR HEL-COR PIPE FOR AIR CONDUCTION

Diam. of Pipe in Inches	*Coefficient of Friction f**	*Diam. of Pipe in Inches*	*Coefficient of Friction f**
6	.029–.033	12	.038–.044
8	.033–.038	15	.041–.047
10	.040–.046	18	.044–.050
		21	.047–.052

*From Darcy-Weisbach formula

are usually removed prior to and replaced after each blast. However, the resistance to collapse of corrugated metal ducts during the blasting operation minimizes damage to the duct and makes removal unnecessary.

Many tunnel contractors make a standard practice of reversing the flow of air through the duct immediately following a detonation to rid the tunnel of blasting fumes as quickly as possible. Normal direction of flow is then restored for the mucking and other operations.

For pipe ventilation, the helical corrugated metal duct combines the strength of a corrugated section with favorable friction characteristics. Fig. 311. The friction characteristics of helically corrugated pipe for various diameters are given in Table 50–1. These are actual test values for lengths of over 100 diameters.

Fig. 312. The heat duct atop these brick kilns in Ohio is corrugated metal pipe.

Fig. 313. Noise deadeners at jet engine test installations have been constructed of Multi-Plate and corrugated metal pipe.

Heat Ducts and Stacks

Asbestos-Bonded corrugated metal pipe is being used for some industrial ventilating applications where corrosive fumes must be handled. Many of these applications have been as vertical stacks.

Cooling or heating concrete aggregates prior to mixing is at times advantageous to attain desirable working and setting properties of the concrete. The use of corrugated metal pipe through the aggregate piles to serve as heat conduits have been very satisfactory in the application. Heat transfer through the walls of the corrugated metal pipe is rapid and its adequate structural strength, high strength-to-weight ratio and complete salvability are definite advantages. Fig. 312.

Silencers

A variation of the exhaust duct has been devised to silence or muffle the terrific noise produced in testing jet airplane engines. One design is illustrated here. Fig. 313.

Crop Drying

Agricultural crops such as wheat, oats, corn, rice, sugar beets, hay and tobacco have their moisture content reduced to permit safe storage, or are cured, by forcing either cold or warm air through them. One method involves the use of a perforated metal floor of Steelox interlocking panels. The other consists of blowing air through pipes with 1-inch perforations under the crops being stored.

Fig. 314. Aggregate handling is expedited by use of liner plate bins such as these at a zinc mine in eastern Tennessee.

CHAPTER FIFTY-ONE

Storage Bins

Types of Bins

The mechanization of coal and aggregate processing, grain handling and other comparable industries has created an increasing demand for economical, easily-erected surge and storage bins to permit greater operating efficiency. To meet the growing demand, modified Armco Liner Plate, Multi-Plate and riveted corrugated metal pipe structures have been utilized to provide very satisfactory, light weight, economical and demountable storage units. Bins of this type are of circular or oval construction. Storage bins may also be built of bin-type retaining wall units. Complete buildings and hangar type structures have also been used for grain storage purposes.

A wide variation of design exists among the types of storage and surge bins required to efficiently handle the many different materials under a wide range of requirements. Figs. 314 and 315.

According to leading authorities, bins may be classified as shallow or deep structures.[1,2] The shallow bin is defined as one in which the plane of rupture of the fill material orginating at the bottom of the structure passes through the surface of the material before it intersects the wall opposite. Conversely, in a deep bin the plane of rupture intersects the wall opposite before cutting the surface of the fill material.

Load Theories and Design

The load is transferred directly to the walls of the structure in increasing amounts as the depth of filling increases for a bin of uniform diameter. When fill heights exceeding 2½ to 3 times the diameter of the bin are reached, all of the weight of the material above that level is transferred directly to the walls of the bin. There is little increase in the lateral pressures beyond a depth of three diameters. When material is withdrawn from the bottom of the bin the pressure may be 10 per cent greater than for the material at rest.

Fig. 315. Coal storage bins can be constructed quickly with liner plates. These three bins in West Virginia have stiffeners extending the full height.

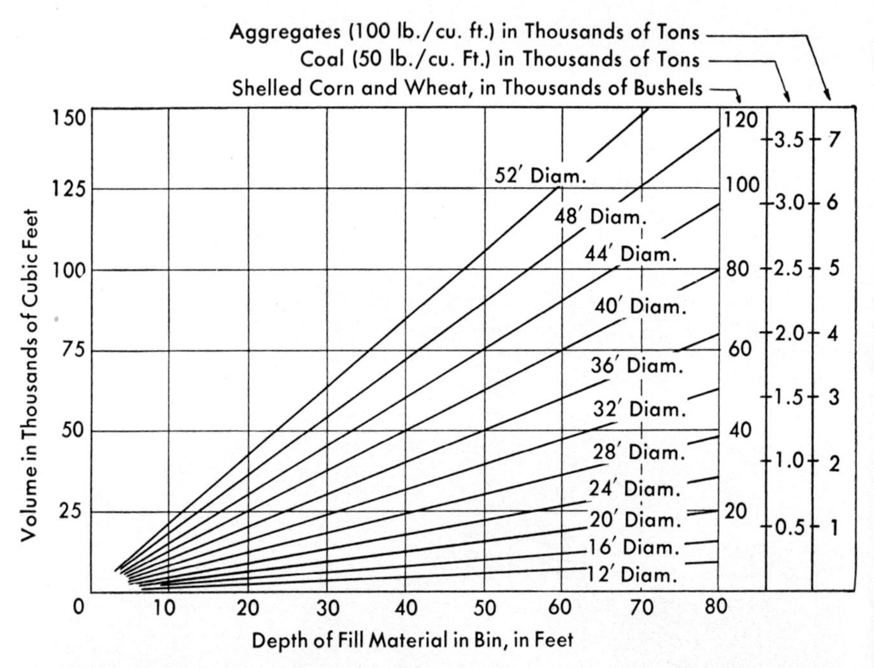

Fig. 316. Chart for determining volumes of aggregates, coal and grain in bins of various diameters.

Shallow Bins

The design of *shallow* bins is normally limited to materials such as sand, coal, coke, ashes, etc. Calculation of the pressures on the walls of a shallow bin is comparable to the calculation of pressures on retaining walls. Space limitation does not permit a full explanation of the theory pertaining to such designs. Complete design data and solutions by both graphic and algebraic methods will be found in references 1 and 2. The designs of the above references include a variety of shallow bin types and loading conditions to meet almost any requirement.

The remainder of this chapter is devoted to the design of circular, straight-walled *deep* bins.

Research on Deep Bins

Model studies have been made by various experimenters to better correlate theory and practice regarding the stresses occurring in deep bins filled with grain. Studies of liner plate bins used to store aggregates, coal and other similar granular materials indicate that design based on the above theory, taking proper account of the variation in unit weight, angle of repose (which is a function of the coefficient of friction) and the ratio of vertical to lateral pressures, will permit a practical correlation with the fundamental laws governing the action of grain in bins.

The conclusions of Ketchum's Chapter XVII, "Experiments on the Pressure of Grain in Deep Bins,"[2] are of such significance as to warrant quotation here:

1. The pressure of grain on bin walls and bottoms follows a law (which for convenience will be called the law of "semi-fluids") which is entirely different from the law of pressure of fluids.

2. The lateral pressure of grain on bin walls is less than the vertical pressure (0.3 to 0.6 of the vertical pressure, depending on grain, etc.) and increases very little after a depth of 2½ to 3 times the width or diameter of the bin is reached.
3. The ratio of lateral to vertical pressures, k, is not a constant, but varies with different grains and bins. The value of k can only be determined by experiment.
4. The pressure of moving grain is very slightly greater than the pressure of grain at rest. . . .
5. Discharge gates in bins should be located at or near the center of the bin.
6. If the discharge gates are located in the sides of the bins, the lateral pressure due to moving grain decreases near the discharge gate and is materially increased on the side opposite the gate. . . .
7. Tie rods decrease the flow but do not materially affect the pressure.
8. The maximum lateral pressures occur immediately after filling, and are slightly greater in a bin filled rapidly than in a bin filled slowly.
9. The calculated pressures by either Janssen's or Airy's formulas agree very closely with actual pressures.
10. The unit pressures determined on small surfaces agree very closely with unit pressures on large surfaces.
11. Grain bins designed by the fluid theory are in many cases unsafe as no provision is made for the side walls to carry the weight of the grain, and the walls are crippled. . . .

Design Formulas

The two basic equations for determining vertical and lateral pressures occurring in a *deep* bin with vertical sides according to Janssen's solution are:

$$V = \frac{w\,R}{k\mu'}\left(1 - e^{-\frac{k\mu' h}{R}}\right)$$

and since $L = kV$

$$L = \frac{w\,R}{\mu}\left(1 - e^{-\frac{k\mu' h}{R}}\right)$$

where:

ϕ = angle of repose of grain
e = 2.718 = base of Naperion logarithms
$\mu = \tan\phi$ = coefficient of friction, grain on grain
$\mu' = \tan\phi$ = coefficient of friction, grain on bin wall
w = weight of grain in lb per cu ft
V = vertical pressure of grain in lb per sq ft
L = lateral pressure of grain in lb per sq ft
A = cross-sectional area of bin in sq ft
U = circumference of bin in ft
$R = \frac{A}{U}$ = hydraulic radius of bin
k = ratio of vertical to lateral pressure
h = depth of grain at any point

[*Text continued on page 429*]

TABLE 51-1 TYPICAL ARMCO LINER PLATE COAL BINS
Material @ 50 lb/cu ft

Bin Capacity in Tons	*Diam. in Feet*	*Height*	*16 Pi Plates Req'd per Ring*	*Number of Rings of Each Gage*				*Total Rings*	*Minimum Size of Stiffener Angles Spaced 24 Pi Inches c to c*	*Weight of Plates, in Lb*	*Weight of Stiffeners, in Lb*	*Total Weight in Lb*
				5	*7*	*10*	*12*					
50	12	15′0″	9			3	7	10	None	3,921		3,921
100	16	19′6″	12	2	6	5		13	None	9,709		9,709
200	20	25′6″	15				17	17	2x2x¼	10,306	814	11,120
300	24	27′0″	18				18	18	2x2x¼	13,095	1,034	14,129
400	24	36′0″	18				24	24	3x2x⅜	17,460	2,549	20,009
500	28	33′0″	21				22	22	2x2x⅜	18,672	2,172	20,844
750	32	37′6″	24				25	25	3x2x⅜	24,250	3,540	27,790
1000	32	49′6″	24	2	2	2	27	33	4x4x⅜	35,540	7,716	43,256
1250	36	49′6″	27	2	2	2	27	33	4x4x⅜	39,982	8,732	48,714
1500	40	48′0″	30	2	2	2	26	32	4x4x⅜	43,213	9,408	52,621
1750	40	57′0″	30	2	2	2	32	38	5x3½x½	50,487	15,504	65,991
2000	44	54′0″	33	2	4	5	25	36	4x4x½	55,643	15,207	70,850
2500	48	57′0″	36	3	12	7	16	38	4x4x½	73,257	17,511	90,768

1. Bin capacity shown is actual capacity, not necessarily usable capacity.
2. Bin designs include surcharge.
3. Bin sizes other than shown are available if required.
4. Bins shown are designed for bottom center unloading.
5. If stiffener angle sizes shown are not obtainable, structural members having equivalent or greater cross-sectional area may be substituted.
6. All stiffener angles are to be placed on the outside of the bin on 24 pi inch center-to-center spacing, and are to extend from the foundation to the top of the bin. Angles having a cross-sectional area 50% less than those shown can be used in upper ⅔ of bin if so desired. Attachment of the stiffeners to the plates should be made by extending three of the five bolts of the vertical joint of alternate rings through the structural angles (see detail under Table 51-2).
7. A steel base plate should be attached to the bottom of each stiffener angle for weight distribution. The base plate should be adequately anchored to the foundation.
8. A curved angle or channel should be installed around the top of the bin for eccentric or off-center loading.
9. Any vertical load on the bin structure resulting from conveyor equipment, roof structure, etc., must be considered in addition to the computed loads in the tables.
10. The structure should be adequately anchored to the foundation with ⅝″ diameter anchor bolts.
11. ASTM: A1 325 high tensile steel ⅝″ diameter x 1½″ bolts will be furnished for bolting joints of 3 and 5-gage rings. All other bolts furnished will be ASTM: A 307 mild steel ⅝″ diameter x 1¼″ bolts.
12. Successive rings should be staggered when erected so that there will be no continuous vertical seam (see detail under Table 51-2).

TABLE 51-2 TYPICAL ARMCO LINER PLATE *AGGREGATE* BINS

Material @ 100 lb/cu ft

Bin Capacity in Tons	*Diam. in Feet*	*Height*	*16 Pi Plates Req'd per Ring*	*Number of Rings of Each Gage*					*Total Rings*	*Size of Stiffener Angles Spaced 24 Pi Inches c to c*	*Weight of Plates, in Lb*	*Weight of Stiffeners, in Lb*	*Total Weight in Lb*
				3	*5*	*7*	*10*	*12*					
100	12	15′0″	9		2	2	2	4	10	None	4,961		4,961
200	16	19′6″	12				2	11	13	2x2x$\frac{1}{4}$	6,557	500	7,057
400	20	25′6″	15			2	2	13	17	2x2x$\frac{3}{8}$	11,409	1,200	12,609
600	24	27′0″	18		2	2	2	12	18	2x2x$\frac{3}{8}$	15,743	1,523	17,266
800	24	36′0″	18		2	2	2	18	24	5x3$\frac{1}{2}$x$\frac{3}{8}$	20,108	4,493	24,601
1000	28	33′0″	21		3	2	2	15	22	3x2x$\frac{1}{2}$	22,534	3,557	26,091
1250	28	42′0″	21	2	3	3	3	17	28	5x3$\frac{1}{2}$x$\frac{1}{2}$	30,384	8,000	38,384
1500	32	37′6″	24	2	3	3	3	14	25	4x4x$\frac{3}{8}$	31,815	5,880	37,695
1750	32	43′6″	24	2	5	3	3	16	29	4x4x$\frac{5}{8}$	37,460	10,927	48,387
2000	32	49′6″	24	2	9	3	6	7	27	6x4x$\frac{5}{8}$	39,783	15,840	55,623
2250	36	45′0″	27	2	11	5	5	7	30	6x4x$\frac{1}{2}$	51,151	13,122	64,273
2500	36	49′6″	27	2	11	5	5	10	33	6x4x$\frac{5}{8}$	54,424	17,820	72,244
3000	40	48′0″	30	8	8	6	10		32	6x6x$\frac{1}{2}$	66,854	18,816	85,670

See footnotes under Table 51-1.

6. All stiffener angles are to be placed on the outside of the bin on 24 pi inch center-to-center spacing, and are to extend from the foundation to the top of the bin. Angles having a cross-sectional area 50% less than those shown can be used in upper ⅔ of bin if so desired. Attachment of the stiffeners to the plates should be made by extending three of the five bolts of the vertical joint of alternate rings through the structural angles (see detail at right).

12. Successive rings should be staggered when erected so that there will be no continuous vertical seam (see detail at right).

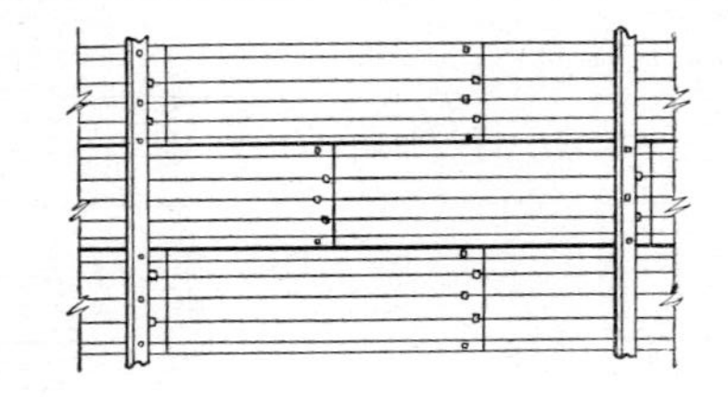

TABLE 51-3 VERTICAL DRAG-DOWN FOR ARMCO LINER PLATE BIN STRUCTURE— PER 24 PI INCH SEGMENT OF CIRCUMFERENCE, IN POUNDS

Diam. in Feet	*No. 16 Pi Plates per Ring*	*No. 24 Pi Inch Segments of Circumference*		*Depth of Fill Material in Bin—in Feet*										
				12	*18*	*24*	*30*	*36*	*42*	*48*	*54*	*60*	*66*	*72*
12	9	6	Corn & Wheat	—*	11,225	18,296	25,370	32,450	40,016	47,100	54,500	62,216	70,316	76,733
			Aggregates	—	15,345	26,730	38,134	49,940	61,950	73,670	85,470	96,750	108,690	120,400
			Coal	—	8,135	14,205	19,640	26,250	32,360	38,465	44,475	50,580	56,590	62,600
16	12	8	Corn & Wheat	—	8,350	16,857	25,544	34,700	43,481	52,268	61,175	70,087	78,987	87,525
			Aggregates	—	11,900	26,730	41,940	50,250	73,260	89,065	103,675	119,080	134,490	149,400
			Coal	—	6,250	13,855	22,140	29,450	37,360	45,465	53,275	61,280	69,590	77,200
20	15	10	Corn & Wheat	—	2,225	12,806	24,040	34,650	45,560	56,260	66,970	77,580	88,390	99,100
			Aggregates	—	—	20,485	39,640	59,050	78,860	97,565	117,465	136,580	155,690	175,900
			Coal	—	—	11,055	20,890	30,700	40,560	50,365	60,175	70,380	80,090	89,100
24	18	12	Corn & Wheat	—	—	11,700	24,400	37,300	50,200	62,600	75,300	88,200	101,000	113,600
			Aggregates	—	—	12,535	35,040	57,450	80,160	103,765	126,075	148,380	171,990	193,900
			Coal	—	—	3,515	17,140	28,850	41,910	54,765	67,775	80,180	93,490	106,690
28	21	14	Corn & Wheat	—	—	4,840	20,400	35,400	51,000	66,200	81,700	97,400	112,300	127,600
			Aggregates	—	—	—	23,940	49,450	77,660	103,265	130,875	158,080	184,540	210,900
			Coal	—	—	—	13,340	26,650	40,560	53,465	67,175	80,800	94,690	107,890
32	24	16	Corn & Wheat	—	—	—	13,800	31,200	48,200	65,500	82,800	99,700	117,000	134,200
			Aggregates	—	—	—	8,010	39,550	70,460	100,765	132,275	161,080	191,490	229,900
			Coal	—	—	—	5,810	20,950	36,100	51,565	67,100	82,580	97,990	113,690
36	27	18	Corn & Wheat	—	—	—	7,600	24,800	45,100	63,700	82,500	101,200	120,000	138,000
			Aggregates	—	—	—	—	23,800	57,860	92,765	127,675	161,080	195,490	229,100
			Coal	—	—	—	—	13,300	30,460	47,865	65,175	82,680	99,900	117,400
40	30	20	Corn & Wheat	—	—	—	—	7,250	27,820	49,000	70,000	91,700	112,800	134,500
			Aggregates	—	—	—	—	—	43,060	80,565	118,675	156,280	195,000	230,900
			Coal	—	—	—	—	—	22,360	41,565	60,775	80,080	99,490	118,700
44	33	22	Corn & Wheat	—	—	—	—	4,690	27,800	51,200	74,400	97,700	121,300	145,000
			Aggregates	—	—	—	—	—	22,340	63,565	105,675	145,580	188,490	232,900
			Coal	—	—	—	—	—	12,290	34,065	54,575	75,780	96,790	117,900
48	36	24	Corn & Wheat	—	—	—	—	—	17,420	42,800	67,800	90,300	118,600	144,100
			Aggregates	—	—	—	—	—	—	42,265	86,875	131,880	178,490	224,900
			Coal	—	—	—	—	—	—	22,115	45,075	68,180	91,190	114,900
52	39	26	Corn & Wheat	—	—	—	—	—	6,000	33,250	58,300	87,900	115,100	142,800
			Aggregates	—	—	—	—	—	—	15,845	64,875	114,080	163,400	213,900
			Coal	—	—	—	—	—	—	8,285	33,875	58,380	83,690	107,900

TABLE 51-4 HORIZONTAL BURSTING STRESS FOR ARMCO LINER PLATE BIN STRUCTURE—PER 18-INCH LAP JOINT, IN POUNDS

Diam. in Feet		*Depth of Fill Material in Bin—in Feet*										
		12	*18*	*24*	*30*	*36*	*42*	*48*	*54*	*60*	*66*	*72*
12	Corn & Wheat	2,025	2,430	2,610	2,700	2,770	2,850	2,850				
	Aggregates	2,790	3,150	3,375	3,555	3,690	3,780	3,780				
	Coal	1,395	1,575	1,688	1,778	1,845	1,890	1,890				
16	Corn & Wheat	3,120	3,780	4,260	4,560	4,740	4,860	4,920				
	Aggregates	4,080	4,980	5,640	6,060	6,360	6,540	6,660				
	Coal	2,040	2,490	2,820	3,030	3,180	3,270	3,330				
20	Corn & Wheat	4,200	5,325	6,150	6,675	7,050	7,350	7,530				
	Aggregates	5,400	6,900	7,950	8,775	9,300	9,600	10,500				
	Coal	2,700	3,450	3,975	4,388	4,650	4,800	5,250				
24	Corn & Wheat	5,220	6,690	8,100	8,946	9,630	10,080	10,440	10,674	10,890	10,980	11,088
	Aggregates	7,020	8,820	10,460	11,430	12,420	13,170	13,680	14,040	14,200	14,200	14,200
	Coal	3,510	4,420	5,230	5,715	6,210	6,585	6,840	7,020	7,100	7,100	7,100
28	Corn & Wheat	6,300	8,820	10,605	11,970	12,810	13,440	13,965	14,280	14,400	14,700	15,120
	Aggregates	7,875	10,710	13,125	14,910	16,380	17,220	18,060	18,690	19,110	19,725	19,725
	Coal	3,938	5,355	6,563	7,455	8,190	8,610	9,030	9,345	9,555	9,863	9,863
32	Corn & Wheat	6,480	8,880	11,040	12,960	14.640	15,840	16,920	17,760	18,288	18,720	19,200
	Aggregates	12,000	14,400	16,800	18,720	20,400	21,480	22,320	23,280	24,000	24,480	25,200
	Coal	6,000	7,200	8,400	9,360	10,200	10,740	11,160	11,640	12,000	12,240	12,600
36	Corn & Wheat	7,020	10,260	13,230	15,850	18,090	19,710	20,790	21,735	22,410	23,085	23,670
	Aggregates	16,770	17,010	19,440	21,600	23,490	25,110	26,730	27,810	29,970	30,780	31,860
	Coal	8,385	8,505	9,720	10,800	11,745	12,555	13,365	13,905	14,985	15,390	15,930
40	Corn & Wheat	8,400	12,300	15,900	18,750	21,000	23,100	24,750	25,950	26,700	27,750	28,350
	Aggregates	12,000	16,800	21,000	24,400	27,600	30,300	33,150	34,500	36,300	37,500	39,000
	Coal	6,000	8,400	10,500	12,200	13,800	15,150	16,575	17,250	18,150	18,750	19,500
44	Corn & Wheat	11,715	14,850	18,480	21,450	24,420	26,730	28,710	30,195	31,350	32,340	33,330
	Aggregates	14,850	20,130	24,090	27,390	30,690	33,660	35,970	37,950	40,260	42,190	43,230
	Coal	7,425	10,065	12,045	13,695	15,345	16,830	17,985	18,975	20,130	21,090	21,615
48	Corn & Wheat	12,960	17,640	21,600	24,840	27,000	30,240	32,400	34,200	36,000	37,760	38,520
	Aggregates	17,280	22,680	27,360	30,960	34,560	37,800	41,040	43,920	46,620	49,320	51,120
	Coal	8,640	11,340	13,680	15,480	17,280	18,900	20,520	21,960	23,310	24,660	25,560
52	Corn & Wheat	13,260	18,720	23,400	27,300	30,420	33,540	36,270	39,000	40,950	42,510	44,070
	Aggregates	18,330	29,960	30,420	35,100	40,170	44,460	47,970	51,090	54,210	56,940	58,890
	Coal	9,165	14,980	15,210	17,550	20,085	22,230	23,985	25,545	27,105	28,470	29,445

P d P

NOTES:
Grain—
K=0.6
$\mu=0.521$
Coal and Aggregates—
K=0.4
$\mu=0.7$
"P" equals the values from the table.

TABLE 51-5 PHYSICAL PROPERTIES OF ARMCO LINER PLATES

Gage	*Allowable End Thrust for 24 Pi In. Section of Armco Liner Plate in Pounds*		*Allowable Lap-Joint* Bolt Strength for Armco Liner Plate in Pounds (18″ Plate Width)*
	Radii less than 90″	*Radii greater than 90″*	
12	3,520	3,000	18,080
10	7,040	3,640	19,480
8	10,550	7,420	24,000
7	12,300	9,050	26,160
5	17,750	12,550	30,400†
3	19,000	16,100	35,200†

*Greater lap-joint strength than that shown in the above table may be obtained by welding.
†ASTM: A 325 heat-treated bolts used.
Allowable load on bolts acting in single shear:
⅝″ diam. ASTM: A 307 3.07 kips (3,070 lb)
⅝″ diam. ASTM: A 325 5.00 kips (5,000 lb)

TABLE 51-6 STANDARD HOT ROLLED STRUCTURAL ANGLES FOR VERTICAL STIFFENERS

Size in Inches	*Weight per Foot in Lb*	*Cross-Sectional Area in Sq In.*	*Size in Inches*	*Weight per Foot in Lb*	*Cross-Sectional Area in Sq In.*
1½x1½x¼	2.34	0.69	4x4 x⅜	9.8	2.86
1¾x1¾x¼	2.77	0.81	4x4 x7/16	11.3	3.31
2 x1½x¼	2.77	0.81	4x4 x½	12.8	3.75
			4x4 x⅝	15.7	4.61
2 x2 x¼	3.19	0.94	4x4 x¾	18.5	5.44
2 x2 x⅜	4.70	1.36			
3 x2 x5/16	5.0	1.47	5x3½x⅜	10.4	3.05
3 x2 x⅜	5.9	1.73	5x3½x7/16	12.0	3.53
3 x2 x½	7.7	2.25	5x3½x½	13.6	4.00
			5x3½x⅝	16.8	4.92
3½x3½x¼	5.8	1.69	5x3½x¾	19.8	5.81
3½x3½x5/16	7.2	2.09			
3½x3½x⅜	8.5	2.48	6x4 x½	16.2	4.75
3½x3½x7/16	9.8	2.87	6x4 x⅝	20.0	5.86
3½x3½x½	11.1	3.25	6x4 x¾	23.6	6.94
			6x6 x½	19.6	5.75
			6x6 x⅝	24.2	7.11
			6x6 x¾	28.7	8.44

Explanation and Use of Tables

The diameters of the circular liner plate storage units shown in Figs. 314, 315 and Tables 51–1 and 51–2 were so chosen that they can be constructed entirely from 16 pi (approximately 50.3) in. net covering length plates. This length plate has been determined as the most economical unit. However, bins of intermediate sizes may be designed in increments of 2 in. in diameter by utilizing a combination of 12, 14 and 16 pi in. length plates. Forces acting on the intermediate sizes may be readily interpolated from the data in the Tables 51–3 and 51–4.

From Table 51–3, vertical drag-down forces acting on a 24 pi (approximately 75.5) in. segment of circumference of the structure caused by the various fill materials listed may be determined directly for the sizes indicated, or interpolated for the intermediate sizes. In computing Tables 51–3 and 51–4, grain-on-grain coefficient of friction was used because it furnishes conservative design criteria. There exists at the present time a great lack of information concerning the problem of the pressures exerted by granular materials stored in deep bins.[4]

The bursting stress per 18-in. width of liner plate occurring at the bottom of various size structures, caused by the lateral pressure exerted by the fill material, may be found in Table 51–4. These values, too, may be interpolated for values corresponding to any intermediate size structure.

The use of the tables for designing a bin storage unit can probably best be correlated by the following example:

Problem: Determine the gage of liner plate; the cross-sectional area of vertical stiffeners (if required) and the height and diameter of a bin to store 38,000 bu of shelled corn or wheat.

Solution: 1. From the curves of Fig. 316, "Volume vs. Depth of Fill Material," there are several diameters and heights of bins which will have the required capacity. If the area on which the bin is to be erected is not restricted as to size, the most economical bin for a given capacity, exclusive of roof and foundation, is one in which the height is equal to the diameter. If the bin is to have a roof structure, the most economical structure for a given capacity will be one in which the height is approximately 1½ times the diameter. A logical choice of dimensions for a bin of the required capacity would be a structure 36 ft in diameter by 48 ft high.

2. From the Table 51–3, "Vertical Drag-Down per 24 pi inch Segment of Circumference," the force at the bottom of the 48-ft depth of fill in a 36-ft diameter bin is 63,700 lb.

3. Table 51–4, "Bursting Stress per 18-Inch Lap Joint," gives a bursting stress (hoop tension) of 20,790 lb at the base of the bin when filled to struck capacity.

4. The gage plates required will be governed by (a) the vertical load (transverse to the corrugations) or (b) the bursting (hoop) stress. From Table 51–5, 8 gage plates will develop the required bursting strength at the base of the bin. Also from this table, the 8 gage will carry the 7,420 lb of 63,700 lb vertical load acting on a 24 pi inch segment of bin wall.

5. The heaviest gage plates (3 gage) will not carry the vertical drag-down load without vertical structural stiffeners. It is more economical to choose plates of a lighter gage and use heavier vertical stiffeners. Therefore, assume that 8 gage plates will be used for the bin. Using 18,000 psi stress for the vertical structurals acting in compression, the required cross-sectional area of the stiffeners will be

$$\frac{63{,}700-7420}{18{,}000} = \frac{56{,}280}{18{,}000} = 3.12 \text{ sq. in.}$$

6. The vertical structural stiffeners should extend from the foundation to such a height that the drag-down of the fill material no longer acts on the walls of the bin. The theoretically required heights may be found in Table 51–3. However, because of possible non-center loading or unloading, and the addition of a roof or loading equipment, it is recommended that all stiffeners be extended to the top of the bin. See Fig. 315 page 421. The upper portion of the stiffeners may be reduced in cross section if desired.

7. The strength in single shear for a ⅝-in. diameter steel bolt is 3070 lb as listed in Table 51–3. Three of the five bolts in the lap-joint may be extended through the vertical structural in alternate 18-in. wide rings or an average of one bolt per foot of the structural length. See detail in Table 51–5. A total of 24 bolts extend through the 24-ft minimum length stiffener. The total load these bolts will carry is 24×3070 lb $= 73{,}680$ lb which is adequate.

A careful check must be made regarding the development of sufficient shear strength of the stiffener bolts. It may be necessary in cases of the larger, higher bins to increase the bolt size, use heat-treated bolts, or weld the structural stiffener to the liner plate to develop the required strength. Values for ⅝ and ¾-in. diameter bolts acting in single shear are presented in Table 51–5. The shear strength of the liner plate and the stiffener sections also is an important consideration and should be investigated along with that of the bolts.

Table 51–6 gives structural angle sizes, weights per foot, cross-sectional area and allowable load in compression. Base plates should be used to distribute the stiffener load over a sufficient area of the footing.

Above the minimum level of the top of the stiffeners, where theoretically the action of the drag-down forces on the walls of the bin are negligible, it is possible to reduce the gage for the plates in this section. This is desirable when the heavier gage plates are used for the lower section of the bin.

It is necessary to maintain sufficient bursting (hoop) strength in the lighter gages, if used for the upper section of the bin, as determined from Table 51–4. Another requirement is maintaining sufficient stiffness at the top of the structure to prevent it from departing from its intended cylindrical shape if subjected to eccentric or off-center loading. One suggested method of accomplishing the desired stiffness is by the addition of a curved angle or channel section to the top ring of plates, if no roof structure is used.

No information has been included regarding the design of bin roof structures, conveyors, elevating equipment, head houses, bottom or side openings or foundations because of their specialized nature. Any vertical load on the bin structure resulting from conveyor equipment, roof structure, etc., must be considered in addition to the computed loads in the tables.

It is necessary to adequately anchor the bin structure to the foundation to prevent its overturn by wind loads while standing empty.

Multi-Plate Bins

Multi-Plate is also being used successfully for storage bin uses. The strength of the 2-in. deep Multi-Plate corrugation, acting under loads transverse to the corrugations, will be approximately 15 per cent less than the values for comparable gages of liner plate as given in Table 51–5. The bolted joint strengths for Multi-Plate may be found in the section on Design for that product.

A large percentage of the existing bin structures constructed of Multi-Plate have been of such height-to-diameter ratios that vertical stiffeners were not required. On those which have required stiffening, fastening the stiffeners to the structure has been accomplished either by field drilling and bolting or by welding the stiffeners to the bin in an amount sufficient to furnish adequate strength.

Prefabricated Grain Storage Bins

Prefabricated corrugated steel bins are being used extensively for small unit storage of grains both for private use and for the Commodity Credit Corporation of the U. S. Government. These are carefully designed units complete with steel roof and floor and may, through minor adaptation, be used for drying as well as storing grains.

Trickling Filters

Another use for Multi-Plate storage units is for the side walls of trickling filter beds for sewage treatment plants instead of the massive monolithic construction normally employed. Multi-Plate provides an easily erected, economical and entirely satisfactory structure for this application. Standard corrugated metal (galvanized or Asbestos-Bonded) is likewise used for such filter tanks. See Fig. 197, page 289.

Bottomless Water Tank

Large, bottomless steel tanks are used in the West for the storage of stock water. It is of course necessary that the bottom be in an impervious soil or be treated to make it reasonably so.

Such tanks are made of standard corrugated metal sheets in diameters from 20 to 60 ft and up to 6 ft high. The vertical joints in the sheets should be staggered. Stiffeners are desirable to prevent vibration and leakage during high winds.

Watertightness

Liner Plate and Multi-Plate bin structures which are erected at a permanent location and must be watertight to seal against the entrance of outside moisture, all vertical and circumferential seams may be welded after erection of the bin. If this method of construction is used, it is possible to eliminate a substantial portion of the bolts, using only enough to accomplish the erection and utilizing the weld to develop the strength of the plates. Another suggested method of attaining practical watertight construction is to "butter" all matching surfaces of the plates with an asphalt mastic of knifing consistency before assembly.

REFERENCES

1. "Earth Pressure, Retaining Walls and Bins," Chapt. VI., by William Cain, First Edition.
2. "The Design of Walls, Bins and Grain Elevators," by Milo S. Ketchum. Third edition. McGraw-Hill Book Co., Inc.
3. "Engineering Data on Grain Storage," compiled by Benton M. Stahl, Published May 1948 by the American Society of Agricultural Engineers.
4. "Lateral and Vertical Pressure of Granular Material in Deep Bins," by Robert A. Caughey, Calvin W. Tooles and Alfred C. Scheer, Iowa Engineering Experiment Station Bulletin 172.

Fig. 317. Proper installation plays an important role in the life of any drainage structure.

SECTION TEN

INSTALLATION INSTRUCTIONS

CHAPTER FIFTY-TWO

Corrugated Metal Drainage Structures

Importance of Good Installation

A well located, properly bedded, accurately assembled and carefully backfilled drainage structure will function properly and efficiently for a long period of time. Small size structures require less care in the details of proper installation than the larger ones but care in handling, base preparation, assembling and backfill will always pay dividends in satisfactory service. Fig. 317.

Corrugated metal structures because of their light weight and resistance to fracture can be installed quickly, easily and without expensive equipment. They are designed to distribute the external loads around the structure and into the backfill. While they can withstand unequal settlement and dimension changes that would cause failure in rigid structures, a well prepared foundation and a well tamped backfill of stable material will satisfy the design assumptions and insure the most satisfactory installation.*

Selection of gages and other design criteria for corrugated metal drainage structures are based on reasonable care being used in installation. Careless installation can quickly undo the work of the designer.

Good installation requires:

Locating structure to fit stream alignment and grade
Installing adequate length for conditions
Excavating accurately to line and grade
Providing a uniform and stable foundation
Handling the material carefully
Assembling the structure properly
Using suitable backfill materials
Placing backfill carefully
Tamping backfill thoroughly
Protecting the structure against heavy concentrated construction loads.

Location and Length

See Chapter 27, page 241.

*For effect of installation conditions on loads reaching a conduit, see Sec. I Chapt. 1 on External Loads and Earth Pressure on Underground Conduits, pages 8, 23, 82.

PART ONE

PREPARATION OF BASE

Excavation to Line and Grade

The trench or streambed must be shaped to fit the bottom of the conduit to line and grade. When a bulldozer or heavy earth-moving equipment is used to excavate for a corrugated metal structure, it is often economical to dig a wide flat base. This is satisfactory if the backfill is carefully tamped under the lower portions of the structure. When excavating is done by hand methods, lines should be strung to limit the boundaries of the excavation and at least one string set parallel to the grade line will assist in maintaining line and grade.

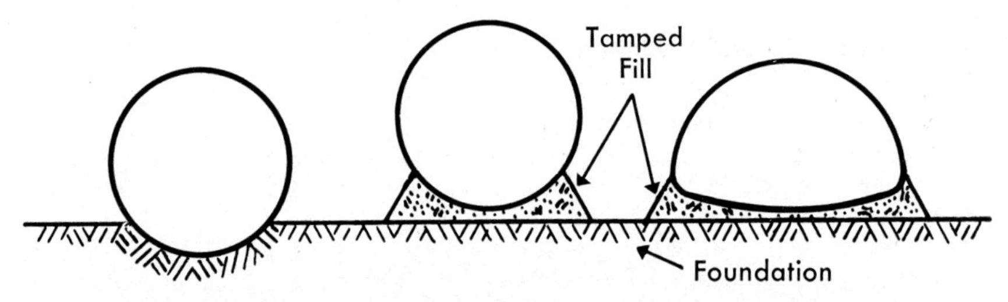

Fig. 318. Methods of bedding corrugated metal structures on wide flat base.

If the structure is to be installed in a trench, the trench should be kept as narrow as possible but sufficiently wide to permit tamping under the haunches. Generally the trench width will not be less than 12 nor more than 24 in. greater than the outside diameter of the pipe structure. A wide trench requires more excavation and backfill and also tends to increase the load on the structure. Make the side walls as vertical as practical, at least to an elevation above the top of the pipe.

When installing the structure in a natural streambed, make sure the base is as uniform and stable as possible for the entire length of the structure. Often a small change in location can improve foundation conditions without affecting the flow. Frequently it will be necessary to stabilize the foundation as described in the second following section.

Uniform Foundation

Corrugated metal drainage structures can settle unevenly without disjointing or breaking. However, for best performance and appearance it is desirable to place them on a firm, uniform foundation that will distribute the load evenly.

All pipe culverts or sewers should be installed with the lower quarter of the circumference firmly supported. Bedding either flexible or rigid pipe by shaping the natural foundation requires careful workmanship to accurately fit the entire length of the structure. Corrugated metal structures can be bedded satisfactorily by excavating to a flat surface and carefully tamping the fill under the haunches. See Figs. 318 and 319.

Fig. 319. Adequate tamping under the haunches is important to good installation.

All pipe and pipe-arch structures should be placed on a stable earth or fine granular foundation. Never install them on sod, frozen earth or on a bed which contains boulders or rock. When granular materials are used for bedding, the fill at the ends of the structure should be sealed against the infiltration of water. This often can be done by bedding the ends in well tamped clay or by using some type of headwall or end section.

Unstable Foundation Soils

When the excavated grade line for the structure crosses both soft and hard spots, the foundation should be made as uniform as practical. Sometimes, the hard spots can be excavated below grade and replaced with softer material. But more often, the soft spots need stabilizing with granular material. Excavating the foundation slightly below the grade line and backfilling with earth shaped to camber the flow line will often cure uneven conditions. See Fig. 321. In any event, abrupt changes from hard to soft foundation should be avoided.

When soft, unstable material occurs at the foundation level, it should be excavated below the flow line grade and backfilled with sand, gravel, crushed stone or other suitable material. Make the width of the base at least twice the diameter of the pipe and as deep as the foundation conditions require. See Fig. 320(a).

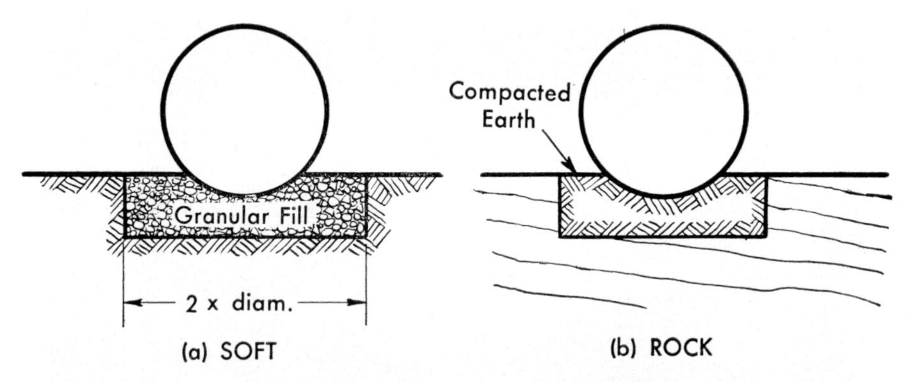

Fig. 320(a). Soft, unstable foundation material should be excavated below the flow grade line and backfilled with sand, gravel, crushed stone, or other suitable material.

Fig. 320(b). When rock is encountered in the foundation, it should be excavated to at least 8 inches below the bottom of the structure.

If the unstable material is in small pockets, it is best to excavate all of the bad foundation and replace it with suitable backfill. Frequently a relatively thin mat (6 to 12 in.) of granular material, well graded, will provide a satisfactory support, but it may be necessary to replace the foundation to a depth of 3 ft if it is very soft. Diameter of pipe and height of fill are controlling factors.

In swampy locations, especially along shore lines or adjacent to large rivers, deep unstable foundations are frequently encountered. If they cannot be readily stabilized with granular material, brush or timber mats may be used to spread the load. Never place a pile bent or a concrete cradle in direct contact with a corrugated metal structure if the structure is to support a fill. The cradle or pipe support should be built with a flat top and covered with an earth cushion. (See Rock Foundations.) This permits the flexible structure to develop side support without concentrating the load at any point on the circumference of the pipe.

When placing large diameter culverts, particularly under high fills, it is often good practice to install perforated pipe subdrainage to prevent subsequent saturation of the foundation and the fill around the pipe. In hilly country, foundation damage from seepage zones in the slopes adjacent to the fill can also be controlled.

Cambered Grade Line

When a culvert is installed under a high fill on a uniformly unstable foundation, raise the elevation of the flow line through the center portion of the structure above its normal position to allow for subsidence when the fill is placed. This is called cambering. Generally enough camber can be obtained by using a flatter grade for the upstream half of the culvert than for the downstream half. The matter of camber must be one of judgment, but do not raise the center so high that water will be pocketed in the pipe. Under high fills the camber should be substantial, especially where foundation conditions are not of the best. Fig. 321.

Rock Foundations

When rock is encountered in the foundation, it should be removed to at least 8 in. below the bottom of the structure and wide enough to avoid any possibility of the pipe resting on the rock. The excavated area is then backfilled with compacted

Fig. 321. Under high fills or where foundation conditions are not of the best, cambering the pipe is helpful. This is on a railroad relocation in Iowa.

earth to provide a cushion for the pipe. See Fig. 320(b).

The depth of cushion placed under the pipe varies with the size of the structure and the height of fill. An 8 to 12-in. thickness is usually sufficient.

Cradling Is Unnecessary

Under no circumstances should a corrugated metal pipe be cradled on or encased in concrete. It is a needless expense which defeats its own purpose by joining two materials of distinctly opposite characteristics—flexibility and rigidity.

Fig. 322. Even where rubber boots are worn, the use of a concrete cradle for corrugated metal pipe is not necessary. An airbase in New Jersey.

PART TWO

ASSEMBLY OF STRUCTURES

Unloading and Handling

Even though corrugated metal drainage products will withstand rough handling without cracking or breaking, they should be unloaded and handled with reasonable care. Lifting or rolling will protect the galvanized or bituminous coating. Dragging the structure over gravel or a rocky surface will injure these coatings and as a result it may adversely affect the durability of the structure. When Paved-Invert pipe is stockpiled in hot climates, the sections should be placed to prevent flow of the asphaltic pavements.

Corrugated metal structures can be lowered down embankments or into deep trenches with the aid of ropes.

Corrugated Metal Pipe

Riveted corrugated metal pipe should be placed with the inside circumferential laps pointing downstream. The longitudinal laps should be at the sides or quarter points, but not in the bottom.

Riveted pipe is supplied in multiples of 2 ft, with maximum individual lengths being governed by shop, transportation or field handling facilities. Culverts of 20 to 30-ft lengths are generally supplied in a single section.

Connecting Bands

The usual method of joining sections of pipe is by means of corrugated connecting bands. "Standard" bands are used for most installations on all sizes of pipe. "Two-piece" bands are used on the larger sizes when the installation conditions are difficult. "Watertight" bands are used on special work where maximum watertightness is essential as in levees, aerial sewers and similar installations. Specially fabricated, bolted or field riveted connections can be provided for jacking, boring, threading and other special installations. See Fig. 323.

The band is first slipped into position over the end of one section of pipe with the band open to receive the next section. The adjoining length is brought to within approximately 1 in. of the first section and the band tightened with the corrugations of the band matching the corrugations of the pipe sections. Care should be taken to keep dirt or gravel out between the pipe and the band so that the corrugations fit snugly. As the plain galvanized band is tightened, it should be tapped with a mallet or hammer to take up slack and insure a tight joint. Merely tightening the bolts will not produce a tight joint on large diameter culverts. Chain hoists, chain or cable cinching devices or C clamps placed around the band to draw it into place, may help to speed up the tightening process.

There is no overlapping of the end corrugations of the pipe sections when band couplers are used. Therefore, for every band used, there is an increase over the rated length of pipe equal to the distance of one corrugation ($2\frac{2}{3}$ in.). In addition, corrugated metal pipe with plain (not rolled) ends has an over-all length $1\frac{1}{2}$ in. greater than the nominal dimension because of the $\frac{3}{4}$-in. lip on each end.

Although the width of the connecting band varies with the diameter of the pipe,

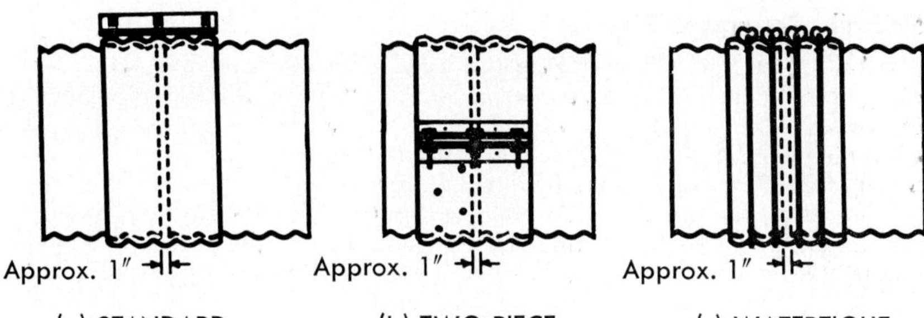

(a) STANDARD

Single piece band with riveted angles thru which bolting is done.

Band width—
7″ for 8″—30″ dia. incl.
12″ for 36″—60″ dia. incl.
24″ for pipe over 60″ dia.

(b) TWO-PIECE

Lower half of band riveted to one end of each pipe section. Upper half may be riveted to the adjoining section or left separate as desired.

Band Width—12″ or 24″

(c) WATERTIGHT

Made of single precurved corrugated sheet which laps itself. Around this is passed ½″ diam. galvanized rods secured by a specially designed silo-type lug. Number of rods as specified.

Band Width—12″ or 24″

NOTES—Bands are usually ordered one gage lighter than the pipe to which they are attached.
When pipe corrugations register properly in the band, the pipe ends will be approximately 1″ apart.
There will be a gain in laying length of the pipe of 2⅔″ for each band.

Fig. 323. Types of connecting bands for corrugated metal pipe.

ranging from 7 in. to 24 in. as shown in Fig. 323, this is of less importance than carefully tightening the band as described above.

Bituminous Coated and Paved Pipe

Paved pipe must be installed with the smooth, thick pavement in the flow line. Otherwise, assembly is the same as for galvanized pipe.

The asphalt that covers approximately 25 per cent of the interior circumference of Paved-Invert pipe fills the corrugations and protects against erosion from abrasive materials. To be effective, it is extremely important that this pavement be placed and centered on the bottom.

Band couplers on coated pipe as well as the surface of the pipe under the band often need to be lubricated with fuel oil or other similar solvent. This allows the band to slip around the pipe and to draw firmly into place. Lubrication is especially needed when the bituminous surfaces are cold. Lubricating and tapping the bands so they can be drawn to proper position will assure a strong joint and maximum watertightness.

Any damaged spots in the bituminous coating where the metal is exposed should be repaired by applying a patch before the structure is backfilled. Use a coating similar to that covering the pipe.

Pipe-Arches

Riveted corrugated metal pipe-arch structures are installed in much the same way as round pipe structures. However, the width of excavation and bedding for a pipe-arch structure is generally not less than 12 nor more than 24 in. wider than its span. Care should be taken either to shape the excavation to the shape of the pipe-arch or to tamp well under the haunches.

Helically Corrugated Pipe

Hel-Cor pipe (helically corrugated) is installed in the same manner as riveted corrugated metal pipe. The connecting bands are made in two pieces and are corrugated to fit the pipe. To assemble, place one half of the band under the first section of pipe. Then lay the second section with the corrugations matching; install the top half of the band on the joint and tighten the bolts.

When using perforated Hel-Cor pipe be sure to rotate each section so that the perforations are in proper position at the bottom. Placing the perforations in position may leave a short distance between the ends of the two lengths of pipe but the opening will be covered by the coupling band.

Fig. 324. Final tightening of bolts on structural plate pipe is left until all sections are in place.

Multi-Plate Pipe and Pipe-Arches

Preparation of the base and the backfill for structural plate pipe and pipe-arches are handled in the same way as described for riveted corrugated metal structures.

Detailed erection instructions for each size and type are shipped along with each structure. These instructions show the position of each plate and the order of assembly for easy erection.

It is important that the bolts be well tightened. This can be done progressively and uniformly, starting at one end of the structure *after all plates are in place.* Fig. 324. The operation should be repeated to be sure the bolts are tight.

The erection of structural plate structures can be speeded by using the proper size structural wrenches, socket wrenches, lining bars, drift pins and handling hooks. When a power wrench is used to tighten the bolts, it is necessary to carefully check the tightening of the nuts because it is very easy for a power wrench to get out of adjustment. Checking can be done with a long-handled structural or socket wrench or with a torque wrench (50 to 250 ft lb of torque).

Structural Plate Arches

Structural plate arches are generally erected on a masonry foundation. The groove or the unbalanced channel in which the arch rests must be accurately built to line and grade for easy assembly of the plates. When the arch is set on a skew, the holes in the unbalanced channels must line up with those in the plates. The layout for the installation of the channels is shown on the special plate assembly drawings that are furnished with each skewed structural plate arch.

For straight-end arches on which headwalls are to be built, allowance should be made in the design for the lip (approx. 2 in.) at each end.

Diaphragms

Diaphragms or metal cut-off walls are used on special installations where there is danger of seepage of water that might cause a washout along the outside of the structure. Typical of such installations are pipes through levees or dams where the pipe may be subjected to a hydraulic head.

Fig. 324a. Three lines of 60-in. Paved-Invert pipe being installed under a levee in Louisiana. Note the square metal diaphragms. Height of cover is to be 50 ft.

The diaphragms should be located midway between two adjacent riveted circumferential seams, as near the center of a pipe length as possible, and at least 4 ft from a field joint. In multiple line installations, diaphragms should be spaced to provide a minimum of 12 in. clearance between the faces of the diaphragms on adjacent pipes to provide space for proper backfilling.

The bottom half of the diaphragm is placed after the excavation for the pipe and before lining and joining the pipe. Generally a narrow trench is excavated for the diaphragm, although it may be driven or jetted into place under some soil conditions. The diaphragm must be lined up to mesh with the corrugations of the pipe. The top half of the diaphragm is placed as soon as the pipe has been placed. The cross trench for the lower half should be backfilled with good fill material and tamped to give maximum compaction.

Multiple Installations

When two or more structures are laid parallel in the same trench or streambed, they should be separated as indicated in Fig. 325. Proper spacing of the pipe in multiple installations allows room to tamp the backfill under and between the pipe, assures adequate side support and allows the fill over the pipe to help compact the backfill between the structures. This tamping and compaction helps prevent washouts during high water or flood stage.

When strutted pipe is used, the diaphragms must be shop fabricated to fit the strutted shape.

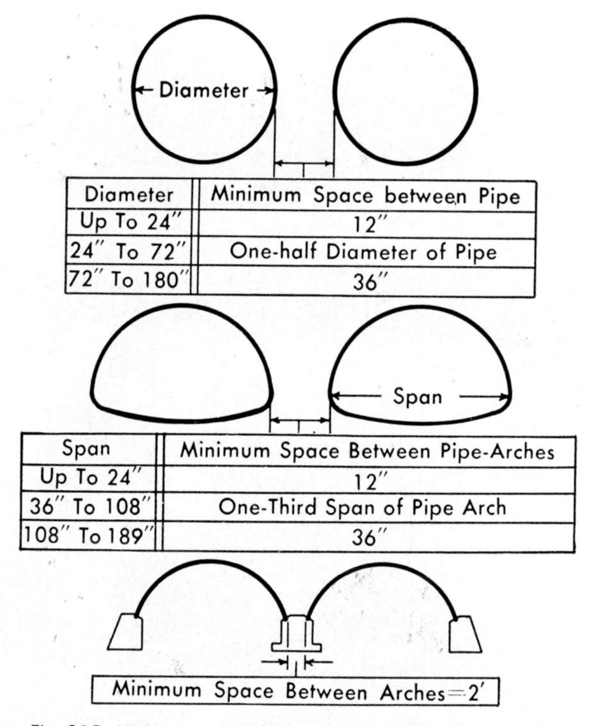

Diameter	Minimum Space between Pipe
Up To 24″	12″
24″ To 72″	One-half Diameter of Pipe
72″ To 180″	36″

Span	Minimum Space Between Pipe-Arches
Up To 24″	12″
36″ To 108″	One-Third Span of Pipe Arch
108″ To 189″	36″

Fig. 325. Minimum permissible spacing for multiple installations.

PART THREE

STRUTTING

LARGE diameter (54 in. diameter and larger) corrugated metal or structural plate pipe tend to deflect as the backfill is placed over them. This deflection is not harmful but may be objectionable from an appearance standpoint.

Deflection and the final shape of the pipe is controlled by (1) selecting the proper gage of pipe or (2) elongating the vertical diameter of the pipe before backfilling by the process known as "strutting" and (3) carefully tamping the backfill. The selection of a heavier gage may eliminate the necessity of strutting. The more carefully the backfill is placed and tamped, the less is the deflection.

Strutting or elongating the vertical diameter of a pipe before backfilling, lets the pipe build up side support as it settles back towards a full round shape under the fill load. It thereby increases the pipe's load-carrying capacity above that allowable for a pipe that has been installed with a round shape. If a method of restraint is built into the elliptical pipe structure to slow down the change in shape while the fill is being placed, the backfill around the pipe will be partly consolidated by the weight of the fill before the pipe starts to deflect. This will also add to the load-carrying capacity of the pipe.

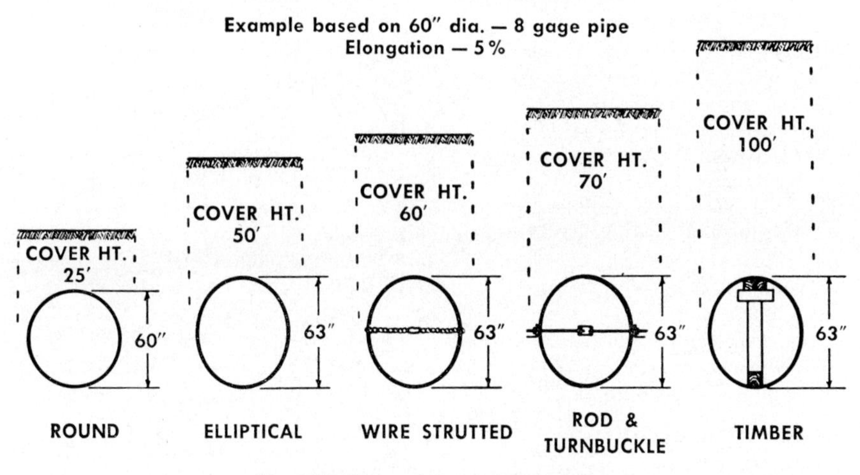

Fig. 326. Effects of shape and strutting.

Methods of Strutting

There are several methods of holding the elliptical shape of a pipe during installation. These are shown in Fig. 326. Also shown are the comparative permissible heights of fill for each type of strutting as well as for elliptical shaped and round pipe.

Elliptical shaping, wire strutting or rod strutting of riveted corrugated pipe is done in the fabricating shop on special order and the pipe is delivered to the job

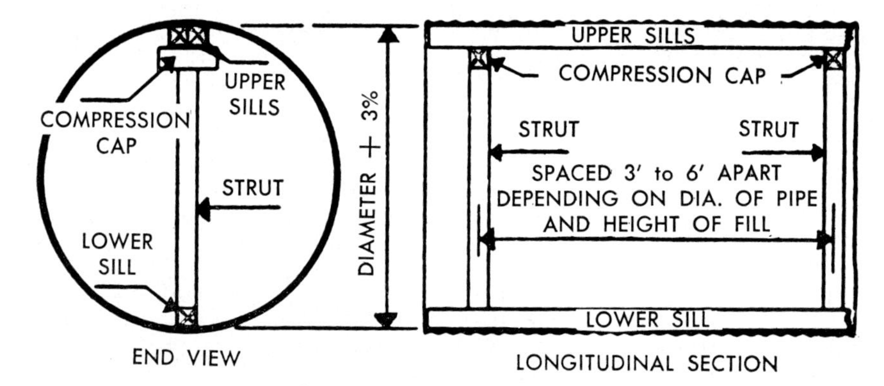

Fig. 327. Details of strutting methods for corrugated metal pipe.

site ready for installation. The wire or rod struts should be horizontal when the pipe is properly placed. Timber strutting is done in the field after the pipe has been laid in place, but before any backfill is started. Wire or rod strutting is best for paved or coated pipe because the strutting is done before the bituminous material is applied and there is no injury to the pavement.

When strutting a Paved-Invert pipe with timber, the pavement can be protected by means of a wide bottom sill shaped to fit the pavement. This method was first used by the U. S. Bureau of Reclamation with excellent results and has also been adopted by others. The shaping of the bottom sill is the only item requiring preparation in addition to that for strutting non-paved pipe.

It is important in all strutted pipe that the struts permit the pipe to deflect slowly as the load is applied. Otherwise there is danger of the pipe bending sharply at the struts. With timber strutting, a *soft* wood compression cap must be placed between the vertical posts and the top sills. See Fig. 328. With rod and turnbuckle strutting, a schedule should be set up to back off the turnbuckles as the fill is placed. All turnbuckles in each line of pipe should be released uniformly throughout the pipe, a turn or two at a time. But some tension should remain in the rods until the fill is completed. Wire struts will generally yield with the load by untwisting or stretching.

After the fill has consolidated, all struts must be removed from the pipe. However, when there is danger of flood water, the struts may have to be removed before the fill has settled completely.

Installing Timber Struts

Timber strutting is done by elongating the vertical diameter, then maintaining the elongation with vertical struts, compression caps and horizontal sills. The amount of elongation, usually 5 per cent for riveted pipe and 3 per cent for structural plate pipe, as well as strut size and spacing are normally given in the plans.

Strutting is done progressively from one end of the structure to the other. Start at one end by placing timber sills in the top and bottom of the pipe and jacking to the required elongation. Then set a vertical strut and soft compression cap in position near the end of the pipe. Remove the first jack and place it further in the pipe. Repeat the process until the pipe is completely strutted.

Two 50-ton jacks are required for heavy gage structural plate pipe and two 25-ton jacks for riveted pipe and light gage structural plate pipe.

Two lines of sills with staggered joints are generally used in the top of the pipe. Compression caps to permit the required deflection are placed with their grain crosswise to the axis of the struts.

The shape of elliptically fabricated pipe may be retained during backfilling by the use of struts or props without the need of jacks.

Do Not Strut Arches or Pipe-Arches

Unlike round corrugated metal structures, arches and pipe-arch structures do not appreciably change their horizontal dimension under load. Additional side support is not created and nothing is gained by strutting.

However, when a pipe-arch is installed on a soft foundation that cannot be stabilized, struts are sometimes used to maintain the vertical dimension while the fill is being placed. The struts should be located on the longitudinal center line of the structure and kept in place until the base has stabilized.

Fig. 328. A soft wood cap between the strut and the top sill permits enough compression so the pipe is not held rigidly under heavy loads.

PART FOUR

BACKFILLING

Importance of Backfilling

The strength of any type drainage structure is to a large extent dependent upon proper backfilling.

Corrugated metal structures, as discussed previously, build up side support as they deflect under load. Therefore, to obtain maximum load-bearing capacities and to prevent washing out and settlement, it is necessary that the backfill be made of good material, properly placed and carefully compacted.

Backfill Material

Selected, drainable backfill material is preferred but most local fill material can be used provided it is carefully placed and compacted. It should be free from large rocks and hard lumps or clods larger than 3 in. in diameter. Do not use frozen fill, sod, cinders or earth containing a high percentage of organic material. Granular material containing a small amount of silt or clay is ideal since it makes a dense, stable fill.

Backfill Around Structure

Fill material under haunches and around the structure should be placed alternately in 6-in. layers on both sides of the pipe to permit thorough tamping. The fill is placed alternately to keep it at the same elevation on both sides of the structure at all times. Figures 329 and 331 show how pipe and pipe-arch structures should be backfilled.

Tamping can be done with hand or mechanical equipment, tamping rollers or

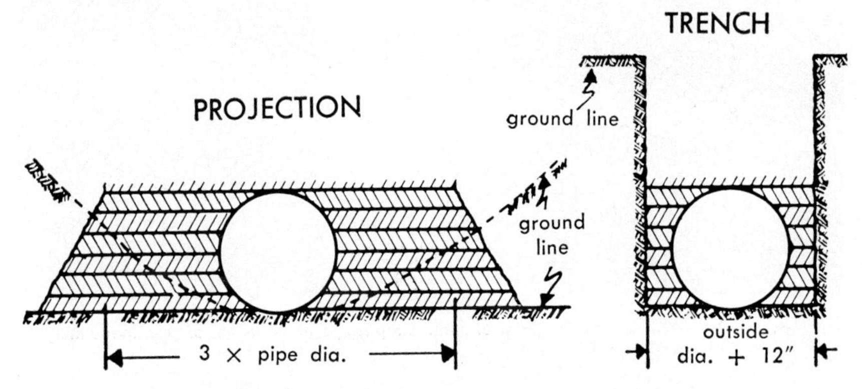

Notes: Place fill in uniform well tamped 6" layers.
Keep fill at same elevation on both sides of pipe.

Fig. 329. Backfill should be placed in uniform well-tamped layers.

Fig. 330. Either hand or mechanical equipment can be used for tamping.

vibrating compactors, depending upon field conditions. Of more importance is that it be done carefully to insure a thoroughly tamped backfill.

Compaction of fills by puddling or jetting is not recommended except for cohesionless, sandy or sandy-gravel material. The reason is that puddling will not work satisfactorily in clayey soils but tends to produce a permanently unstable condition.

In backfilling around and over a structure, the loads of heavy earth-moving or compacting equipment may exceed those for which the structure was designed. Therefore, it is always advisable that the structure be covered adequately before direct loads are applied.

Tamping Equipment

Hand Equipment. For tamping under the haunches of a structure, a pole or 2 x 4 is generally needed to work in the small areas. Hand tampers for compacting horizontal layers should weigh not less than 20 lb and have a tamping face not larger than 6 x 6 in. Ordinary "sidewalk" tampers are generally too light.

Mechanical Tampers. Most types of power tampers are satisfactory and can be used in all except the most confined areas. However, they must be used carefully and completely over the entire area of each layer to obtain the desired compaction. Avoid striking the structure with power tamping tools.

Tamping Rollers. Where space permits, sheepsfoot, rubber-tired and other types of tamping rollers can be used to compact the backfill around the structure. If rollers are used, the fill adjacent to the structure should be tamped with hand or power equipment. Be sure to keep the rollers from hitting the structure. Smooth rollers are generally not satisfactory for compacting fills.

Vibrating Compactors. Vibrating equipment can be used to compact granular backfills but generally is unsatisfactory for clay or other plastic soils.

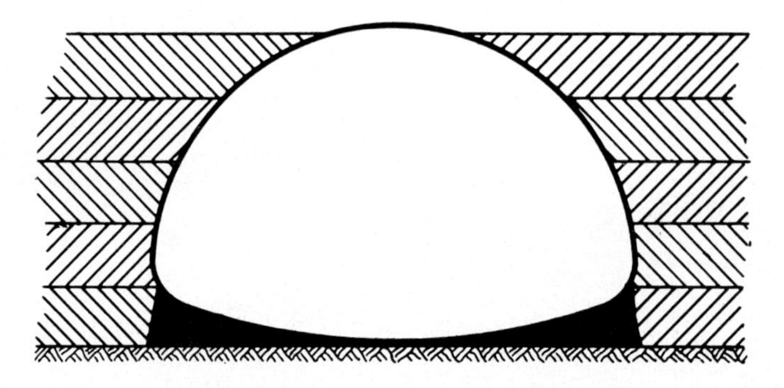

Tamp fill carefully under bottom of pipe-arches.
Place fill in uniform well tamped 6" layers.
Keep fill at same elevation on both sides.

Fig. 331. Care must be taken in backfilling pipe-arches to insure compaction underneath the haunches.

Backfill on Arches

Care must be taken in backfilling arches, especially half-circle arches, because they have a tendency to shift sideways or to "peak up" under the backfilling loads. The ideal way is to cover an arch in layers—each layer conforming to the shape of the arch. If one side is backfilled more than the other, the arch will move away from the larger load. If both sides are backfilled equally and tamped thoroughly, the top of the arch may peak up unless enough fill has been placed over it to resist the upward thrust. See Fig. 332.

Arches Without Headwalls

When backfilling arches without headwalls or with headwalls that are not sufficiently strong to maintain the shape of the arch, the first fill should be placed midway between the ends of the arch. This fill should be kept in as narrow a strip as possible until the top of the arch is reached. The remainder of the backfill should be placed from the top of the arch, starting at the center and working both ways to the ends. By this means, illustrated in Fig. 332, only a minimum of side pressure is developed until the top is loaded.

Arches With Headwalls

In backfilling arches with headwalls heavy enough to maintain the shape of the arch, it is advisable to place the fill against one headwall until the top of the arch is reached. Then proceed by dumping off the top in layers toward the opposite headwall.

IDEAL METHOD

Build fill over arch in layers conforming to the arch shape.

PRACTICAL METHOD

RIGID HEADWALL

Start filling of headwalls and work towards center.

NO HEADWALL

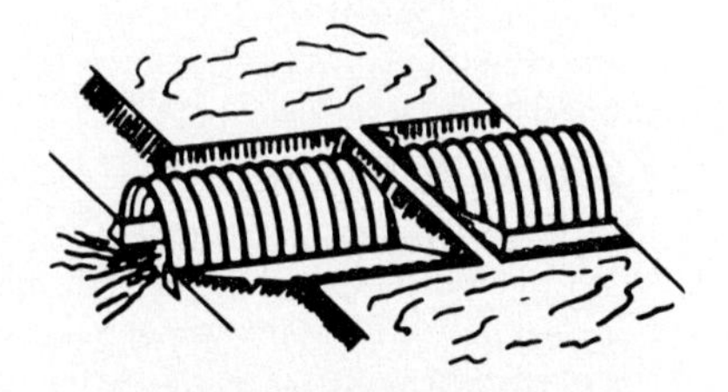

Start filling midway between the ends and work both ways.

Fill as narrow a strip as possible by distributing the fill material around and over the arch in uniform layers. Then proceed by placing the remainder of the fill from the top of the arch. The fill material adjacent to the arch should be thoroughly tamped and deposited evenly on both sides.

EFFECTS OF BAD BACKFILLING

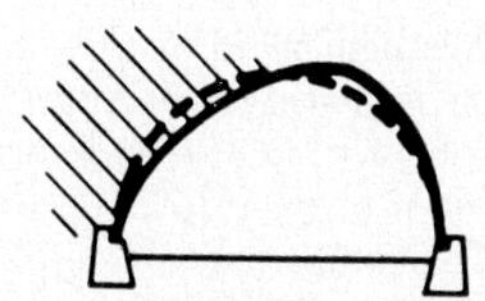

Filling on one side only may cause the arch to shift sidewise.

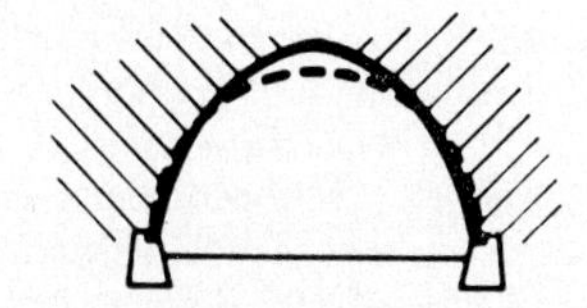

Filling too much along both sides before fill is placed over top may cause the crown to rise.

Fig. 332. Methods of backfilling arches.

Completing the Fill Over Structure

Material used to complete the fill over a corrugated metal structure should be essentially the same as that used for the backfill and placed and compacted in the same manner. Distribute and compact the fill evenly to a depth equal to the height of the structure or the entire fill if it is shallow.

In trenches, fill material should be tamped in layers from the top of the structure to the original ground level. This assures thorough compaction and eliminates settlement. Do not compact fill in trenches by puddling or jetting with water.

Protection of Structure from Equipment

It is important to protect drainage structures during construction for several reasons. The fill has not consolidated to develop maximum strength in the structure and heavy construction equipment can impose concentrated loads far in excess of those the structure would normally carry.

Frequently, more than normal fill is needed to protect the structure during construction, especially if heavy equipment is used. The minimum cover required for highway loading of corrugated metal pipe, pipe-arch and arch installations is shown on page 106. How much additional protective fill is needed depends upon the wheel loads of equipment used as well as their frequency.

Providing extra fill is a simple way to protect the job from possible damage by excessive loads.

Trestle Replacements

Trestle replacements with culvert structures should be given careful inspection. They generally involve fairly high fills and large diameter pipe. Obtaining a good foundation and a well compacted backfill is often difficult when working around the old trestle timbers and a better fill can be made if the timbers can be removed before the fill is placed.

Dumping from the top of the trestle should be avoided if possible and the dirt must be placed in thin horizontal layers and well compacted to an elevation well above the top of the pipe. Vegetation and other objectionable materials should be removed from the surface before the fill is started and where slopes exist that will cause wedge action to increase fill pressures, the slopes should be benched or step cut before filling. Experience has shown that water pockets frequently occur in trestle fills and particular care should be exercised to provide subdrains for all seeps and pockets showing in the base of the fill. Seeps have a tendency to drain toward the culvert structures, soften the backfills and cause structural difficulties.

End Finish

Metal end sections can be attached to the pipe as it is being laid or they can be placed after the culvert barrel has been backfilled. The end section must be accurately lined with the culvert in order that the connection will fit the end corrugation properly. Before the end section is placed, a trench of proper size is excavated for the toe plate. The backfill in the trench should be well tamped and backfill carefully placed around the end section. Fig. 333.

If rigid, reinforced concrete headwalls are to be used, it is preferable that the culvert be backfilled before the headwall is built. There is some possibility that the deflection of the pipe may crack the headwall. This is most likely to occur on strutted pipe culverts, hence the struts should be removed before rigid headwalls are placed. Headwalls should be placed on solid foundations because settlement of the heavy headwall may drag the pipe out of place.

Fig. 333. Metal end sections provide efficient finish on this culvert on the road to the Grand Canyon, Arizona.

Dry or cemented rubble masonry or cement bag headwalls are frequently used on large structures for erosion protection. They are generally placed on a prepared slope after the structure has been installed and the grade completed.

Large Diameters or High Fills

The installation of large size structures or structures under very high fills requires an investigation of the site to be certain that the foundation under both the structure and the fill adjacent to the structure is adequate and will remain stable. Careful assembly of the structure is important and a well compacted backfill of selected material is necessary. To be sure these conditions are met, the foreman and superintendent should understand the principles of good construction which have been outlined in this chapter. They should realize the importance of following the specified methods. Experience has shown that close, authoritative inspection is the economical way of obtaining good installations.

Fig. 334. Left: Two men handle 20 ft length of perforated pipe. Right: A simple bolted coupling is used.

CHAPTER FIFTY-THREE

Perforated Pipe Subdrains

GROUND water may be from several sources—underground flow in thin or thick pervious strata, springs or other concentrated flows, percolation from rainfall or standing surface water, percolation through cracks and fissures. Control of such surface water is accomplished by means of an underdrain or subdrain.

A pipe subdrain is made up of four parts: a perforated pipe in a trench with a pervious backfill or filter, and provided with an outlet. These must be properly done if the subdrain is to function satisfactorily over a long period of time.

The Outlet

An underdrain system requires a suitable stream or sewer into which the water may be discharged.

The outlet end of the pipe should be kept high enough so that it cannot become clogged by debris, sediment or ice. A coarse wire screen over the end or a flap gate will prevent rodents from entering the pipe and building nests. Cantilevering the end of the pipe and deflecting it to enter the outlet stream at an angle will generally protect against undermining.

The Trench

Construction of an underdrain system is generally started at the downstream or outlet end. This allows the ground water to drain out of the trench and keeps the bottom as dry as possible during construction.

When the water-bearing strata extend to depths that cannot be drained to natural outlets, the subdrain may have to be placed in the water-bearing strata to lower the natural water table. Usually, however, it is better for the subdrain to be deep enough so that the flow line of the pipe is below the water-bearing stratum.

Depth of the trench will also be governed by the slope of the pipe, the trench bottom and the pipe flow line being about identical. Subdrainage laterals should generally be placed on a minimum grade of 0.3 ft in 100 ft. Mains should be on the same minimum grade, although 0.1 ft in 100 ft is permissible if necessary.

The trench should be kept as narrow as practicable and still permit jointing to be done. The minimum is the inside diameter of the pipe plus 9 in. See page 313.

Underdrain pipe should be laid on a stable base. If the bottom of the trench is in an impervious layer that has become wet and puddled, it may be necessary to add granular material to stabilize the bottom. However, the depth of granular material should not be such as to encourage the flow of water under the subdrain pipe.

Subdrain Pipe

Installation of corrugated metal pipe has been described on pages 433–451. For subdrainage pipe an additional precaution is in regard to the perforations. These should be placed at the lower quarter points except where the pipe crosses pervious strata where the water would be lost and cause further damage. See Fig. 335. Placing the holes as shown, lowers the water table most for a given depth of trench and reduces any tendency for backfill material to flow into the pipe. The unperforated segment in the bottom will handle normal flow of water intercepted by a drain.

Catchbasins, manholes, risers and fittings such as tees, wyes, elbows and reducers should preferably be placed in the line at the time the pipe is being laid.

Backfill or "Filter"

The subdrain trench must be backfilled with a fine, graded pervious (granular) material that will serve as a "filter" to keep fine soil from entering and clogging the drain pipe.

Gradation of the filter material recommended is shown as No. 1 in the accom-

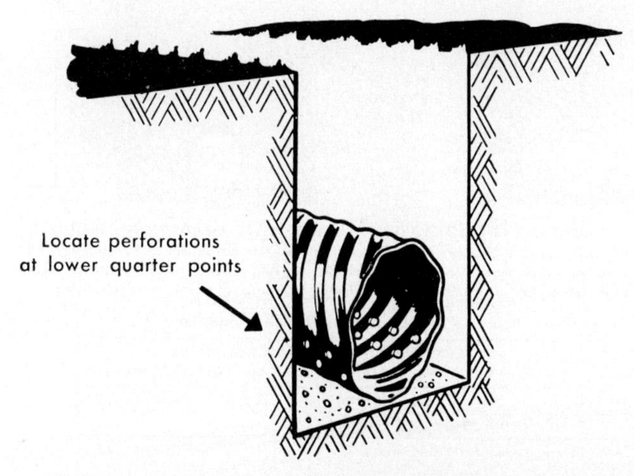

Fig. 335. Pipe should be generally installed with the perforations down.

panying table (Fig. 335a). Many bank-run sands and concrete sands and gravel aggregates will meet these requirements. Graded crushed stone not of a self-cementing nature may also be used. Material having not more than 10 per cent of its weight in particles larger than ⅜-in. size, but otherwise meeting the No. 1 gradation, will make a satisfactory filter. It is important that the fine material be in contact with the sides of the trench throughout the water-bearing strata, thereby preventing washing of soil fines from the trench walls and clogging the coarse filter and the pipe.

Filter material should be placed in layers and should be tamped. Filter material should be carried to within 6 in. of the ground surface, and the remainder of the trench filled with earth thoroughly compacted. Where surface interception is desired and silting not likely to occur, the filter material can be carried to the surface.

When subdrain pipes with open joints (instead of perforations) are used, it is generally necessary to use two different backfill materials. A coarse filter material (No. 2 on chart) is placed around the pipe to prevent the entrance of fine material into the pipe. Second, the fine filter material described above must be used to prevent washing of soil fines from the trench walls.

Where perforated short-sectional clay or concrete pipe is used, the joints between sections must be filled with cement mortar. Merely laying burlap or roofing paper over the joints will not prevent entrance of the fine graded filter material.

Retaining Walls and Abutments

Perforated corrugated metal pipe installed as drains for retaining walls and for the back of bridge abutments must be installed in a backfill of pervious material as indicated for underdrains or subdrains. While drains may be placed on more than one elevation for high abutments, the bottom drain should be placed at the lowest level that will drain when water in the stream is at normal low water level.

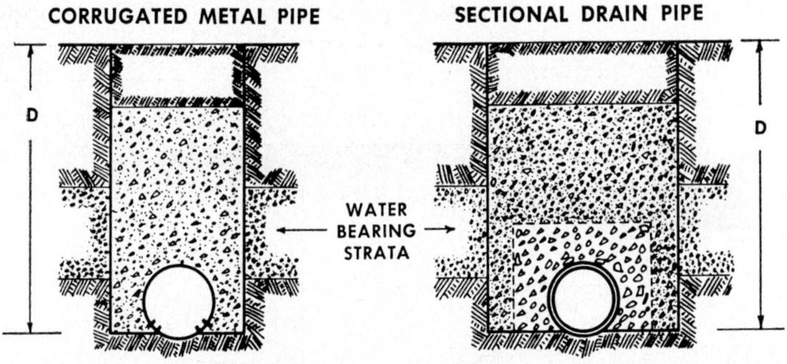

CORRUGATED METAL PIPE

SECTIONAL DRAIN PIPE

D

WATER BEARING STRATA

D

ONLY ONE FILTER GRADATION NEEDED
Gradation No. 1 is used to prevent migration of soil particles from trench wall which would cause silting of underdrain and settlement of surface.

TWO FILTER GRADATIONS REQUIRED
Gradation No. 2 is necessary in conjunction with Gradation No. 1 to prevent fine filter material washing into large opening at joints and clogging the pipe.

Depth "D" should be varied to suit installation conditions.

FILTER * GRADATION	PERCENT PASSING STD. A.S.T.M. SIEVE 1½	1	⅜	No. 4	No. 8	No. 16	No. 50	No. 100
No. 1	——	——	100	95-100	——	45-80	10-30	0-10
No. 2	100	90-100	25-60	5-40	0-20	——	——	——

*C.A.A. Recommended Filter Gradations.

Fig. 335a. Recommended filters for two types of subdrains—perforated and open joints.

CHAPTER FIFTY-FOUR

Jacking

NEW openings for culverts, sewers, conduits, underpasses, etc. are frequently required under existing railroads, highways, streets, runways, levees and other engineering works. Four methods of placing such openings are: open trenching, jacking, tunneling and boring. These methods are discussed in this and following chapters.

Open trenching is the most commonly used method and is well adapted to new construction and to replacements under shallow fills and areas of light traffic. This method is described in detail in the preceding chapters.

The *jacking* method of installation, in use for the past quarter century, offers important advantages such as protection of the general public and expensive surface installations, and fast, uninterrupted movement of traffic. Fig. 336.

Fig. 336. Jacking provides an efficient means of installing culverts under busy thoroughfares.

Diameters

Diameters of pipes from 28 in. up to 96 in. have been installed by the jacking method with no settlement of surface structures and no interruption of traffic. However, the most common sizes being jacked today range from 30 to 60 in. One essential of this method is that the structure be large enough to allow working space for a man to excavate ahead of the pipe without being too cramped and 36-in. diameter seems to be the minimum for the average size man. The maximum size that can be jacked depends on several factors of which the main ones are: ground conditions, height of cover and safety.

Lengths

The length of pipe that can be jacked is variable and depends on the pipe diameter, ground conditions and the pressures required to push the pipe. Therefore, a thorough investigation should be made of these factors before setting up a job which is to be done entirely by the jacking method. Lengths of over 200 ft have been installed by this method, but ground conditions had to approach the ideal and the pipe had to be kept in motion on a 24-hour basis to keep it from "freezing" tight. Where the pipe does "freeze up" it is possible, under most conditions, to move to the opposite side of the fill and to jack the balance of the pipe to meet the end that is already in place. To do this and make a proper junction of the two pipes, it will be necessary for line and grade to be accurately set and closely watched.

Depth of Cover

The cover over pipe to be jacked on railroads should be at least one diameter, with a minimum of 3 ft to get below the ballast line and into stable material. Under highway slabs that are reinforced, the cover can be a minimum for providing a cushion between bottom of slab and top of pipe. However, under bituminous type pavements the cover should be equal to that used under railroads.

Acceptance

This method of installing new openings has become standard procedure for most railroads and numerous highway departments and has resulted in saving time, money and material, plus a factor of safety which is all-important to present day movement of traffic. Jacking also avoids the cost and nuisance of repeated maintenance of the fill due to settlement which is usually necessary when the open trench method of installation is used. For levee or dike installations jacking avoids sacrificing valuable land and the building of new set-back levees.

Jacking Procedure[1]

Testing of Soil

Jacking should not be attempted in dry sand, in gravelly soil that is known to contain large boulders, through fills where logs or stumps are known to exist or where it is impractical or uneconomical to lower the water table below the excavation.

In all questionable soil conditions, the soil should be tested by boring or sampling before jacking is decided upon. This is neither costly nor time-consuming.

Approach Trench

When pipe is to be jacked through fills higher than the diameter of the pipe, plus the required minimum cover, no working pit is necessary. However, it is desirable

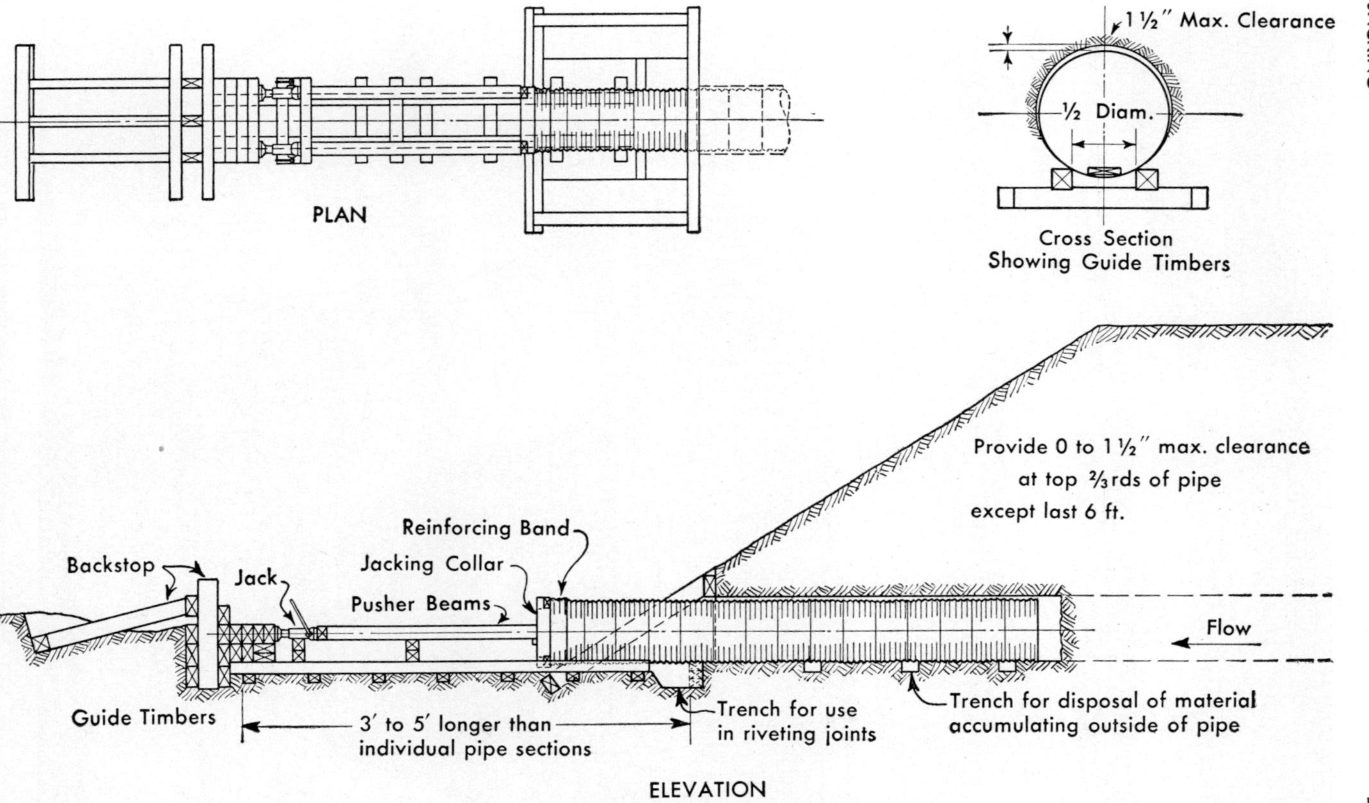

Fig. 337. Setup for typical jacking operation.

Fig. 338. Jacking 36-in. corrugated metal pipe under main line railroad.

to excavate an approach trench into the fill far enough to provide a jacking face of 3 ft or more above the pipe. This open face should be shored securely to prevent slipping or raveling of the embankment. Provision for a sump should be made in one corner of the approach trench or pit.

Backstop and Guides

A substantial backstop is necessary to take the thrust of the jack. A 60 to 80-ft length jacking job in reasonably good soil often develops 150 to 300 tons of jacking resistance.[2] The backstop is usually of heavy timbers.

The timbers or steel rails that support the pipe as it enters the bore must be accurately placed on line and grade. Both line and grade should be checked at least once per shift as the work progresses. Fig. 337.

Pipe for Jacking

For corrugated pipe to be jacked, the sections are especially prepared for making field joints by riveting or bolting. The use of a jacking band to reinforce the end receiving the thrust is recommended especially for long lines or large diameters. When jacking through loose or gravelly soils, smooth steel sheets of light gage should be bolted to the top and bottom of the pipe sections.

Equipment

Necessary equipment for jacking includes an electric power plant for lights, pumps, excavating tools, muck handling equipment and jacks. Often an air compressor for air spades and breakers is justified. A wheel-barrow is economical for pipe 48 in. and larger. For smaller pipe, some type of skip or dolly-mounted dirt box is required.

Any of several types of jacks can be used. These should have a capacity of at least 35 tons and be operated in pairs. Travel of jacks should be at least 13 in. Small track jacks can be used to start the pipe. Fig. 338.

Working Crew

A crew of four men and a sub-foreman, per shift, provides the necessary manpower. However, during the preliminary work of excavating the working pit and placing the backstop, more men can be employed, such as by combining two shifts.

One man digs at the head of the pipe. A second man loads the dirt buggy. The other two remove the excavated material and they jack the pipe. All hands join in lowering a section of pipe into the trench and making the field connection.

Jacking Operation

As material is excavated ahead of the pipe, the pipe is jacked in to follow this excavation. The distance dug ahead of the pipe rarely exceeds 12 to 18 in. Some loose soils may reduce this to 3 or 4 in.

Excavation should be about 1 in. more than the outside diameter of the pipe at the top, and taper off towards the invert.

REFERENCES

1. For details see "Jacking Culverts Through Fills," by C. M. Colvin, in *Western Construction*, San Francisco, April 1953.
2. Where excavation is carried ahead of pipe, the pressure may be 125 psf of surface area of imbedded pipe. Where jacking is progressed ahead of the excavation, the pressure may be 600 psf, according to Jacob Feld in Bull. No. 14, Highway Research Board, 1948.

Fig. 339. Another method of installing small conduits under streets and railroads is by boring.

CHAPTER FIFTY-FIVE

Boring

Boring is another means of installing conduits and culverts without disturbing surface structures or traffic. This method is generally confined to pipe diameters from 1 in. to 36 in. Various types of machines on the market are built to perform this operation.

There are two basic methods for accomplishing the objective, the first of which is to push the conduit pipe into the fill as the boring auger drills out the ground. Fig. 339. The second one consists of drilling the hole through the fill and pushing the conduit pipe into the hole after the drill auger has completed the bore. Both of these methods have their advantages, but if there is any doubt concerning the ground conditions, the first method is the safer of the two and offers greater protection to the surface structure under which the conduit is being placed.

For example, if the second method is used and a sand pocket is encountered in what is otherwise a good stable fill, it is easy to imagine that a void in the fill could be created that would cause a lot of trouble. The use of boring equipment for installing small diameter tubing is illustrated on page 358.

Location of Holes

Since these boring installations are generally of small diameters, the possibility of being stopped by encountering boulders, rocks or utility lines should be taken into consideration and alternate locations for the conduit should be provided. In some locations, rocks and boulders are prevalent, while in other areas the possibility of encountering such obstacles is remote. Hence the engineer and the contractor must guide their thinking accordingly. Where obstacles are encountered in fills, it may be necessary to abandon that exact location. However, by starting a new hole at a distance of as little as 1 foot either side may make it possible to miss the obstacle and go through with a successful installation.

There have been cases where as many as six holes were drilled before a clear path was found for the boring tool.

There are machines that will bore through rock and coal, but sometimes it is not economically practical to adapt these rock cutters to earth augers. Most boring augers will penetrate soft rock, wood or brick, but experience and "feel" are required to judge the practicability of going ahead when such obstacles are encountered. Line and grade may suffer because of these obstacles and even though it is possible to complete the bore, it may not be satisfactory for the purpose intended. Under such circumstances it may be wiser to abandon the bore when the obstacle is encountered and move a few feet to try again for a clear pathway.

The horizontal boring method of installation is not an exact science and hence requires experienced personnel, good investigation of ground conditions, good equipment and flexibility of thinking.

Instructions

Detailed instructions are not available. However, in general, the information given in the preceding chapter on Jacking applies here.

Fig. 340. Liner plate shaft used in the installation of a new sewer line in Charleston, West Virginia.

CHAPTER FIFTY-SIX

Tunneling

ANOTHER method for installation of culvert openings, sewers, conduits, etc. under surface structures is by tunneling. Tunneling may be done with timbers and lagging or by the use of metal liner plates, supplemented in the larger tunnels by metal ribs. Because of the fire hazard, cost and scarcity of timber, this material is giving way to metal tunnel linings. Liner plates for holding back the ground while the tunnel moves ahead are described in Chapt. 48, page 400, and the efficient use of these plates to install underground openings is finding its way into more projects every year. In some of these projects the liner plates may serve as the finished structure while in others the plates serve only as a temporary support for the "bore" until a monolithic lining can be placed.

Under present traffic conditions the engineer should give full and detailed consideration to the use of tunneling before allowing his railroad, streets or highways to be broken open for any purpose whatsoever except under circumstances of absolute necessity. For instance, a street in a business district should not be torn up for new sewers and utility lines if doing so will interfere with business for merchants, restaurants and hotels lining both sides of the street due to traffic stoppage or congestion. Fig. 340.

Precautions

Although there is no mystery about tunneling, it does consist of the employment of knowledge and experience plus the right tools and materials to gain the objective. Hence, experienced contractors or other qualified personnel should be employed on all tunnel work. Breaking through the sheeting of a pit to get tunneling started can be a risky operation. Also, working a tunnel face in soft wet ground or "sugar sand" can cause trouble if experienced personnel is not employed.

Procedure

A first step in any tunneling job is to excavate and shore one or more working pits. These should be large enough to contain a compressor, pump, lighting equipment and tools. Provision must be made for hoisting the muck dug from the tunnel.

Before beginning excavation of the tunnel, a short section of liner plate should be assembled and set up in the pit accurately on line and grade, as a guide to subsequent operations. Frequent instrument checks on line and grade are essential.

The excavation for the tunnel should be kept to the outside diameter of the liner plates and any voids that might occur due to boulders, loss of face materials, etc. which might cause voids back of the liner plate, should be immediately filled with well compacted material or pressure grout to avoid any settlement of the overburden. The use of hay or straw will help prevent loose material from running and causing large voids behind the liner plate. These temporary fillers should be replaced with more permanent materials before the job is completed.

In soft, unstable ground, various methods of advancing the tunnel are used such as the "shield"; "poling plate"; "poling board" (see Fig. 341) or "splinter";

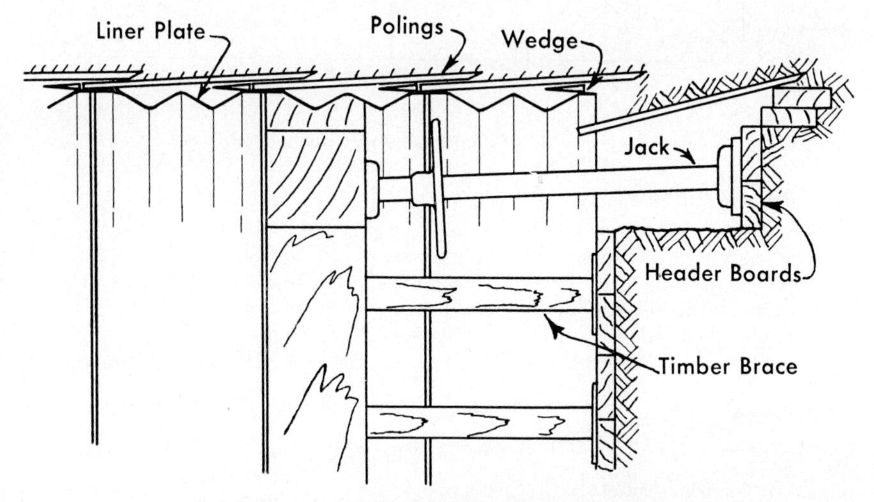

Fig. 341. Typical set-up for tunneling with Armco Liner Plates.

"benching" and "needle beam" method. These are used singly or in combination depending on ground conditions, diameter of the "bore" and type of loads the tunnel is carrying.

When unstable ground is anticipated, a percentage of the liner plates should be provided with grout holes and nipples to facilitate grouting of voids.

Using light-weight tunnel liner plates for vertical shafts, mine slope entries, caissons for bridge piers, etc. is entirely practical and saves the extra excavation that would be required where heavy timbers were contemplated.

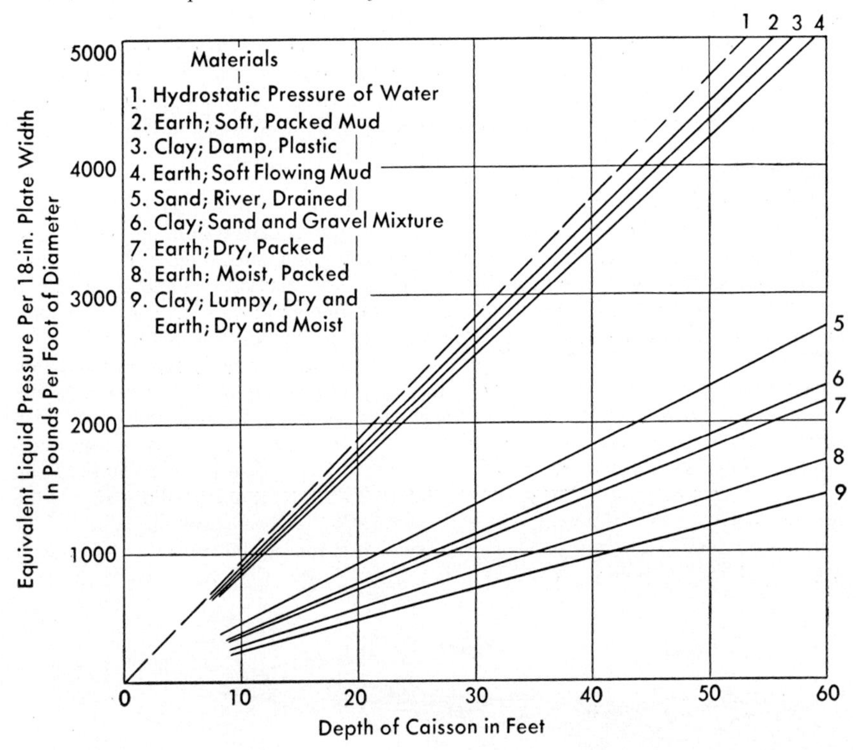

Fig. 342. Equivalent fluid pressure for caisson construction.

Caisson Construction

The load carried by an 18-in. wide liner joint plate (lap) at a specified depth may be computed by multiplying the pressure shown in Fig. 342 by one-half the diameter of the caisson in feet. Then it is necessary to choose the gage of liner plate to carry this load with the desired factor of safety.

Example: Determine the load for a caisson 20 ft in diameter, 40 ft deep, in damp plastic clay. From Fig. 342, the load per 18-in. ring per ft of diameter is 3500 lb Then $3500 \times \frac{20}{2}$ ft $= 35{,}000$ lb per joint. Ultimate lap joint strength for 3 ga. plates with ASTM A-325 high tensile steel bolts $= 131{,}500$ lb (From Fig. 43, page 52). Factor of safety $= \frac{131{,}500}{35{,}000} = 3.76$.

Fig. 343. Old structures can be revitalized by lining with corrugated metal pipe.

CHAPTER FIFTY-SEVEN

Lining

THERE comes a time when tunnels, conduits and culverts begin to deteriorate and lose strength. A decision must be made as to whether the structure should be rehabilitated or replaced. The decision is usually based on economics. Also, due to changing conditions, some old structures must be strengthened to take care of present and future loads which are greater than those for which the structures were originally designed.

Discussion is confined to some of the economical methods used to rehabilitate and strengthen drainage openings, small bridges, sewers, etc.

Masonry and Concrete Arches: These structures begin to deteriorate from natural causes after being in service for a period of years. Mortar comes out of the joints, the stones become loose and alternate freezing and thawing causes trouble. Concrete begins to crack and spall off or heavy loads cause foundation settlement, resulting in cracking and spalling. Consequently, the structure needs to be strengthened or must be replaced. Rehabilitation in numerous cases is the most economical and can be accomplished with minimum effort.

Lining such a structure with a structural plate or liner plate arch will require a minimum of space, thereby saving a maximum amount of the original waterway area. These metal arches can be supported on new concrete side walls or on original bench walls where feasible as illustrated in Fig. 344.. Tables 11-9, page 131, and 14-3, page 142, show recommended minimum gages for arches of 6 to 30-ft span. Although these tables cover railroad loadings the same principle can be applied to highway structures.

Pressure Grouting

By pressure grouting the space between the old and new structures, further collapse of the old structure is prevented and concentrated pressures on the new lining avoided. Two-inch grout couplings welded into the liner plates can be furnished at proper intervals for convenience in grouting.

Grouting should be carefully done and frequent checks made to see that voids are being thoroughly filled. In fact, due to shrinkage of the grout after "set up", the top row of grout holes should be "check grouted" after grout placement is completed to be sure any voids due to shrinkage have been filled.

Lining Materials

As mentioned above, either structural plate or liner plate can be used as the liners. The one chosen depends on the condition of the old structure, the room available in which to work and the accessibility of the site. Small arches, 6 ft or less, can be lined with riveted corrugated metal sections. Each product will accomplish the same objective and the choice will be determined by the size of the structure and method of installation used. Each product can be set in channels thoroughly anchored to a proper base. The plates in turn will rest in these channels to get the proper load bearing requirements.

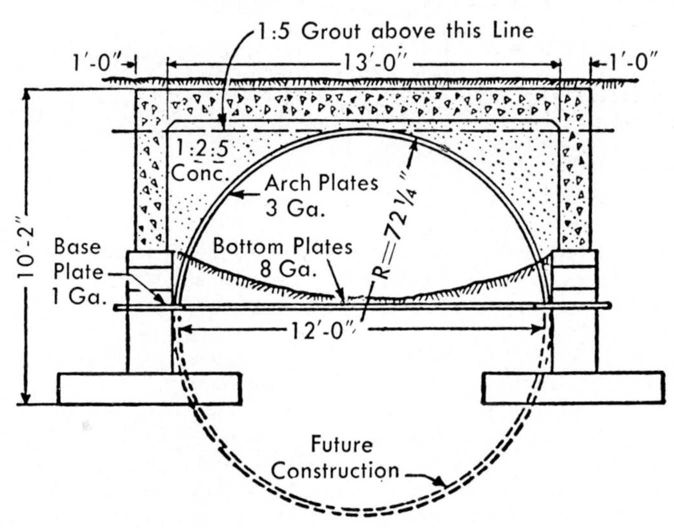

Fig. 344. Cross-section of 1100-ft concrete box culvert reinforced with steel arch to withstand heavier plane loads on midwestern airport.

Hundreds of lineal feet of masonry arches have been given new life by this lining method over the past 20 years and the results have been very satisfactory.

Other Shapes of Structures

This same method of relining can be applied to full round, elliptical or other shapes of structures that have begun to show signs of deterioration or collapse. New corrugated metal pipe, structural plate or liner plate can be threaded inside the old structure to give it new life for long trouble-free service. Frequently, due to excessive deflection or joint settlement, the diameter of the new lining will necessarily be much smaller in order to have clearance for threading. In such cases it sometimes is necessary to jack or tunnel a supplementary opening alongside the present structure to make up for the lost waterway area in the old culvert. It also happens that changes in runoff conditions may not require as large an opening as originally installed. In these cases, a reduction in waterway area due to "threading" is not serious. These changing conditions should be investigated before the engineer sets forth his requirements.

This method of rehabilitation can also be applied to storm or sanitary sewers which are beginning to show signs of weakening. Fig. 345. Methods of installation of liners for sewers will vary with the size of the sewer and the type of liner to be used but the basic principles applying to this type of job would be the same as those used in "threading" or lining a culvert that is relatively short and open at both ends.

Fig. 345. Specially fabricated corrugated metal pipe, egg-shaped, was used to line a fading sewer. Views show sections before and during installation.

CHAPTER FIFTY-EIGHT

Bridge Filling

ON RAILROADS and highways there are innumerable small bridges built of timber, concrete and steel, or a combination of these materials, that are larger than the drainage area demands. Maintenance on these bridges becomes quite costly as the structure ages. Eventually, arrangements must be made for major repairs or complete replacement. At that time a complete investigation should be made of the actual waterway opening required, the importance of the structure from a traffic standpoint, consideration of fire hazard, elimination of maintenance and the most economical material to be used.

Economics of materials does not necessarily mean low first cost. Reduced maintenance cost, long trouble-free life, ease of installation without traffic interruptions and capital investment should be considered along with the cost of retiring the old structure.

Structural plate and corrugated metal pipe have been used quite extensively over the past 20 years for filling and replacing timber trestles on railroads, and small steel, wood or concrete spans on county and state highway systems. The success of applying these metal structures is evidenced by the growing acceptance of their use. In some instances one opening is sufficient to take care of the waterway while in other cases a whole battery of pipes may be necessary. Drainage area

Fig. 346. This massive trestle was replaced with an easy to maintain culvert and fill.

Fig. 347. Old highway bridges can be readily replaced with the culvert and fill method.

and available headroom will determine the size and number of pipes required. Fig. 346 and 347.

Proper foundation, strutting and tamping of the backfill are very important and these operations are of sufficient importance to warrant repeating. Where the pipe or pipes are close to existing pile bents and cross bracing, a good job of backfilling and tamping should be mandatory at these spots. It would be preferable to surround the pipe with pit run gravel or other types of pervious material (except cinders or slag) rather than clay. Precautions should, however, be taken to seal the upstream end against seepage under and alongside the pipe—a cause of failures.

Impervious materials can be used on top of the pervious material to build up the fill, but since water will follow the line of piling and cross bracing and could cause soft spots around the pipes, it would be better to have a place for such water to collect on the outside and seep into the culvert before it can do harm to the fill. This is particularly true where structural plate is used. After the fill has consolidated, this pervious material will gradually cease to function as a water collector. However, it should be there at the time of installation to help eliminate soft spots alongside the pipe that tend to form from rains that fall during the fill build up.

In case of replacement of railroad trestles, the caps and stringers should remain in place to handle traffic until the fill has become consolidated. Otherwise the railroad should be willing to raise track that settles with the fill. In case of highway bridge replacements, a temporary surface should be placed on the new fill until consolidation is final.

CHAPTER FIFTY-NINE

Bin Walls

ARMCO bin-type retaining walls are gravity type walls assembled from prefabricated parts. Stability of the wall comes largely from the weight of the fill confined within the bins. Resistance against sliding is provided by the friction of the confined fill on the foundation and by extending the wall into foundation material.

Bin-type walls can be erected by hand methods, placing one piece at a time. They can also be erected by making up sub-assemblies that can be placed with light cranes. Fig. 348.

Excavation

The earth can be excavated with heavy construction equipment to the elevation of the natural ground line and into the bank a short distance beyond the rear of the wall. The final excavation, from the ground line to the base of the columns, should be done by hand in the form of trenches just wide enough to allow the bottom members of the wall to be placed. This will reduce the volume of excavation and make it easy to accurately excavate the area under the base plates without disturbing any more of the natural ground than necessary.

Fig. 348. On large retaining walls, it is frequently most economical to assemble transverse sections into units.

Fig. 349. Backfill should be placed in uniform layers and then tamped.

Preparing the Foundation

The foundation under the wall should be cleared of all sod, debris and unstable soil. When the wall is placed on rock or other nonyielding foundation, a cushion of soil should be placed under the base plates to permit the entire wall to adjust to small differential settlements and avoid concentration of loads on any individual members of the wall.

The elevation of the foundation should be set low enough to prevent undercutting of the foundation if a ditch or stream carries water along the face of the wall. The depth required will vary with the velocity and direction of the currents or the amount of wave action. *On good foundation not subject to erosion, a shallow footing depth may be used.*

The base plates must be accurately placed to line, grade and slope. A simple template may be constructed for establishing the position of the base plates for walls placed on 1:6 batter. When the walls are designed to be installed on other than the standard batter or placed vertically, the same method can be used by adjusting the template or batter block dimensions.

Subdrainage of retaining walls, using perforated metal pipe is generally desirable to eliminate the possibility of hydrostatic pressure developing behind the wall or saturating the foundation. See Chapt. 47, page 378. Such a subdrain should be placed at the back of the wall, below the lowest member, if a suitable outlet can be provided.

Assembly

Assembly of the wall can be handled either by building the wall piece by piece or by making a sub-assembly of the transverse section members (bearing plates, columns, spacers and connecting channels), erecting it as a unit and then placing the stringers. The latter method requires a small hoist for handling the transverse sections but will prove economical for long walls. Fig. 348. In either case, it is important to check the columns for batter and line as they are placed and before the assembly bolts are tightened.

The wall can be backfilled as it is erected, provided caution is used to see that the columns are held in correct position while the backfill is being placed. A stringer and spacer temporarily placed at the top of the columns will assist in holding the columns in line. For higher walls when a column splice is required, it is often advantageous to backfill up to the splice before the upper portion of the column is placed.

Backfill

The fill should have a high percentage of graded granular material with a maximum size of 3 in. Bank-run sand or fine gravel is ideal; heavy clays should be avoided if possible, but may be used if extreme care is taken in tamping the fill. No lumps, sod, cinders or frozen material should be used.

First fill and carefully tamp the trenches around the base of the wall. Place the balance of fill material in 6-in. layers and tamp each layer thoroughly to minimize settlement in the fill but avoid overtamping. Fig. 349. While the fill material should be *placed to fill* all members of the wall, it is *advisable not to tamp* the fill into the stringers and spacers.

The backfill between the wall and natural ground should be kept approximately level with fill inside the bins at all times. The fill over the wall should be shaped to avoid having surface water standing in the area. Paved ditches or storm sewers should be used to carry away surface water when a nearly level surface is required behind the wall.

When a perforated metal pipe underdrain is specified behind the wall, a properly graded pervious granular backfill material must be used over the underdrain and extend above the elevation of any seepage zones.

Fig. 350. A bin type retaining wall used to permit widening a highway in New York State.

CHAPTER SIXTY

Sheeting

THE driving of sheeting requires *skilled operators,* particularly if satisfactory and economical results are to be obtained. This statement applies to any type sheeting: wood, heavy steel sections or cold-formed sheets.

The importance of proper driving equipment and the proper use of it must be stressed. The American Society of Civil Engineers in its Manual of Engineering Practice—No. 27 (1946) on Pile Foundations and Pile Structures—has the following recommendation on driving load-carrying piles and they apply equally well to steel sheet piles.

"*Selecting Weight and Striking Velocity of Hammer.*—The type, length, dimensions and material having been chosen for the pipe, in view of the soil conditions and the load to be carried, the type, size, weight and velocity at impact of the hammer (or of equivalent gravity fall) must be chosen subject to the conditions that it deliver sufficient energy without injury to the pile. Selection may be made on the basis of weight of striking part (ram) and foot-pounds delivered per blow. The matter resolves itself into a practical decision, since it is not feasible to compute the various resistances that must be overcome. Good judgment, based upon knowledge of the local conditions and upon experience in pile driving, is essential, and advice of specialists would be of value."

Kinds of Soils Encountered

Moist, silty soils or silty-clay soils are relatively easy to penetrate. Driving in clay soils will vary from easy to difficult or impossible. The same is true of sand. Confined quicksand is very difficult to penetrate by driving and will require the use of a water jet. Gravel-sand mixtures may contain large-size stones that will prevent the penetration of the piling.

Suggestions on Equipment

No definite recommendations can be given on the size and kind of driving equipment that should be used unless all the conditions are known. Suppose you were given several different kinds of nails—finishing, small and large spikes, boat spikes, etc.—to drive into different kinds and thicknesses of wood, and had available several sizes of hammers and sledges. You would pick the hammer that would best meet the conditions. The character of the soil mass through which the piling is to be driven, the moisture content of the soil, the length and weight of the sheeting and whether excavation is done ahead of driving are facts that must be known in order to select the proper driving equipment for handling sheeting. Fig. 351.

Table 60-1, which is based on manufacturers' catalogs, gives an idea of the range of equipment that is available for driving sheeting. Data on the heavy, large size drivers which would be used for deep foundations has been omitted. No data are given for the "paving-breaker" type of hammer, which is frequently advertised as a sheeting driver, since it is *not suitable for most driving conditions.* It has a tendency to batter the top of the sheeting.

TABLE 60-1 TYPES OF DRIVING EQUIPMENT FOR SHEETING

Description of Hammer	*Double-Acting*						*Single-Acting*			*Differential*
Weight, lb	105	145	343	675	1500	2900	8000	11,000	3700	4274
Ram Weight, lb	5	21	48	68	200	400	3000	5,000	1800	1800
Stroke, in.	4½	3¾	5¼	5¾	7	8¾	36	39	24	10½
Strokes, no./min.	1000	500	500	400	300	275	65	60	80	150
Energy, ft-lb/blow	.....	.....	.....	.....	1000	2500	9000	16,250	3600	3600
Length, in.	25	47	37	62	57	63	148	159	114	77½
Compressed Air, cu ft	60	70	70	110	250	400	400	600	220	308
Total Penetration, ft	5–6	6–10	10–15	10–15	15–20	20–30	.....	......	15–25	15–25*

Penetration is in average material with hammer operating at rated speed.
*Based on driving two sheets simultaneously.

Weight of Hammer

A hand maul or a light pneumatic hammer may be satisfactory for pushing sheeting in a trench where the bottom can be excavated ahead of driving and when the earth loads on the sheeting are light. If the sheeting is to be driven in advance of excavation or the side pressures are heavy, then heavier equipment such as a drop hammer, or a pneumatic or steam pile driver will be needed. The use of heavy driving equipment will usually show faster driving with less injury to the sheeting for any given condition. Light equipment tends to batter the top edge and slow down the driving.

The driving equipment must be capable of supplying ample foot-pounds of energy to move the sheeting easily. A driver which strikes a heavy blow with a low velocity at impact will do the most work with the least amount of damage to the sheeting. Long, heavy sheet piles require more energy to start them moving than do short, light sections. In this respect, the heavy hot rolled sections will require heavier drivers than those for light-weight sheeting. The friction of the soil on the sheeting surfaces and force required for penetration of the leading edge are factors that are very hard to evaluate. In order to select the proper driving equipment, it is essential to know local conditions and have experience with various types of driving equipment in the soil formations that will be encountered.

Hold Sheeting Firmly; Drive Squarely

Regardless of the type of equipment used, it is essential that the sheeting be held firmly in place during driving. In addition, the driver must be held on the top of the sheeting so that all blows are axial to the sheeting and squarely centered on the top surface. There is no real substitute for a good set of leads that will hold the sheeting firmly in place and the driver in proper position during driving. Fig. 351.

In trench work where the sheeting is held by wales, it is sometimes possible to hold the hammer on top of the sheeting by means of a crane or a tripod, but the hammer tends to bounce around and cause bending and bruising of the pile. Light pneumatic equipment must be held so that the blows are axial. For driving sheeting, as opposed to "pushing" it, the hand tools strike such a light blow that the driving is very slow, resulting in bending and bruising of the top of the pile.

Medium size single or double-acting hammers will give a much more satisfactory performance when held in leads than when swung on a cable. The leads can be short and need not be as elaborate as would be required for driving long foundation piling but they must be supported to hold the driver in line with the sheeting, and they should be guyed to hold the sheeting in line. A light to medium weight gravity hammer (1200 to 2500 lb) may give good results if properly guided and used with a 2 to 5-ft drop.

Driving Heads Not Always Needed

Driving heads, such as can be furnished with sheeting, are designed to spread the load over a larger area of the top of a sheet than would be the case if the driving equipment were used without the head. Therefore, the head should be used only when driving with hand tools or the light pneumatic or gasoline drivers. The driving head is unnecessary and may even be detrimental when used in conjunction with gravity hammers or single or double-acting pile hammers. These drivers have a wide flat surface that will cover the entire top end of one—and in some cases two or more—sheet piles. The driving head, if used in this case, would concentrate the blow on a smaller portion of the pile than would be the case if the driver were centered and held squarely on the top end of the sheeting and the blow

Fig. 351. Proper driving equipment for handling steel sheeting depends upon the character of the soil as well as the length and weight of the sheeting.

Fig. 352. Driving steel sheeting for erosion protection along a causeway in Florida.

struck through the wide base of the driver. If proper driving equipment is used, the special driving head is seldom necessary.

Jets are generally necessary when driving into fine, well compacted sand or quicksand. They are used in conjunction with driving equipment and the water flow must be controlled to displace just enough material to allow the sheeting to be driven.

Keeping the Sheeting Plumb

Driving a long row of interlocking sheeting requires careful operation to keep the top from progressively leaning toward the undriven end of the row. Each piece must be carefully lined and plumbed (some contractors use a mason's level on each section) before starting to drive it, and the section must be held firmly in place until it is driven to full penetration. A very satisfactory method is to set up the individual sections well in advance and then drive the row in a stair-step fashion, driving each piece 1 or 2 ft at a time.

Closing the interlock on the bottom leading edge of the sheeting will frequently prevent small pebbles from entering the interlock and interfering with the driving of the following section. Crawling out of plumb can be partly avoided by placing one or two 20 penny spikes in the fold at the top of the interlock of the last piece of sheeting driven, after the adjacent piece has been placed for driving. Each section of sheeting should be straight and free from kinks before it is placed for driving.

CHAPTER SIXTY-ONE

Beam Type Guardrail

Location of Rail

The proper location of guardrail may be shown on the plans. Often its location is left to the discretion of the construction engineer or to the maintenance supervisor.

In general, the rail should be located near the shoulder line to give a maximum width of roadway and shoulder. However, the distance from the back of the post line to the slope should not be less than 1½ or 2 ft in order to give adequate support against overturning. At the throat of narrow bridges, the approach guardrail should be placed on the traffic side of the bridge end post so that a vehicle cannot strike the end post. Abrupt changes in direction should be avoided when possible. For further details on location, see Design of Guardrail, Chapter 49, pages 407–414.

Posts

Spacing of posts on 12½-ft centers should be done with reasonable accuracy and care, especially if pre-drilled posts are used. Ordinarily, however, a post can be moved at the top sufficiently to line it up and space it accurately.

Posts may be driven or holes may be dug or drilled depending on the kind of soil and presence of rock or boulders. Driving or drilling equipment should be adequate to handle any condition encountered. Fig. 353.

Fig. 353. A tractor-mounted auger is convenient for making guardrail post holes in most soils.

Wood posts may be left high and later trimmed to a uniform height. Metal or concrete posts should be set or driven to grade. Depth below ground is usually 3 to 3½ ft; height above ground is approximately 2 ft. Normally the center of the rail is at automobile bumper height—18 in. above the ground.

Backfilling of dug or drilled holes should not be completed until the rail is in place and lined up. Backfill should consist of dry earth or granular material, well tamped. Posts need not be set in concrete unless unusually soft materials require it.

If the top of the posts are flush with the top of the rail, wings of snow removal equipment can "ride" the top of the rail without damage to either.

Assembling the Rail

The easiest way of assembling beam-type guardrail is to begin at the end farthest from approaching traffic, placing one panel of the rail at a time on the posts, without putting the nut on the long post bolt until the next panel is in place. The two corrugation crests should always be towards traffic so that the bolts are in the valleys or post side. Fig. 354.

Fig. 354. Two men can handle a single section of Flex-Beam Guardrail.

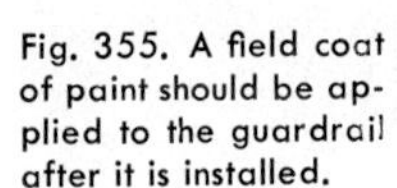

Fig. 355. A field coat of paint should be applied to the guardrail after it is installed.

Then the six short splice bolts are inserted and the nuts left loose. Tightening of all bolts is done during the final aligning process.

The end wing is installed just like any other panel and always with the end flared back. The lap at all posts should be such that a vehicle does not strike the end of the metal.

Painting

Beam-type guardrail comes with a mill primer coat of paint to prevent rusting. A field coat of paint should be applied after the rail is installed and finally aligned. Fig. 355.

White paint is considered to have the best visibility. However, orange color and aluminum paints are also used. Black diagonal striping of the rail can be done for special warnings. The use of reflector buttons and tapes on the rail is also possible.

Maintenance

Panels or posts damaged by collisions should be promptly repaired or replaced. Meanwhile, due to the beam strength of beam-type guardrail, the remainder of the rail provides effective protection.

Damaged panels can readily be unbolted, removed and replaced by the maintenance crew. Posts should be realigned or replaced as necessary, with care being taken to tamp the earth around each affected post.

Periodic repainting of the panels and posts is desirable to maintain high visibility and to prolong the life of the rail and posts. It is essential that dust, dirt, grease and any loose paint be removed before painting. Rusted spots or streaks should be wire brushed to remove loose rust.

Bridge Rail

On new bridges of deck girder or slab construction, the guardrail posts are generally so spaced as to be in some fraction (usually one-half) of the standard guardrail panel length (12½ ft). However, for both new and old construction, and especially on truss bridges, the guardrail panels can be specially shop cut and punched or can be field drilled. Special brackets may be needed for bolting the rail to girders, beams or truss members.

Bridge rail is generally attached at the same level as road guard. In many cases it may be a continuation of the road guard from the approaches. On truss bridges a second or higher line of rail can be placed to protect the members from being struck by truck or trailer bodies or by their loads. See page 410.

Curved Installations

The application of deep corrugated beam-type guardrail to curved installations is as simple as for straight lines since no tensioning is required for this type of rail. Flex-Beam Guardrail may be obtained shop curved to any desired radius 20 ft or greater.

For radii of 150 ft and over, the elements may be erected in a smooth curve without the necessity of shop curving since the lap joint of beam-type guardrail is as strong in bending as the rail element. Successful field installations with radii as small as 75 ft may be made by attaching several sections of rail to the ones to be curved and using the extra sections as a lever. The extra lever sections are then removed and used elsewhere. When available, the power of trucks or tractors can be utilized for field curving of guardrail sections.

CHAPTER SIXTY-TWO

Metal Bridge Plank

Where Used

Metal bridge plank is used principally in the reflooring of highway bridges which have worn wooden floors. There are also many places where it may be economically used in the design of new bridges. Besides providing a new, quiet floor, it serves to stiffen the bridge laterally. It has been successfully used since 1946.

Essentially the metal bridge plank is a steel plate 24 in. wide, with 6-in. by 2-in. trapezoidal corrugations. Fig. 357. Maximum lengths are 20 ft for 12 gage, 16 ft for 10 gage and 12 ft for 7 gage. These lengths are welded together, end to end, to form planks across the bridge floor. Physical properties and recommended spans are given in Table 62-1.

Present Stringer System

To prevent excessive deflections of the floor and consequent rupturing of the metal and the pavement, care should be taken to properly support all stringers with their tops reasonably well aligned before applying the metal planks. Blocking shims under the ends of stringers may be necessary to bring them up to good alignment so the planks are supported uniformly at each stringer.

Fig. 356. Installing Armco metal bridge plank to replace an old wooden floor.

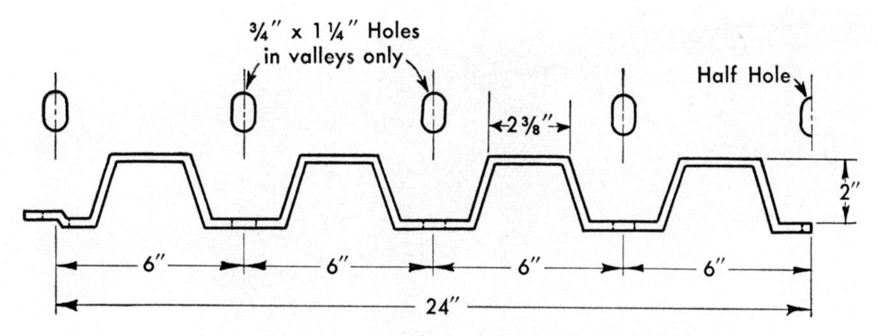

Fig. 357. Details of metal bridge plank.

A very light, limber stringer system can also cause excessive deflection of a bridge floor and result in premature failure of the flooring material. The same is true of a system of stringers having different stiffnesses.

Complete replacement of the present stringer system may be necessary in some cases, either with steel or timber. Steel is preferable because it permits securely welding the metal floor plank.

Welding

Provided the stringer system has been properly leveled, supported and tightened, and a smooth floor laid, the welds on the bridge deck material need carry only a limited amount of stress. Nonetheless, the welder should be one who can pass the qualifying tests of the American Welding Society for bridge construction as outlined in their handbook.

Metal bridge plank is welded from the top through slotted holes punched to match bridge stringer spacings. Fig. 356. These holes are ¾ x 1¼ in.

These same holes can be used if the planks are to be bolted or lag screwed to wooden stringers.

TABLE 62-1 PHYSICAL PROPERTIES OF ARMCO METAL BRIDGE PLANK AND TENTATIVE RECOMMENDED MAXIMUM SPANS FOR 6"x2" TRAPEZOIDAL CORRUGATION

Gage	*Equivalent Thickness in In.*	*Section Modulus In. Cubed/In.*	*Weight Lb per Sq Ft*	*Maximum Span—in In.**	
				H-20 and H-15	*H-10*
7	.1793	.162	10.7	30	39
10	.1345	.124	8.0	25	32
12	.1046	.098	6.2	22	28

Average weight of surfacing is 28.1 lb per sq ft based on 2 in. over metal at center line and 1 in. at edges. Pavement at 135 lb per cu ft.

*For ASTM:245-48T, Grade "C"; center to center of stringers except where stringers have very heavy and wide flanges; then from edge to edge of stringer flanges.

Fig. 358. Bituminous pavements are applied to metal bridge plank in two courses.

Bituminous Pavement

Bituminous pavements have been used successfully with metal bridge plank floors. The only precautions necessary are to make the pavement of such consistency that it will not shove under the action of traffic and that it be made smooth. Wherever dense graded, not too rich mixes have been used, and well compacted into place, no trouble is likely to occur. The best guide to proper pavement construction on these floors is the experience of the local highway department. Fig. 358.

CHAPTER SIXTY-THREE

Armco Gates

Recommendations for the installation of the various types of Armco Gates will be discussed under four general headings: slide head gates, flap gates, radial gates and roller gates. See table of water control gates, Table 46–2, page 376.

Slide Head Gates (Models 50-10, 30-05, 101 and 115)

These models are machined and adjusted before they leave the factory. For best results the gate should be in position before the concrete is placed. The gate slide must be in position in the wedge blocks. This will prevent springing of the seat casting.

If the concrete is placed before the gate is in position, a recess must be provided for the seat spigot. Leave the proper space for later "grouting-in" of the gate. Anchor bolts should be secured in position in the forms and held in perfect alignment when the concrete is placed. When the gate is installed, it should be placed on the anchor bolts with the slide engaging the wedge blocks. Block the gate in position and carefully grout in the seat. The gate seat should never be tightened to an uneven concrete surface, as it would spring and permit leakage.

Lift and stem guides should be carefully aligned parallel to the gate faces. This will insure smooth operation of the entire assembly. Detailed drawings and instructions are usually supplied by the manufacturer. Fig. 359.

Fig. 359. A battery of 72-in. gates located in Texas City, Texas.

Models 10-00 and 5-00

Care should be taken to avoid twisting the welded steel framework during installation. These models do not have wedges nor are they machined. Twisted framework will not allow water pressure to correctly seat the gate and will result in excessive leakage.

After the gates are installed, they should be carefully inspected to make sure all concrete is removed from the slots and seating surfaces and that the slide moves freely.

On Model 10-00 the guides, stem, gate and lifts should all be in perfect alignment. This will permit the gate to be raised and lowered without binding.

Flap Gates

Install flap gates with seating faces in a vertical plane, or with the bottom of the seating surface projecting slightly forward, so the gate will not hang open when not operating. This will also assure seating of the gates under small heads.

The ring or seat casting is comparatively light and can be easily warped. It should not be tightened against an uneven concrete surface. Concrete should be thoroughly worked around the gate seat while being placed. This should be done carefully as too much force might cause warpage. On most sizes, it is necessary to have a slight recess in the concrete at the top of the gate ears. This allows the link to move in and out and the gate to function properly. Fig. 360.

After installation, care should be taken in removing all concrete that might have stuck to the seating faces or at any point to hinder operation of the gate.

Fig. 360. Installing battery of 72-in. culverts with flap gates and diaphragms under a levee in Oregon.

Where flap gates are to be installed on very low and unstable ground, the recommendations in the next chapter will be found very helpful.

Radial Gates

Side walls must be vertical and parallel. The bottom of the channel should be level and at right angles to the side walls.

Both pin bearings must be installed at exactly the same elevation with the bearings at right angles to the wall. The center line of the hole in each bearing should also be at the correct distance from the location of the center line of the drumshaft of the hoist. In the area where the rubber side seals are in contact with the concrete, the concrete should be carefully smoothed. This smooth concrete will help in obtaining the desired seal and in prolonging the life of the rubber. A steel plate may also be imbedded for contact with the seal.

Perfect alignment of all parts can be assured by setting the gate into position with pins in bearings and pin plate before pouring concrete walls, or leaving windows in walls to set parts into for grouting bearing in place. Fig. 361.

Roller Gates

Side walls must be vertical. The bottom of the channel should be level and perpendicular to the side walls. Both channels for rollers must be vertical and parallel to each other. Contact surfaces for seals should be troweled smooth or have steel plates imbedded for seal contact.

Stems should be plumb. If stem guides are used, they must be correctly aligned to permit the stem to work freely. The distance between lifts should be carefully maintained when placing anchor bolts for the lifts.

Fig. 361. A 10 x 10 ft radial gate on the Kern River in California.

CHAPTER SIXTY-FOUR

Flap Gate Drainage Structures Through Levees and Dikes

CORRUGATED pipes fitted with flap gates can be employed successfully wherever it is practicable to maintain levees or dikes. While the difficulties increase with the larger sizes (48 to 96-in.) in wet, soft soils, this is even more true of alternate structures. Some of these latter require stable, unchanging foundations which may be secured only at great expense.

Size of Pipe

The size of the pipe is determined by the rainfall runoff and the length of time required to drain the land. In many cases, reclaimed lands became completely submerged during the winter due to the rise in the river and sloughs adjoining these lands. Knowing the rate at which this river water recedes after flood periods, and the length of time one can allow for draining the lands, the sizes of gates can be determined. When making levees on unreclaimed land, it is usually the best practice to install gates at the ends of the natural drainage ditches and this makes it possible by investigating the flow in these channels to determine more accurately the sizes of structures required.

Methods of Transporting

Drainage gates and pipes are delivered by boat, barge or tractor sled and sometimes floated and towed. The last method is advisable only where the pipe is made watertight either by close riveting or dipping in asphaltic compound. When towing, the ends are closed by bolting down the covers of the gates or, if the gates are not supplied, by tying canvas heads to the ends of the pipe.

Installing the Pipe

For details of installing pipe, especially on soft ground, see Chapter 52, page 435. The use of granular materials or stable soils under the pipe cannot be over-emphasized. When open granular materials are used for bedding, the ends of the structure should be sealed against seepage of water by using well tamped clay or some type of headwall or cut-off. Also, if there is any choice, the best materials should be used in filling around the pipe.

When installing pipes in battery, care should be taken to see that they are far enough apart so that trash entering one pipe, or floating against the levee, cannot loop itself between the culverts. This would form an obstruction to flow into both pipes affected. To avoid this condition, pipes should be placed with their centers at least 1½ diameters apart.

It should be noted that the satisfactory working of flap gates requires that they be placed vertically—that is, if the pipe slopes downward where the gate is attached, the shutter will not close tightly, and if it slopes upward it will not open until more water has accumulated behind it than would otherwise be necessary. If any deviation is made from vertical, it should be with the bottom of the seating surface slightly forward from the top surface.

Protection of Gates

Pipes with flap gates should be placed as deeply as possible in the levees. If it is possible to place them so that at low tide level the gates are entirely submerged, it should be done. Keeping the gates submerged greatly protects them from weathering and also keeps the trash that floats on the surface of the water from entering. Sometimes this cannot be done on account of silt conditions, but in all cases the gates should be low enough so that at extremely low tide the water is not lower than the bottom of the pipe.

By placing the gates deeply in the water, as mentioned above, they are protected from the greater part of the floating debris and wave action. Additional protection, such as anchored floating logs, or screens should be provided in front of drainage gates to guard against floating debris and to protect them from being broken by heavy pieces of timber, or barges floating against them.

When installing gates, one must be very careful to see that the outlet ends are placed so as not to become silted up due to their discharging in very shallow water

Fig. 362. Flap gate (Model 102) on 42-in. culvert through a dike at Sackville, New Brunswick. The gate, propped open for inspection, is protected by a recessed metal headwall.

or into a channel where there is not enough velocity to carry off the silt. Whenever possible, it is best to install the gates and pipes with their outlets discharging in ditches or deep canals. By keeping the levees well out near the deep water or so that at low tide there is not an accumulation of mud at the outlet side of the gates, the gates can be kept always free from silt. When the dredger is borrowing earth to build levees, it should always take from the outside or tidal side rather than from the side to be drained.

When the gates are subject to wave action, such as when they discharge into a wide bay or into the ocean, a pile or concrete seawall should be built in front of the gate and high enough to protect it from wave action and floating debris.

Protection may also be given to a gate by recessing it in a timber and metal headwall as shown in Fig. 362.

Where Headwall Is Necessary

Headwalls are necessary where the earth is very soft and likely to wash, and where there is considerable current in the canal where the pipe and gate are installed. When headwalls are to be used they should not be installed at the time the gate is put in, but rather about six months later. The levee in the meantime will have been given a chance to shrink and the pipes to settle and become more firmly lodged.

Headwalls in soft material should not be made of concrete unless the headwall is supported on a well designed pile foundation. The reason is that as the weight of the concrete headwall will tend to bear on the pipe near the gate due to the slow sinking of the soft material surrounding such an installation, preventing the gate from seating properly. A steel sheeting or concrete headwall extending halfway up on the pipe is recommended where needed.

Fig. 363 shows a type of end protection which can be used when the ground is a little softer than that described above—not dense enough to support the

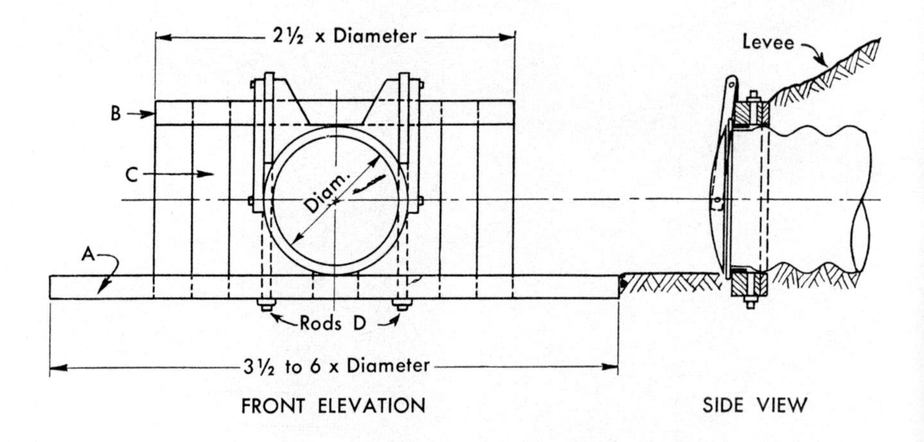

Fig. 363. Timber headwall for soft ground.

drainage structure without the aid of some sort of headwall. A long sill "A" is placed directly under the ring of the gate behind the flange. Another piece similar to "A" is used as a header at the top as "B". These two timbers are tied together and clamped to the gate by means of threaded rods and nuts "D". Then the whole structure is planked at the back by means of planks "C". This type of headwall forms a good protection to the levee on both sides of the gate, and also a certain amount of buoyancy to help support the added weight of the cast iron ring and cover. It is good practice to install such a headwall with all gates and corrugated pipes, disregarding the conditions of the soil. A headwall of this kind is far better than concrete because of its light weight and its tendency to buoy up the gate rather than to pull it down.

A modified form of this headwall for soft, mushy soils is shown in Fig. 364.

Multiple Pipes

Regarding the use of a few large diameter structures rather than two or more smaller ones, it should be remembered that in places where the soil is exceedingly wet and like quicksand, a concentration of a large volume of water in one spot is likely to cause undercutting beneath the gate structure. Rather than concentrate this water in one place, it would be better to spread it along the length of the levee and discharge it at intervals of say from 50 to 100 ft, through smaller structures. Where the head of water is great enough to fill a large diameter pipe (48 to 96 in.), it would be great enough to undermine the soft strata directly under the gate structures.

Rather than concentrate a large volume of water of this kind against one gate and attempt to have that gate function under a head high enough to fill the pipe in cases where the ground is very soft, it may be better to install several gates of somewhat larger diameter than would be necessary for capacity alone, and by so doing cut down the velocity of the discharging water.

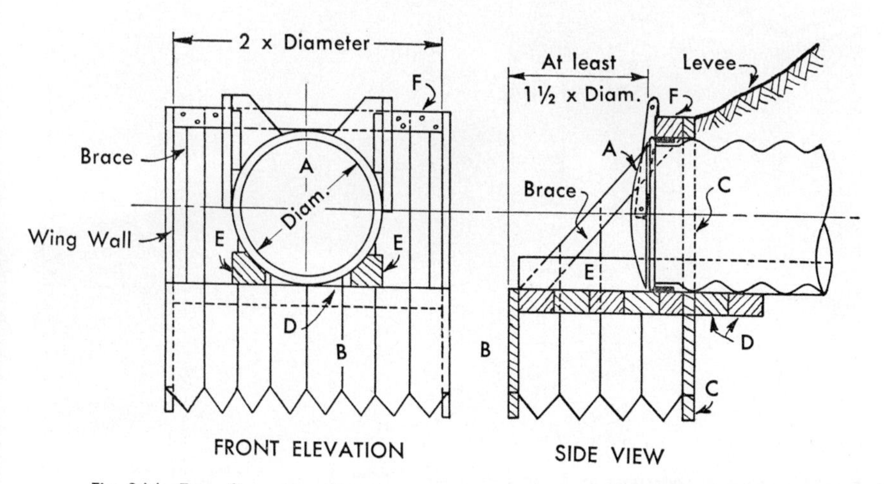

Fig. 364. For soft, mushy soils, greater support is provided by this timber headwall.

Fig. 365. Vehicular underpass of Armco liner plate tunneled through a 35-ft rock fill in southern Kentucky.

SECTION ELEVEN

TABLES

PART ONE

Conversion Tables

TABLE 65-1 LENGTH

Ordinary Units

1 foot = 12 inches
1 yard = 3 feet
1 mile = 5280 feet
1 nautical mi. = 1.1516 statute mi.
1° of latitude at the equator = 69.16 statute mi.
= 60 nautical mi.
1 acre = 208.71 ft. on one side of square

Old Surveyors' Units

1 link = 7.92 inches
1 rod = 25 links = 16.5 ft.
1 chain = 100 links = 66 ft.
1 mile = 320 rods = 8 furlongs

Metric Units

10 millimeters (mm.) = 1 centimeter (cm.)
10 cm. = 1 decimeter (dm.)
10 dm. = 1 meter (m.)
1000 m. = 1 kilometer (about ⅝ mi.) (km.)

Equivalents

1 inch = 2.5400 centimeters
1 foot = 0.3048 meters
1 statute mi. = 1.60935 kilometers
1 nautical mi. = 1.853 kilometers
1 centimeter = 0.39370 inches
1 meter = 3.28 feet
1 kilometer = 3280.83 feet = 0.62137 mile

TABLE 65-2 AREA

Ordinary Units

1 square foot	=144 square inches
1 square yard	=9 sq. ft.
	=1296 sq. in.
1 acre	=43,560 sq. ft.
	=4840 sq. yds.
1 sq. mile	=27,878,400 sq. ft.
	=3,097,600 sq. yds.
	=640 acres
	=1 section of land (U.S.)

Equivalents

1 square centimeter	=0.155 square inch
1 square meter	=10.76 square feet
	=1.196 square yards
1 hectare	=2.47 acres
1 square kilometer	=0.386 square mile
1 square inch	=6.45 square centimeters
1 square foot	=0.0929 square meter
1 square yard	=0.836 square meter
1 acre	=0.405 hectare
1 square mile	=2.59 square kilometers

TABLE 65-3 VOLUME AND CAPACITY

Ordinary Units

1 cu. ft. of water at 39.1° F.	=62.425 lb.
1 United States gallon	=231 cu. in.
1 imperial gallon	=277.274 cu. in.
1 cubic inch of water	=0.004329 U. S. gallon
	=0.003607 imperial gallon
	=0.036126 pound
1 cubic foot of water	=1728 cu. in.
	=7.480519 U. S. gallons
	=6.232103 imperial gallons
	=62.4250 pounds
1 cubic yard	=27 cu. ft. =46,656 cu. in.
1 pint	=4 gills
1 quart	=2 pints
1 gallon	=4 quarts
1 U. S. gallon	=231 cu. in.
	=0.133681 cu. ft.
	=0.083311 imperial gallon
	=8.345 lb.
1 barrel	=31.5 gallons =4.21 cu. ft.
1 U. S. bushel	=1.2445 cu. ft.
1 fluid ounce	=1.8047 cu. in.
1 acre foot	=43,560 cu. ft.
	=1,613.3 cu. yds.
1 acre inch	=3,630 cu. ft.

Ordinary Units (Continued)

1 million U. S. gallons = 133,681 cu. ft.
= 3.0689 acre-ft.
1 ft. depth on 1 sq. mi. = 27,878,400 cu. ft.
= 640 acre-ft.
1 inch depth on 1 sq. mi. = 2,323,200 cu. ft.
= 53.333 acre-ft.

Metric Units (liquid capacity)

1 centiliter (cl.) = 10 milliliters (ml.)
1 deciliter (dl.) = 10 centiliters
1 liter (l.) = 10 deciliters (about 1 quart)
1 dekaliter (dkl.) = 10 liters
1 hectoliter (hl.) = 10 dekaliters
1 kiloliter = 10 hectoliters

Equivalents

1 cu. in. = 16.387 cu. cm.
1 cu. ft. = 0.0283 cu. m.
1 cu. yd. = 0.765 cu. m.
1 cu. cm. = 0.0610 cu. in.
1 cu. m. = 35.3 cu. ft.
= 1.308 cu. yds.
1 liter = 61.023378 cu. in.
= 0.035314 cu. ft.
= 0.264170 U. S. liquid gallon
= 0.2201 imperial gallon
1 milliliter = 0.0338 liquid ounce
1 U. S. liquid ounce = 29.57 milliliters
1 U. S. liquid quart = 0.946 liter
1 U. S. liquid gallon = 3.785 liters

TABLE 65-4 WEIGHT

Ordinary Units

1 pound = 16 ounces (avoirdupois)
1 ton = 2000 lb.
1 long ton = 2240 lb.
1 lb. of water (39.1° F.) = 27.681217 cu. in.
= 0.016019 cu. ft.
= 0.119832 U. S. gallon
= 0.099833 imperial gallon
= 0.453617 liter

Metric Units

1 centigram (cg.) = 10 milligrams (mg.)
1 decigram (dg.) = 10 centigrams
1 gram (g.) = 10 decigrams (about 15 grains)
1 dekagram (dkg.) = 10 grams
1 hectogram (hg.) = 10 dekagrams
1 kilogram (kg.) = 10 hectograms
1 metric ton = 1000 kilograms

TABLE 65-4 WEIGHT (Continued)

Equivalents

1 gram	=15.43 grains
	=0.0353 avoirdupois ounce
1 kilogram	= 2.205 avoirdupois pounds
1 metric ton	= 0.984 gross or long ton
	= 1.102 net or short tons
1 avoirdupois ounce	=28.35 grams
1 avoirdupois pound	= 0.4536 kilogram

TABLE 65-5 PRESSURE

Comparison of Heads of Water in Feet with Pressures in Various Units

One foot of water at 39.1° F. =62.425 pounds per square foot
= 0.4335 pounds per square inch
= 0.0295 atmosphere
= 0.8826 inch of mercury at 30° F.
=773.3 feet of air at 32° F. and atmospheric pressure
One pound on the square foot, at 39.1° F. =0.01602 foot of water
One pound on the square inch, at 39.1° F. =2.307 feet of water
One atmosphere of 29.922 inches of mercury=33.9 feet of water
One inch of mercury at 32° F. =1.133 feet of water
One foot of air at 32° F. and 1 atmosphere=0.001293 foot of water
One foot of average sea water=1.026 feet of pure water
One foot of water at 62° F. =62.355 pounds per square foot
=0.43302 pound per square inch
One inch of water at 62° F. =0.5774 ounce=0.036085 pound per square inch
One pound of water on the square inch at 62° F. =2.3094 feet of water
One ounce of water on the square inch at 62° F. =1.732 inches of water
1 atmosphere at sea level (32° F.) =14.697 lbs. per sq. in.
=29.921 in. of mercury
1 inch of mercury (32° F.) =0.49119 lb. per sq. in.

TABLE 65-6 FLOWING WATER

C. F. S. =cubic feet per second, or second feet
G. P. M. =gallons per minute
1 C. F. S. =60 cu. ft. per min.
=86,400 cu. ft. per 24 hrs.
=448.83 U. S. gals. per min.
=646,317 U. S. gals. per 24 hrs.
=1.9835 acre-foot per 24 hrs. (usually taken as 2)
=1 acre-inch per hour (approximate)
=.028317 cu. meters per second
=2446.59 cu. meters per day
=50 Miners inches, Idaho, Kan., Neb., New Mex., N. Dak., S. Dak.

1 C. F. S. = 40 Miners inches, Ariz., Calif., Mont., and Oregon
= 38.4 Miners inches, Colorado
= 36 Miners inches, British Columbia
1 inch depth per hour = 645.33 C. F. S. per sq. mi.
1 inch depth per day = 26.889 C. F. S. per sq. mi.
1 acre-inch per hour = 1.0083 C. F. S. (usually taken as unity)
1 U. S. G. P. M. = 1440 U. S. gals. per 24 hrs.
= 0.00442 acre-feet per 24 hrs.
= 0.0891 Miners inches, Ariz., Calif.
1 million U. S. gal. per day = 1.5472 C. F. S.
= 3.07 acre-feet
= 2.629 cu. meters per min.

TABLE 65-7 MISCELLANEOUS

Temperature

Freezing point of water = 32° Fahrenheit
= 0° Centigrade
Boiling point of water (at normal air pressure) = 212° Fahrenheit
= 100° Centigrade
1 degree Fahrenheit = 0.5556 degree (Centigrade)
1 degree Centigrade = 1.8 degrees Fahrenheit

Circular Measure

1 minute (′) = 60 seconds (″)
1 degree (°) = 60 minutes
1 right angle = 90 degrees
1 circumference = 360 degrees

Time Measure

1 minute = 60 seconds
1 hour = 60 minutes = 3600 seconds
1 day = 24 hours = 1440 minutes
1 week = 7 days
1 year = 365 days, 5 hr., 48 min., 48 sec.

Ice and Snow

(From Clark.) 1 cubic foot of ice at 32° F. weighs 57.50 pounds; 1 pound of ice at 32° F. has a volume of 0.0174 cubic foot = 30.067 cubic inches.

Relative volume of ice to water at 32° F., 1.0855, the expansion in passing into the solid state being 8.55 per cent. Specific gravity of ice = 0.922, water at 62° F. being 1.

At high pressures the melting-point of ice is lower than 32° F., being at the rate of 0.0133° F. for each additional atmosphere of pressure.

Specific heat of ice is 0.504, that of water being 1.

1 cubic foot of fresh snow, according to humidity of atmosphere, weighs 5 pounds to 12 pounds. 1 cubic foot of snow moistened and compacted by rain weighs 15 pounds to 50 pounds (Trautwine).

TABLE 65-8 CONVERSION OF MINUTES INTO DECIMALS OF A DEGREE

0′30″	.00833	20′30″	.34167	40′30″	.67500
1 00	.01667	21 00	.35000	41 00	.68333
30	.02500	30	.35833	30	.69167
2 00	.03333	22 00	.36667	42 00	.70000
30	.04167	30	.37500	30	.70833
3 00	.05000	23 00	.38333	43 00	.71667
30	.05833	30	.39167	30	.72500
4 00	.06667	24 00	.40000	44 00	.73333
30	.07500	30	.40833	30	.74167
5 00	.08333	25 00	.41667	45 00	.75000
30	.09167	30	.42500	30	.75833
6 00	.10000	26 00	.43333	46 00	.76667
30	.10833	30	.44167	30	.77500
7 00	.11667	27 00	.45000	47 00	.78333
30	.12500	30	.45833	30	.79167
8 00	.13333	28 00	.46667	48 00	.80000
30	.14167	30	.47500	30	.80833
9 00	.15000	29 00	.48333	49 00	.81667
30	.15833	30	.49167	30	.82500
10 00	.16667	30 00	.50000	50 00	.83333
10 30	.17500	30 30	.50833	50 30	.84167
11 00	.18333	31 00	.51667	51 00	.85000
30	.19167	30	.52500	30	.85833
12 00	.20000	32 00	.53333	52 00	.86667
30	.20833	30	.54167	30	.87500
13 00	.21667	33 00	.55000	53 00	.88333
30	.22500	30	.55833	30	.89167
14 00	.23333	34 00	.56667	54 00	.90000
30	.24167	30	.57500	30	.90833
15 00	.25000	35 00	.58333	55 00	.91667
30	.25833	30	.59167	30	.92500
16 00	.26667	36 00	.60000	56 00	.93333
30	.27500	30	.60833	30	.94167
17 00	.28333	37 00	.61667	57 00	.95000
30	.29167	30	.62500	30	.95833
18 00	.30000	38 00	.63333	58 00	.96667
30	.30833	30	.64167	30	.97500
19 00	.31667	39 00	.65000	59 00	.98333
30	.32500	30	.65833	30	.99167
20 00	.33333	40 00	.66667	60 00	1.00000

TABLE 65-9 INCHES AND FRACTIONS EXPRESSED IN DECIMALS OF A FOOT

Inches	Fractions of Inches							
	0	1/8	1/4	3/8	1/2	5/8	3/4	7/8
0	.0000	.0104	.0208	.0313	.0417	.0521	.0625	.0729
1	.0833	.0937	.1042	.1146	.1250	.1354	.1458	.1562
2	.1667	.1771	.1875	.1979	.2083	.2188	.2292	.2396
3	.2500	.2604	.2708	.2813	.2917	.3021	.3125	.3229
4	.3333	.3437	.3542	.3646	.3750	.3854	.3958	.4062
5	.4167	.4271	.4375	.4479	.4583	.4688	.4792	.4896
6	.5000	.5104	.5208	.5313	.5417	.5521	.5625	.5729
7	.5833	.5937	.6042	.6146	.6250	.6354	.6458	.6562
8	.6667	.6771	.6875	.6979	.7083	.7188	.7292	.7396
9	.7500	.7604	.7708	.7813	.7917	.8021	.8125	.8229
10	.8333	.8437	.8542	.8646	.8750	.8854	.8958	.9062
11	.9167	.9271	.9375	.9479	.9583	.9688	.9792	.9896
12	1.0000	....	....	....	....	....	....	....

From King's "Handbook of Hydraulics."

TABLE 65-10 SLOPE IN INCHES REDUCED TO FEET
(For Use with Formulas)

In. per 100 Ft	*Ft per 100 Ft*	*Ft per Mile*	*In. per 100 Ft*	*Ft per 100 Ft*	*Ft per Mile*
1/4	.0208	1.098	1/4	.5208	27.498
1/2	.0417	2.202	1/2	.5417	28.602
3/4	.0625	3.300	3/4	.5625	29.700
1	.0833	4.398	7	.5833	30.798
1/4	.1042	5.502	1/4	.6042	31.902
1/2	.1250	6.600	1/2	.6250	33.000
3/4	.1458	7.698	3/4	.6458	34.098
2	.1667	8.802	8	.6667	35.202
1/4	.1875	9.900	1/4	.6875	36.300
1/2	.2083	10.998	1/2	.7083	37.398
3/4	.2292	12.102	3/4	.7292	38.502
3	.2500	13.200	9	.7500	39.600
1/4	.2708	14.298	1/4	.7708	40.698
1/2	.2917	15.402	1/2	.7917	41.802
3/4	.3125	16.500	3/4	.8125	42.900
4	.3333	17.598	10	.8333	43.998
1/4	.3542	18.702	1/4	.8542	45.102
1/2	.3750	19.800	1/2	.8750	46.200
3/4	.3958	20.898	3/4	.8958	47.298
5	.4167	22.002	11	.9167	48.402
1/4	.4375	23.100	1/4	.9375	49.500
1/2	.4583	24.198	1/2	.9583	50.598
3/4	.4792	25.302	3/4	.9792	51.702
6	.5000	26.400	12	1.0000	52.800

PART TWO

General Tables

TABLE 65-11 AREAS OF PLANE FIGURES*

Triangle:	Base × ½ perpendicular height
	$\sqrt{s(s-a)\quad(s-b)\quad(s-c)}$
	$s = \frac{1}{2}$ sum of the three sides a, b and c
Trapezium:	Sum of areas of the two triangles
Trapezoid:	½ sum of parallel sides × perpendicular height
Parallelogram:	Base × perpendicular height
Regular Polygon:	½ sum of sides × inside radius
Circle:	$\pi r^2 = 0.78540 \times \text{dia.}^2 = 0.07958 \times \text{circumference}^2$
Sector of Circle:	$\frac{\pi r^2 A°}{360} = 0.0087266\ r^2 A° = \text{arc} \times \frac{1}{2}\ \text{radius}$
Segment of Circle:	$\frac{r^2}{2}\left(\frac{\pi A°}{180} - \sin A°\right)$
Circle of same area as square:	diameter = side × 1.12838
Square of same area as circle:	side = diameter × 0.88623
Ellipse:	Long diameter × short diameter × 0.78540
Parabola:	Base × ⅔ perpendicular height

Irregular Plane Surface:

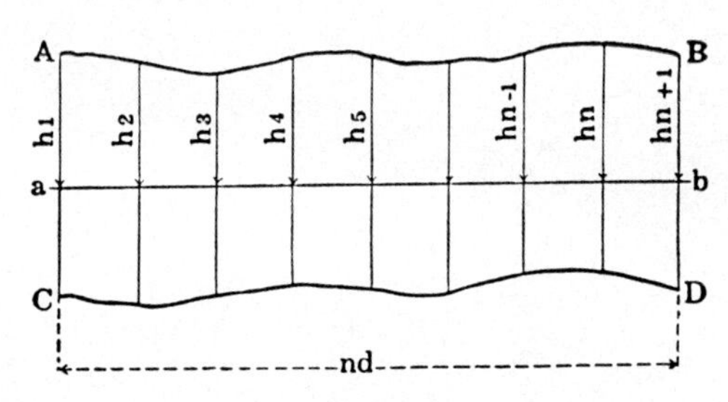

Divide any plane surface A, B, C, D, along a line a-b into an even number, n, of parallel and sufficiently small strips, d, whose ordinates are h_1, h_2, h_3, h_4, h_5 .... h_{n-1}, h_n, h_{n+1}, and considering contours between three ordinates as parabolic curves, then for section $ABCD$,

$$\text{Area} = \frac{d}{3}\left[\ h_1 + h_{n+1} + 4(h_2 + h_4 + h_6 \ldots + h_n) + 2(h_3 + h_5 + h_7 \ldots + h_{n-1})\ \right]$$

or, approximately, Area = Sum of ordinates × width, d.

*From Carnegie's "Pocket Companion."

TABLE 65-12 NATURAL TRIGONOMETRIC FUNCTIONS

Angle	*Sin.*	*Cosec.*	*Tan.*	*Cotan.*	*Sec.*	*Cos.*	
0°	0.000	......	0.000	......	1.000	1.000	90°
1°	0.017	57.30	0.017	57.29	1.000	1.000	89°
2°	0.035	28.65	0.035	28.64	1.001	0.999	88°
3°	0.052	19.11	0.052	19.08	1.001	0.999	87°
4°	0.070	14.34	0.070	14.30	1.002	0.998	86°
5°	0.087	11.47	0.087	11.43	1.004	0.996	85°
6°	0.105	9.567	0.105	9.514	1.006	0.995	84°
7°	0.122	8.206	0.123	8.144	1.008	0.993	83°
8°	0.139	7.185	0.141	7.115	1.010	0.990	82°
9°	0.156	6.392	0.158	6.314	1.012	0.988	81°
10°	0.174	5.759	0.176	5.671	1.015	0.985	80°
11°	0.191	5.241	0.194	5.145	1.019	0.982	79°
12°	0.208	4.810	0.213	4.705	1.022	0.978	78°
13°	0.225	4.445	0.231	4.331	1.026	0.974	77°
14°	0.242	4.134	0.249	4.011	1.031	0.970	76°
15°	0.259	3.864	0.268	3.732	1.035	0.966	75°
16°	0.276	3.628	0.287	3.487	1.040	0.961	74°
17°	0.292	3.420	0.306	3.271	1.046	0.956	73°
18°	0.309	3.236	0.325	3.078	1.051	0.951	72°
19°	0.326	3.072	0.344	2.904	1.058	0.946	71°
20°	0.342	2.924	0.364	2.747	1.064	0.940	70°
21°	0.358	2.790	0.384	2.605	1.071	0.934	69°
22°	0.375	2.669	0.404	2.475	1.079	0.927	68°
23°	0.391	2.559	0.424	2.356	1.086	0.921	67°
24°	0.407	2.459	0.445	2.246	1.095	0.914	66°
25°	0.423	2.366	0.466	2.145	1.103	0.906	65°
26°	0.438	2.281	0.488	2.050	1.113	0.899	64°
27°	0.454	2.203	0.510	1.963	1.122	0.891	63°
28°	0.469	2.130	0.532	1.881	1.133	0.883	62°
29°	0.485	2.063	0.554	1.804	1.143	0.875	61°
30°	0.500	2.000	0.577	1.732	1.155	0.866	60°
31°	0.515	1.942	0.601	1.664	1.167	0.857	59°
32°	0.530	1.887	0.625	1.600	1.179	0.848	58°
33°	0.545	1.836	0.649	1.540	1.192	0.839	57°
34°	0.559	1.788	0.675	1.483	1.206	0.829	56°
35°	0.574	1.743	0.700	1.428	1.221	0.819	55°
36°	0.588	1.701	0.727	1.376	1.236	0.809	54°
37°	0.602	1.662	0.754	1.327	1.252	0.799	53°
38°	0.616	1.624	0.781	1.280	1.269	0.788	52°
39°	0.629	1.589	0.810	1.235	1.287	0.777	51°
40°	0.643	1.556	0.839	1.192	1.305	0.766	50°
41°	0.656	1.524	0.869	1.150	1.325	0.755	49°
42°	0.669	1.494	0.900	1.111	1.346	0.743	48°
43°	0.682	1.466	0.933	1.072	1.367	0.731	47°
44°	0.695	1.440	0.966	1.036	1.390	0.719	46°
45°	0.707	1.414	1.000	1.000	1.414	0.707	45°
	Cos.	*Sec.*	*Cotan.*	*Tan.*	*Cosec.*	*Sin.*	*Angle*

TABLE 65-13 TRIGONOMETRIC FORMULAS*

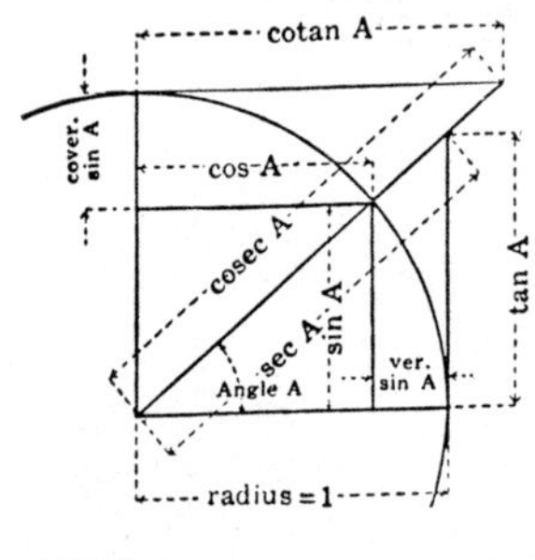

Radius, $1 = \sin^2 A + \cos^2 A$

$= \sin A \operatorname{cosec} A = \cos A \sec A = \tan A \cot A$

Sine $\quad A = \dfrac{\cos A}{\cot A} = \dfrac{1}{\operatorname{cosec} A} = \cos A \tan A = \sqrt{1-\cos^2 A}$

Cosine $\quad A = \dfrac{\sin A}{\tan A} = \dfrac{1}{\sec A} = \sin A \cot A = \sqrt{1-\sin^2 A}$

Tangent $\quad A = \dfrac{\sin A}{\cos A} = \dfrac{1}{\cot A} = \sin A \sec A$

Cotangent $\quad A = \dfrac{\cos A}{\sin A} = \dfrac{1}{\tan A} = \cos A \operatorname{cosec} A$

Secant $\quad A = \dfrac{\tan A}{\sin A} = \dfrac{1}{\cos A}$

Cosecant $\quad A = \dfrac{\cot A}{\cos A} = \dfrac{1}{\sin A}$

*From Carnegie's "Pocket Companion."

TABLE 65-14 DECIMALS OF AN INCH FOR EACH 1/64TH

32nds	*64ths*	*Decimal*	*Fraction*	*32nds*	*64ths*	*Decimal*	*Fraction*
	1	.015625			33	.515625	
1	2	.03125		17	34	.53125	
	3	.046875			35	.546875	
2	4	.0625	1/16	18	36	.5625	9/16
	5	.078125			37	.578125	
3	6	.09375		19	38	.59375	
	7	.109375			39	.609375	
4	8	.125	1/8	20	40	.625	5/8
	9	.140625			41	.640625	
5	10	.15625		21	42	.65625	
	11	.171875			43	.671875	
6	12	.1875	3/16	22	44	.6875	11/16
	13	.203125			45	.703125	
7	14	.21875		23	46	.71875	
	15	.234375			47	.734375	
8	16	.25	1/4	24	48	.75	3/4
	17	.265625			49	.765625	
9	18	.28125		25	50	.78125	
	19	.296875			51	.796875	
10	20	.3125	5/16	26	52	.8125	13/16
	21	.328125			53	.828125	
11	22	.34375		27	54	.84375	
	23	.359375			55	.859375	
12	24	.375	3/8	28	56	.875	7/8
	25	.390625			57	.890625	
13	26	.40625		29	58	.90625	
	27	.421875			59	.921875	
14	28	.4375	7/16	30	60	.9375	15/16
	29	.453125			61	.953125	
15	30	.46875		31	62	.96875	
	31	.484375			63	.984375	
16	32	.5	1/2	32	64	1.000000	

TABLE 65-15 PROPERTIES OF THE CIRCLE*

Circumference of Circle of Dia. $1 = \pi = 3.14159265$

Circumference of Circle $= 2\,\pi\,r$

Dia. of Circle = Circumference $\times$ 0.31831

Diameter of Circle of equal periphery as square	= side	$\times$ 1.27324
Side of Square of equal periphery as circle	= diameter	$\times$ 0.78540
Diameter of Circle circumscribed about square	= side	$\times$ 1.41421
Side of Square inscribed in Circle	= diameter	$\times$ 0.70711

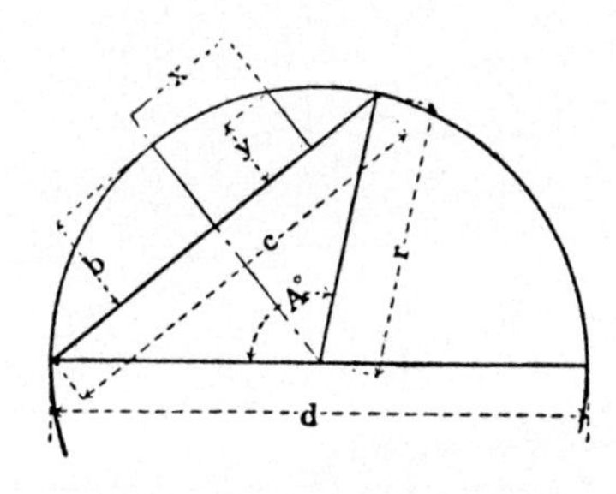

Arc, $a = \dfrac{\pi\, r\, A^\circ}{180} = 0.017453\, r\, A^\circ$

Angle, $A = \dfrac{180^\circ\, a}{\pi\, r} = 57.29578\, \dfrac{a}{r}$

Radius, $r = \dfrac{4\,b^2 + c^2}{8\,b}$ Diameter, $d = \dfrac{4\,b^2 + c^2}{4\,b}$

Chord, $c = 2\sqrt{2\,b\,r - b^2} = 2\,r\,\sin\dfrac{A^\circ}{2}$

Rise, $b = r - \tfrac{1}{2}\sqrt{4\,r^2 - c^2} = \dfrac{c}{2}\tan\dfrac{A^\circ}{4} = 2\,r\,\sin^2\dfrac{A}{4}$

Rise, $b = r + y - \sqrt{r^2 - x^2}$ $y = b - r + \sqrt{r^2 - x^2}$ $x = \sqrt{r^2 - (r + y - b)^2}$

$\pi = 3.14159265$, $\log = 0.4971499$

$\dfrac{1}{\pi} = 0.3183099$, $\log = \bar{1}.5028501$

$\pi^2 = 9.8696044$, $\log = 0.9942997$

$\dfrac{1}{\pi^2} = 0.1013212$, $\log = \bar{1}.0057003$

$\sqrt{\pi} = 1.7724539$, $\log = 0.2485749$

$\sqrt{\dfrac{1}{\pi}} = 0.5641896$, $\log = 1.7514251$

$\dfrac{\pi}{180} = 0.0174533$, $\log = \bar{2}.2418774$

$\dfrac{180}{\pi} = 57.2957795$, $\log = 1.7581226$

*From Carnegie's "Pocket Companion."

TABLE 65-16 AREAS OF CIRCLES

Diameter in Inches	Area: Square Inches	Area: Square Feet	Diameter in. Inches	Area: Square Inches	Area: Square Feet	Diameter in. Inches	Area: Square Inches	Area: Square Feet
1.0	0.7854	.005454	4.0	12.5664	.087266	7.0	38.4845	.267254
.1	0.9503	.006599	.1	13.2025	.091684	.1	39.5919	.274944
.2	1.1310	.007854	.2	13.8544	.096211	.2	40.7150	.282743
.25	1.2272	.008522	.25	14.1863	.098516	.25	41.2825	.286684
.3	1.3273	.009218	.3	14.5220	.100847	.3	41.8539	.290652
.4	1.5394	.010690	.4	15.2053	.105592	.4	43.0084	.298669
.5	1.7671	.012272	.5	15.9043	.110446	.5	44.1786	.306796
.6	2.0106	.013963	.6	16.6190	.115410	.6	45.3646	.315032
.7	2.2698	.015763	.7	17.3494	.120482	.7	46.5663	.323377
.75	2.4053	.016703	.75	17.7205	.123059	.75	47.1730	.327590
.8	2.5447	.017671	.8	18.0956	.125664	.8	47.7836	.331831
.9	2.8353	.019689	.9	18.8574	.130954	.9	49.0167	.340394
2.0	3.1416	.021816	5.0	19.6350	.136354	8.0	50.2655	.349066
.1	3.4636	.024053	.1	20.4282	.141863	.1	51.5300	.357847
.2	3.8013	.026398	.2	21.2372	.147480	.2	52.8102	.366737
.25	3.9761	.027612	.25	21.6475	.150330	.25	53.4562	.371223
.3	4.1548	.028852	.3	22.0618	.153207	.3	54.1061	.375736
.4	4.5239	.031416	.4	22.9022	.159043	.4	55.4177	.384845
.5	4.9087	.034088	.5	23.7583	.164988	.5	56.7450	.394063
.6	5.3093	.036870	.6	24.6301	.171042	.6	58.0880	.403389
.7	5.7256	.039760	.7	25.5176	.177205	.7	59.4468	.412825
.75	5.9396	.041247	.75	25.9672	.180328	.75	60.1320	.417584
.8	6.1575	.042760	.8	26.4208	.183477	.8	60.8212	.422370
.9	6.6052	.045869	.9	27.3397	.189859	.9	62.2114	.432024
3.0	7.0686	.049087	6.0	28.2743	.196350	9.0	63.6173	.441786
.1	7.5477	.052414	.1	29.2247	.202949	.1	65.0388	.451658
.2	8.0425	.055851	.2	30.1907	.209658	.2	66.4761	.461640
.25	8.2958	.057609	.25	30.6796	.213053	.25	67.2006	.466671
.3	8.5530	.059396	.3	31.1725	.216475	.3	67.9291	.471730
.4	9.0792	.063050	.4	32.1699	.223402	.4	69.3978	.481929
.5	9.6211	.066813	.5	33.1831	.230438	.5	70.8822	.492237
.6	10.1788	.070686	.6	34.2119	.237583	.6	72.3823	.502654
.7	10.7521	.074667	.7	35.2565	.244837	.7	73.8981	.513181
.75	11.0447	.076699	.75	35.7847	.248505	.75	74.6619	.518486
.8	11.3411	.078758	.8	36.3168	.252200	.8	75.4296	.523817
.9	11.9459	.082958	.9	37.3928	.259672	.9	76.9769	.534561

The above table may be used for finding the areas of circles whose diameters are not within the limits of the table. Since the areas vary as the squares of their diameters, the given diameter may be divided (or multiplied) by 10, and the area found from the table under the resulting diameter corrected by moving the decimal point two places to the right (or left). Thus to find the area of a 22-inch circle:

From table, area of 2.2-inch circle—3.8013 sq. in.—.026398 sq. ft.

Therefore area of 22-inch circle—380.13 sq. in.—2.64 sq. ft.

Again, to find the area of a 0.75-inch circle:

From table, area of 7.5-inch circle—44.1786 sq. in.—0.306796 sq. ft.

Therefore area of 0.75-inch circle—0.4418 sq. in.—0.00307 sq. ft.

It will also be apparent that the *first two* columns in the table may be used for any unit of measure.

TABLE 65-17 FUNCTIONS OF NUMBERS 1 TO 99

No.	Square	Cube	Square Root	Cubic Root	Logarithm	1000 × Reciprocal	No. = Diameter Circum.	No. = Diameter Area
1	1	1	1.0000	1.0000	0.00000	1000.000	3.142	0.7854
2	4	8	1.4142	1.2599	0.30103	500.000	6.283	3.1416
3	9	27	1.7321	1.4422	0.47712	333.333	9.425	7.0686
4	16	64	2.0000	1.5874	0.60206	250.000	12.566	12.5664
5	25	125	2.2361	1.7100	0.69897	200.000	15.708	19.6350
6	36	216	2.4495	1.8171	0.77815	166.667	18.850	28.2743
7	49	343	2.6458	1.9129	0.84510	142.857	21.991	38.4845
8	64	512	2.8284	2.0000	0.90309	125.000	25.133	50.2655
9	81	729	3.0000	2.0801	0.95424	111.111	28.274	63.6173
10	100	1000	3.1623	2.1544	1.00000	100.000	31.416	78.5398
11	121	1331	3.3166	2.2240	1.04139	90.9091	34.558	95.0332
12	144	1728	3.4641	2.2894	1.07918	83.3333	37.699	113.097
13	169	2197	3.6056	2.3513	1.11394	76.9231	40.841	132.732
14	196	2744	3.7417	2.4101	1.14613	71.4286	43.982	153.938
15	225	3375	3.8730	2.4662	1.17609	66.6667	47.124	176.715
16	256	4096	4.0000	2.5198	1.20412	62.5000	50.265	201.062
17	289	4913	4.1231	2.5713	1.23045	58.8235	53.407	226.980
18	324	5832	4.2426	2.6207	1.25527	55.5556	56.549	254.469
19	361	6859	4.3589	2.6684	1.27875	52.6316	59.690	283.529
20	400	8000	4.4721	2.7144	1.30103	50.0000	62.832	314.159
21	441	9261	4.5826	2.7589	1.32222	47.6190	65.973	346.361
22	484	10648	4.6904	2.8020	1.34242	45.4545	69.115	380.133
23	529	12167	4.7958	2.8439	1.36173	43.4783	72.257	415.476
24	576	13824	4.8990	2.8845	1.38021	41.6667	75.398	452.389
25	625	15625	5.0000	2.9240	1.39794	40.0000	78.540	490.874
26	676	17576	5.0990	2.9625	1.41497	38.4615	81.681	530.929
27	729	19683	5.1962	3.0000	1.43136	37.0370	84.823	572.555
28	784	21952	5.2915	3.0366	1.44716	35.7143	87.965	615.752
29	841	24389	5.3852	3.0723	1.46240	34.4828	91.106	660.520
30	900	27000	5.4772	3.1072	1.47712	33.3333	94.248	706.858
31	961	29791	5.5678	3.1414	1.49136	32.2581	97.389	754.768
32	1024	32768	5.6569	3.1748	1.50515	31.2500	100.531	804.248
33	1089	35937	5.7446	3.2075	1.51851	30.3030	103.673	855.299
34	1156	39304	5.8310	3.2396	1.53148	29.4118	106.814	907.920
35	1225	42875	5.9161	3.2711	1.54407	28.5714	109.956	962.113
36	1296	46656	6.0000	3.3019	1.55630	27.7778	113.097	1017.88
37	1369	50653	6.0828	3.3322	1.56820	27.0270	116.239	1075.21
38	1444	54872	6.1644	3.3620	1.57978	26.3158	119.381	1134.11
39	1521	59319	6.2450	3.3912	1.59106	25.6410	122.522	1194.59
40	1600	64000	6.3246	3.4200	1.60206	25.0000	125.66	1256.64
41	1681	68921	6.4031	3.4482	1.61278	24.3902	128.81	1320.25
42	1764	74088	6.4807	3.4760	1.62325	23.8095	131.95	1385.44
43	1849	79507	6.5574	3.5034	1.63347	23.2558	135.09	1452.20
44	1936	85184	6.6332	3.5303	1.64345	22.7273	138.23	1520.53
45	2025	91125	6.7082	3.5569	1.65321	22.2222	141.37	1590.43
46	2116	97336	6.7823	3.5830	1.66276	21.7391	144.51	1661.90
47	2209	103823	6.8557	3.6088	1.67210	21.2766	147.65	1734.94
48	2304	110592	6.9282	3.6342	1.68124	20.8333	150.80	1809.56
49	2401	117649	7.0000	3.6593	1.69020	20.4082	153.94	1885.74

From Carnegie's "Pocket Companion."

[Continued on next page]

TABLE 65-17 FUNCTIONS OF NUMBERS 1 TO 99 (Continued)

No.	*Square*	*Cube*	*Square Root*	*Cubic Root*	*Logarithm*	*1000 × Reciprocal*	*No. = Diameter*	
							Circum.	*Area*
50	2500	125000	7.0711	3.6840	1.69897	20.0000	157.08	1963.50
51	2601	132651	7.1414	3.7084	1.70757	19.6078	160.22	2042.82
52	2704	140608	7.2111	3.7325	1.71600	19.2308	163.36	2123.72
53	2809	148877	7.2801	3.7563	1.72428	18.8679	166.50	2206.18
54	2916	157464	7.3485	3.7798	1.73239	18.5185	169.65	2290.22
55	3025	166375	7.4162	3.8030	1.74036	18.1818	172.79	2375.83
56	3136	175616	7.4838	3.8259	1.74819	17.8571	175.93	2463.01
57	3249	185193	7.5498	3.8485	1.75587	17.5439	179.07	2551.76
58	3364	195112	7.6158	3.8709	1.76343	17.2414	182.21	2642.08
59	3481	205379	7.6811	3.8930	1.77085	16.9492	185.35	2733.97
60	3600	216000	7.7460	3.9149	1.77815	16.6667	188.50	2827.43
61	3721	226981	7.8102	3.9365	1.78533	16.3934	191.64	2922.47
62	3844	238328	7.8740	3.9579	1.79239	16.1290	194.78	3019.07
63	3969	250047	7.9373	3.9791	1.79934	15.8730	197.92	3117.25
64	4096	262144	8.0000	4.0000	1.80618	15.6250	201.06	3216.99
65	4225	274625	8.0623	4.0207	1.81291	15.3846	204.20	3318.31
66	4356	287496	8.1240	4.0412	1.81954	15.1515	207.35	3421.19
67	4489	300763	8.1854	4.0615	1.82607	14.9254	210.49	3525.65
68	4624	314432	8.2462	4.0817	1.83251	14.7059	213.63	3631.68
69	4761	328509	8.3066	4.1016	1.83885	14.4928	216.77	3739.28
70	4900	343000	8.3666	4.1213	1.84510	14.2857	219.91	3848.45
71	5041	357911	8.4261	4.1408	1.85126	14.0845	223.05	3959.19
72	5184	373248	8.4853	4.1602	1.85733	13.8889	226.19	4071.50
73	5329	389017	8.5440	4.1793	1.86332	13.6986	229.34	4185.39
74	5476	405224	8.6023	4.1983	1.86923	13.5135	232.48	4300.84
75	5625	421875	8.6603	4.2172	1.87506	13.3333	235.62	4417.86
76	5776	438976	8.7178	4.2358	1.88081	13.1579	238.76	4536.46
77	5929	456533	8.7750	4.2543	1.88649	12.9870	241.90	4656.63
78	6084	474552	8.8318	4.2727	1.89209	12.8205	245.04	4778.36
79	6241	493039	8.8882	4.2908	1.89763	12.6582	248.19	4901.67
80	6400	512000	8.9443	4.3089	1.90309	12.5000	251.33	5026.55
81	6561	531441	9.0000	4.3267	1.90849	12.3457	254.47	5153.00
82	6724	551366	9.0554	4.3445	1.91381	12.1951	257.61	5281.02
83	6889	571787	9.1104	4.3621	1.91908	12.0482	260.75	5410.61
84	7056	592704	9.1652	4.3795	1.92428	11.9048	263.89	5541.77
85	7225	614125	9.2195	4.3968	1.92942	11.7647	267.04	5674.50
86	7396	636056	9.2736	4.4140	1.93450	11.6279	270.18	5808.80
87	7569	658503	9.3274	4.4310	1.93952	11.4943	273.32	5944.68
88	7744	681472	9.3808	4.4480	1.94448	11.3636	276.46	6082.12
89	7921	704969	9.4340	4.4647	1.94939	11.2360	279.60	6221.14
90	8100	729000	9.4868	4.4814	1.95424	11.1111	282.74	6361.73
91	8281	753571	9.5394	4.4979	1.95904	10.9890	285.88	6503.88
92	8464	778688	9.5917	4.5144	1.96379	10.8696	289.03	6647.61
93	8649	804357	9.6437	4.5307	1.96848	10.7527	292.17	6792.91
94	8836	830584	9.6954	4.5468	1.97313	10.6383	295.31	6939.78
95	9025	857375	9.7468	4.5629	1.97772	10.5263	298.45	7088.22
96	9216	884736	9.7980	4.5789	1.98227	10.4167	301.59	7238.23
97	9409	912673	9.8489	4.5947	1.98677	10.3093	304.73	7389.81
98	9604	941192	9.8995	4.6104	1.99123	10.2041	307.88	7542.96
99	9801	970299	9.9499	4.6261	1.99564	10.1010	311.02	7697.69

From Carnegie's "Pocket Companion."

TABLE 65-18 TWO-THIRDS POWERS OF NUMBERS

No.	*.00*	*.01*	*.02*	*.03*	*.04*	*.05*	*.06*	*.07*	*.08*	*.09*
.0	.000	.046	.074	.097	.117	.136	.153	.170	.186	.201
.1	.215	.229	.243	.256	.269	.282	.295	.307	.319	.331
.2	.342	.353	.364	.375	.386	.397	.407	.418	.428	.438
.3	.448	.458	.468	.477	.487	.497	.506	.515	.525	.534
.4	.543	.552	.561	.570	.578	.587	.596	.604	.613	.622
.5	.630	.638	.647	.655	.663	.671	.679	.687	.695	.703
.6	.711	.719	.727	.735	.743	.750	.758	.765	.773	.781
.7	.788	.796	.803	.811	.818	.825	.832	.840	.847	.855
.8	.862	.869	.876	.883	.890	.897	.904	.911	.918	.925
.9	.932	.939	.946	.953	.960	.966	.973	.980	.987	.993
1.0	1.000	1.007	1.013	1.020	1.027	1.033	1.040	1.046	1.053	1.059
1.1	1.065	1.072	1.078	1.085	1.091	1.097	1.104	1.110	1.117	1.123
1.2	1.129	1.136	1.142	1.148	1.154	1.160	1.167	1.173	1.179	1.185
1.3	1.191	1.197	1.203	1.209	1.215	1.221	1.227	1.233	1.239	1.245
1.4	1.251	1.257	1.263	1.269	1.275	1.281	1.287	1.293	1.299	1.305
1.5	1.310	1.316	1.322	1.328	1.334	1.339	1.345	1.351	1.357	1.362
1.6	1.368	1.374	1.379	1.385	1.391	1.396	1.402	1.408	1.413	1.419
1.7	1.424	1.430	1.436	1.441	1.447	1.452	1.458	1.463	1.469	1.474
1.8	1.480	1.485	1.491	1.496	1.502	1.507	1.513	1.518	1.523	1.529
1.9	1.534	1.539	1.545	1.550	1.556	1.561	1.566	1.571	1.577	1.582
2.0	1.587	1.593	1.598	1.603	1.608	1.613	1.619	1.624	1.629	1.634
2.1	1.639	1.645	1.650	1.655	1.660	1.665	1.671	1.676	1.681	1.686
2.2	1.691	1.697	1.702	1.707	1.712	1.717	1.722	1.727	1.732	1.737
2.3	1.742	1.747	1.752	1.757	1.762	1.767	1.772	1.777	1.782	1.787
2.4	1.792	1.797	1.802	1.807	1.812	1.817	1.822	1.827	1.832	1.837
2.5	1.842	1.847	1.852	1.857	1.862	1.867	1.871	1.876	1.881	1.886
2.6	1.891	1.896	1.900	1.905	1.910	1.915	1.920	1.925	1.929	1.934
2.7	1.939	1.944	1.949	1.953	1.958	1.963	1.968	1.972	1.977	1.982
2.8	1.987	1.992	1.996	2.001	2.006	2.010	2.015	2.020	2.024	2.029
2.9	2.034	2.038	2.043	2.048	2.052	2.057	2.062	2.066	2.071	2.075
3.0	2.080	2.085	2.089	2.094	2.099	2.103	2.108	2.112	2.117	2.122
3.1	2.126	2.131	2.135	2.140	2.144	2.149	2.153	2.158	2.163	2.167
3.2	2.172	2.176	2.180	2.185	2.190	2.194	2.199	2.203	2.208	2.212
3.3	2.217	2.221	2.226	2.230	2.234	2.239	2.243	2.248	2.252	2.257
3.4	2.261	2.265	2.270	2.274	2.279	2.283	2.288	2.292	2.296	2.301
3.5	2.305	2.310	2.314	2.318	2.323	2.327	2.331	2.336	2.340	2.345
3.6	2.349	2.353	2.358	2.362	2.366	2.371	2.375	2.379	2.384	2.388
3.7	2.392	2.397	2.401	2.405	2.409	2.414	2.418	2.422	2.427	2.431
3.8	2.435	2.439	2.444	2.448	2.452	2.457	2.461	2.465	2.469	2.474
3.9	2.478	2.482	2.486	2.490	2.495	2.499	2.503	2.507	2.511	2.516
4.0	2.520	2.524	2.528	2.532	2.537	2.541	2.545	2.549	2.553	2.558
4.1	2.562	2.566	2.570	2.574	2.579	2.583	2.587	2.591	2.595	2.599
4.2	2.603	2.607	2.611	2.616	2.620	2.624	2.628	2.632	2.636	2.640
4.3	2.644	2.648	2.653	2.657	2.661	2.665	2.669	2.673	2.677	2.681
4.4	2.685	2.689	2.693	2.698	2.702	2.706	2.710	2.714	2.718	2.722
4.5	2.726	2.730	2.734	2.738	2.742	2.746	2.750	2.754	2.758	2.762
4.6	2.766	2.770	2.774	2.778	2.782	2.786	2.790	2.794	2.798	2.802
4.7	2.806	2.810	2.814	2.818	2.822	2.826	2.830	2.834	2.838	2.842
4.8	2.846	2.850	2.854	2.858	2.862	2.865	2.869	2.873	2.877	2.881
4.9	2.885	2.889	2.893	2.897	2.901	2.904	2.908	2.912	2.916	2.920

From King's "Handbook of Hydraulics."

TABLE 65-19 SQUARE ROOTS OF DECIMAL NUMBERS

For Use in Manning's Formula

Number	.–*0*	.–*1*	.–*2*	.–*3*	.–*4*	.–*5*	.–*6*	.–*7*	.–*8*	.–*9*
.00001	.003162	.003317	.003464	.003606	.003742	.003873	.004000	.004123	.004243	.004359
.00002	.004472	.004583	.004690	.004796	.004899	.005000	.005099	.005196	.005292	.005385
.00003	.005477	.005568	.005657	.005745	.005831	.005916	.006000	.006083	.006164	.006245
.00004	.006325	.006403	.006481	.006557	.006633	.006708	.006782	.006856	.006928	.007000
.00005	.007071	.007141	.007211	.007280	.007348	.007416	.007483	.007550	.007616	.007681
.00006	.007746	.007810	.007874	.007937	.008000	.008062	.008124	.008185	.008246	.008307
.00007	.008367	.008426	.008485	.008544	.008602	.008660	.008718	.008775	.008832	.008888
.00008	.008944	.009000	.009055	.009110	.009165	.009220	.009274	.009327	.009381	.009434
.00009	.009487	.009539	.009592	.009644	.009695	.009747	.009798	.009849	.009899	.009950
.00010	.010000	.010050	.010100	.010149	.010198	.010247	.010296	.010344	.010392	.010440
.0001	.01000	.01049	.01095	.01140	.01183	.01225	.01265	.01304	.01342	.01378
.0002	.01414	.01449	.01483	.01517	.01549	.01581	.01612	.01643	.01673	.01703
.0003	.01732	.01761	.01789	.01817	.01844	.01871	.01897	.01924	.01949	.01975
.0004	.02000	.02025	.02049	.02074	.02098	.02121	.02145	.02168	.02191	.02214
.0005	.02236	.02258	.02280	.02302	.02324	.02345	.02366	.02387	.02408	.02429
.0006	.02449	.02470	.02490	.02510	.02530	.02550	.02569	.02588	.02608	.02627
.0007	.02646	.02665	.02683	.02702	.02720	.02739	.02757	.02775	.02793	.02811
.0008	.02828	.02846	.02864	.02881	.02898	.02915	.02933	.02950	.02966	.02983
.0009	.03000	.03017	.03033	.03050	.03066	.03082	.03098	.03114	.03130	.03146
.0010	.03162	.03178	.03194	.03209	.03225	.03240	.03256	.03271	.03286	.03302
.001	.03162	.03317	.03464	.03606	.03742	.03873	.04000	.04123	.04243	.04359
.002	.04472	.04583	.04690	.04796	.04899	.05000	.05099	.05196	.05292	.05385
.003	.05477	.05568	.05657	.05745	.05831	.05916	.06000	.06083	.06164	.06245
.004	.06325	.06403	.06481	.06557	.06633	.06708	.06782	.06856	.06928	.07000
.005	.07071	.07141	.07211	.07280	.07348	.07416	.07483	.07550	.07616	.07681
.006	.07746	.07810	.07874	.07937	.08000	.08062	.08124	.08185	.08246	.08307
.007	.08367	.08426	.08485	.08544	.08602	.08660	.08718	.08775	.08832	.08888
.008	.08944	.09000	.09055	.09110	.09165	.09220	.09274	.09327	.09381	.09434
.009	.09487	.09539	.09592	.09644	.09695	.09747	.09798	.09849	.09899	.09950
.010	.10000	.10050	.10100	.10149	.10198	.10247	.10296	.10344	.10392	.10440
.01	.1000	.1049	.1095	.1140	.1183	.1225	.1265	.1304	.1342	.1378
.02	.1414	.1449	.1483	.1517	.1549	.1581	.1612	.1643	.1673	.1703
.03	.1732	.1761	.1789	.1817	.1844	.1871	.1897	.1924	.1949	.1975
.04	.2000	.2025	.2049	.2074	.2098	.2121	.2145	.2168	.2191	.2214
.05	.2236	.2258	.2280	.2302	.2324	.2345	.2366	.2387	.2408	.2429
.06	.2449	.2470	.2490	.2510	.2530	.2550	.2569	.2588	.2608	.2627
.07	.2646	.2665	.2683	.2702	.2720	.2739	.2757	.2775	.2793	.2811
.08	.2828	.2846	.2864	.2881	.2898	.2915	.2933	.2950	.2966	.2983
.09	.3000	.3017	.3033	.3050	.3066	.3082	.3098	.3114	.3130	.3146
.10	.3162	.3178	.3194	.3209	.3225	.3240	.3256	.3271	.3286	.3302

From King's "Handbook of Hydraulics."

TABLE 65-20 U. S. STANDARD GAGES FOR SHEET AND PLATE IRON AND STEEL (Black)

Established by Act of Congress, July 1, 1893
(With revisions, 1945)

Number of Gage	*Approximate Thickness*				*Weight*		
	Fractions of an Inch	*Decimal Parts of an Inch*		*Milli-meters*	*per Square Foot in Ounces Avoir-dupois*	*per Square Foot in Pounds Avoir-dupois*	*per Square Meter in Kilo-grams*
	*Wrought Iron**	*Wrought Iron**	*Steel*†	*Steel*†			
0000000	1-2	0.5	0.4782	12.146	320	20.	97.65
000000	15-32	.46875	.4484	11.389	300	18.75	91.55
00000	7-16	.4375	.4185	10.630	280	17.50	85.44
0000	13-32	.40625	.3886	9.870	260	16.25	79.33
000	3-8	.375	.3587	9.111	240	15.	73.24
00	11-32	.34375	.3288	8.352	220	13.75	67.13
0	5-16	.3125	.2989	7.592	200	12.50	61.03
1	9-32	.28125	.2690	6.833	180	11.25	54.93
2	17-64	.265625	.2541	6.454	170	10.625	51.88
3	1-4	.25	.2391	6.073	160	10.	48.82
4	15-64	.234375	.2242	5.695	150	9.375	45.77
5	7-32	.21875	.2092	5.314	140	8.75	42.72
6	13-64	.203125	.1943	4.935	130	8.125	39.67
7	3-16	.1875	.1793	4.554	120	7.5	36.62
8	11-64	.171875	.1644	4.176	110	6.875	33.57
9	5-32	.15625	.1495	3.797	100	6.25	30.52
10	9-64	.140625	.1345	3.416	90	5.625	27.46
11	1-8	.125	.1196	3.038	80	5.	24.41
12	7-64	.109375	.1046	2.657	70	4.375	21.36
13	3-32	.09375	.0897	2.278	60	3.75	18.31
14	5-64	.078125	.0747	1.897	50	3.125	15.26
15	9-128	.0703125	.0673	1.709	45	2.8125	13.73
16	1-16	.0625	.0598	1.519	40	2.5	12.21
17	9-160	.05625	.0538	1.367	36	2.25	10.99
18	1-20	.05	.0478	1.214	32	2.	9.765
19	7-160	.04375	.0418	1.062	28	1.75	8.544
20	3-80	.0375	.0359	0.912	24	1.50	7.324
21	11-320	.034375	.0329	.836	22	1.375	6.713
22	1-32	.03125	.0299	.759	20	1.25	6.103
23	9-320	.028125	.0269	.683	18	1.125	5.49
24	1-40	.025	.0239	.607	16	1.	4.882
25	7-320	.021875	.0209	.531	14	0.875	4.272
26	3-160	.01875	.0179	.455	12	.75	3.662
27	11-640	.0171875	.0164	.417	11	.6875	3.357
28	1-64	.015625	.0149	.378	10	.625	3.052

By Act of Congress, the gage numbers are based on the *weight* per square foot in ounces (sixth column) and not on thickness.

*The thickness given in the Congressional table is for wrought iron and not for steel.

†The thickness for *steel* is from tables compiled by the American Iron and Steel Institute, November 1942, based on 41.82 pounds per square foot per inch thick.

Example: A 16 gage sheet of either wrought iron or steel *weighs* 40 ounces per square foot. The wrought iron is approximately .0625 inch thick whereas the steel is .0598 inch thick.

TABLE 65-21 AVERAGE WEIGHT OF VARIOUS MATERIALS USED IN CONSTRUCTION IN POUNDS PER CUBIC FOOT

Substance	*Weight*	*Substance*	*Weight*
Clay, Earth and Mud:		Masonry and its Materials—(Continued):	
Clay	122–162	Sand, pure quartz, dry, loose	87–106
Earth, dry and loose	72–80	Sand, pure quartz, dry, slightly shaken	92–110
Earth, dry and shaken	82–92	Sand, pure quartz, dry, rammed	100–120
Earth, dry and moderately rammed	90–100	Sand, natural, dry, loose	80–110
Earth, slightly moist, loose	70–76	Sand, nautral, dry, shaken	85–125
Earth, more moist, loose	66–68	Sand, wet, voids full of water	118–128
Earth, more moist, shaken	75–90	Stone	135–195
Earth, more moist, moderately rammed	90–100	Stone, quarried, loosely piled	80–110
Earth, as soft flowing mud	104–112	Stone, broken, loose	77–112
Earth, as soft mud well pressed into a box	110–120	Stone, broken, rammed	79–121
Mud, dry, close	80–110		
Mud, wet, moderately pressed	110–130		
Mud, wet, fluid	104–120	Metal and Alloys:	
		Brass (copper and zinc)	487–524
Masonry and its Materials:		Bronze (copper and tin)	524–537
Brick, best pressed	150	Copper, cast	537–548
Brick, common hard	125	Copper, rolled	548–562
Brick, soft, inferior	100	Iron and steel, cast	438–483
Brickwork, pressed brick, fine joints	140	Average	450
Brickwork, medium quality	125	Iron and steel, wrought	475–494
Brickwork, coarse, inferior soft bricks	100	Average	480
Cement, pulverized, loose	72–105	Spelter or zinc	425–450
Cement, pressed	115	Tin, cast	450–470
Cement, set	168–187	Steel	490
Concrete, 1:3:6	140	Tin	459
Gravel, loose	82–125	Zinc	438
Gravel, rammed	90–145	Mercury (32°F.)	849
Masonry of granite or stone of like weight:			
Well-dressed	165	Woods (Dry)*	
Well-scabbled rubble, 20 per cent mortar	154	White oak	46.4
Roughly scabbled rubble, 25 to 35 per cent mortar	150	White pine	25.6
Well-scabbled dry rubble	138	Southern long-leaf pine	38.1
Roughly scabbled dry rubble	125	Douglas fir	32.1
Masonry of sandstone or stone of like weight, weighs about seven-eights of the above.		Short-leaf yellow pine	38.4
Mortar, hardened	90–115	Norway pine	30.2
		Spruce and eastern fir	25.0
		Hemlock	26–32
		Cypress	29.8
		Cedar	23.1
		Chestnut	41.0
		California redwood	26.2
		California spruce	25.0

*The weights of green or unseasoned timbers are 20 to 40 per cent greater.
From King's "Handbook of Hydraulics."

TABLE 65-22 COMPRESSIVE AND TENSILE STRENGTH OF VARIOUS MATERIALS

Material	*Stresses in Thousands of Pounds*	
	Tensile Strength	*Compressive Strength*
Metals:		
Aluminum	24–35	12
Brass	18–24	20
Bronze	28.5	42
Copper	32–35	32
Gold	20–30	—
Iron (Cast)	15–18	80
Iron (Wrought)	27–35	46
Lead	2.5	—
Silver	40	—
Steel	55–65	55–65
Tin	3.5–4.6	6
Zinc	7–16	—
Stones:		
Feldspar	—	—
Gneiss	—	—
Granite	1.20	12
Graphite	—	—
Limestone	0.8	8
Marble	0.8	8
Sandstone	0.15	5
Slate	3.0	10
Mineral Substances:		
Brick	0.2	10
Brickwork	—	—
Clay	—	—
Earth, dry, loose	—	—
Earth, moist, loose	—	—
Earth, packed	—	—
Mud, wet	—	—
Portland Cement	0.74	7.04
Sand, dry	—	—
Sand, wet	—	—
Glass	3.0	30

TABLE 65-23 SAFE BEARING VALUE OF SOILS (Baker)

Kind of Material	*Safe Bearing Power in Tons per Square Foot*
Rock (Poor)	5 tons per square foot
Rock (Solid and First Quality)	25 tons per square foot
Dry Clay	4 tons per square foot
Medium Dry Clay	2 tons per square foot
Soft Clay	1 ton per square foot
Cemented Gravel	8 tons per square foot
Compact Sand	4 tons per square foot
Clean Dry Sand	2 tons per square foot
Quicksand and Alluvial Soil	½ ton per square foot

TABLE 65-24 AREA OF STEEL REINFORCEMENT PER FOOT WIDTH OF SLAB

Size of Bar	Spacing of Bars in Inches																		
	3	3½	4	4½	5	5½	6	6½	7	7½	8	8½	9	9½	10	10½	11	11½	12
	Area of Steel in Square Inches																		
¼ round*	0.20	0.17	0.15	0.13	0.12	0.11	0.10	0.09	0.08	0.08	0.07	0.07	0.07	0.06	0.06	0.06	0.05	0.05	0.05
¼ square*	0.25	0.21	0.19	0.17	0.15	0.14	0.13	0.12	0.11	0.10	0.09	0.09	0.08	0.08	0.08	0.07	0.07	0.07	0.06
⅜ round	0.44	0.38	0.33	0.29	0.26	0.24	0.22	0.20	0.19	0.18	0.17	0.16	0.15	0.14	0.13	0.13	0.12	0.11	0.11
⅜ square*	0.56	0.48	0.42	0.37	0.34	0.31	0.28	0.26	0.24	0.23	0.21	0.20	0.19	0.18	0.17	0.16	0.15	0.15	0.14
½ round	0.78	0.67	0.59	0.52	0.47	0.43	0.39	0.36	0.34	0.31	0.29	0.28	0.26	0.25	0.23	0.22	0.21	0.20	0.20
½ square	1.00	0.86	0.75	0.67	0.60	0.55	0.50	0.46	0.43	0.40	0.38	0.35	0.33	0.32	0.30	0.29	0.27	0.26	0.25
⅝ round	1.23	1.05	0.92	0.82	0.74	0.67	0.61	0.57	0.53	0.49	0.46	0.43	0.41	0.39	0.37	0.35	0.33	0.32	0.31
⅝ square*	1.56	1.34	1.17	1.04	0.94	0.85	0.78	0.72	0.67	0.63	0.59	0.55	0.52	0.49	0.47	0.45	0.43	0.41	0.39
¾ round	1.77	1.51	1.33	1.18	1.06	0.96	0.88	0.82	0.76	0.71	0.66	0.62	0.59	0.56	0.53	0.51	0.48	0.46	0.44
¾ square*	2.25	1.93	1.69	1.50	1.35	1.23	1.13	1.04	0.97	0.90	0.84	0.80	0.75	0.71	0.68	0.64	0.61	0.59	0.56
⅞ round	2.40	2.06	1.80	1.60	1.44	1.31	1.20	1.11	1.03	0.96	0.90	0.85	0.80	0.76	0.72	0.69	0.66	0.63	0.60
⅞ square*	3.06	2.62	2.30	2.04	1.84	1.67	1.53	1.42	1.31	1.23	1.15	1.08	1.02	0.97	0.92	0.88	0.83	0.80	0.77
1 round	3.14	2.69	2.36	2.09	1.88	1.71	1.57	1.45	1.35	1.26	1.18	1.11	1.05	0.99	0.94	0.90	0.86	0.82	0.79
1 square	4.00	3.43	3.00	2.67	2.40	2.18	2.00	1.85	1.72	1.60	1.50	1.41	1.33	1.26	1.20	1.14	1.09	1.08	1.00
1⅛ round*	3.98	3.41	2.98	2.65	2.38	2.17	1.99	1.83	1.70	1.59	1.49	1.40	1.33	1.26	1.20	1.14	1.09	1.08	0.99
1⅛ square	5.06	4.34	3.80	3.37	3.04	2.76	2.53	2.34	2.17	2.02	1.90	1.79	1.69	1.60	1.52	1.45	1.38	1.32	1.27
1¼ round*	4.91	4.20	3.68	3.27	2.95	2.68	2.45	2.27	2.10	1.96	1.84	1.73	1.64	1.55	1.47	1.40	1.34	1.28	1.23
1¼ square	6.25	5.36	4.69	4.17	3.75	3.41	3.13	2.89	2.68	2.50	2.34	2.21	2.08	1.97	1.88	1.79	1.70	1.63	1.56

*Not standard, and seldom stocked.

TABLE 65-25 AREAS AND WEIGHTS OF CORRUGATED METAL PIPE

Based on U. S. Standard Gages for Sheet and Plate Iron and Steel

Nominal Diam. in Inches	*Area in Square Feet*	*Computed Weight per Linear Foot of Finished Pipe Exclusive of End Finish (Based on 20′ Length of Pipe) Pounds*				
		Galvanized Sheet Gage Number				
		16	*14*	*12*	*10*	*8*
8	.349	7.3	....	....	....	....
10	.545	9.0	....	....	....	....
12	.785	10.5	13.1	....	....	....
15	1.227	12.9	16.1	....	....	....
18	1.767	15.3	19.1	26.4	....	....
21	2.405	17.7	22.1	30.6	....	....
24	3.142	20.4	25.2	34.7	44.2	....
30	4.909	....	30.9	43.0	54.8	....
36	7.069	....	37.1	51.0	65.4	79.4
42	9.621	....	43.6	59.5	76.8	93.2
48	12.566	....	....	68.0	87.4	106.1
54	15.904	....	....	77.8	99.4	120.7
60	19.635	....	....	....	108.9	133.5
66	23.758	....	....	....	120.6	146.4
72	28.274	....	....	....	130.4	159.3
78	33.183	....	....	....	142.4	172.8
84	38.485	....	....	....	153.5	185.2
96	50.265	....	....	....	174.7	212.1
108	63.617	....	....	....	196.8	238.9

TABLE 65-26 AREA, WETTED PERIMETER, AND HYDRAULIC RADIUS OF PARTIALLY FILLED CIRCULAR CONDUIT SECTIONS

$\frac{d}{D}$	$\frac{area}{D^2}$	$\frac{wet.\ per.}{D}$	$\frac{hyd.\ rad.}{D}$	$\frac{d}{D}$	$\frac{area}{D^2}$	$\frac{wet.\ per.}{D}$	$\frac{hyd.\ rad.}{D}$
0.01	0.0013	0.2003	0.0066	0.51	0.4027	1.5908	0.2531
0.02	0.0037	0.2838	0.0132	0.52	0.4127	1.6108	0.2561
0.03	0.0069	0.3482	0.0197	0.53	0.4227	1.6308	0.2591
0.04	0.0105	0.4027	0.0262	0.54	0.4327	1.6509	0.2620
0.05	0.0147	0.4510	0.0326	0.55	0.4426	1.6710	0.2649
0.06	0.0192	0.4949	0.0389	0.56	0.4526	1.6911	0.2676
0.07	0.0242	0.5355	0.0451	0.57	0.4625	1.7113	0.2703
0.08	0.0294	0.5735	0.0513	0.58	0.4723	1.7315	0.2728
0.09	0.0350	0.6094	0.0574	0.59	0.4822	1.7518	0.2753
0.10	0.0409	0.6435	0.0635	0.60	0.4920	1.7722	0.2776
0.11	0.0470	0.6761	0.0695	0.61	0.5018	1.7926	0.2797
0.12	0.0534	0.7075	0.0754	0.62	0.5115	1.8132	0.2818
0.13	0.0600	0.7377	0.0813	0.63	0.5212	1.8338	0.2839
0.14	0.0668	0.7670	0.0871	0.64	0.5308	1.8546	0.2860
0.15	0.0739	0.7954	0.0929	0.65	0.5404	1.8755	0.2881
0.16	0.0811	0.8230	0.0986	0.66	0.5499	1.8965	0.2899
0.17	0.0885	0.8500	0.1042	0.67	0.5594	1.9177	0.2917
0.18	0.0961	0.8763	0.1097	0.68	0.5687	1.9391	0.2935
0.19	0.1039	0.9020	0.1152	0.69	0.5780	1.9606	0.2950
0.20	0.1118	0.9273	0.1206	0.70	0.5872	1.9823	0.2962
0.21	0.1199	0.9521	0.1259	0.71	0.5964	2.0042	0.2973
0.22	0.1281	0.9764	0.1312	0.72	0.6054	2.0264	0.2984
0.23	0.1365	1.0003	0.1364	0.73	0.6143	2.0488	0.2995
0.24	0.1449	1.0239	0.1416	0.74	0.6231	2.0714	0.3006
0.25	0.1535	1.0472	0.1466	0.75	0.6318	2.0944	0.3017
0.26	0.1623	1.0701	0.1516	0.76	0.6404	2.1176	0.3025
0.27	0.1711	1.0928	0.1566	0.77	0.6489	2.1412	0.3032
0.28	0.1800	1.1152	0.1614	0.78	0.6573	2.1652	0.3037
0.29	0.1890	1.1373	0.1662	0.79	0.6655	2.1895	0.3040
0.30	0.1982	1.1593	0.1709	0.80	0.6736	2.2143	0.3042
0.31	0.2074	1.1810	0.1755	0.81	0.6815	2.2395	0.3044
0.32	0.2167	1.2025	0.1801	0.82	0.6893	2.2653	0.3043
0.33	0.2260	1.2239	0.1848	0.83	0.6969	2.2916	0.3041
0.34	0.2355	1.2451	0.1891	0.84	0.7043	2.3186	0.3038
0.35	0.2450	1.2661	0.1935	0.85	0.7115	2.3462	0.3033
0.36	0.2546	1.2870	0.1978	0.86	0.7186	2.3746	0.3026
0.37	0.2642	1.3078	0.2020	0.87	0.7254	2.4038	0.3017
0.38	0.2739	1.3284	0.2061	0.88	0.7320	2.4341	0.3008
0.39	0.2836	1.3490	0.2102	0.89	0.7384	2.4655	0.2996
0.40	0.2934	1.3694	0.2142	0.90	0.7445	2.4981	0.2980
0.41	0.3032	1.3898	0.2181	0.91	0.7504	2.5322	0.2963
0.42	0.3130	1.4101	0.2220	0.92	0.7560	2.5681	0.2944
0.43	0.3229	1.4303	0.2257	0.93	0.7613	2.6061	0.2922
0.44	0.3328	1.4505	0.2294	0.94	0.7662	2.6467	0.2896
0.45	0.3428	1.4706	0.2331	0.95	0.7707	2.6906	0.2864
0.46	0.3527	1.4907	0.2366	0.96	0.7749	2.7389	0.2830
0.47	0.3627	1.5108	0.2400	0.97	0.7785	2.7934	0.2787
0.48	0.3727	1.5308	0.2434	0.98	0.7816	2.8578	0.2735
0.49	0.3827	1.5508	0.2467	0.99	0.7841	2.9412	0.2665
0.50	0.3927	1.5708	0.2500	1.00	0.7854	3.1416	0.2500

Fig. 366. Multi-Plate pipe, 12½ ft in diameter, 226 ft long, under 57 ft of cover in Montana.

APPENDIX A

UNDERGROUND CONDUITS

An Appraisal of Modern Research

BY M. G. SPANGLER, M. ASCE

Paper No. 2337

Reprinted by permission from *TRANSACTIONS*

AMERICAN SOCIETY OF CIVIL ENGINEERS

Volume 113, 1948, page 316

The following reprint includes
the original paper
by M. G. Spangler but with discussions only
by E. F. Kelley and George E. Shafer.

AMERICAN SOCIETY OF CIVIL ENGINEERS

Founded November 5, 1852

DISCUSSIONS

Paper No. 2337

UNDERGROUND CONDUITS—AN APPRAISAL OF MODERN RESEARCH

BY M. G. SPANGLER,[1] M. ASCE

WITH DISCUSSION BY MESSRS. WILSON V. BINGER, JACOB FELD, ZDENĚK BAŽANT, JR., ANSON MARSTON, GEORGE E. SHAFER, E. F. KELLEY, BAILEY TREMPER, AND M. G. SPANGLER.

SYNOPSIS

The increasingly successful application of scientific principles of mechanics to the analysis of soil has characterized engineering development during the first twoscore years of the twentieth century. A number of problems that involve the soil as an integral part of the finished structure and which a generation or two ago were considered by many to be too complex to be subject to orderly classification and solution are yielding to the onslaught of organized research.

One notable example of problems in this category concerns the design of underground structures such as conduits, sewers, drains, culverts, water mains, and gas lines. Conduits of this general type have been used by mankind for at least 3,000 years, being found among the earliest examples of the practice of the engineering arts; but not until about 1910 was serious effort directed toward the development of a rational method for determining the magnitude and character of the loads to which underground conduits were subjected in service due to the earth overburden and other load sources. In those early days, Anson Marston, Past-President and Hon. M. ASCE, then director of the Engineering Experiment Station at Iowa State College in Ames, inaugurated a research program which has been continuously active under his direction. The purpose of this paper is to review Dean Marston's theory of loads on, and supporting strengths of, underground conduits and to record the experimental background, together with working values of many of the constants required for the practical application of the theory.

NOTE.—Published in June, 1947, *Proceedings*. Positions and titles given are those in effect when the paper or discussion was received for publication.

[1] Research Associate Prof., Civ. Eng. Dept., Iowa Eng. Experiment Station, Iowa State College, Ames, Iowa.

Load Classification of Underground Conduits

Underground conduits, in general, may be divided into two main classes on the basis of construction conditions under which they are installed—that is (1) ditch conduits and (2) projecting conduits.

(1) "Ditch conduits" are structures installed and completely buried in narrow ditches in relatively passive or undisturbed soil. Examples of this class of conduits are sewers, drains, and water mains (see Fig. 1(*a*)).

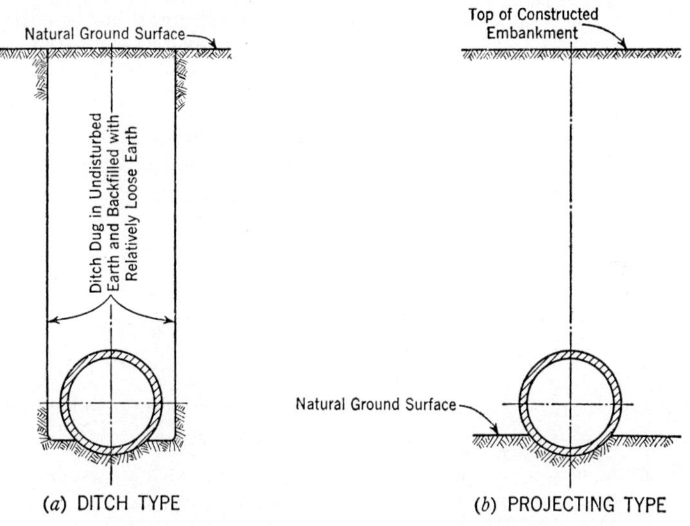

Fig. 1.—Essential Elements of Typical Conduits

(2) "Projecting Conduits" are structures installed in shallow bedding with the top of the conduit projecting above the surface of the natural ground, and then covered with an embankment, as shown in Fig. 1(*b*). Railway and highway culverts are good illustrations of this class of conduits. Conduits installed in ditches wider than about two or three times their maximum horizontal breadth may also be treated as projecting conduits.

Notation

The letter symbols in this paper are defined where they first appear, in text or by illustration, and are assembled for reference in Appendix I. Discussers are requested to conform to this usage.

Loads on Ditch Conduits

When a conduit is placed in a ditch not wider than about two or three times its outside breadth, and covered with earth, the backfill will tend to settle downward. This downward movement or tendency for movement of the soil in the ditch above the pipe produces vertical frictional forces or shearing stresses along the sides of the ditch which act upward on the prism of soil within the ditch and help to support the backfill material. Assuming the cohesion between the backfill material and the sides of the ditch to be negligible, the magnitude of these vertical shearing stresses is equal to the active lateral pressure exerted by the earth backfill against the sides of the ditch, multiplied by the tangent of the angle of friction between the two materials. This assumption of negligible cohesion is justified because: (*a*) Even when the ditch is dug in, and backfilled with, cohesive material, considerable time must elapse before effective cohesion between the backfill material and the sides of the ditch can develop after backfilling; and (*b*) the assumption of no cohesion yields the maximum probable load on the conduit. The maximum load may develop at any time during the life of the conduit due to heavy rainfall or other causes which may eliminate or greatly reduce cohesion between the backfill and the sides of the ditch.

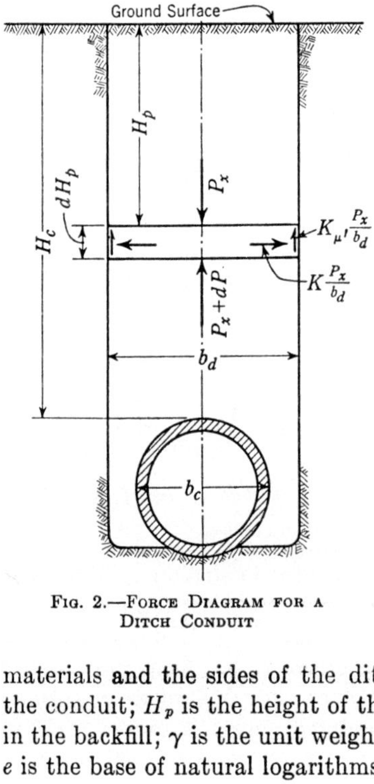

Fig. 2.—Force Diagram for a Ditch Conduit

Let Fig. 2 represent the section of a unit length of ditch conduit and consider a horizontal element of the fill material having a height dH_p at a distance H_p below the ground surface. Equating[2] the vertical forces acting on this element:

$$P + dP + 2\,K\,\mu'\,\frac{P}{b_d}\,dH_p = P + \gamma\,b_d\,dH_p \quad (1a)$$

This is a linear differential equation, the solution for which is

$$P = \gamma\,b_d^2\,\frac{1 - e^{-\alpha H_p}}{2\,K\,\mu'} \quad (1b)$$

in which P equals the total vertical pressure on a horizontal plane in the backfill, in pounds per linear foot; μ' is the coefficient of sliding friction between the fill materials and the sides of the ditch; b_d is the width of ditch at the top of the conduit; H_p is the height of the ground surface above any horizontal plane in the backfill; γ is the unit weight of filling material, in pounds per cubic foot; e is the base of natural logarithms; and, to simplify typography:

$$\alpha = \frac{2\,K\,\mu'}{b_d} \quad (2a)$$

The ratio K of active lateral pressure to vertical pressure, is defined as

$$K = \frac{\sqrt{\mu^2 + 1} - \mu}{\sqrt{\mu^2 + 1} + \mu} \quad (2b)$$

in which μ is the coefficient of internal friction of the filling material. The coefficient μ' may be equal to or less than μ, but it cannot be greater.

When $H_p = H_c$, Eq. 1*b* gives the total vertical pressure within the ditch at the level of the top of the pipe. The proportion of this total pressure that

[2] "The Theory of Loads on Pipes in Ditches and Tests of Cement and Clay Drain Tile and Sewer Pipe," by A. Marston and A. O. Anderson, *Bulletin No. 31*, Iowa Eng. Experiment Station, Ames, Iowa, 1913, p. 32.

will be carried by the conduit will depend upon the relative rigidity of the conduit and of the fill material between the sides of the conduit and the sides of the ditch. In the case of very rigid pipes, such as burned clay, concrete, or heavy cast-iron pipe, the side fills may be relatively compressible and the pipe itself will carry practically all the load, P. On the other hand, if the pipe is a relatively flexible, thin-walled pipe and the side fills are thoroughly tamped in at the sides of the pipe, the stiffness of the side fills may approach that of the conduit and the load on the structure will be reduced by the amount of load the side fills are capable of carrying.

For the case of rigid ditch conduits with relatively compressible side fills, the load will be:

$$W_c = C_d \gamma b^2_d \quad (3a)$$

For the case of flexible pipes and thoroughly compacted side fills having the same degree of stiffness as the pipes, the load will be:

$$W_c = C_d \gamma b_c b_d \quad (3b)$$

in which W_c is the total load on the conduit, and:

$$C_d = \frac{1 - e^{-\alpha H_c}}{2 K u'} \quad (3c)$$

Eq. 3*a* has been verified many times by experiment and by observation of the performance of actual sewers and drains. The results of two of Dean Marston's early load experiments on rigid pipes are shown in Fig. 3, together with loads calculated by Eq. 3*a*.

Evaluation of Eqs. 3*a* and 3*b* may be simplified by the use of Fig. 4 in which values of C_d for various values of H_c/b_d have been plotted for several kinds of filling materials having different coefficients of internal friction.

The width of ditch, b_d, is the actual width of a normal, parallel-sided ditch. In case the ditch is constructed with sloping sides, or the conduit is placed in a subditch at the bottom of a wider trench, experiments[3] have shown that the width of ditch at or slightly below the top of the pipe is the proper width to use when determining the load.

These ditch conduit formulas (Eqs. 3*a* and 3*b*), with proper selection of the physical factors involved, give the maximum loads to which any particular conduit may be subjected in service. On the other hand, because of the development of cohesion, any particular conduit may escape the maximum load for a long time, sometimes until its removal for other causes than load failure. Experiments and field observations show that the load on a conduit at the time the fill is completed is usually less than it will be at some later time. This condition accounts for the fact that sewers and other conduits which have been observed to be structurally sound immediately upon completion are sometimes found to be cracked some months or years later.

[3] "Loads on Pipe in Wide Ditches," by W. J. Schlick, *Bulletin No. 108*, Iowa Eng. Experiment Station, Ames, Iowa, 1932.

Loads on Projecting Conduits

Projecting conduits, as defined and as the name implies, are placed with their tops projecting some distance above the natural ground surface. They may be of any shape, such as circular, rectangular, or elliptical; may be made of any material, such as concrete, burned clay, cast iron, corrugated metal, or wood; and may possess any degree of rigidity from the very rigid concrete pipes and monolithic box culverts to the very flexible, lightweight corrugated metal pipes.

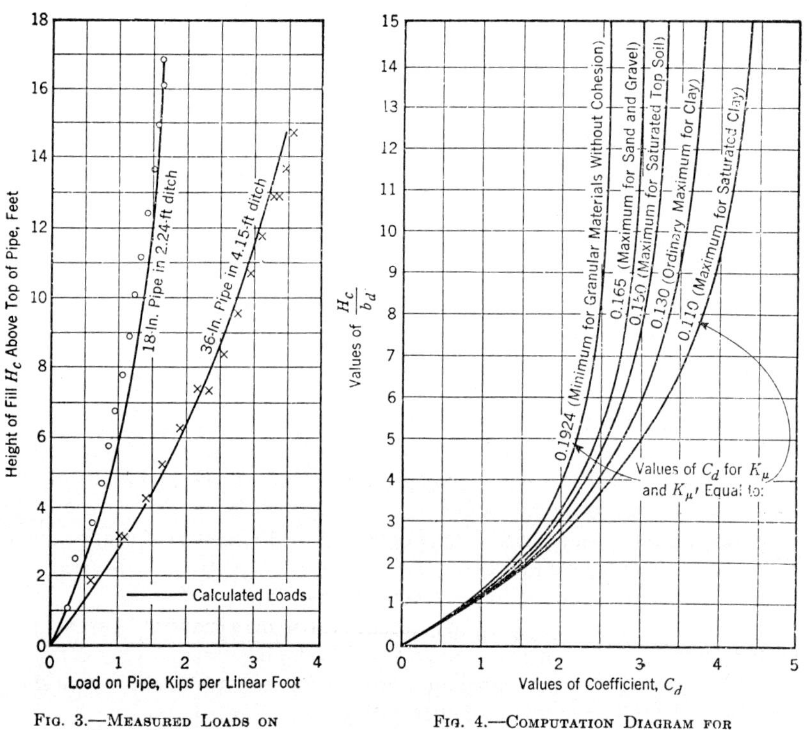

Fig. 3.—Measured Loads on Ditch Conduits

Fig. 4.—Computation Diagram for Ditch Conduits

As a basic case for studying the action of an embankment over this type of conduit, consider first a rigid structure resting on an earth foundation which settles under the load the same amount as the natural ground adjacent to the structure (see Fig. 5). Then in the embankment built over the conduit, there are three masses or prisms of soil, one of which, called the "interior prism," is directly over the conduit between the vertical planes tangent to the sides. The other two masses of soil, called the "exterior prisms," are those on each side of the structure adjacent to the tangent vertical planes.

It is evident that the height of the interior prism will be less than that of the exterior prisms by the amount which the conduit projects above the natural ground. In accordance with the well-known phenomenon that a high prism of soil will settle more than a lower prism, there is a tendency for the exterior prism to settle more than the interior prism and for friction forces or shearing stresses to be exerted along the tangent vertical planes bounding the interior prism. These shearing stresses are transmitted to the conduit, making the load on the structure greater than the weight of the interior prism of soil. The magnitude of the shearing stresses (again neglecting cohesion) is assumed to be equal to the active lateral pressure at these planes, multiplied by the coefficient of internal friction of the fill material. It is recognized that definite shearing planes between the interior and exterior prisms of soil do not actually exist in an earth embankment and that, in all probability, the shearing stresses are transferred from one prism to another through more or less narrow zones of the filling material. Nevertheless, actual vertical shearing planes are assumed for convenience in developing the theory, and load measuring experiments indicate that the assumption is valid.

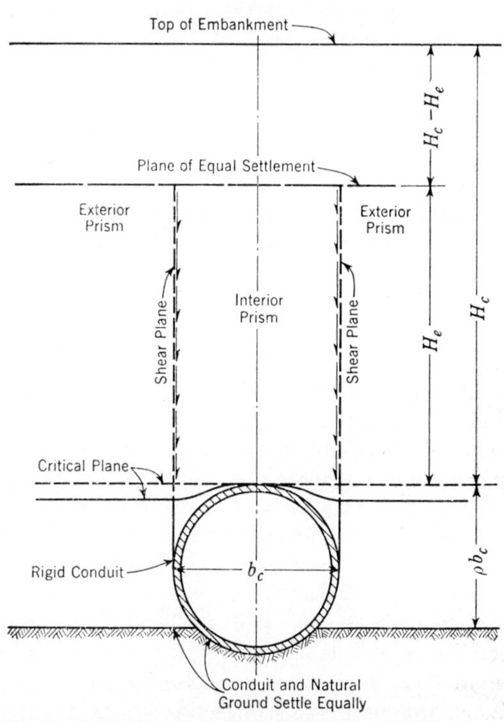

FIG. 5.—BASIC CASE FOR CONSIDERING THE ACTION OF AN EMBANKMENT OVER A PROJECTING CONDUIT

If the embankment is not very high, these shearing stresses may extend upward from the conduit completely to the top of the embankment. In the case of higher fills, the shearing stresses will not extend to the surface, but will terminate at some horizontal plane between the top of the conduit and the top of the embankment, known as the "plane of equal settlement." The distance between the top of the conduit and this plane is called the "height of equal settlement, H_e."

The plane of equal settlement is defined as the horizontal plane in the embankment at and above which the settlements of the interior and exterior prisms of soil are equal. Above the plane of equal settlement there is no tendency for relative movement between the three adjacent prisms and no shearing stresses are generated along the boundaries of the interior prism above this plane, whereas, below it, relative movements do have a tendency to occur and shearing stresses are developed.

A plane of equal settlement in this basic case results from the transfer of pressure, by shear, from the exterior prisms to the interior prism. Since the vertical deformation of a prism of material due to its own weight is a function of the height as well as characteristic of the material, normally the summation of deformations from the bottom of a prism upward will be at a greater rate in a high prism than in a lower one if the prisms act independently of one another. In the case of projecting conduits, however, the exterior prisms of soil transfer a part of their vertical pressure to the interior prism and the rate of summation of vertical deformations will be reduced in the exterior prisms and increased in the interior prism because of this stress transfer. Therefore, the total summation of deformations in the interior prism will approach that in the exterior prisms, and the height at which the deformations become equal is the height of equal settlement.

The existence of a plane of equal settlement was first announced by Dean Marston in 1922[4] on the basis of pure mathematical reasoning and a formula for evaluating its height was developed at that time. Since then the actual existence of such a plane has been demonstrated by measurements of the settlements and of the loads on a number of experimental conduits.

This basic settlement situation is practically always modified by two additional factors which must be considered in the development of a general theory of fill loads. The first of these is the settlement of the undisturbed subgrade under the exterior prisms adjacent to the conduit; and the second, the settlement of the top of the conduit. The settlement of the subgrade adjacent to the conduit augments the downward movement of the two exterior prisms of earth. The settlement of the top of the conduit (which is equal to the sum of the settlement of its foundation and the distortion or shortening of its vertical dimension) has the tendency to neutralize this action by reducing the relative movement between the interior and exterior prisms. Indeed, if the conduit is sufficiently flexible, if it is placed on a very yielding foundation, or if both conditions hold true, the top of the conduit may settle enough to permit the interior prism to move downward a greater amount than the exterior prisms. When this occurs, the direction of the induced shearing stresses is reversed and the stresses are subtractive from the weight of the prism of earth over the conduit. The rate of summation of settlements in relation to height above the conduit for the interior prism is less than that in the exterior prisms due to the reduced pressure. Nevertheless, there still may be a plane of equal settlement, even if the direction of relative movements is reversed, because the total settlement is augmented by the settlement of the top of the conduit, which causes the entire interior prism to move downward.

In this connection it is convenient to define a "critical plane" which is the horizontal plane in the fill material at the level of the top of the conduit at the beginning of construction of the embankment and before settlements have begun to develop. With this definition in mind, the aforementioned facts concerning direction of the induced shearing stresses may be simplified by stating that, when the critical plane settles more than the top of the conduit, the shearing stresses act downward on the interior prism and that, when it settles less, they act upward.

---

[4] "Second Progress Report to the Joint Concrete Culvert Pipe Committee," by Anson Marston, April 7, 1922 (mimeographed).

A neutral or transition case occurs when the top of the conduit settles downward an amount just equal to the settlement of the critical plane. When this case occurs, the plane of equal settlement is right at the top of the conduit and coincident with the critical plane; the interior and exterior prisms of soil move downward equally throughout their full height and no shearing stresses are induced, with the result that the load on the structure is equal to the weight of the prism of soil directly over it. Some typical settlement situations affecting loads on projecting conduits are illustrated in Fig. 6. (The solid

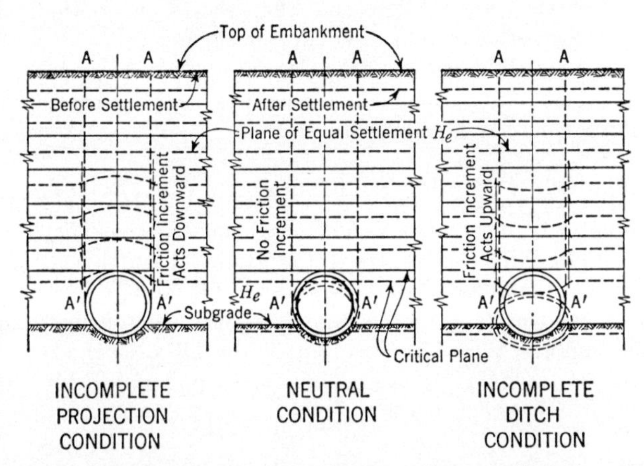

Fig. 6.—Typical Settlement Conditions Affecting Loads on Projecting Conduits

horizontal lines represent imaginary planes of embankment before settlement. The broken lines represent the same planes after settlement.[5])

In the mathematical analysis of loads on projecting conduits, the net effect of all these settlement factors, both as to magnitude and direction of the relative movements of the three prisms of soil, is combined into an abstract ratio known as the "settlement ratio," which is defined as the ratio of the difference between the settlement of the critical plane and the top of the conduit, to the deformation of the fill material adjacent to the conduit within the vertical distance between the top of the conduit and the natural ground line. Dean Marston defined this ratio on the basis of the settlements of the various elements which are produced by that section of the fill above the plane of equal settlement.

For purposes of calculating the external vertical loads on projecting conduits, the field conditions affecting the loads are conveniently grouped into four subclassifications based on the magnitude of the settlement of the interior prism relative to that of the exterior prisms and, therefore, the direction of the shearing stresses, and the height of the embankment in relation to the height of equal settlement. These four conditions are: (1) The complete projection condition, (2) the incomplete projection condition, (3) the complete ditch condition, and (4) the incomplete ditch condition.

[5] "Investigation of Loads on Three Cast Iron Pipe Culverts Under Rock Fills," by M. G. Spangler, *Bulletin No. 104*, Iowa Eng. Experiment Station, Ames, Iowa, 1931, p. 26, Fig. 11.

They are defined as follows:

(1) The "complete projection condition" prevails when the top of the conduit settles less than the critical plane and when the height of the embankment is less than the theoretical height of equal settlement.

(2) The "incomplete projection condition" prevails when the top of the conduit settles less than the critical plane and when the height of the embankment is greater than the height of equal settlement.

(3) The "complete ditch condition" prevails when the top of the conduit settles more than the critical plane and when the height of the embankment is less than the theoretical height of equal settlement.

(4) The "incomplete ditch condition" prevails when the top of the conduit settles more than the critical plane and when the height of the embankment is greater than the height of equal settlement.

MATHEMATICAL DERIVATION OF LOAD FORMULAS FOR PROJECTING CONDUITS

Dean Marston defines[4,6] the various settlements, y, as the "* * * increments due to the addition at or above the height of equal settlement of any [the same for all] incremental uniform layer of fill materials." A settlement ratio is defined as the ratio of the difference between the settlement of the critical plane and the top of the conduit of the fill adjacent to the conduit within the height $\rho\, b_c$ (Fig. 5) caused by the fill material above the plane of equal settlement. In other words:

$$\delta = \frac{(y_m + y_g) - (y_f + y_c)}{y_m} \qquad (4a)$$

in which y_g is the settlement of the embankment subgrade adjacent to the conduit, in feet; y_f is the settlement of the flow line of the conduit; y_c is the deflection of the conduit—that is, the shortening of its vertical dimension; and y_m is the deformation of the filling material adjacent to the conduit within the height $\rho\, b_c$ in feet—that is:

$$y_m = \frac{(H_c - H_e)\,\gamma}{E_f}\,\rho\, b_c \qquad (4b)$$

in which E_f is the modulus of deformation of the filling material. The settlement of the "critical plane," in this notation is $y_m + y_g$ and the settlement of the top of the conduit is $y_f + y_c$. In Eq. 4a, δ is negative for the "incomplete" ditch condition and positive for the "incomplete" projection condition.

Considering first the complete ditch and projection conditions (Fig. 7(a)), in which $H_c < H_e$, the vertical forces on any thin horizontal element of the interior prism may be equated as follows:

$$P + dP = P + \gamma\, b_c\, dH_p \pm 2\, K\, \mu \frac{H_p}{b_c}\, dH_p \qquad (5a)$$

[6] "The Theory of External Loads on Closed Conduits in the Light of the Latest Experiments," by Anson Marston, *Bulletin No. 96*, Iowa Eng. Experiment Station, Ames, Iowa, 1930.

The solution of this equation is

$$P = \gamma\, b^2_c \frac{e^{\pm \beta H_p} - 1}{\pm 2\, K\, \mu} \quad \text{(5b)}$$

in which μ is the coefficient of internal friction of the filling material, and to simplify typography (compare Eq. 2a):

$$\beta = \frac{2\, K\, \mu}{b_c} \quad \text{(5c)}$$

At the top of the conduit, $P = W_c$ and $H_p = H_c$; therefore:

$$W_c = C_c\, \gamma\, b^2_c \quad \text{(6a)}$$

in which the load coefficient for projecting conduits is represented by:

$$C_c = \frac{e^{\pm \beta H_c} - 1}{\pm 2\, K\, \mu} \quad \text{(6b)}$$

in which H_c is the height above the top of a conduit. In Eq. 6b the plus signs are used for the complete projection condition and the minus signs for the complete ditch condition.

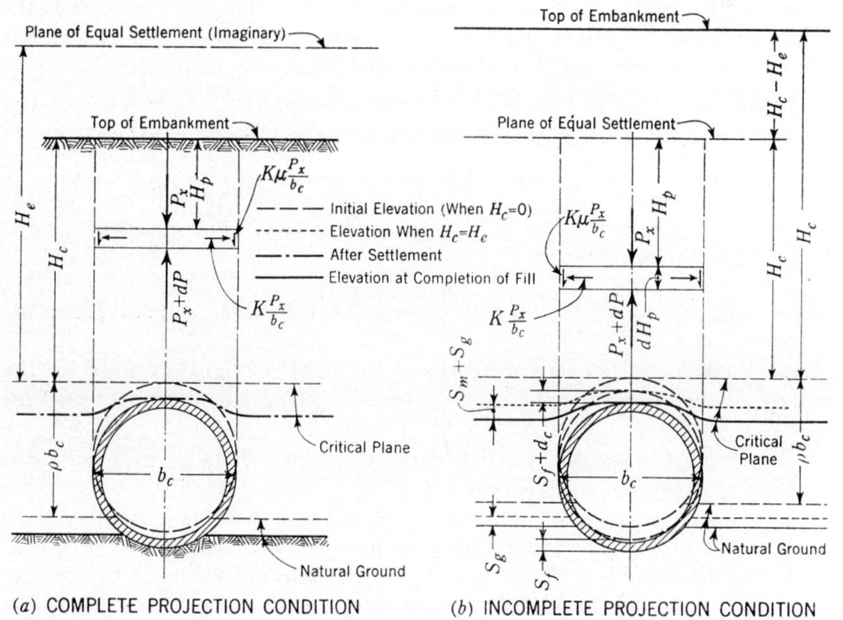

(a) COMPLETE PROJECTION CONDITION (b) INCOMPLETE PROJECTION CONDITION

Fig. 7.—Forces Acting on a Projecting Conduit

Considering the incomplete ditch and the incomplete projection conditions (Fig. 7(b)), in which $H_c > H_e$, and again equating the vertical forces on a thin horizontal element:

$$P + dP = P + \gamma\, b_c\, dH_p \pm 2\, K\, \mu \frac{P}{b_c}\, dH_p \quad \text{(7a)}$$

When $H_p = 0$, $P = (H_c - H_e)\,\gamma\, b_c$ and the solution of this differential equation (Eq. 7*a*) is:

$$P = \frac{\gamma\, b^2_c}{2\,K\,\mu} \pm \frac{\gamma\, b^2_c}{2\,K\,\mu}\, e^{\pm\beta H_p} + (H_c - H_e)\,\gamma\, b_c\, e^{\pm\beta H_p} \quad \text{(7b)}$$

At the top of the conduit, $P = W_c$ and $H_p = H_e$; therefore, in Eq. 6*a*, the load coefficient C_c becomes:

$$C_c = \frac{e^{\pm\beta H_e} - 1}{\pm\, 2\,K\,\mu} + \left(\frac{H_c}{b_c} - \frac{H_e}{b_c}\right) e^{\pm\beta H_e} \quad \text{(8)}$$

As before, the plus signs are applicable to the incomplete projection condition and the minus signs apply to the incomplete ditch condition.

To derive an expression for evaluating H_e, the following two conditions are assumed:

a. The internal friction in the embankment materials distributes the infinitely small increments or decrements of pressure from shear into the interior prism below the plane of equal settlement in such manner that their effect on settlement may be assumed to be substantially the same as for uniform vertical pressure; and

b. The internal friction in the embankment materials distributes the infinitely small decrements or increments of pressure from shear into the exterior prisms so completely that their effect on settlement may be neglected.

Equating the settlements in the exterior prisms and the settlements in the interior prism caused by the fill material above the plane of equal settlement:

$$\frac{(H_c - H_e)\,\gamma}{E_f}\, H_e + y_m + y_o = \int_0^{H_e} \frac{(H_c - H_e)\,\gamma}{E_f}\, e^{\pm\beta H_p}\, dH_p + y_f + y_c \quad \text{(9)}$$

In Eq. 9, using Eqs. 4:

$$e^{\pm\beta H_e} \mp 2\,K\,\mu\,\frac{H_e}{b_c} = \pm\, 2\,K\,\mu\,\delta\,\rho + 1 \quad \text{(10)}$$

In the three quantities of Eq. 10 the +, −, and + signs are used for the projection condition; and the −, +, and − signs, respectively, are used for the ditch condition.

Eq. 10 must be solved by trial, since it contains H_e as an exponent of e, the base of natural logarithms (see Eq. 5*c*).

As in the case of ditch conduits, the solution of these various expressions for loads on projecting conduits is made easy by the construction of a load coefficient diagram,[7,8] as shown in Fig. 8. For selected values of the "settlement" ratio and the "projection" ratio $(\delta\,\rho)$ and given values of H_c/b_c the proper value of the coefficient C_c is read from the curves and substituted in Eq. 6*a*. Comparisons between actual weighed loads in carefully conducted experiments and loads computed by Dean Marston's load theory are shown in Fig. 9.

[7] "The Theory of External Loads on Closed Conduits in the Light of the Latest Experiments," by Anson Marston, *Bulletin No. 96*, Iowa Eng. Experiment Station, Ames, Iowa, 1930, p. 14, Fig. 3.

[8] "The Supporting Strength of Rigid Pipe Culverts," by M. G. Spangler, *Bulletin No. 112*, Iowa Eng. Experiment Station, Ames, Iowa, 1933, p. 46, Fig. 18.

Several alternate methods of determining the value of H_e have been investigated, including an analysis in which the settlement ratio was based on the total settlements of the various elements of the fill and of the conduit caused by the total height of embankment. The loads obtained by this alternate analysis were nearly the same as those obtained by Dean Marston's original analysis, being somewhat less for high values of $\frac{H_e}{b_c}$ and $\delta\,\rho$.

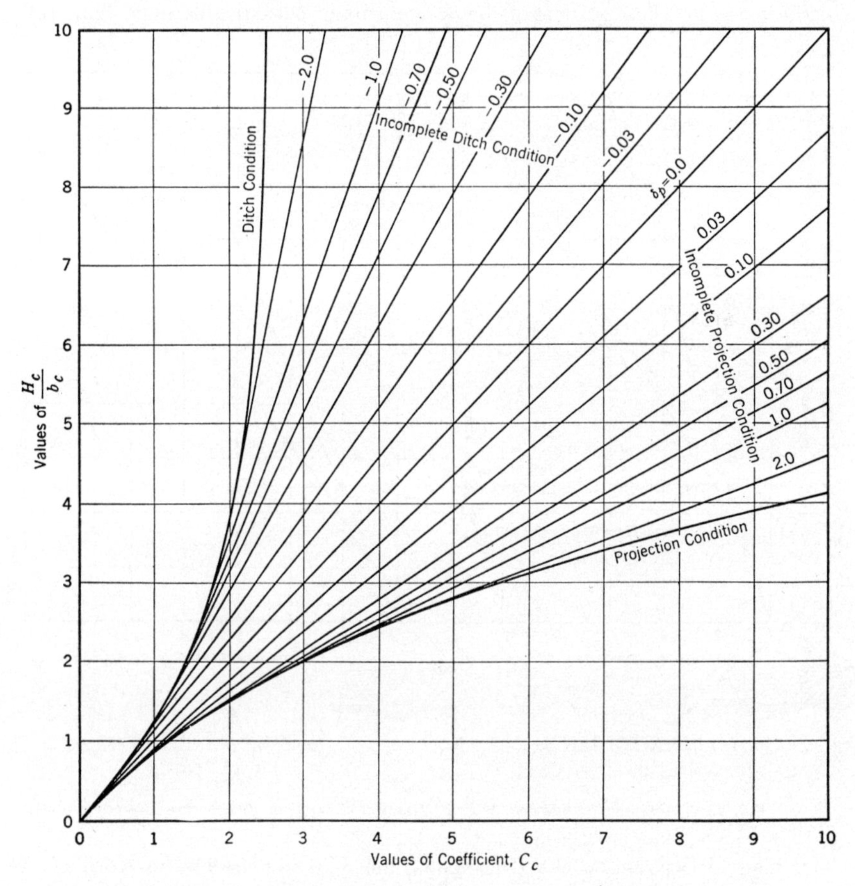

Fig. 8.—Computation Diagram for External Loads on Conduits ($K\mu = 0.1924$)

Working values of μ, the coefficient of internal friction of the embankment material, may be determined by soil tests in a particular case. However, Dean Marston has shown that the variation in load on a projecting conduit is relatively small for wide variations of the coefficient of internal friction. For example, when this coefficient varies from about 0.3 to 1.0, corresponding to angles of friction from about 17° to 45°, the product $K\mu$ varies from about 0.17 to 0.1924 and back to 0.17. Since the load is dependent upon the product $K\mu$ and not on μ alone, a value of $K\mu = 0.19$ may reasonably be chosen as a safe working value for most cases of projecting conduit loads.

Time Effect on Loads

To study the effect of time on the loads produced on culverts by earth embankments, three test culverts supported on weighing devices were built and loaded with a 15-ft embankment late in the fall of 1927, and observations of the loads on these structures have been made periodically since that date.

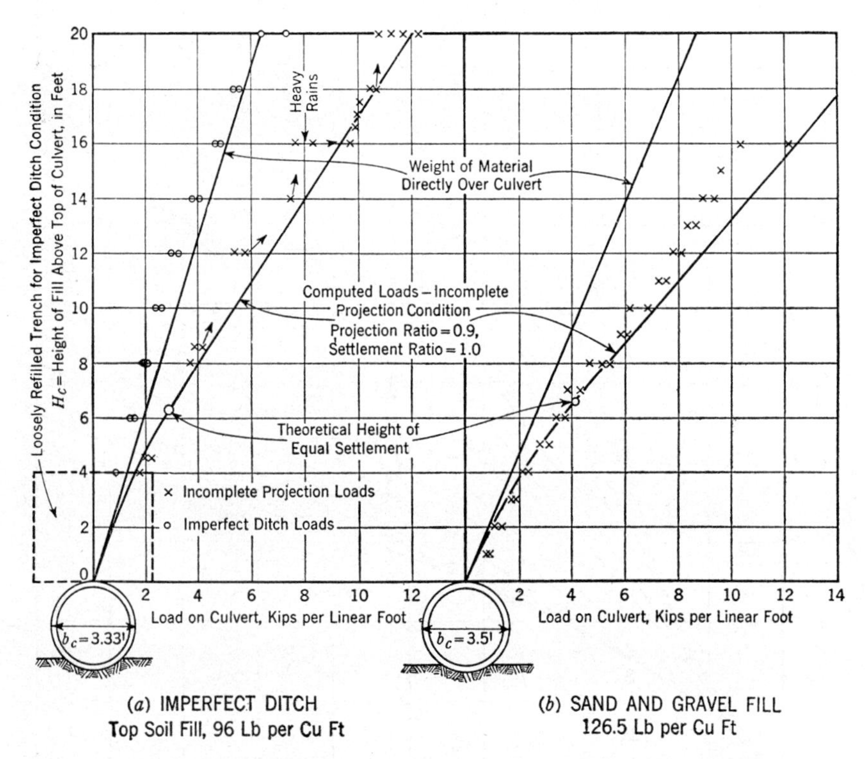

Fig. 9.—Comparison Between Actual Weighed Loads on Projecting Conduits

This load history shows that the maximum load was reached in April of the following spring after the fill was completed, after which the load fell off somewhat, reaching a low point about 10% below the maximum in the following October and November. Since that date, the load has fluctuated between these approximate limits, reaching the maximum for each year early in the spring and the minimum late in the fall.

Eq. 10 for H_e has been derived for the assumed case in which the fill material has a uniform modulus of deformation throughout; and it is emphasized that the value of H_e is independent of the value of this modulus. In other words, even if the fill material is thoroughly compacted during placement and a high value of the compression modulus is attained, the direction of the relative settlements of the interior and exterior prisms and the height of equal settlement will not be affected thereby.

The settlement ratio is wholly rational in the theoretical analysis of loads on projecting conduits. However, except in unusual cases it will not be practicable to predict the value to use in the design of a given structure on the basis of individual study and analysis of the soil at a proposed site. It has been deemed advisable and appropriate, therefore, to consider the settlement ratio as a semi-empirical factor and to determine proper design values on the basis of the observed performance of projecting conduits in service.

Rather extensive field measurements of the settlement characteristics of some actual culverts under the highways of Iowa and southern Minnesota, which have been conducted by the Iowa Engineering Experiment Station in cooperation with the Public Roads Administration, Federal Works Agency, tentatively indicate the following working values for the settlement ratio—for rigid culverts on:

Foundation material	δ
Rock or other unyielding material	+ 1.0
Ordinary earth	+ 0.5 to + 0.8

Observations of the settlement ratio have been made on a few flexible type culverts in actual service, but the number of specimens is limited. These measured values ranged from 0 to + 0.7 and they varied directly with the values of the modulus of passive pressure of the side-fill materials. It appears, therefore, that high quality densification of the side fills around a flexible pipe, for the purpose of increasing the modulus of passive pressure, tends to increase the load on the pipe. However, the ultimate deflection of the pipe is decreased by this practice, since the increase in supporting strength of the pipe more than offsets the effect of the increased load.

Unusual installation conditions may cause exceptional values of the settlement ratio and of the load to develop. For example, a case has come to the writer's attention where a highway fill was built across a salt marsh underlain with stiff clay at about 10 ft or 12 ft below the surface. A concrete pipe culvert was built prior to construction of the fill. To reduce the expected settlement of the culvert and to increase its supporting strength, the pipes were laid in a well-designed concrete cradle, which in turn was supported on piles driven into the clay stratum. Shortly after the fill was completed this culvert collapsed, even though it was constructed of excellent reinforced concrete pipe. Although no settlement data are available, it seems probable that the fill material at the sides (the "exterior prisms") settled a very large amount due to the soft spongy character of the marsh bed, whereas the culvert resting on piles driven to the stiff clay could not settle. Under these conditions the critical plane probably settled much more than the top of the culvert, causing a very high positive value of the settlement ratio and a very high load to develop.

Imperfect Ditch Conduits

In the early days of Dean Marston's researches on conduit loads, he was impressed by the very high loads that may develop on projecting conduits when the conditions are such that large shearing forces add to the weight of the prism of soil directly over the conduit, and he strove to devise a method of construction that would reduce or eliminate these shearing forces, or would possibly reverse their direction so that they would act benevolently as in the case of ditch conduits. With this objective in mind, he developed the imperfect ditch method of construction in which the soil on both sides and above the conduit for some distance above its top is thoroughly compacted by rolling, tamping, or any other suitable method. Then a ditch is constructed in this compacted fill by removing the prism of material directly over the conduit. The ditch is refilled with very loose compressible material, after which the embankment is completed in a normal manner.

The purpose of this method of construction is accomplished by creating a condition wherein it is certain that the prism of material directly over the conduit will settle more than the adjacent prism; the ditch in the artificially compacted material must be deep enough and the refilling material must be loose enough to insure this action. Straw or other highly compressible material may be used as part of the ditch backfill to augment the settlement of the interior prism. The efficacy of this method of construction was demonstrated by a series of experiments conducted by Dean Marston from 1919 to 1921, in which the load on a conduit was measured, first, when the fill was constructed in the ordinary manner for a projecting conduit, and, second, when the fill was constructed by the imperfect ditch method. The loads measured in these experiments are shown in Fig. 9(*a*).

Surface Loads

In addition to external loads imposed by the filling material around and above underground conduits, these structures are also subjected to loads resulting from highway, railway, or airplane traffic or from other types of loads applied at the surface and transmitted through the soil to the underground structure. Such loads are of major importance when a conduit is placed under a trafficway with a relatively shallow covering of earth.

John H. Griffith, M. ASCE, was among the first to suggest the applicability of the Boussinesq solution[9] for the distribution of stress in a semi-infinite elastic solid to various problems of stress distribution in soils in a report prepared for a subcommittee on soils of the United States Bureau of Standards of which he was chairman. Extensive experiments[10,11] on both ditch and projecting conduits subsequent to this suggestion have shown that a concentrated surface load, such as a truck wheel, is transmitted through the soil covering to the underground structure substantially in accord with the Boussinesq solution.

[9] "Revised Report of Subcommittee on Soils," U. S. Bureau of Standards, *Proceedings*, ASCE, Vol. XLVI, 1920, pp. 916–941.

[10] "The Causes of Structural Failures of Sewers," by Anson Marston and M. G. Spangler, *Proceedings*, Am. Soc. of Municipal Engrs., Vol. 38, 1933, p. 236.

[11] "Experimental Determinations of Static and Impact Loads Transmitted to Culverts," by M. G. Spangler, Clyde Mason, and Robley Winfrey, *Bulletin No. 79*, Iowa Eng. Experiment Station, Ames, Iowa, 1926.

From these facts, the load on an underground conduit due to a concentrated surface load may be expressed as:

$$W_P = \frac{1}{L} F_i C_t P_0 \ldots\ldots\ldots\ldots\ldots\ldots\ldots (11)$$

in which W_P is the average load on an underground conduit due to a concentrated surface load, in pounds per linear foot; P_0 is a concentrated surface load, in pounds; F_i is an impact factor; L is the length of the conduit, in feet; and C_t is a coefficient for load on an underground conduit due to a concentrated surface load.

The coefficient C_t may be calculated by dividing the area of the top of the conduit or its horizontal projection, $L\, b_c$, into a number of small areas as illustrated in Fig. 10, and summing up the total pressure on all these small areas, according to the formula:

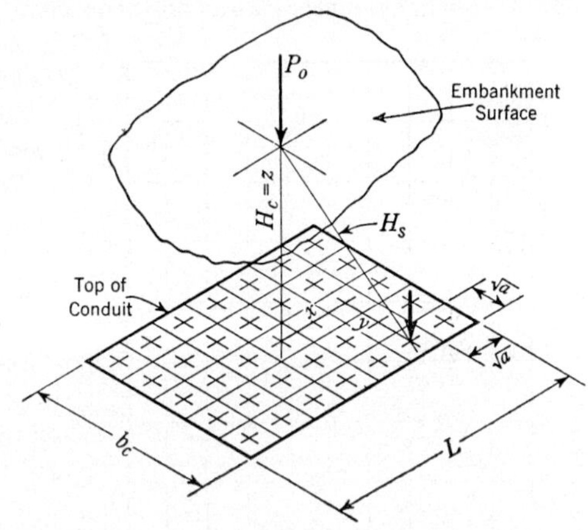

Fig. 10.—Computation of the Concentrated Surface Load Transmitted to an Underground Conduit

$$C_t = a \sum \frac{3}{2\,\pi} \frac{H^3_c}{H^5_s} \ldots (12a)$$

in which a is the area of an element, in square feet; H_c is the vertical height from the top of the conduit to the embankment surface, in feet; and H_s is the slant height, in feet, from the center of each element to the point of application of the load; that is: $H_s = \sqrt{x^2 + y^2 + z^2}$, in feet.

Early in 1929 D. L. Holl integrated this expression for C_t and obtained:

$$C_t = 1 - \frac{2}{\pi}\left\{\left[\sin^{-1} H_c \sqrt{\frac{\frac{L^2}{4} + \frac{b^2_c}{4} + H^2_c}{\left(\frac{L^2}{4} + H^2_c\right)\left(\frac{b^2_c}{4} + H^2_c\right)}}\right] - \frac{\frac{L\, b_c\, H_c}{4}}{\sqrt{\frac{L^2}{4} + \frac{b^2_c}{4} + H^2_c}}\left(\frac{1}{\frac{L^2}{4} + H^2_c} + \frac{1}{\frac{b^2_c}{4} + H^2_c}\right)\right\} \ldots\ldots\ldots (12b)$$

Eq. 12*b* can be evaluated[12] readily by the table prepared by N. M. Newmark,[13] M.ASCE, for determining stresses in the soil beneath uniformly loaded rectangular foundations.

[12] "A Method of Computing Live Loads Transmitted to Underground Conduits," by M. G. Spangler and Richard L. Hennessy, *Proceedings*, Highway Research Board, National Research Council, Vol. 26, 1946, p. 179.

[13] "Simplified Computation of Vertical Pressures in Elastic Foundations," by Nathan M. Newmark, *Circular No. 24*, Eng. Experiment Station, Univ. of Illinois, Urbana, Ill., 1935.

Values of C_t for conduits 3 ft long of various widths, b_c, are shown[14] in Fig. 11 for various heights of fill up to 10 ft. When fill loads and surface loads are combined to obtain the design load on an underground conduit, the minimum load will be found to occur when the height of fill is relatively low over the top of the structure.

The impact factor, F_i, is equal to unity when the surface load is static. When it is moving, as in the case of truck or airplane wheels, the value of F_i may vary widely depending on speed of the vehicle, vibratory action, wing uplift, and most important, on roughness characteristics of the roadway surface. Experiments[9] have indicated design values of F_i ranging from 1.5 to 2.0 for highway traffic on an unsurfaced roadway.

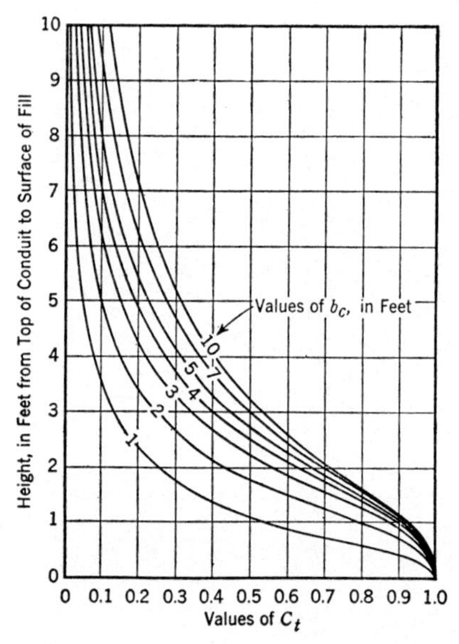

Fig. 11.—Concentrated Surface Load Coefficients for Underground (L = 3 Ft)

Professor Griffith gave extensive consideration to problems of the transmission of stress through soils and the applicability of the Boussinesq classical solution to them. In 1929 he developed a generalized expression[15] for the intensity of vertical pressure in a soil mass due to a concentrated surface load in the form:

$$P_z = \frac{\nu}{2\pi} P_0 \frac{\cos^{\nu+2}\theta}{z^2} \quad \ldots (13)$$

in which P_z is the intensity of pressure at a point in the soil mass; P_0 is the concentrated load applied at a point on the surface; θ is the angle formed with the vertical by the radius vector from the point of application of the surface load to the point considered; z is the vertical distance from the surface to the point; and ν is a disposable parameter, often referred to as the "concentration" factor or "dispersion" factor.

Professor Holl[16] has utilized Eq. 13 in the solution of a number of problems dealing with the transmission of surface loads through soil masses.

The Supporting Strength of Underground Conduits

Underground conduits are constructed in a wide variety of shapes and of many different structural materials. In general, the load on a conduit is independent of its shape and the material of which it is made. In contrast, the supporting strength of a conduit is intimately dependent upon its shape and the kind and quality of material of which it is made. The remainder of this

[14] "The Theory of External Loads on Closed Conduits in the Light of the Latest Experiments," by Anson Marston, *Bulletin No. 96*, Iowa Eng. Experiment Station, Ames, Iowa, 1931, p. 19, Fig. 5.

[15] "Dynamics of Earth and Other Macroscopic Matter," by John H. Griffith, *Bulletin No. 117*, Iowa Eng. Experiment Station, Ames, Iowa, 1934.

[16] "Stress Transmission in Earths," by D. L. Holl, *Proceedings*, Highway Research Board, National Research Council, Vol. 20, 1940, p. 709.

paper will be devoted to a discussion of the supporting strength of a number of commonly used types of conduits.

Monolithic Arch and Box Culverts or Sewers.—These monolithic types of reinforced concrete structures may be designed satisfactorily by any current procedures for analysis of rigid frame structures. Numerous measurements of the distribution of the vertical load on both rectangular and circular shaped culverts due to the earth overburden have indicated that it is essentially uniformly distributed over the width of the conduit and may be so considered for design purposes. Culverts may or may not be subjected to active lateral pressure on all or part of their side-wall areas, depending on the local situation.

Some laboratory experiments[17] on the supporting strength of monolithic box culverts indicate that the actual supporting strength exceeds the calculated strength until the concrete of the top slab cracks, after which the actual strength very closely approximates the calculated strength.

Rigid Circular Pipes.—Rigid circular pipes, which are usually pre-cast of such materials as burned clay, plain or reinforced concrete, or cast iron, are difficult to analyze by principles of mechanics; and, since they are usually relatively small structures, their supporting strength can be most easily determined by testing a representative group of specimens in the laboratory. Several methods of testing short sections of circular pipes have been devised[18] —the two-edge bearing, the three-edge bearing, the sand bearing, and the Minnesota bearing tests—the details of which are shown in Fig. 12. Of these,

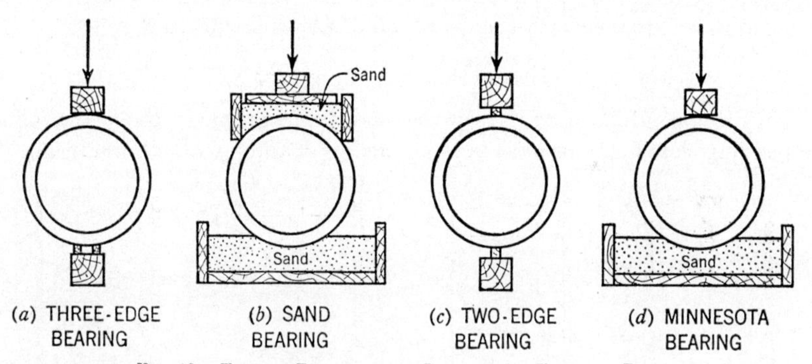

Fig. 12.—Typical Bearings for Laboratory Tests of Pipes

the three-edge bearing test (Fig. 12(*a*)) is the simplest and most easily performed. At the same time it gives accurate and uniform results, and for these reasons it is widely used in tests to determine the strength of pipes, although some engineers prefer the sand bearing test (Fig. 12(*b*)) because of the wider distribution of both the applied load and reaction.

The test load and reaction on the pipe are distributed differently in each of these types of tests and the ultimate load or supporting strength will like-

[17] "The Supporting Strength of Reinforced Concrete Box Culverts," by George C. Pagels, thesis presented to Iowa State College, Ames, Iowa, in 1935 in partial fulfilment of the requirements for the degree of Master of Science.

[18] "The Supporting Strength of Rigid Pipe Culverts," by M..G. Spangler, *Bulletin No. 112*, Iowa Eng. Experiment Station, Ames, Iowa, 1933, p. 13, Fig. 5.

wise be different. It is convenient to express the supporting strength of a pipe in terms of its strength when tested by the three-edged bearing method, taken as unity, by a load factor or strength ratio which is defined as the ratio of the strength of a pipe under any stated condition of loading to its three-edge bearing test strength. The following values of load factor or strength ratio for the other three test methods shown in Fig. 12 are applicable:

Test	Load factor
Sand bearing	1.5
Two-edge bearing	1.0
Minnesota bearing	1.1

Likewise when a pipe is placed and loaded in an actual field installation, the loads and reactions will be distributed much differently than in the test loading; and, in certain cases, lateral pressures will be exerted against the sides of the pipe thereby increasing its ability to support vertical loads.

A wide variety of bedding conditions affecting the load and reaction distribution and the lateral pressure situation may be encountered in sewerage, water works, and culvert construction practice; and a wide variety of supporting strengths of a given conduit may be obtained simply by varying the installation conditions. It is feasible to establish and define classifications of bedding conditions covering a range of practical attainments and determine a load factor for each classification which, when multiplied by the three-edge bearing laboratory strength of the pipe, will give the safe supporting strength for pipes installed in accordance with the definition of that classification.

Ditch Conduit Beddings

For ditch conduits used in sewerage and drainage construction, the following bedding classifications have been defined[19,20,21] and are illustrated in Fig. 13.

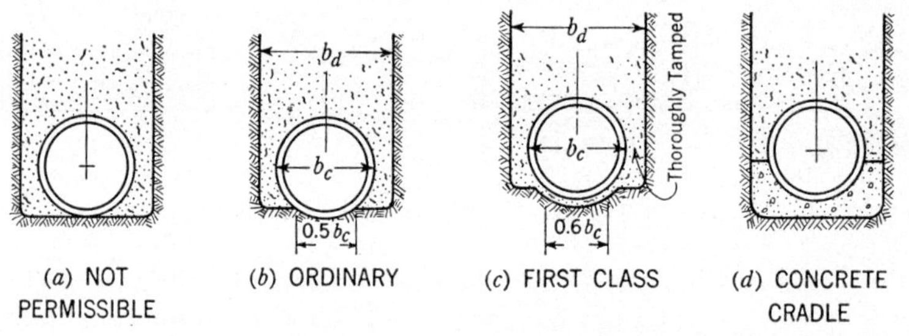

Fig. 13.—Typical Bedding Specifications for Sewers and Other Ditch Conduits

Bedding conditions for cast-iron pipe in water works construction will be discussed subsequently.

[19] "The Supporting Strength of Sewer Pipe in Ditches and Methods of Testing Sewer Pipe in Laboratories to Determine Their Ordinary Supporting Strength," by Anson Marston, W. J. Schlick, and H. F. Clemmer, *Bulletin No. 47*, Iowa Eng. Experiment Station, Ames, Iowa, 1917.

[20] "Supporting Strength of Drain Tile and Sewer Pipe Under Different Pipe-Laying Conditions," by W. J. Schlick, *Bulletin No. 57*, Iowa Eng. Experiment Station, Ames, Iowa, 1920.

[21] "Concrete Cradles for Large Pipe Conduits," by W. J. Schlick and James W. Johnson, *Bulletin No. 80*, Iowa Eng. Experiment Station, Ames, Iowa, 1926.

1. "Impermissible" bedding (Fig. 13(*a*)) is that method of bedding ditch conduits in which little or no care is exercised to shape the foundation to fit the lower part of the conduit exterior and to refill all spaces under and around the conduit.

2. "Ordinary" bedding (Fig. 13(*b*)) is that method of bedding ditch conduits in which the conduit is placed with "ordinary" care in an earth foundation shaped to fit the lower part of the conduit exterior with reasonable closeness for a width of at least 50% of the conduit breadth. The remainder of the conduit is surrounded to a height of at least 0.5 ft above its top by granular materials, shovel placed and shovel tamped to fill completely all spaces under and adjacent to the conduit—all under the general direction of a competent engineer.

3. "First-class" bedding (Fig. 13(*c*)) is that method of bedding ditch conduits in which the conduit is set on fine granular materials in an earth foundation carefully shaped to fit the lower part of the conduit exterior for a width of at least 60% of the conduit breadth. The remainder of the conduit is entirely surrounded to a height of at least 1.0 ft above its top by granular materials carefully placed by hand to fill, completely, all spaces under and adjacent to the conduit. The fill is tamped thoroughly on each side and under the conduit as far as practicable in layers not exceeding 0.5 ft thick—all under the direction of a competent engineer represented by a competent inspector constantly present during the operation.

4. "Concrete-cradle" bedding is that method of bedding conduits in which the lower part of the conduit exterior is set in plain or reinforced concrete, of suitable thickness, under the lowest part of the conduit exterior and extending upward on each side of the conduit for a greater or less proportion of its height.

The load factor for each of these bedding classifications has been determined experimentally to be:

Figure No.	Bedding	Load factor
13(*a*)	Impermissible	1.1
13(*b*)	Ordinary	1.5
13(*c*)	First class	1.9
13(*d*)	Concrete cradle	2.2 to 3.4

Projecting Conduit Beddings

In culvert construction practice, rigid pipes are often installed as projecting conduits and the fill material may exert an active lateral pressure against the sides of the pipes, which tends to increase the supporting strength of the structure. The supporting strength of a projecting conduit, therefore, is a function of both the distribution of the vertical load and the reaction on the pipe, and the magnitude and distribution of the active lateral pressure on sides which are exposed to the embankment filling material.

Because of the large number of possible combinations of reaction distributions and effective lateral pressure distributions, the experimental determination of load factors for projecting conduits has been supplemented by analytical studies of the stress situation in pipe rings under various combinations of loads and lateral pressures.[22] By definition, the load factor is

$$F_p = \frac{R_c}{R_{eb}} \qquad (14a)$$

in which F_p is the load factor; R_c is the supporting strength of the pipe in any stated loading condition; and R_{eb} is the three-edge bearing supporting strength of the pipe.

Except for the normal variations in physical properties of the material of which culvert pipes are made, it is sufficiently accurate to assume that the outer fiber stress at the point and at the time of rupture will be the same whether the pipe is loaded in a testing machine or in an actual embankment. Therefore, the thin ring elastic theory and the flexure formula may be used to express the outer fiber stress in terms of the loads on the pipe in the field and laboratory loadings; and, by equating these expressions, the load factor is readily determined. When the field loading situation is such that the pipe cracks first at the bottom, this process leads to the formula:

$$F_p = \frac{1.431}{X_P - X_A \kappa_t} \qquad (14b)$$

in which X_P is a parameter which is a function of the distribution of the vertical load and vertical reaction; X_A is a parameter which is a function of the area of the vertical projection of the pipe on which the active lateral pressure of the fill material acts; and κ_t is the ratio of the total lateral pressure to the total vertical load.

When the load and reaction situation causes the pipe to crack first at the top (which is usually the case when pipes are bedded in concrete cradle), X'_P and X'_A should be substituted for X_P and X_A in Eq. 14*b*. Values of the parameters X_A and X'_A for various projection ratios are as follows:

Projection ratio, p	Values of X_A	Values of X'_A
0	0	0.150
0.3	0.217	0.743
0.5	0.423	0.856
0.7	0.549	0.811
0.9	0.655	0.678
1.0	0.638	0.638

As in the case of ditch conduits, it is convenient to name and define several classes of bedding conditions for projecting conduits and to determine a value of X_P or X'_P for each class. These classes of bedding are defined as follows:[23]

1. "Impermissible projection bedding" is that method of bedding projecting conduits in which little or no care is exercised either to shape the foundation surface to fit the lower part of the conduit exterior or to fill all spaces under and around the conduit with granular materials. This type of bedding also includes the case of conduits on rock foundations in which an earth cushion is

[22] "The Supporting Strength of Rigid Pipe Culverts," by M. G. Spangler, *Bulletin No. 112*, Iowa Eng. Experiment Station, Ames, Iowa, 1933.

[23] *Ibid.*, p. 15, Fig. 6.

provided under the conduit, but is so shallow that the conduit, as it settles under the influence of vertical load, approaches contact with the rock.

2. "Ordinary projection bedding" is that method of bedding projecting conduits under embankments in which the conduit is bedded with "ordinary" care in an earth foundation shaped to fit the lower part of the conduit exterior with reasonable closeness for at least 10% of its over-all height. The remainder of the conduit is surrounded by granular materials, placed by shovel to fill all spaces completely under and adjacent to the conduit—all under the general direction of a competent engineer. In the case of rock foundations, the pipes are bedded on an earth cushion, having a thickness under the pipe of not less than 0.5 in. per foot of height of fill, with a minimum allowable thickness of 8 in.

3. "First-class projection bedding" is that method of bedding projecting conduits, having a projection ratio not greater than 0.70, in which the conduit is carefully bedded on fine granular materials in an earth foundation carefully shaped to fit the lower part of the conduit exterior for at least 10% of its over-all height. The earth filling material is thoroughly rammed and tamped, in layers not more than 6 in. deep, around the conduit for the remainder of the lower 30% of its height—all under the direction of a competent engineer, represented by a competent inspector constantly present during the operation. In the case of rock foundations, the pipes are bedded in an earth cushion having a depth as provided under ordinary projection bedding.

4. "Concrete-cradle projection bedding" is that method of bedding conduits in which the lower part of the conduit exterior is bedded in a cradle, constructed of 2,000-lb concrete, or better, having a minimum thickness under the pipe of one fourth of the nominal internal diameter and extending up the sides of the pipe for a height equal to one fourth of the outside diameter. The values of X_P for these bedding classes are as follows:

Type of projection bedding	Value of X_P
Impermissible	1.310
Ordinary	0.840
First class	0.707
Concrete cradle (X'_P)	0.505

Working values of the load factor F_P, computed for rigid culvert pipes installed as projecting conduits on ordinary, first-class, and concrete-cradle beddings, with various projection ratios and a value of the settlement ratio of 0.7 are shown in Fig. 14. The general correctness of the foregoing analytical method of determining load factors has been established by a series of experiments in which ten pipe culverts of four kinds of material—plain concrete, reinforced concrete, burned clay, and cast iron—were loaded by earth embankments and their supporting strengths determined. Then samples of pipes representative of each of the ten culverts were tested in the laboratory by the three-edge bearing test and the ratios of the field and laboratory strengths were obtained.[24]

[24] "The Supporting Strength of Rigid Pipe Culverts," by M. G. Spangler, *Bulletin No. 112*, Iowa Eng. Experiment Station, Ames, Iowa, 1933, p. 53.

Concrete-Incased Clay Pipe

Circumstances may arise under which an engineer may wish to increase the strength of clay pipes by incasing them in concrete. Some extensive experiments[25] in which commercial vitrified salt-glazed clay pipe was incased in plain concrete and the combined structure tested in both sand and three-edge bearings have indicated that the test strength is only slightly greater than the sum of the individual supporting strengths of the clay pipe and of the incase-

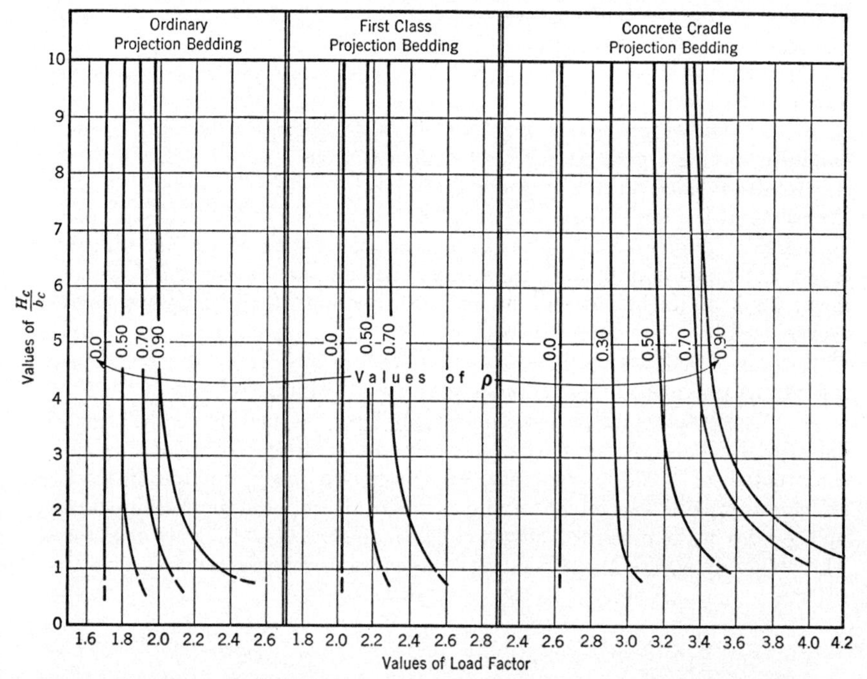

Fig. 14.—Working Values of the Load Factor for Projecting Conduits ($\delta = 0.70$)

ment. The action of the incased pipe was very nearly that of two independent but concentric rings—the supporting strength of the combined structure being very much less than if the two materials had acted as a unit in resisting the stresses due to the test load. As a result of these experiments, computations have been made of the three-edge bearing supporting strength of A.S.T.M. (American Society for Testing Materials) standard sewer pipe when incased in concrete of various thicknesses. The results of these computations are shown in Fig. 15.

The Supporting Strength of Cast-Iron Pipe When Subjected to Internal Pressure

When used for the transportation of water, gas, or other fluids, cast-iron pipe conduits not only are subjected to the ring stresses produced by the

[25] "Supporting Strength of Concrete-Incased Clay Pipe," by W. J. Schlick, *Bulletin No. 93*, Iowa Eng. Experiment Station, Ames, Iowa, 1929.

external loads due to backfilling and surface loads, but in addition must resist the stresses produced by the internal fluid pressure as well. Since 1939 completed studies[26, 27, 28] on the supporting strength of this kind of pipe under combined loads and pressures indicated an approximately parabolic relationship between the magnitude of the external load and the internal pressure which is required to cause failure of the pipe. The external loads may be those for any loading condition, although usually it will be most convenient to test the pipe in three-edge bearings and then apply the proper strength ratio or load factor to calculate the equivalent supporting strength under any particular field condition of installation.

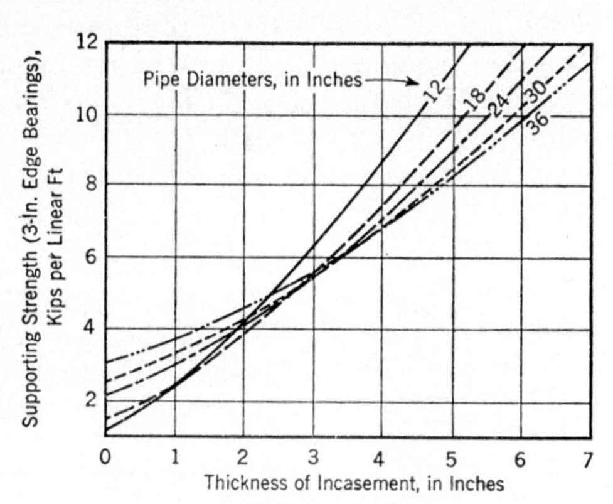

FIG. 15.—SUPPORTING STRENGTHS (AT 70° F) OF STANDARD A.S.T.M. SEWER PIPE, INCASED IN 3,000-LB CONCERTE

Safe design values of the strength ratio have been determined for cast-iron pit-cast pipes installed under six different field conditions, as follows:

Condition	Trench	Backfill
A	Flat bottom	Untamped
B	Flat bottom	Firmly tamped under and around pipe
C	Pipe laid on blocks	Untamped
D	Pipe laid on blocks	Firmly tamped under and around pipe
E	Shaped bottom	Untamped
F	Shaped bottom	Firmly tamped under and around pipe

Quoting W. J. Schlick,[29] M. ASCE:

"The safe design values of the strength ratio for these field conditions are shown for nominal pipe diameters from 4" to 60" [in Fig. 16]. The values shown in this figure have been adopted by Sectional Committee A21 of the American Standards Association, with whom this research work was conducted on a cooperative basis. They are based directly upon the experimental results although those adopted for conditions B and F have been reduced from the experimental values in the belief that the tamped earth beddings in the laboratory tests were more carefully made and therefore more effective than is safe to assume for field conditions."

[26] "A Proposed New Method for Determining Barrel Thicknesses of Cast Iron Pipe," by T. H. Wiggin, M. L. Enger, and W. J. Schlick, *Journal*, A.W.W.A., May, 1939, p 841.

[27] "American Recommended Practice Manual for Computation of Strength and Thickness of Cast Iron Pipe" (A21.1), A.S.A., 1939.

[28] "Supporting Strength of Cast-Iron Pipe for Water and Gas Service," by W. J. Schlick, *Bulletin. No. 146*, Iowa Eng. Experiment Station, Ames, Iowa, 1940.

[29] *Ibid.*, p. 8, Fig. 2.

FLEXIBLE PIPES

In general, it may be stated that underground conduits derive their capacity to support the earth above them from two sources: First, the inherent strength of the pipe to resist external pressures; and, second, the lateral pressure of the soil at the sides of the pipe. In rigid pipes such as those made of concrete, cast iron, and burned clay, the inherent strength of the pipe is the predominant source of supporting strength.

In flexible pipes such as corrugated metal culverts and thin-walled steel conduits, the situation is reversed. The pipe itself has relatively little inherent strength, and a large part of its capability of supporting vertical load must be derived from the passive pressures induced as the sides move outward against the soil.

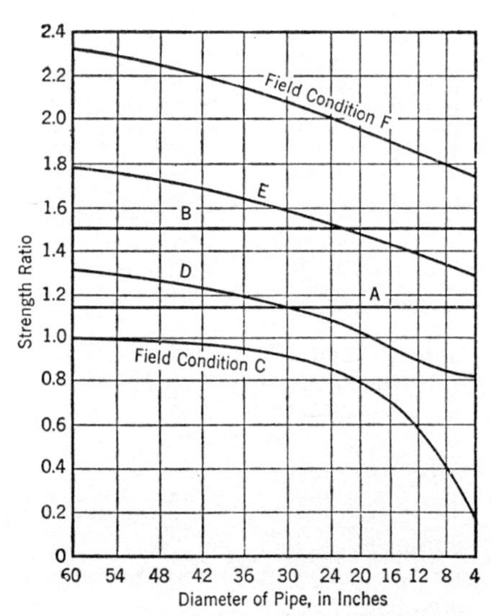

FIG. 16.—WORKING VALUES OF STRENGTH RATIO FOR CAST-IRON PIT-CAST PIPE IN SIX FIELD CONDITIONS

Another major difference between the rigid types of conduits and the flexible types is that the latter fail by deflection rather than by rupture of the pipe walls, as do the former. The action of a flexible pipe under embankment loading is one of large deflection change unaccompanied by rupture of the pipe wall; and, for this reason, the design of the flexible types of conduits should be based upon the deflection of the ring rather than upon stress in the side walls as in the case of the rigid types. This statement is predicated on the assumption that the longitudinal joints in the flexible pipe are sufficiently strong to develop the pipe wall as a continuous ring.

Laboratory tests[30] of short sections of corrugated metal culvert pipes of various diameters and gages of metal have indicated that the elastic theory of flexure as applied to thin rings by Claude W. L. Filkins and Edwin J. Fort,[31] M. ASCE, is applicable to these flexible conduits, even if the deflections and changes in radius of the elastic ring are relatively very large. Therefore, if the loads and pressures acting on a flexible pipe are known or can be assumed confidently, the deflection of the pipe can be determined by this theory within the elastic limit of the pipe material. Typical results of laboratory measurements of diameter changes under three-edge loading conditions are shown in Fig. 17.

---

[30] "The Structural Design of Flexible Pipe Culverts," by M. G. Spangler, *Bulletin No. 153*, Iowa Eng. Experiment Station, Ames, Iowa, 1941.

[31] "Stresses and Deflections in Circular Rings Under Various Conditions of Loading," by Claude W. L. Filkins and Edwin J. Fort, *Transactions*, Assn. of Civ. Engrs. of Cornell Univ., Ithaca, N. Y., Vol. IV, 1896, pp. 99–112.

A number of field loading experiments on corrugated metal pipe culverts, in which the vertical and lateral pressures and the deflections of the pipes were measured have led to the following conclusions regarding soil pressures and deflections of flexible conduits:

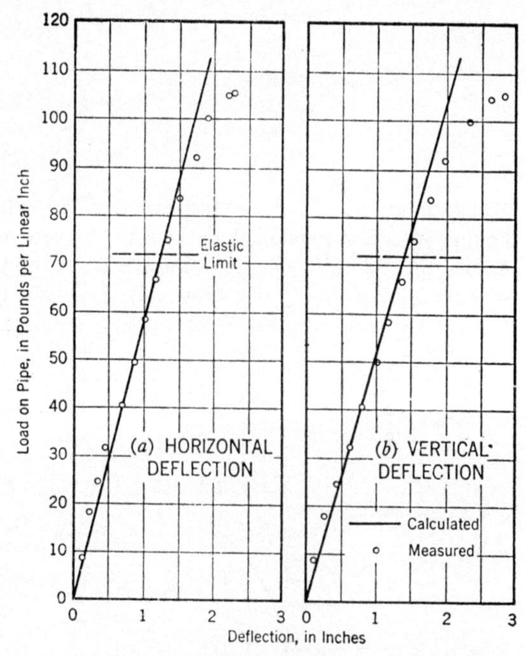

FIG. 17.—LOAD-DEFLECTION DIAGRAMS FOR A 42-IN. CORRUGATED CULVERT PIPE ON THREE-EDGE BEARINGS

1. The vertical load may be determined by Dean Marston's theory of loads on conduits; it is distributed approximately uniformly over the breadth of the pipe.

2. The vertical reaction is equal to the vertical load and is distributed approximately uniformly over the width of bedding of the pipe.

3. The horizontal pressure on each side of the pipe is distributed parabolically over the middle of 100° of the pipe, and the maximum unit pressure (which occurs at the ends of the horizontal diameter of the pipe) is equal to the modulus of passive resistance of the fill material multiplied by one half of the horizontal deflection of the pipe.

4. The pipe may continue to deform for some period of time after the maximum fill load has developed, due to continuing deformation of the side fills under lateral pressure. The assumed loading is shown graphically[32] in Fig. 18. The expression for horizontal deflection resulting from these hypotheses is:

$$\Delta = F_d \frac{F_k W_c r^3}{E I + 0.061 \epsilon r^4} \qquad (15)$$

in which Δ is the horizontal deflection of the pipe, in inches; F_d is the deflection lag factor; F_k is a bedding constant, depending upon the bedding angle; W_c is the vertical load per unit length of the pipe, in pounds per inch; r is the mean radius of the pipe, in inches; E is the modulus of elasticity of the pipe material, in inches; I is the moment of inertia per unit length of cross section of pipe wall, in inches^4 per inch; and ϵ is the modulus of passive resistance of the enveloping soil, in pounds per square inch per inch.

[32] "The Structural Design of Flexible Pipe Culverts," by M. G. Spangler, *Bulletin No. 153*, Iowa Eng. Experiment Station, Ames, Iowa, 1941, p. 26, Fig. 17.

Values of the bedding constant, F_k, for various values of the bedding angle are:

Degrees	Bedding constant, F_k
0	0.110
15	0.108
22.5	0.105
30	0.102
45	0.096
60	0.090
90	0.083

The modulus of passive resistance of the side filling material is defined as the unit pressure developed as the side of a pipe moves outward a unit distance against the side fill. Little is known concerning the nature of this modulus. In the Rankine theory of lateral soil pressures, the limiting value of the ratio of passive horizontal pressure to vertical pressure which a granular soil without

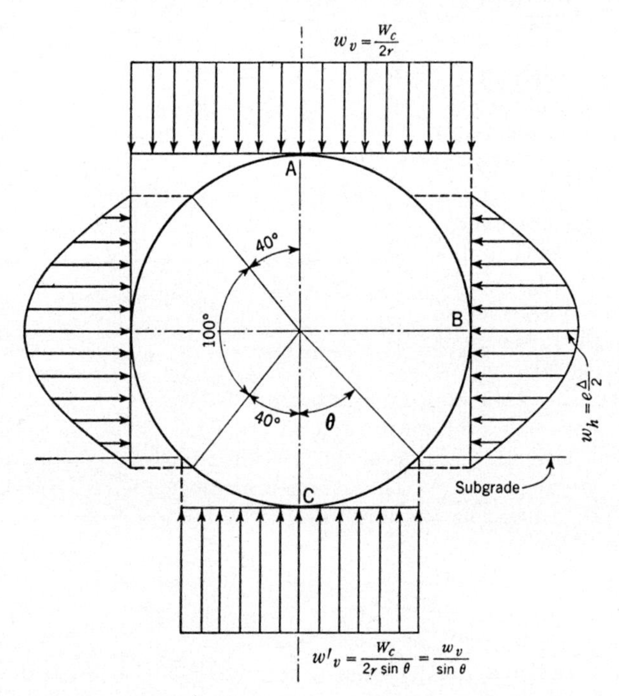

FIG. 18.—THE DISTRIBUTION OF PRESSURES AROUND A FLEXIBLE PIPE UNDER AN EARTH FILL

cohesion can develop is shown to be the reciprocal of the active pressure ratio. However, this theory does not give a clue as to the amount of movement required to develop the limiting value of passive pressure, and it would seem that the actual passive pressure may be any value less than the maximum, depending on soil characteristics and amount of movement of the sides of the pipe.

Several facts concerning the value of the modulus of passive resistance of side fills adjacent to experimental flexible culvert pipes have been observed. First, this modulus varies widely with soil characteristics. Measurements have indicated a value for a gravel material approximately three times as great as for a loam material. Also in the case of a silty clay soil material, the modulus of passive resistance was approximately doubled by hand tamping as compared to the value for the same material in a relatively loose, shovel-placed condition. The second fact that has been observed is that when a flexible pipe is installed without struts the horizontal movement of the sides of the pipe and the passive resistance pressure at the sides of the pipe increase in a linear relationship with the height of fill, indicating a constant value of the modulus of passive resistance pressure as the height of fill is built up.

Field observations of several flexible pipe culverts in service, completed in 1946, have indicated that the settlement ratio, the modulus of passive pressure, and the deflection lag factor are all intimately interrelated. These studies also indicate that the structural performance of this type of conduit is greatly influenced by the character of the side fills and that time and effort spent in compacting the soil at the sides of the pipe will be amply repaid in better performance of the structure as a whole.

Summary

Dean Marston's theory of loads and supporting strengths of underground conduits serves to highlight the many factors, in addition to the height of fill and the conduit strength, which contribute to the structural success or failure of such structures. It is a guide to sound design procedure and to good construction practice in this field of engineering.

For example, the theoretical analysis of ditch conduits indicates that the width of ditch has a marked effect upon the load which the conduit must carry and field observations tend to verify this indication. Good practice, therefore, requires that the design width of ditch be held to a practical minimum value and that this design width be adhered to in construction.

In the case of projecting conduits, such factors as the projection ratio and the settlement ratio have an important bearing on the load which the soil overburden produces on the structure, and knowledge of the characteristics of the site which influence these ratios is necessary before an accurate load analysis can be made. These characteristics are concealed to a very great extent when an embankment is built so that it is usually not possible to determine the load on a projecting conduit after it is completed merely by observing the height of fill and the character of the soil covering. Likewise, the bedding characteristics of a conduit, and the conditions governing the development of lateral earth pressures on the structure, both of which influence its field supporting strength, cannot be determined readily after construction is completed. It is not feasible, therefore, to base one's judgment of the safe height of fill which can be constructed over a given type of conduit in one location, on the height of fill which the same type of conduit may be successfully supporting in another location, unless it is known that all factors which influence load and supporting strength are the same in both locations.

APPENDIX. NOTATION

The following letter symbols, adopted for use in this paper and in its discussion, conform essentially with ASCE *Manual of Engineering Practice No. 22*, "Soil Mechanics Nomenclature":

a = an area element (see Fig. 10);
b = horizontal breadth or width, with subscripts denoting:
  c = conduit;
  d = width of ditch at top of conduit;
C = load coefficient, with subscripts denoting:
  c = projecting conduits;
  d = ditch conduits;
  t = load on the underground conduit transmitted by concentrated load on the surface;
E = modulus of elasticity of the pipe material; Young's modulus;
E_f = modulus of deformation of the filling material;
e = base of natural logarithms;
F = factor, with subscripts denoting:
  d = deflection lag;
  i = impact;
  k = bedding constant;
  p = load;
H = height of fill, with subscripts denoting:
  c = height to ground surface above top of conduit;
  e = height to the plane of equal settlement from the top of a pipe; this is the "height of equal settlement";
  p = height to top of backfill from any horizontal plane;
  s = slant height from the center of an elementary area in Fig. 10 to the point of application of a load;
I = moment of inertia per unit length of cross section of pipe wall;
K = ratio of lateral pressure at a point to vertical pressure; hydrostatic pressure ratio;
L = longitudinal length of the conduit;
P = total vertical pressure on a horizontal plane in the backfill, or within the interior prism:
  P_0 = the pressure of a concentrated load at the surface;
  P_z = total at any point distant z from the surface;
R = supporting strength or resistance of a pipe, with subscripts denoting:
  c = strength in any stated loading condition;
  eb = strength for the case of three-edge bearing;
r = mean radius of the pipe;
W = weight or total load, with subscripts denoting:
  c = load on an underground conduit;
  P = load transmitted by a concentrated surface force;
w = load per unit area, with subscripts denoting:

h = horizontal unit load;
v = vertical unit load;

X = a parameter symbol, denoting by subscripts a function of:
A = the area of the vertical projection of the pipe on which the active lateral pressure of the fill material acts;
P = the distribution of the vertical load and vertical reaction;
When the load and reaction situation (Eq. 14*b*) causes the pipe to crack first at the top the parameter symbol is primed, thus: X';

y = vertical deflection or vertical settlement, corresponding to Δ = horizontal deflection, the subscripts denoting:
c = deflection of the conduit or the shortening of its vertical dimension;
f = settlement of the flow line of the conduit;
g = settlement of embankment subgrade adjacent to the conduit;
m = deformation of the filling material adjacent to the conduit within the height $\rho\, b_c$;

z = distances along the z-axis, also vertical distance from the surface to a given point;

α = a substitution symbol involving b_d introduced to simplify typography (see Eq. 2*a*);

β = a substitution symbol involving b_c introduced to simplify typography (see Eq. 5*c*);

γ = unit weight of filling material;

Δ = horizontal deflection;

δ = a settlement ratio defined by Eq. 4*a*;

ϵ = modulus of passive resistance of the enveloping soil;

θ = angle formed with the vertical by the radius vector from the point of application of the surface load to the point considered (Eq. 13), also the angle to the intersection of a pipe trench with the ground surface (Fig. 18);

κ_t = ratio of total lateral pressure to total vertical load;

μ = coefficient of internal friction between fill materials; μ' = coefficient of sliding friction between the fill materials and the sides of the ditch;

ν = concentration factor or dispersion factor; a disposable parameter; and

ρ = projection ratio; ratio of the vertical distance between the top of the conduit and the natural ground surface adjacent to the conduit, to b_c; the conduit projection is $\rho\, b_c$.

George E. Shafer,[45] Assoc. M. ASCE.—This summary of valuable research on underground conduits should stimulate more practical use of the proved but too little accepted methods of determining the loads that drainage structures must withstand. For more than twenty years the writer has followed and helped disseminate the results of various research on culvert loads and design. Field experience during this period justified the feeling that much money has been wasted because engineers have not made use of the data available.

The writer had the pleasure of cooperating with Anson Marston, Past-President and Hon. M. ASCE, in the derivation and verification of the equations for "complete" and "incomplete" ditch condition discussed in the forepart of

[45] Chf. Engr., Armco Drainage and Metal Products, Inc., Middletown, Ohio.

Professor Spangler's paper. Referring to the section, "Flexible Pipes," the writer and his associates were perhaps the first to recognize that flexible pipes do not fail as soon as the metal is stressed beyond the elastic limit, but continue to function structurally until the deflection resulted in a change in shape to the extent of reversing the curvature in the top or bottom of the structure. If one agrees with the author that structural failure of corrugated metal structures is due to excessive deflection, the problem then is to determine a method of predicting deflection.

Referring to Fig. 22, a flexible pipe is in equilibrium when the inherent strength of the pipe, R_I, plus the side support, W_H (developed in the earth as passive pressure due to outward movement of the sides of the pipe), is equal to the vertical load, W_c, on the pipe and its accompanying reaction.

How much a pipe deflects depends on all three factors—the larger the values of R_I and W_H the smaller will be the vertical deflection, y_c, and the larger the value of W_c, the greater that deflection. Therefore,

$$y_c = f\left(\frac{W_c}{R_I + W_H}\right) \qquad (25)$$

Eq. 15 is in this form and includes those three factors.

Prior research on the design of flexible structures resulted in an empirical equation for deflection. This research should be considered, so that the results of the two equations can be compared. In 1926, after it was fully recognized that flexible structures fail by change in shape (excessive deflection), the writer and his associates set out to determine: (1) The law of deflection, so that structural performance could be predicted, and (2) the maximum permissible deflection, so that some part of the maximum could be used as a safe design deflection.

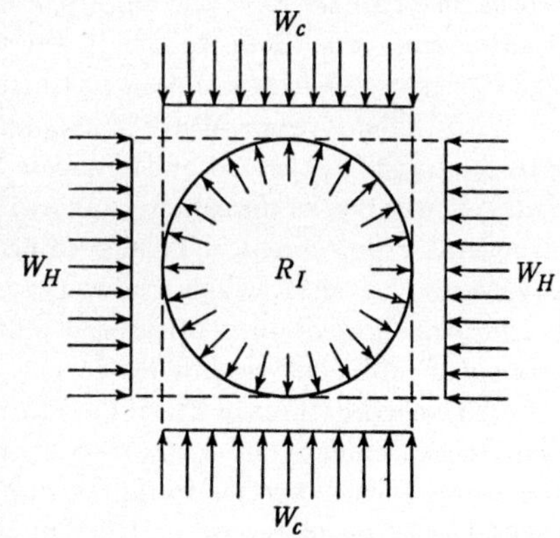

FIG. 22.—CONDUIT LOADING DIAGRAM

As to the law of deflections, it was known that deflection would vary directly as some power of the fill height, H, and the diameter, D, and inversely as the thickness of metal, t. Thus,

$$y_c = k\,\frac{H^m\,D^n}{t^s} \qquad (26)$$

Using the deflection data from the American Railway Engineering Association (A.R.E.A.) investigation,[46] wherein the deflections were accurately measured as the fill was slowly made (permitting partial settlement to take place), along with measurements taken on numerous large diameter, high fill, unstrutted structures under both highway and railroad service, the values of k, m, n, and s were determined.

[46] "Culvert Load Determination," *Bulletin No. 284*, A.R.E.A., 1926.

The maximum deflection before failure occurred was readily determined by inspecting numerous, large diameter pipe installations with shallow cover of the "horse and buggy" days in California. With better roads and flatter grades, many of these structures, because of their good material and structural performance, were left in place and extended to permit the fill height to be increased. In some cases, the additional cover was sufficient to cause considerable additional deflection. The maximum recorded was 22% at a localized point. The average safe maximum deflection was determined as 20% of the vertical diameter. Using the conservative factor of safety of 4, the design deflection was established at 5%.

During the thirty years prior to 1926, when the empirical equation for riveted corrugated pipe was derived, the use of corrugated pipe was steadily increasing. By 1926 there were in use approximately 100,000,000 ft of average size corrugated pipe. With acceptance and use, gage tables based on experience had been compiled. Each large producer had his own gage table; however, all were practically the same. A new gage table based on the empirical equation using 5% deflection checked very closely with the old gage tables then in use, which were based on experience. Both were based on average installation conditions.

At that time, especially in certain parts of the United States, there were some questions regarding the durability of light gage, metal drainage structures. Gages that satisfied structural requirements often had to be increased because of durability requirements. For this reason, a gage table based solely on the equation was impractical. One of the objectives of the A.R.E.A. investigation[46] was a rational design for flexible pipe. The objective was never obtained; the empirical equation likewise fell short of the A.R.E.A. objective. It was also realized that the empirical equation was new and somewhat radical in principle. For these reasons it was not published. Like a new and untried tool it was used with discretion until its merit was established.

With the more general use of asphalt coated and paved invert pipe, plus the introduction of asbestos bonded sheets to insure adhesion of the asphalt to the metal, it was not so necessary to increase the gage of metal over and above the structural requirement. This permitted a more rigid use of the empirical equation. By 1931, when a new type of large diameter metal pipe made by bolting corrugated curve structural plates together in the field was introduced, there was sufficient confidence in the original empirical equation for riveted pipe with corrugations of $2\frac{2}{3}$ in. by $\frac{1}{2}$ in. so that a new equation was derived from field measurements of unstrutted structural plate pipe as soon as sufficient structures were in service to represent a good average. The equation was later revised as more installations were made and a new equation was derived for field strutted structures. These equations served to predict deflection. The bolted longitudinal seam was designed separately. Thousands of riveted and bolted structures have been designed on the basis of the empirical equations with almost faultless structural performance.

None of the equations have been published—not because they were considered trade secrets, but because the men who derived them knew their limitations.

The equations have just one application—to determine the required thickness of metal for a given diameter of pipe and height of cover or dead load. A tabular form giving the required gage for all structurally safe combinations of diameter and fill height is a gage table. Such tables, based on all three equations, have been available since the equations were derived. In some cases, light gages have been modified because of durability requirements; and, in others, to take care of various live load conditions. Since a gage table is far more convenient to use than an equation, the public or profession has not suffered because the exact equations were not known. The form of the equation and the fact that the gage tables were based on an empirical equation were published in 1937.[47]

When Professor Spangler proposed his investigation on the structural design of corrugated pipe various members of the industry took interest and cooperated. Those familiar with the empirical design hoped a rational design that would take into account installation conditions, type of soil, and other factors would result, so that, when possible, a more economical design could be used. When the investigation was completed and Eq. 15 was published, its use was investigated. The apparent weakness of the equation at that time necessitated the selection of the proper value of ϵ (modulus of passive resistance of the soil) to use for various soils. Later, the writer tried to use the equation to verify some live load tests and extend them into a gage table for airport loading. Again it was difficult to find the proper value of ϵ.

Perhaps the best way to discuss the application of Eq. 15 is to compare the permissible heights of cover for a range of diameters and gages with those obtained by the empirical equation. In Table 2, the heights of cover for Eq. 15 are based on $\Delta = 0.1\ r$, or 5% deflection, with $F_d = 1.5$, $F_k = 0.1$, $E = 30{,}000{,}000$, and $\epsilon = 20$. In general, the two equations agree fairly well for certain combinations of diameter and gage, but vary widely for other combinations. Eq. 15 does not give as much value to difference in gage as does the empirical equation and as is warranted by experience. It also permits higher fills for large diameters and light gages.

TABLE 2.—Comparison of Fill Heights, in Feet, Obtained by Empirical Equation and by Eq. 15

Gage	24 In. in Diameter		48 In. in Diameter		72 In. in Diameter	
	Empirical	Eq. 15	Empirical	Eq. 15	Empirical	Eq. 15
16	26	24.2	7.2	15.9	3.5	21.7
12	62	36.6	18	17.4	8.8	22.2
8	140	53.7	39	19.6	18.5	22.2

Those engaged in the manufacture and distribution of flexible drainage structures see a definite need for a rational method of design. Not because design based on experience, such as the empirical equation, is wrong, but because it is possible that the full economy of flexible construction is not utilized in all cases. Furthermore, engineers prefer a rational approach to any prob-

[47] "Handbook of Culvert and Drainage Practice," Armco Culvert Mfrs. Assn., Middletown, Ohio, 1937.

lem, even though they use empirical methods in the solution of many problems. The rational approach also leads to a clearer understanding of the basic principles involved.

With this desire for a rational design in mind, the writer makes the following comments on each factor in Eq. 15 in the hope that by constructive criticism a solution will be evolved that will form the basis of all flexible conduit design.

Referring back to Eq. 25, the simplified form of Eq. 15, the writer has already implied agreement with the Marston theory for determining the vertical load on flexible structures. The part of Eq. 15 involving inherent strength R_I is based on the elastic theory of a closed ring. Referring to Fig. 23, this means that the load-deflection relation is a straight line and may coincide with the actual deflection curve from two-edge bearing tests for small deflections, or may deviate appreciably when the ring is stressed beyond the elastic limit.

Regardless of whether the load for two-edge bearing is determined from the equation,[30]

$$y_c = 0.149 \frac{P r^3}{E I} \qquad (27)$$

or for the factor of Eq. 15 corresponding to R_I in Eq. 25, the result is the same, when F_d and F_k are assumed equal to 1.5 and 0.1, respectively. Therefore, the strength that is built into the pipe can be determined by Eq. 27. It is realized that Eq. 27 does not apply beyond the elastic limit of the metal, yet the comparison is made on the basis of 5% deflection, slightly beyond the limit, because that deflection has become standard practice in the design of corrugated metal pipe. In Table 3, values of P or W are given for 5% deflection and for a representative range of diameters and gages. The data on two-edge bearing loads does not include the Iowa tests, but does include unpublished data from several other investigations.

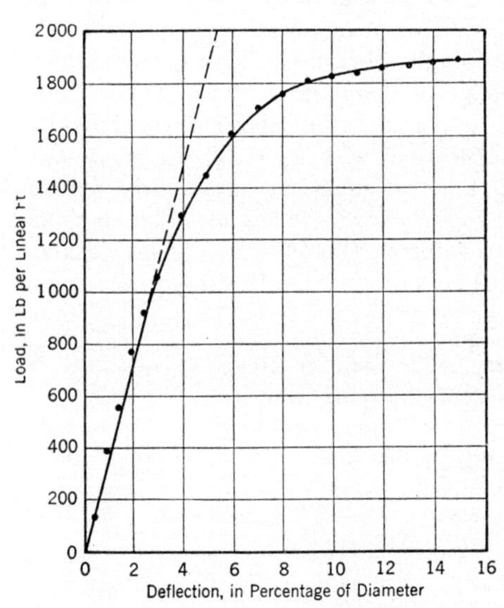

Fig. 23.—Load-Deflection Curve for 36-In. Diameter Corrugated Metal Pipe (Wall Thickness, 0.112 In.; ½-In. Corrugations)

The loads determined by Eq. 27 for pipe 24 in. in diameter are approximately 2¼ times those from tests, and for pipe 72 in. in diameter they are approximately equal. If the effect of gage is considered regardless of diameter, Eq. 27 shows 8-gage pipe to be approximately 2¾ times stronger than 16-gage pipe, whereas the test data show this ratio to be approximately 4. These differences tend to affect the final design resulting from Eq. 15 by failing to show the full effect due to gage, regardless of diameter. This is a general comment regarding the use of Eq. 15 in actual practice. There are two other factors that should be considered with the foregoing data: (1) How much stronger is a flexible pipe in uniform vertical loading, as compared with concentrated loading, and (2) how much does uniform loading raise the elastic limit over that for concentrated loading?

TABLE 3.—COMPARISON OF INHERENT PIPE STRENGTHS[a] AS DETERMINED BY EQ. 27 AND BY ACTUAL TESTS

Gage	24 In. in Diameter		48 In. in Diameter		72 In. in Diameter	
	Iowa[b]	Test[c]	Iowa	Test	Iowa	Test
16	3,530	1,300	880	500	375	295
12	6,080	2,826	1,510	1,110	675	665
8	9,630	5,220	2,370	2,100	1,060	1,190

[a] Load in pounds per foot at 5% deflection. [b] Calculated by Eq. 27. [c] Determined by actual tests.

The usually accepted conversion factor for uniform loading from two-edge or three-edge bearing for rigid pipe is 1.5. According to the elastic theory, either by deflection of the ring or for moment in the ring, the factor should be approximately 2.0. It is the writer's opinion that a ratio of 2.0 is conservative.

Undoubtedly the elastic limit is higher (Fig. 23) for uniform loading as compared to concentrated loading, because of the more gradual and uniform change in shape or curvature under uniform load. Just how much the limit is raised is difficult to determine. If the change is small, then factors in Eq. 15 entering into inherent strength should be changed so that instead of being based on the elastic theory they would be based on actual concentrated load test data corrected for uniform vertical load. The average concentrated loads per foot of pipe to produce 5% deflection can be determined from the empirical equation,

$$P = \frac{4.825 \times 10^6 \, t^{1.40}}{D^{1.35}} \qquad (28)$$

in which t is the thickness of the metal in inches (corrugations $2\frac{2}{3}$ in. by $\frac{1}{2}$ in.) and D is the pipe diameter in inches.

The side support part of Eq. 15 is based on certain assumptions, two of which will be discussed:

1. " * * * the horizontal pressure on the (side of a) pipe at any point bears a nearly constant relationship to the horizontal movement of the point."[30]

2. The distribution of passive pressure on the sides of the pipe is assumed symmetrical about the horizontal axis.

Considering first the assumption that horizontal pressure has a constant relationship to movement of the pipe sides, it is true that the Iowa data support this contention. Earlier research work[35] at the University of North Carolina

(Chapel Hill) seems to offer verification, except for very low fills. Referring to Fig. 24, the assumption is correct when the pressure and movement curves are straight lines. The pressure curves are straight lines, but the deflection is not a straight line for low fill heights. The deflection curve for Professor Spangler's first experiment has a similar characteristic.

If the pressure movement ratio is constant, the value of ϵ should be a constant for any soil characteristic and should not vary with fill height, or with the degree of rigidity of the pipe. There seems to be evidence that ϵ varies with fill height, or pipe rigidity—or both. Considering first the data supporting the claim that ϵ varies with fill height, in Fig. 24 the value of ϵ calculated using Eq. 15 varies from less than 30 for a 1-ft fill to more than 70 for a 12-ft fill. Similar values of ϵ for the 20-in. pipe in the same investigation are not as con-

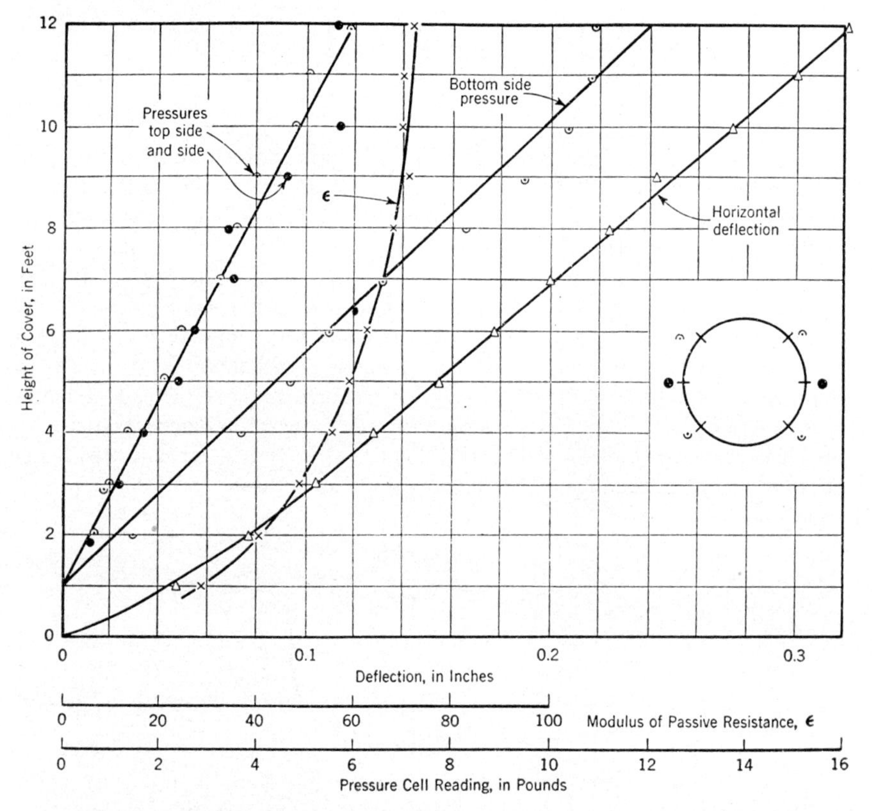

FIG. 24.—PRESSURE DEFLECTION DATA FROM UNIVERSITY OF NORTH CAROLINA STUDIES ON 30-IN. DIAMETER CORRUGATED METAL PIPE (WALL THICKNESS 0.108 IN.)

sistent as those plotted in Fig. 24 for the 30-in. pipe, but do vary from 28 for a 2-ft cover to 56 for an 8-ft cover.

In 1928 accurate deflection measurements were taken on a rather large number of metal pipes installed in a new line of the Union Pacific Railroad Company. Original diameters were measured before backfilling, and final readings were taken nine years later. The number of unstrutted structures for which there was complete data (diameter, gage, average load, two-edge bearing strength at 5% deflection, and calculated ϵ according to Eq. 15) are shown in Table 4. Also included in Table 4 are similar data on two other investigations—those at the University of North Carolina[30] and the unpublished data on a live load test made by the writer. As further proof that ϵ may vary with the fill height, note how the average ϵ decreased with the average fill. The thirty-eight structures included in this investigation were installed under various conditions. For that reason, a comparison between individual structures is unwarranted, although a comparison between the averages for any pipe size seems permissible.

Referring to Table 4(*b*), the North Carolina tests were carefully made so that all pipes were installed and backfilled as nearly alike as possible. The three pipes listed are those that can be considered as flexible, the most flexible being a smooth pipe that had to be braced to hold the circular shape until the

TABLE 4.—COMPUTED VALUES OF ϵ FROM VARIOUS TEST PROGRAMS

No. of structures	Diameter (in.)	Gage	Average Load		Bearing strength of pipe[a] (lb)	Computed ϵ	Col.6 / Col.7
			Dead (ft of fill)	Live			
(1)	(2)	(3)	(4)	(5)	(6)	(7)	(8)
(*a*) UNION PACIFIC RAILROAD COMPANY							
3	24	10	34	E60	3,950	62	64
16	36	10	17	E60	2,300	38	61
19	48	8	5	E60	2,100	18	117
(*b*) UNIVERSITY OF NORTH CAROLINA							
1	30[b]	12	12	0	....[c]	29	....
1	30	12	12	0	1,620	47	36.3
1	30[d]	$\frac{5}{16}$ in.	12	0	....[c]	89	....
(*c*) LIVE LOAD							
1	24	14	1	Truck with dual tires	1,780	262[e]	6.8
1	24	12	1		2,820	339[e]	8.3
1	48	12	1		1,110	149[e]	7.5
1	48	10	1		1,580	188[e]	8.4

[a] Two-edge bearing strength at 5% deflection. [b] Smooth pipe, very flexible. [c] Unknown. [d] Steel tube. [e] Average for three different live loads (4,635 lb, 8,700 lb, and 13,695 lb) per wheel.

pipe was covered with sharp bank sand. The second and third pipes were progressively more rigid, as evidenced by the fact that the load factors (the percentage of load directly above the pipe actually carried by the pipe under 12-ft fill) were 61, 80, and 87, respectively. The values of ϵ, as calculated from Eq. 15 are 29, 45, and 85, respectively. These data tend to show that ϵ is a function of pipe rigidity. In Table 4(*c*) live load is the predominant load. All structures were carefully installed under the same installation conditions and loaded in the same manner. In this case ϵ varies with the pipe rigidity.

It will be noted that the ratio of two-edge bearing strength at 5% deflection to ϵ is much more constant than the values of ϵ.

To summarize the data in Table 4, there is evidence to show that ϵ varies with pipe rigidity more than with fill height. Nevertheless, in the Union Pacific data (Table 4(*a*)) for 36-in., 10-gage pipe and the 48-in., 8-gage pipe, the rigidity is approximately the same, where average ϵ varies from 38 for an average fill of 17 ft to 18 for a fill of 5 ft. This, added to the variation in ϵ shown in Fig. 24 for the same pipe under varying fill heights, leads the writer to believe that ϵ may vary both with fill height and pipe rigidity.

It is unfortunate that all the pipes in the author's third experiment, the major part of his tests wherein conditions were identical, were of approximately the same rigidity. In selecting the size and gage of pipe to use, the aim was to keep them as flexible as possible within the limits of practicability. The inherent or two-edge bearing strengths of the four pipes in the third experiment, according to the writer's data, are shown in Table 5. Had the tested pipe been of widely different degrees of rigidity, the resulting data might have indicated that ϵ is a function of pipe rigidity.

TABLE 5.—TWO-EDGE BEARING LOAD FOR PIPES OF THE AUTHOR'S THIRD EXPERIMENT

Diameter (in.) (1)	Gage (2)	Two-edge bearing load[a] (lb) (3)
36	16	750
42	14	840
48	14	685
60	1	815

[a] At 5% deflection.

Considering the second assumption, that the passive pressure on the sides of the pipe is symmetrical about the horizontal axis, the right half of Fig. 25 shows the development by Professor Spangler of a "witch-shaped" (witch of Agnesi) curve representing the locus of the horizontal movement of all points on the half circle, as the circle changes to an ellipse, their horizontal axes being coincident. In actual installations the inverts are coincident if there is no settlement. The left side of Fig. 25 shows the approximate shape of the locus based on coincident inverts and the same parabolic curve Professor Spangler used, which closely simulates the witch curve. The new center of the parabola is below the horizontal axis of the pipe by an amount equal to $y/2$. Actually, the difference in shape of the sides is not great, but the difference in shape combined with increased pressure below the horizontal could appreciably change the pressure diagram or composite loading.

Referring to the North Carolina data[35] for the 30-in. pipe, the pressure curves in Fig. 24, which were drawn to show the increase in pressure starting at a 1-ft fill, show the average pressure 45° above the horizontal "top side" to be approximately equal to the average side pressure. The average pressure 45° below the horizontal "bottom side" is more than twice the side pressure. This does not mean that the horizontal component of the measured pressure on the bottom side is greater than the horizontal component on the top side. It does, however, indicate that there can be a high pressure under the haunches of the pipe. Professor Spangler's composite loading, on which Eq. 15 is based, is shown on the right side of Fig. 26. The pressure at a point 45° below the horizontal, according to this loading, is very small. The data justified that assumption, but the writer believes that, had the pipe in the tests deflected more, or had the pipe been installed under 100% projection, the load diagram would be similar to that shown on the left side.

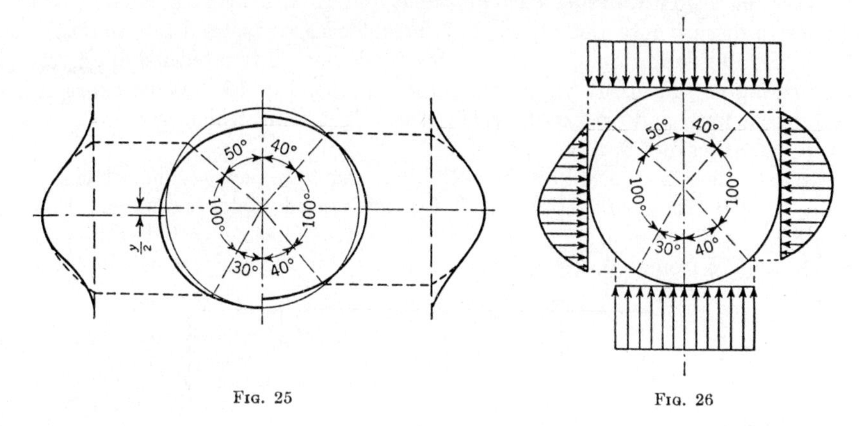

Fig. 25

Fig. 26

As further proof of greater pressure under the haunches than that assumed by the author, the averages of all the pressure cell readings for the three flexible pipes in the 30-in. size tested at North Carolina[35] are shown in Fig. 27. These pressures are in pounds per square inch, and are the average increase in pressure due to any additional foot of fill from 0 ft to 12 ft. These data show that, with the exception of the top point, the greatest pressure is at the haunches, or 45° below the sides. Previously published data[48] show the haunches to be points of low pressure for low fills, with a trend toward more uniform pressures for higher fills. Such a revised pressure diagram would complicate the mathematical analysis but would, in the writer's opinion, more nearly fit field conditions for design deflections and the usual installation conditions, wherein the foundation is often quite yielding.

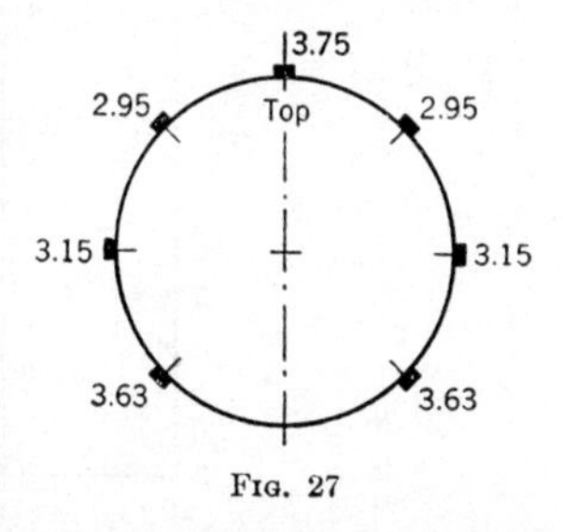

Fig. 27

To summarize, Professor Spangler's investigation and interpretation are steps in the right direction. It is unfortunate that the test pipes in the third experiment were all of virtually the same inherent strength. This, plus the fact that the range of diameters was small, apparently led to a solution that gives undue value to the side support factor for large diameters. Additional data are needed on working values of ϵ, especially under live load conditions. Whether there are sufficient test data available from all sources to revise Eq. 15, so that the results will be more consistent with actual practice, is unknown to the writer. It is emphasized again that the comments in this discussion are intended to be constructive and to encourage ideas and data that will eventually lead to a solution of a rather complex problem.

---

[48] "The Structural Design of Flexible Pipe Culverts," by M. G. Spangler, *Bulletin No. 153*, Iowa Eng. Experiment Station, Ames, Iowa, 1941, Figs. 24 and 25.

E. F. KELLEY,[49] ESQ.—This is an excellent summary of the results of the research work on underground conduits that has been carried on over a period of years by the Iowa Engineering Experiment Station at Ames, under the direction of Anson Marston, Past-President and Hon. M. ASCE. The writer desires to discuss only Eq. 15, which is presented as a method for computing the horizontal deflection of a flexible pipe, such as a corrugated metal culvert. By making certain assumptions and substitutions, Eq. 15 may be expressed in different form and used to determine the height of fill which will produce a given deflection of a flexible pipe culvert.

In experiments reported by the author[50] it was found that δ, the settlement ratio, ranged from -0.14 to -0.76 for corrugated metal culverts. Elsewhere,[51] as a result of other experiments, the author has suggested settlement ratios ranging from -0.4 to $+0.8$. Therefore, for the purpose of simplifica-

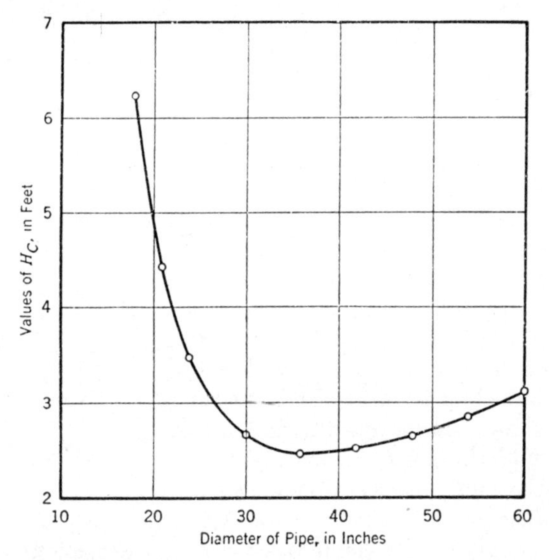

FIG. 28.—RELATION BETWEEN HEIGHT OF FILL, H_c, AND DIAMETER OF 16-GAGE CORRUGATED METAL PIPE, COMPUTED BY EQ. 15 FOR A DEFLECTION OF 1% OF THE PIPE DIAMETER

tion and illustration it is considered sufficiently accurate to assume the settlement ratio equal to zero.

It is apparent from Fig. 8 that when $\delta = 0$, $\delta\,\rho = 0$ and

$$C_c = \frac{H_c}{b_c} \qquad (29)$$

Also, with b_c expressed in feet and r in inches,

$$b_c = \frac{2\,r}{12} \qquad (30)$$

[49] Chf., Div. of Physical Research, Public Roads Administration, Washington, D. C.

[50] "The Structural Design of Flexible Pipe Culverts," by M. G. Spangler, *Bulletin No. 153*, Iowa Eng. Experiment Station, Ames, Iowa, 1941, p. 56.

[51] "Analysis of Loads and Supporting Strengths, and Principles of Design for Highway Culverts," by M. G. Spangler, *Proceedings*, Highway Research Board, National Research Council, Vol. 26, 1946, p. 198.

Substituting Eqs. 29 and 30 in Eq. 6*a*,

$$W_c = \frac{H_c \gamma r}{6} \quad \text{.......................} (31)$$

Thus, if W_c is expressed in pounds per linear foot of pipe, Eq. 15 may be reduced to the form,

$$H_c = \frac{72 \Delta (E I + 0.061 \epsilon r^4)}{F_d F_k \gamma r^4} \quad \text{.................} (32)$$

Computed values of H_c for corrugated metal pipe having diameters from 18 in. to 60 in., inclusive, are shown in Fig. 28. For the purpose of the computation it was assumed that: $\Delta = 1\%$ of the pipe diameter ($= 0.02\,r$); $E = 30{,}000{,}000$ lb per sq in.; $I = 0.001766$ in.^{4} per in., a value computed for 16-gage corrugated metal; $\epsilon = 20$ lb per sq in. per in.; $F_d = 1.5$; $F_k = 0.10$, corresponding to a bedding angle of about 35°; and $\gamma = 120$ lb per cu ft.

It is quite generally agreed that the deflection of corrugated metal pipes in service should be limited to a maximum of 5% of the pipe diameter. However, as the author has pointed out, Eq. 15 is applicable only within the elastic range of the pipe metal and it is not known that a 5% deflection of a pipe in service is within this range. It is known that, when corrugated metal pipe is subjected to the three-edge bearing test, a deflection of 5% is generally outside the elastic range, whereas a deflection of 1% is well within it. It is for this reason that, for purposes of illustration, the relatively small deflection of 1% of the pipe diameter has been selected.

For the smaller sizes of pipe Fig. 28 shows, as would be expected, that H_c decreases as the diameter of pipe increases. However, the minimum value of H_c is obtained for a diameter of 36 in.; thereafter the value of H_c increases with increases in the pipe diameter. Such results are unreasonable and cannot be accepted as correct.

There may be one or more reasons for the questionable results shown in Fig. 28. It may be that empirical Eq. 15, although applicable within the range of the author's experiments, may not have a general application. It may be also that the writer's assumption of a constant settlement ratio or a constant value of the modulus of passive resistance, or both, may be incorrect.

These questions, and the further question as to whether a deflection of a pipe in service of the order of 5% is within the elastic range of the pipe metal, lead to the conclusion that, on the basis of present knowledge, Eq. 15 cannot be accepted for use in the design of flexible pipe culverts.

M. G. Spangler,[54] M. ASCE.—The time and effort put forth in preparing this paper have been more than compensated for by the stimulating ideas which have been expressed by the various discussers. Of particular value are the data presented by Mr. Binger relative to the pressures measured on a concrete box culvert under a 50-ft fill on the Panama Railroad. The close correlation between the measured pressures and those indicated by the Marston theory when applied to the conditions of the installation serve, powerfully, to reinforce the confidence which engineers may place in the principles involved in the theoretical development.

Mr. Binger's data are significant for two reasons: First, they show the load produced by a fill two and one-half times higher than any previous fill for which loads have been measured; and, second, the fill was compacted by modern heavy equipment during construction.

Mr. Feld is entirely justified in referring to the researches on underground conduit loads which were conducted at the University of North Carolina in Chapel Hill. In preparing any paper the matter of scope becomes highly important and in this case it was decided to limit the paper to the work which had been done at Iowa State College in Ames. Dean Marston has made an exhaustive study of the reports covering the North Carolina experiments and has concluded that the measured loads in those tests conform closely to the results calculated by the Marston theory, as he has stated in his discussion.

It is difficult to subscribe to Mr. Feld's characterization of the problems discussed in the paper as purely academic. Although it is true, as everyone knows, that methods of earth handling and construction have undergone radical changes during the past quarter of a century, the principles of stress transfer embodied in the Marston theory are ageless and will be applicable many years hence when present-day construction methods become outmoded. The ditch conduit analysis may be applied with equal validity to a hand-dug or a machine-dug trench without reference to the slope or irregularity of the sides, provided the correct ditch-width factor is used in the analysis. If the backfill material is placed in the condition which Mr. Feld describes as "better" than relatively loose earth, considerable harm may result in that the loads on the pipe may be very greatly increased as compared to the loads under the more usual manner of backfilling. In the example cited where the backfills of drainage trenches became relatively hard lines in the subgrade, there is little doubt in the writer's mind but that the load at the base of the trench was relatively high, because the transferred shearing stresses would be additive to the weight of the backfill instead of subtractive as in the more usual case.

The method of constructing projecting conduits in trenches dug through compacted embankments has distinct advantages from the standpoint of loads produced on the structure, in addition to the advantages mentioned by Mr. Feld, since placing the pipes in ditches tends to cause the shear stress increments to act upward on the prism of material in the ditch, provided the backfill is loosely placed. The California Highway Department has developed methods

[54] Research Prof., Civ. Eng. Dept., Iowa Eng. Experiment Station, Iowa State College, Ames, Iowa.

of construction based on this principle which appear to be efficient in reducing loads on the pipes. These procedures, together with excellent bedding and backfilling practices, have permitted a substantial increase in safe heights of fill over drainage conduits under highways in that state. However, it seems doubtful whether the practice of building an embankment first and then trenching through it to construct a drainage line can ever be widely applicable, inasmuch as climatic conditions in many localities are such that a heavy rainstorm between the time of completion of the embankment and the construction of the trench through it might be very detrimental or even disastrous. The favorable load condition produced by this method of construction is recognized, however, and it is clearly within the scope of the Marston load theory. The deeper the trench through the embankment in relation to the trench width, and the more loosely the backfill is placed in the region immediately above the conduit, the farther toward the left side of Fig. 8 the situation falls and the less will be the load on the structure.

Mr. Tremper's remarks indicate that similarly good results are being obtained in the State of Washington by installing pipe culverts in sidehill ditches to one side of the watercourse. Where practicable, this procedure would appear to be better than that suggested by Mr. Feld, because drainage water could be cared for in the natural watercourse during construction of the culvert. The discussions by both Messrs. Feld and Tremper lend emphasis to the more favorable load situation that can be achieved in culvert construction when specific attention is given to creating conditions in which pressures are transferred by shear from the interior prism of soil to the exterior masses.

From Prague, Czechoslovakia, comes a very interesting analysis of concrete pipe rings from which values of the load factor for cradled pipe have been determined. There is no difference of opinion between Professor Bažant and the writer relative to the analytical determination of bending moments in a reinforced concrete pipe. This procedure is precisely that employed by the writer prior to 1933 which led to the development of Eq. 14*b*. The difficulties in design arise when one attempts to convert the calculated moments into stresses in the steel and concrete of which the pipes are made.

Professor Bažant's calculated load factors shown in Table 1 are approximately 10% greater than the average experimental values obtained by W. J. Schlick, M. ASCE, and James W. Johnson.[55] These differences are not significant and readily may be accounted for by the fact that the sand-bearing load was assumed to be uniformly distributed in the analysis, whereas it is known that the pressure in the test is greater at the center of the bearing than at the sides and that it approaches a parabolic distribution.

However, several circumstances and assumptions connected with the analysis contained in the discussion lead to the conclusion that the correlation shown in Table 1 may be more coincidental than basic. For example, it is assumed that: "The maximum moment occurs at points a and b, where the first cracks

[55] "Concrete Cradles for Large Pipe Conduits," by W. J. Schlick and James W. Johnson, *Bulletin No. 80*, Iowa Eng. Experiment Station, Ames, Iowa, 1926, p. 39.

occur * * *." In the Schlick and Johnson experiments, 94% of the cradled specimens cracked first at the top of the pipe. The first cracks in the remaining 6% occurred simultaneously either at the top and bottom or at the top and sides of the pipe. Also, in every case the cradle cracked in the region below the bottom crack in the pipe and at the same time that the bottom crack occurred. In no case did the first cracks occur at the junction of the pipe wall and the cradle as assumed by Professor Bažant.

The comparison between computed and experimental values of the load factor for ultimate loads is probably not valid, even though the values appear to be reasonably close numerically, because at ultimate load the pipe and the cradle have long since ceased to be a continuous arch body. At ultimate loadings, the experimental pipes were cracked in many places, the cradles were broken into two parts, and the bond between the cradles and the pipes was destroyed, so that the structures were considerably different after they were cracked from the structures which Professor Bažant analyzed. For these reasons it would seem that a comparison between calculated and observed load factors at "first crack" load would be much more appropriate. Such comparisons for the three cradle types included in Table 1 show that the calculated load factors exceed the observed values by 18%, 37%, and 35%, respectively.

Mr. Shafer's discussion is a most welcome addition to the literature on the supporting strength of flexible pipe conduits. He has had wide experience in this field, has made extensive observations of the performance of this type of structure, and has brought rare good judgment to the interpretation of his observations. The writer has a very high regard for the utility of Mr. Shafer's empirical Eq. 26. It has served both the industry and the users of metal culvert pipes very well since its inception in 1926.

In the writer's opinion, however, the flexible pipe problem is far too complex to rely solely on experience for a solution. Theory is needed to supplement judgment and to guide the interpretation of the shotgun pattern of the facts gleaned in the field. The empirical formula falls short in the achievement of scientific design of flexible pipe culverts and tends to stifle progress in that direction, since it does not take into account several important variables that influence the problem. One of these is the passive resistance of the soil side fills, which is widely recognized as a highly important factor (probably the most important single factor) on which pipe deflection depends. The empirical formula throws all the effect of side pressure into the factor k, and the best that can be expected under these circumstances is the determination of "average" deflection, which may be greatly exceeded in individual cases. Very few field data are available to the profession from which to judge the correlation between actual deflections developed in the field and deflections predicted by the empirical formula. Such data as the writer has seen show a very wide range of deflections, many individual specimens being in excess of 100% above the "average," and extreme cases being from 400% to 500% above.

Another variable factor which the empirical formula submerges in the "average" is the relationship between the height of fill and the load on a culvert. It is unfortunate, but nonetheless true, that the load and the height of fill are not related by a constant factor for all culverts. This fact is clearly shown by Fig. 8. In the present state of knowledge it is difficult to predict values of the settlement ratio, which has such an important effect on the relationship between load and height of fill. Nevertheless, it is present and effective in every culvert installation and scientific progress demands that it be recognized and studied. This same comment applies to the projection ratio, except that the latter factor is more easily determined for a specific pipe installation.

For these reasons and others, the writer does not consider that the fill height data given in Table 2 are validly comparable. It would be the purest coincidence if the fill heights shown in the parallel columns were in agreement. The only valid check on Eq. 15 is a comparison of the deflections computed by the formula with actual measured values when all the factors relative to a culvert installation which influence the deflections are known or can be estimated with a reasonable degree of precision.

When Eq. 15 was developed and published, it was intended to be used to compute the deflection of a flexible pipe culvert when the diameter of the pipe and its physical properties (the height of fill, the settlement ratio, the projection ratio, the width of bedding, the unit weight of the fill, and the character of the soil as it influences passive resistance pressures) are known. Immediately after publication, many engineers turned the formula around and attempted to use it to calculate a fill height that would produce some predetermined deflection of the pipe. This practice has led to some difficulties and erroneous concepts concerning the formula. Mr. Kelley rejects the formula as giving unreasonable results, because the fill height to produce a given deflection, expressed as a constant percentage of pipe diameter, is larger for large pipe than it is for some smaller pipe sizes. His point would be well taken if it could be definitely stated that, when two pipes of different diameters have deflected under a fill an amount equal to 5% of their diameters, they have both progressed the same distance toward failure and are, therefore, on a comparable basis as far as strength is concerned. The writer does not believe this is true.

This premise opens the whole question as to the theory of failure of flexible pipes and a suitable criterion for an allowable design limit. The metal pipe industry has for many years suggested a deflection limit of 5% of the diameter as being a suitable criterion and many engineers have accepted this value. The writer has looked on the 5% limit as a good value to "shoot at," but he has come to realize that neither it nor any other constant percentage-of-diameter deflection represents the same strength situation for all diameters of pipes. As evidence on this point, the writer has investigated the pipes for which Fig. 28 was drawn by computing the fill heights to produce a constant value of bending moment at the bottom of the pipes. The equation for the moment at the bottom of a flexible pipe under field loading conditions (for a bedding angle of 35°) is[56]

$$M = 0.176\, W_c\, r - 0.166\, h\, r^2 \quad \text{..............} (33a)$$

[56] "The Structural Design of Flexible Pipe Culverts," by M. G. Spangler, *Bulletin No. 153*, Iowa Eng. Experiment Station, Ames, Iowa, 1941, p. 58.

in which

$$h = \epsilon \frac{\Delta}{2} \qquad (33b)$$

Substituting Eq. 15 in Eq. 33*a* and using the same values of various factors that were used by Mr. Kelley, it is possible to compute heights of fill over the various diameter pipes to produce the same bending moment in each of the pipes. The bending moment in the 36-in. pipe of Fig. 28 was arbitrarily chosen as the common value for all the pipes. The results are shown in Fig. 29. On the basis of this criterion the height of fill decreases with increasing pipe diameter, which seems to be more reasonable. Since both Eq. 15 and Eq. 33 are based on the elastic analysis, the author believes that Fig. 28 throws a cloud of uncertainty on the validity of applying a constant percentage-of-diameter deflection limit to all sizes of pipe, rather than on the validity of Eq. 15.

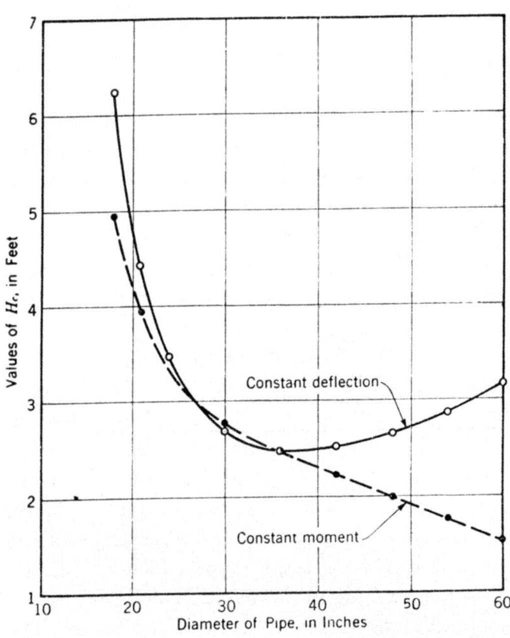

Fig. 29.—Height of Fill Versus Pipe Diameter

Mr. Shafer goes further and applies the 5% limit to pipes loaded in two-edge bearings and compares the loads to produce this deflection by elastic analysis and by actual test. Since the smaller sized pipes tested were obviously loaded beyond the elastic limit of the metal, the calculated loads to produce 5% deflection were considerably greater than the test loads. This discrepancy between calculated loads and test loads is cited by Mr. Shafer as an indication of a weakness in Eq. 15. The writer believes that the comparisons in Table 3 are wholly fortuitous and irrelevant and that Mr. Shafer's conclusions based on them are not valid.

In support of this contention, it is pointed out that, if the test specimens had been made of metal having a higher elastic limit, the difference between the loads calculated by Eq. 27 and the test loads would have been materially less. In Fig. 23, the metal in the 36-in. pipe for which load-deflection data are plotted apparently reached its elastic limit at a load of 1,056 lb per lin ft, or 88 lb per lin in. The bending moment at the top and bottom of a circular ring loaded in two-edge bearing is[57]

$$M = 0.318\,P\,r \quad (34)$$

in which P is the load per unit length of pipe; and r is the radius of the pipe. By the flexure formula,

$$s = \frac{M\,c}{I} \quad (35)$$

The elastic limit of the metal in this pipe is approximately 46,000 lb per sq in. by Eqs. 34 and 35.

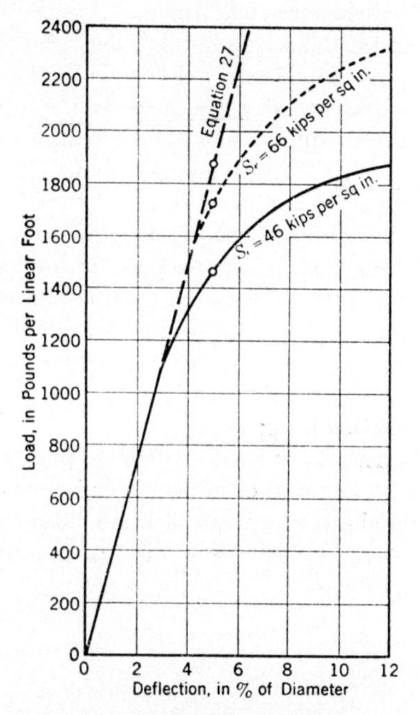

Fig. 30.—Load-Deflection Diagram for Corrugated Metal Pipe Culverts

Corrugated metal pipe culverts are made of many different kinds of iron and steel, ranging from commercially pure iron having a relatively low elastic limit to copper and copper-molybdenum iron or steel alloys having high elastic limits. In the research work on which Eq. 15 was based, the metal pipes furnished for the tests by four different manufacturers varied in elastic limits from 47,800 lb per sq in. to 65,500 lb per sq in. If the 36-in. pipe of Fig. 23 had been made of metal having an elastic limit of 66,000 lb per sq in. instead of 46,000 lb per sq in., the load-deflection diagram would have been approximately as shown by the dotted line in Fig. 30 and the difference between actual loads and those computed by Eq. 27 would have been much less.

Likewise, the data shown in Table 3 are intimately dependent on the elastic limits of the particular pipes tested. It is the writer's view that these data do not provide a proper basis for generalization without some detailed knowledge of the elastic limits of the metals from which the test specimens were made.

The data in Table 3 are irrelevant because the load and reaction in a two-edge bearing test are much more concentrated than in the field loading for which Eq. 15 was developed and it seems probable that the difference between computed loads and actual loads would be much less in the latter case, even when the pipe metal is stressed beyond its elastic limit at localized points—that is, the load-deflection curve under field loading would probably deviate from a straight-line elastic relationship much less rapidly than under concentrated loading. Mr. Shafer appears to agree with this view. Obviously, also, pipes made of metal having a high elastic limit would deviate less from the elastic line and would have less deflection for a given load than would pipes made from low elastic limit metal.

[57] "The Structural Design of Flexible Pipe Culverts," by M. G. Spangler, *Bulletin No. 153*, Iowa Eng. Experiment Station, Ames, Iowa, 1941, p. 14.

The data shown in Table 3 again raise the question of whether it is valid to apply a constant limiting deflection to all sizes of pipe. Mr. Shafer has given an interesting account of the origin of the commonly accepted 5% limit. He would do the profession a service if he would publish the data on which the values were established. It is pertinent to ask whether the "average safe maximum deflection" which was observed was the same percentage value for all pipe diameters.

Mr. Shafer has raised some appropriate questions concerning the nature of the modulus of passive resistance of soils, and the writer agrees that there is much yet to be learned about this property and its application to the flexible pipe problem. It is hoped that future research, both in the laboratory and in the field, will shed further light on this factor concerning which so little factual data exist. In particular, information is needed to determine more definitely the relationship between passive pressures and movement of the sides of the pipe, the distribution of the passive pressures, the effect of fill height and pipe rigidity on the passive pressure modulus, and soil test procedures on which to base estimates of the value of the modulus for design use. Such added information is needed in order to refine and improve Eq. 15 and to develop a parallel formula for strutted flexible pipe culverts.

The author is deeply indebted to those who have discussed the paper and wishes to express to them his personal thanks. He believes the discussions have added materially to the understanding of the underground conduit problem.

GENERAL INDEX

Items in bold face indicate sections and chapters, or prime references.
Tables are indicated by T.
See also Table of Contents, pages v to vii.

A

Abutment, bridge
  drainage of, 343, 454
Accelerated tests, corrosion, 148
Acid corrosion test, 148
Acidity, soil and water, 168
Aerial pipe sewers, T15-1, 60, 144
Aerial surveys, 225
Aggregate storage bins, 420, 425, 426–427
Aggregate tunnels, 399
Agricultural Engineering magazine, 339
Agricultural Subdrainage (see also Reclamation), 333–339
Airport Design Standards, T13-1, 135
  Minimum height of cover for
    various kinds of pipe, T13-2, 136
    c.m. pipe-arches, T13-3, T13-4, 137
    M.P. pipe-arches, T13-5, T13-6, 138
    Multi-Plate pipe, T13-7, 139
Airport Drainage, 344–354
  design for strength, 134–139
  size of pipe, 272–280, 349–352
  surface runoff, 252, 349
Air shafts, 399, 415
Alabama State Highway Dept., 18
Alignment (see also Mal-alignment)
  culvert, 150–151, **242–243**
  subdrain, 353
Alkali, alkalinity, 156, 169
Allen, Kenneth; sewage flow, 268
American Assn. of State Highway Officials, 36, 38, 71, 79, 105, 107, 166, 171, 314, 411, 413
American Railway Bridge and Bldg. Assn., 166
American Railway Eng. Assn., 12–14, 31, 59, 126, 161, 166, 173
  roadway drainage, 254, 323
  specifications, 71, 73, 124, 315
American Society for Testing Materials, 28, 49, 112–116, 129, 130, 147, 428, 481
American Society of Agricultural Engineers, 431
American Soc. of Civil Engineers, 21, 31, 171, 211, 473
American Water Works Assn., 34
Analysis metal, 172
  soil, 296
Anchorage for sectional pipe culv., 259
Anderson, A. O.; drain tile tests, 21
Angle of repose (see also Slope)
  soil, 30, 211, 379
Angles, structural, T51-6, 428
Appurtenances, Sewer, 281–290
Arches, Liner Plate (See Liner Plate)
  Multi-Plate (see Multi-Plate)
Arches, standard corrugated (see conveyor covers, Part circle culverts)
Area (see also Size of waterway)
  arches, T8-14, 86, 90–93, 236
  circles or pipe, 74, 235, 498, 502, 503, 511
  circular segments, T65-11, 498
  conduits, partly filled, 511
  drained (size, character), 229, 236
  drop-inlet culverts, T26-4, 234
  equivalent units, T65-2, 492
  part circle culverts, 293
  pipes, T26-5, 235
  pipe-arches, 77, 84, 237
  plane figures, T65-11, 498
  tunnels, T48-1, 400
Arid soil conditions, 169
Armco (refers to Armco Steel Corporation or Armco Drainage & Metal Products, Inc. or their products)
Armco (see Asbestos-Bonded, Corrugated metal pipe (standard, nestable, helical lock-seam), Bin-type retaining walls, Corrugated metal sheets, Flex-Beam Guardrail, Jacking, Liner Plate, Multi-Plate, Part circle culverts, Paved-Invert, Sewers, Sheeting, etc.)
Armco Culvert Mfrs. Assn.; Armco Drainage Products Assn.; Armco Drainage & Metal Products, Inc., 3, 21, 29, 34, 38, 45, 46, 54, 57, 63, 153, 163, 177, 257
Armco International Corporation, The, 3

Armco Research Laboratories, 4, 44, 46, 54, 161
Armco Steel Corporation, 3, 14, 25, 148
Asbestos-Bonded pipe
  durability, 161, 163, 175
  weights, T8-4, T8-7, 74, 77
  sewer, 121, 144, 162
Asphalt coating and lining (see Bituminous)
Assembly, corr. metal structures, 438–442
  retaining walls, 471
Assn. of American Railroads, 29
Aston, James; corrosion, 171
Athletic field drainage, 331
Auger, soil, 306, 345

B

Babbitt, H. E.; sewage flow, 268, 289
Backfill (see also Fill, Filter, Tamp)
  costs, 182
  Instructions, 446–450
  material, re strength, 67
  pervious (various ref.), 314, 342, 453
  retaining walls, 472
  threaded pipe, 469
Backflow, backwater, 371
Bailey, M. H.; durability, 158, 163, 177
Baker, I. O.; soils, 509
Baker, R. C.; durability, 161
Baker, R. F.; landslides, 356
Ballast section, 254
Band (see Coupling)
Barnard, R. E.; pile shell research, 34
Baseball diamond drainage, 331
Base (see Sub-base, Foundation)
Base plates, bin-wall, 381, 385
Baumann, E. R.; septic tanks, 289
Batter, retaining wall, 381–383
Beam strength test
  bridge plank, steel, 45
  corrugated pipe, riveted, T7-1, 60–61, 69
  Flex-Beam guardrail, T5-3, 44
  Hel-Cor pipe, 61
  structural plates, curved, 38, 41
Beam Type guardrail, 408
  installation instr., 477–479
Bearing value of soils, 302, 323, 380, 509
Bedding (see also Foundation)
  conditions for trench conduits, 8
  costs, 184
  of conduits, 434
Bending moment, 57–59
Better Roads magazine, 240, 317
Beveled ends, culvert, 247
Bibliographies, soil studies, 310, 356
Binger, W. V.; U. S. Engrs., 9
Bins, storage and surge, 420–431
  tests on liner plate joints, T6-1, 51–53
Bin-wall (retaining wall), 363, 380
  installation, 470–472
Bituminous coated pipe
  durability design, 174
  installation instructions, 439
Bituminous coated pipe—Continued
  leakage test, T4-1, 34
  watertightness, 372
  weights, T8-4, T8-6, 74, 77
Bituminous pavement, bridge roadway, 482
Bolts; bolted joints
  advantages, 48
  failure, 50
  high tensile steel, 49, 81
Boring
  installing small diam. pipe, 358, 406
  instructions, 461
Borings (see Auger)
Boussinesq, load formula, 23
Branch, Y-fittings, 283
  sewer, 286
Braune, G. M.; U. of N. C.
  load research, 11
Bridge (see Abutments)
  Culverts vs. Small Bridges, 236–239
  drainage, 340–343
  filling, 468–469
  plank
    corrugation, 37
    deflection tests, 45
    Installation, 480–482
  rail, 411, 413, 479
  replacement, 239, 468
  surface drainage, 252
Brown, J. B., 206
Bruce, A. G.; highway design, 171
Bulkheads, sheeting, 389
Bureau of Public Roads (see U. S. Bureau of Public Roads)
Bursting stress in bins, T51-4, 427
Buttresses, landslide, 356

C

Cain, Wm.; U. of N. C.
  load research, 11, 431
Caissons, bridge piers, 464
California State Hy. Comm., 44
California, Univ. of, 206, 339, 354
Camber, grade line, 19, 245, 435–437
Canadian Dept. of Transport, 135
Cantilever culvert outlet, 245, 335, 360
Capacity (see also Discharge, Size)
  airport drains, 272–280
  bridge, 238
  culvert, 224–240, 278
  ditch, 206–211
  drop inlets, 234
  sanitary sewers, 280
  sewers, 265–268, 272–280
  soil-carrying, of water, 210
  spillway, 365
  subdrains, T37-1, 312
  units, equivalent, T65-3, 492–493
  weir notch, 365
Capillary moisture, 308, 322, 333, 335
Carnegie's Pocket Companion, tables, 498, 500, 501, 503–504

Cast iron pipe, 7, 69, 183
Catchbasin (see also Inlets), 284, 346, 349
Cathodic protection, 176
Cattle passes (see Underpasses)
Caughey, R. A.; bin pressures, 431
Cemetery subdrainage, 329
Channel, stream, Design of, 206–211, 361
Channels, unbalanced, 81
Check dams, 365
Chemical Characteristics of Water and Soil Which Affect Durability, 167–171
Chezy flow formula, 206
Chicago & North Western RR
  subdrainage installation, 325
Cinders, 169
Circle, area, T65-11, T65-16–17, 498, 502–504
  properties, T65-15, 501
Circular, measure, T65-7, 495
Circumference of circles, T65-15, T65-17, 501, 503
  segment, areas, T65-11, 498
Civil Aeronautics Admin., 71, 134, 304, 350
Civil Engineering magazine, 240
Clark; properties of ice and snow, T65-7, 495
Clarkeson, J.; highway design, 171
Clay drain tile (see Vitrified clay)
Coal bins, T51-1, 420, 424, 426, 427
Coatings
  bituminous (non-metallic), 174
  galvanized, 161, 169, 173
  protective, durability, 147–177
  watertightness, 369
Coefficient, roughness, *n*, ditch, 208
  air pipe, T50-1, 418
  imperviousness, 266
  pipe lines, 271
  subsurface drainage, 352
Cofferdams, 389
Cohesion of soil, 301
Column strength, T15-2, 144
Columns, bin-wall, 381, 385
Column tests
  on pipe, 62, 63
  on plates, 40–41
Colvin, C. M.; jacking, 459
Combined surface and subsurface drainage, airport, 348
Commodity Credit Corp., 431
Compaction (see Settlement and Tamping)
Compression caps, 444
Compression tests on joints, 51–53
Concentration, time of, 198, 200, 350, 352
Concrete
  arch lining, 465
  cradle, 9, 436, 437
  ditch checks, 361-363
  encasement, 437
  gutters, 364
  pipe
    cost studies, 186
    headwall need, 259
    rating, durability, 151
    rigidity, 7, 68
    roughness coefficient, 271
Concrete, pipe—Continued
    subdrain, 454
    weights, 183
Concrete Pipe Handbook, 183
Conduit (see also Culvert, Pipe)
  flexible, 7
  "negative projecting," 8
  "projecting," 7
  public utility, 397, 399
  "trench," 7
  types, 67
  underground, 5, Appendix A
Connections (see also Bolts, Joints, Seams)
  band, 72, 438
  riveted, field, 72
  Sewer appurtenances, 281–290
Construction costs, drainage, 179–193
Conversion tables, 491–497
Conveyor covers, 69
Cooper, railroad loading, 23, 124
Cornell University
  theory of flexure, 63
Corps of Engineers (see U. S.)
Core wall, 368
Corner sections, steel sheeting, 390
Corrosion, cause of deterioration, 167
Corrugated metal pipe, standard [see also Corr. metal pipe (helical lock-seam), Corr. metal sheets, Culverts, Multi-Plate, Paved-invert, Perforated pipe, Sewers]
  background, 69
  coefficient of roughness, 271
  conduits, tunnels, underpasses, 405
  cost of installation, 186
  ditch enclosure, 363
  durability rating, 150
  fabrication details, 72–76
  fittings, 283
  gages, highway, T9-2, T9-3, 107
  gages, sewer, T10-1, T10-2, 118–119
  gages, railway, T11-1, 125
  gages, levee, T12-1, 133
  gages, airport, T13-2, 136
  instructions for installing, 433–451
  manhole, 282, 285
  nesting, 181
  sluiceway, 368, 371
  small bridge, 236
  spillways, 365
  strength (see Strength)
  weights, T8-4, 73, 74, 183
Corrugated metal pipe (helical lock-seam)
  beam strength, T7-1, 61
  column strength, T7-2, 63
  crushing strength, 25
  fittings, 283
Corrugated metal sheets
  physical properties, 36
Corrugated metal plates (see Multi-Plate)
Corrugated metal structures (pipe, arches, and pipe-arches)
  durability design, 172–177
  installation instructions, 433–451

Corrugated pipe-arch
fabrication details, 76–77
gages, highway, T9-4, 108
gages, sewer, T10-3, 119
gages, railway, T11-2, 125
gages, airport, T13-3, T13-4, 137
weights, T8-6, 77
Corrugations
strength, influence on, 41
type and dimensions, 35–37, 39
Cost (see also Economy)
Installation, 179–193
assembling Multi-Plate, 187
detour provision, 188
end finish, 191
engineering and inspection, 180
equipment and tools, 188
excava. and backfill, 182–184
guardrail, 193
items studied, 180
lay, line and join, 185
maintenance, 193
material cost, 180
miscellaneous factors, 190
preparing bed; placing new structure, 184
railroad freight, 181
removing old structure, 184
replacing surface, 188
retaining walls, 192
salvage value, 193
slow orders, 189
strutting, 188
supervision, overhead, 190
total, 180
transportation and handling, 181–182
truck haulage, 182
Couplings
standard band, 72
watertightness, 33, 75, 286, 287
Cover, minimum height of
airports, T13-2 to T13-7, 136–139
highway loading, T9-1, 106
Cradling, concrete, 9, 436, 437
Cribbing, 356
Critical
slope, 215, 222, 365
section, 212
velocity, 212
Crossing, grade, 328
Cross-section of roadway, 251, 254
Crown, 251
Cube of numbers, T65-17, 503–504
Cube roots, T65-17, 503–504
Culvert (see also Corrugated metal, Multi-Plate, Pipe, etc.)
alignment, 242
bridge, 236–239
definition, 224
design, size, 224–240
drop-inlet, 234, 245
durability, 147–177
end finish, 258–264
equalizer, 248
Culvert—Continued
extension, 259
farm entrance, 248
grade, 244–245
headwalls, 258–264
hydraulics of, 224–240
installation costs, 179–193
installation instructions, 432–451
investigations, durability, 154–161
location and length, 241–249
levee, 256–257, 372
multiple, 238
part circle, 291–293
paved invert (see Paved Invert)
relief, 249
relocation, 193
sizes (see also Size of Waterway), 224–240
skew, 243, 247
vs. small bridge, 236–239
Curve data, for bin-walls, T47-1, 386-387
guardrail, 414, 479
Cutoff wall (see also Diaphragm)
sheeting, 261, 389
Cuts, drainage of wet, 320, 321, 325, 343

D

Dalrymple, Tate; streamflow, 240
Dam, 234, 365, 367
Decimals
degree, of a, T65-8, 496
feet, conversion, T65-9, 497
inches, conversion, T65-10, T65-14, 497, 500
square roots of, T65-19, 506
Deck drain, half circle, 342
Deflection (see also Flexible)
angles, retaining wall, T47-2, 387
effect on load, 11
Flexible culverts, T1-1, 15
function of gage and load, 55, 70
law of, 70
Multi-Plate pipe, T1-3, 18
pipe-arch tests, T1-2, 16
railroad culverts, 160
tests, laboratory, 55
Denver & Rio Grande Western RR, 14
Depth of fill on pipe (see Cover)
Depth of subdrains
airport, 352, 354
recommended, 337
Design
Airport Drainage, 344–354
Airport, Loadings, 134–139
Size of pipe, 272–280
Asbestos-Bonded metal, 175
Corrugated Metal Structures, 66–103
Culvert Location and Length, 241–249
Culvert Sizes, 224–240
Culverts under Levees, 256–257
Culverts Vs. Small Bridges, 236–239
Drainage of Bridges and Grade Separations, 340–343

Design—Continued
  Durability, 165–177
  End Finish of Culverts, 258–264
  Guardrail and Bridge Rail, 407–414
  Highway Loadings and Gages, 105–117
  Highway Surface Drainage, 250–253
  Hydraulics of Culverts, 224–240
  Hydraulics of Sewers, 269–280
  Part Circle Culverts, 291–293
  Pipe, Corr. Metal, 72–76
  Principles and Practices (Size), 194–293
  Levee Loadings, 132–133
  Liner Plate Gages, 140–143
  Multi-Plate Structures
    arches, 86–103
    pipe, 81–82
    pipe-arches, 83–85
  Open Channels, 206–211
  Railway Loadings and Gages, 124–131
  Railway Surface Drainage, 254–255
  Retaining Walls, 378–388
  Selection of Materials on Durability Basis, 172–177
  Sewers, 265–268
  Sewer Appurtenances, 281–290
  Sewer Loadings and Gages, 118–123
  Sheeting, Steel, 389–396
  Storage Bins, 420–431
  Strength of Conduits, 65–145
  Subdrains, 311–316
  Subsurface Drainage, 294–339
  Surface Drainage, 250–255
  Tunnels, Underpasses, Conduits, 397–406
  Ventilation, 415–419
Deterioration
  material and structural, 150–152, 167
Detour costs, 188
Dewatering of excavation, 190
Diaphragms, 369, 372, 441
Dike culverts, 256, 371, 486–489
Discharge (see also Capacity, Runoff, Size)
  circular conduits, 280
  Culvert, 226–233
  Sewer, 272–280
  Subdrains, 312–313, 318, 352
Disjointing
  culvert pipe, 30, 363, 368
  subdrains, 353
Disturbance factors in sewers, 270
Ditch
  capacities, 207-210
  checks, 361
  diversion, 345, 360
  enclosure (see also Stream enclosure), 345, 363, 366
  lining, 364
  spillway (= check), 361
  surface drainage, 253, 255
  velocities, permissible, 207, 210
Diversion ditch, 360
Downs, W. S.; culvert survey, 158
Downspouts, 253, 342
Drag-down, vertical, on bins, T51-3, 426
Drainage
  Agricultural, 333–339
  Airport, 344–354
  area (size, character, etc.), 200, 226, 266
  Bridges and Grade Separations, 340–343
  Gates, 373–377
  Highway Surface, 250–253
  Land Reclamation, 371–377
  landslide, 356
  openings, methods of providing, 455
  Railway Surface, 254–255
  retaining wall, 378, 380
  Special Problems, 340–377
  Street, 281, 291
  Subsurface, 294–339
  Surface, 250–255, 344
Drain pipe (see Culverts, Subdrains, Sewers)
Driving steel sheeting, 392
Drop-down, hydraulic, 212
Drop-inlet, 234, 245, 360, 363, 368, 370
Drying crops, 419
Ducts, air, heat, 417, 418
Dunlop; airport engineering, 354
Durability, 147–177
  airport drains, 353
  Design, 165–177
  Field Investigations, 148, 154–163
  Metals and Coatings, 172–177
  Methods of Determining, 147–153
  Studies, metals and coatings, 147–177

E

Earth Control, 379–396
Economic Factors, 179–193
  large diameter culverts, 236–239
  part circle culverts, 291
  separate vs. combined sewer, 265
Efficiency
  bolted joint, 49
  hydraulic, 243, 244, 354
Elastic theory of flexure, 57
Elasticity, modulus of stand. corr. metal, 36
Elbow, fittings, 283
Elliptical liner plate underpasses, 143, 401
Elliptical pipe, 82
Elongation, vertical diameter, 443
Embankment
  load tests under, 7, 9, 12, 18, 30
  protector, 359
  settlement (see Settlement)
  soil characteristics, T36-5, 302
Empirical formula, earth pressures, 379
  strength, 66
  rainfall runoff, 196
Encasement of corr. metal, 437
Enclosures (see Ditch enclosures and Stream enclosures)
End Finish of Culverts, 76, 258–264, 450, 488
End sections, metal
  dimensions, T31-1, T31-2, 262–263
  durability, 176
  erosion prevention, 243

End sections, metal—Continued
installation costs, T22-3, 191
Encroachment (see Erosion)
Engineering costs, 180
Engineering News-Record, 21, 135, 148, 158, 186, 271
Eno, F. H.; subsoil investigations, 309
Entrance
of culvert, 243
culverts, private and side road, 248
loss, 269
Equalizer culvert, 248
Equipment
costs; use of, 188
jacking, 459
pile driving, sheeting, 473, 474
strutting, 444
tamping, 447
Equivalents, conversion tables, 491–497
Erie RR; tunneling, 327
Erosion; Scour
at end of culvert, 243, 245, 360
bank, preventing, 366
ditch, prevention, 209, 243, 361–365
invert, 150, 154, 369
Roadway Prevention, 359–367
shoulders, 349
transverse gullies, 360
Excavation (see also Trenching)
bin-walls, 470
costs, 182–184
jacking method, 459
Explosion door, 417
Expressway (see also Turnpikes)
Bronx-Whitestone, 282
Extension
culvert, 259, 360

F

Fabricated metal products, date of introduction, T16-3, 153
Fabrication
corrugated pipe, T8-3, T8-4, 72–76
corrugated pipe-arch, T8-5, T8-6, 76–77
Multi-Plate structures, T8-8, T8-9, T8-10, 78–80
pipe for jacking, 459
Factor of safety, 68, 70, 81, 224, 231, 233
Fan ducts, 417
Farm entrance, 248
Farm ponds, 369
Federa. of Sewage Works Assns., 171
Feld, Jacob; jacking pressures, 459
Field Investigations, durability, 148
measurements of settlement, deflection, 8, 17
Filkins, Claude W. L.; elastic rings, 63
Fill (see also Backfill)
permissible height or depth, 81, 82, 105–143
soft, 320, 324
Filter material, subdrain, 313–315, 454
Fittings, pipe (see also Connections), 282
Sewer Appurtenances, 281–290
Flap gates, 372–376, 484, 486–489
Flange type sheeting, 389
Flared entrance, culvert, 233, 360
Flex-Beam (see Guardrail)
Flexible (flexibility) type of culvert or conduit (see also Corrugated metal, Deflection, Strength, etc.), 7, 68
Flood Control and Land Reclamation, 371–377
Flow (see Hydraulics)
Flowing water, equivalents, T65-6, 494–495
Flourescein (ground water tracer), 306
Flumes, 364, 365
Folwell, A. P.; sewerage reference, 280
Footings (see Foundations)
Force, tractive hydraulic, T24-2, 210
Forces (see Pressures, Loads)
destructive, materially, 147
Ford, paved, 249
Formulas
bending moment, 58
Chezy, 206
Darcy-Weisbach (air), 418
deflection, 70
discharge, weir notch, 365
ditch check spacing, 361
durability rating, 151
earth pressures, 379
hydraulic, complexity, 210
Jarvis-Myers, runoff, 227
Kutter, 270, 272, 273
Manning, 206, 270, 351
pressures in deep bins (Janssen), 423
Ramser, 234
rational, 266, 350
strength (empirical), 66, 70
subsurface runoff, 313
surface runoff, 226, 266
Talbot (runoff), 226
trigonometric, T65-13, 500
Fort, Edwin J.; elastic rings, 63
Fortier, Samuel; hydraulics, 207
Foster, Edgar E.; rainfall, 197
Foundation (see also Bearing power, Subgrade)
bin-walls, 471
character of, 67, 318, 324
corrugated metal structures, 434
Multi-Plate arches, 93–103
retaining walls, 380
subdrain, 354
Fowler, Geo. L.; strength research, 59
Fractions, conversion to decimals, T65-14, 500
Free moisture (see Gravitational)
Free outlet, 218, 231, 365
Freezing (see Frost)
Freight
car capacity, 181
charges, 181
French drains, 313, 338
Friction loss in sewers (see also Coefficient of roughness), 270

Frost action, 31, 353
Frost boils and heaving, 305, 309, 347
Frost, R. E.; soil mapping, 310
Fuller, Earl I.; frost, 317
Functions
  of numbers, T65-17, 503–504
  trigonometric, T65-12, 499

G

Gage
  Bridge Plank, Armco metal, 481
  Corr. Metal Pipe, T8-4, 74
    H-20 live load, unstrutted, T9-2, 107
    H-20 live load, strutted, T9-3, 107
    H-10 live load, trench cond., T10-1, 118
    H-20 live load, trench cond., T10-2, 119
    E-70 live load, unstrutted and strutted, T11-1, 125
    Under levees and dams, T12-1, 133
    Under airports, T13-2, 136
  Corrugated Metal Pipe-arches
    H-20 live load, T9-4, 108
    H-10 live load, trench cond., T10-3, 119
    E-70 live load, T11-2, 125
    under airfield pvmt., rigid, T13-3, 137
    under airfield pvmt., flexible, T13-4, 137
  Highway Loadings, 105–117
  Multi-Plate Arches
    H-20 live load, T9-13, 116
    H-15 live load, T9-14, 116
    H-10 live load, T9-15, 117
    No live load, T9-16, 117
    H-10 live load, sewer, T10-8, 123
    H-20 live load, sewer, T10-9, 123
    E-70 live load, T11-7, T11-9, 130, 131
    E-50 live load, T11-8, 130
  Multi-Plate Pipe
    H-20 live load, unstrutted, T9-5, 109
    H-20 live load, strutted, T9-6, 110
    No live load, unstrutted, T9-7, 111
    No live load, strutted, T9-8, 111
    H-10 live load, trench cond., T10-4, 120
    H-20 live load, trench cond., T10-5, 120
    E-70 live load, unstrutted, T11-3, 126
    E-70 live load, strutted, T11-4, 127
    Airport loading, T13-7, 139
  Multi-Plate Pipe-arches
    H-20 live load, T9-9, 112
    H-15 live load, T9-10, 113
    H-10 live load, T9-11, 114
    No live load, T9-12, 115
    H-10 live load, sewer, T10-6, 122
    H-20 live load, sewer, T10-7, 122
    E-70 live load, T11-5, 128
    E-50 live load, T11-6, 129

Gage, Multi-Plate Pipe-arches—Continued
    Airport loading, T13-5, T13-6, 138
  multiple, 81
  part circle culverts, 292
  Railway Loadings, 124–131
  steel sheeting, T47-3, 390
  Tunnel Liner Plate, 140–143, 402
    H-20 live load, T14-1, 140
    E-70 live load, T14-2, 141
    E-70, arch relining, T14-3, 142
    H-20, elliptical, T14-4, 143
    E-70, elliptical, T14-5, 143
  strain, 18
  U. S. Standard, sheets and plate iron and steel, T65-20, 507
Gaging stations, rainfall, 195
Galvanizing (see Spelter), 173
Gates, Drainage, 177, 369, **373–377**
  available models, T46-2, 376
  dimensions, Model 100, T46-1, 374
  installation instructions, 483–485, 486–489
Georgia State Hy. Dept., 148
Gilliland, J. L.; corrosion, 177
Golf course drainage, 329
Grade (see also Slope)
  culvert, 244–245
  ditch, 361, 365
  storm sewer, 272
  subdrain, 316, 453
Grade crossing drainage, 328
Grade Separation Structures, 340–343
Grain bins, 420, 426, 431
Granular base, 436
Gravitational moisture, movement and control, 308, 333
Gridiron system of drains, 336
Griffin, Ira P.; airfields, 345
Ground water (see also Capillary, Gravitational, Hygroscopic, Moisture), 270, 307
Grouting, 406, 463, 466
Guardrail
  Design, 407–414
  durability, 177
  impact tests, 43–45
  installation costs, 193
  Installation Instructions, 477–479
  joints, tension tests, T6-2, 54
Gullies (see Erosion)
Gutters, 252, 360

H

Hand excavation, 182
Hand placing, 184
Hanson, W. E.; foundations, 310
Hardenbergh, W. A.; sewerage, 171, 268
Hauling, truck, 182
Head
  flow under, 224
  loss, 269
  permissible on gates, 374–376

Headwalls, 258–264
drainage gate, 488–489
installation, 448
metal end sections, 262–264
sheeting, 261
Heaving
frost action, 309
track, 323
Height, permissible fill (see also Cover), 81, 82, 105–143
Hel-Cor pipe (see Corr. metal pipe—lock-seam), 25, 37, 61, 63, 283, 315, 417, 418, 440
Helical (see Corr. metal pipe—lock-seam)
Herring-bone system, drains, 336
High fills, culverts under, 18, 451
Highwater records, 226
Highway culvert inspections, 154–158
Highway Magazine, The, 158, 163, 177
Highway Research Board, 17, 29, 54, 105, 148, 239, 300, 304, 309, 339, 356, 459
Highway Subdrainage, 317–322
Highway Surface Drainage, 250–253
Hittle, J. E.; aerial mapping, 310
Horonjeff, Robt.; airport design, 354
Housel, W. S.; tunnel liner research, 51
Hydraulic
considerations, culvert, 224
efficiency of culvert, 260
equivalents, T65-6, 494–495
Open Channels, 206–211
radius, 206, 279, 511
Theory of Critical Flow, 212–223
traffic, 154
Hydraulics of Sewers, 269–280
Hydrology (see also Capacity, Flow), 195–205
Hydrostatic pressure, 59
Hygroscopic moisture, 307, 335

I

Ice, properties of, T65-7, 495
Illinois Central Railroad, 12
Illinois, University of
strength research, 21, 38, 54, 57, 62
septic tank research, 289
Impact (see Load, surface)
airplane, 135, 353
guardrail, 43–45, 407
part circle culverts, 291
Research, 22–29
Impervious (see also Perviousness)
relative values, T23-5, 201
Industrial tunnels, 398
Industrial wastes, 268
Infiltration
sewers, 268
subdrains, 314
surface water, 354
Inlet (see also Catchbasin)
culvert, droptype, 234, 245
effect on capacity of culvert, 233
sewer, 281
Inlet—Continued
subdrain, 314
Inspection
culvert size, 226
Highway Culverts, 154–158
Multi-Plate pipe and arch, 157
Railway Culverts, 159–161
sewers, 162
Installation
conditions of; methods, 67, 131
Cost Studies, 179–193
Instructions, 432–489
Armco Gates, 483–485
Beam-Type Guardrail, 477–479
Bin Walls, 388, 470–472
Boring, 460–461
Bridge Filling, 468–469
Corrugated Metal Structures, 433–451
Flap Gate Drainage Structures, 486–489
Jacking, 455–459
Lining, 465–467
Metal Bridge Plank, 480–482
part circle culverts, 293
Perforated Pipe Subdrains, 452–454
Sheeting, 473–476
Tunneling, 405, 462–464
simplicity of culvert, 238
Intake (see Inlet)
Intensity of storms, 196
Internal Pressures, 32–34
Intercepting ditches, 253, 255
Intercepting drains, 311, 319, 324, 343, 346, 348
Interception
ground water, 308, 311, 344
surface water, 251, 345
Interference, traffic, 189
Interlocking sheeting, 389, 476
Introduction of fabrica. metal products, T16-3, 153
Invert (see also Paved Invert), 174
Investigation (see Durability, Culvert, Research)
Iowa Agricultural Experi. Station, 339
Iowa State College, Engineering Experiment Station
load research, 7, 11, 24, 56, 70, 339, 365, 431
subdrainage research, 312
Iowa, University of
flow research, 231
Isohyetal maps, rainfall, 196
Izzard, Carl F.; drainage, 239

J

Jacking Method
Instructions, 456–459
small diameter pipe, 357, 460
tunnels, 405
Janda, H. F.; load research, 11
Jarvis-Myers runoff formula, 227

Joints, pipe (see also Connections, Disjointing)
- bolted, research on, 47–54
- effect on cost, 184–185
- effect on flow, 270
- inspection of, 150–151
- riveted, strength test, 48
- sewer, 287
- tightness, 358

Jones; airport design, 354
Journal of Agri. Research
- rainfall frequency—intensity, 201

K

Kelley, E. F.; USBPR, 148
Ketchum, Milo S.; bin stresses, 431
King, H. W.
- tables, general, 497, 505, 506, 508
- use of Manning formula, 206, 365

King, J. A.; tile drainage, 339
Kirkham, Don; subdrainage, 339
Kropf, W. J.; culvert life, 21, 158
Kutter
- formula, 272, 273
- value of *n*, 270

L

Labor
- costs, 184–193
- jacking method, 459

Laboratory tests; (see also Research)
- durability, 148
- flow, 210–212
- strength, 38–46, 47–54, 55–63

Lake, artificial, 369
Landing field (see Airport)
Landslides, 355–358
- causes, 355
- drainage, 356–358
- remedies, 355–358, 388

Lang, F. C.; subgrade stabilization, 318
Larew, H. G.; landslides, 356
Large diameter pipe, 366, 451
Laterals, 336
Leakage (see Watertight, Infiltration)
Length and Location, Culvert, 241–249
Length, culvert and drain pipe
- computation of, 246
- effect on cost, 185
- gain due to connection, 439
- pipe for jacking, 456
- standard for corr. metal pipe, 72
- table, conversion, T65-1, 491

Levee, 371
- drainage of, 256
- gages of corr. metal pipe, 133
- installing culverts, 486–489

Level water table, 319
Life expectancy, 148, 149, 152, 166
Lift-operated gates, 373–377, 483
Line (see Alignment)
Liner Plate
- areas, plate combinations, T48-1, T48-2, 400–401
- arch or culvert lining, 466
- durability, 176
- gages, highway, T14-1, 140
- gages, railway, T14-2, 141
- gages, railway arch relining, T14-3, 142
- gages, highway, elliptical, T14-4, 143
- gages, railway, elliptical, T14-5, 143
- joints, 51–53
- tunnel lining, 462

Lining (see also Threading)
- arch, 97
- **conduits, 465-467**
- ditch, 364
- tunnel, 462

Liquid limits, soils, 300
Load (see also Impact, Pressure, Landslides, etc.)
- **Airport Loadings, 134–139**
- beam, 60
- construction, 105
- cracking, 28
- **Dead, 5–21, 94**
- distribution on wales, 393
- factors, 67
- **highway, 105–117**
- impact (see Impact)
- legal limits, 105
- levee loadings, 132–133
- live (see surface loads)
- miscellaneous, 144–145
- **Railroad loadings (and gages), 124–131**
- **Sewer loadings (and gages), 118–123**
- **Research on, 5–63**
- **Surface, 22–29, 94**
- **theory, 5**

Loading costs (and unloading), 181
Location, Culvert
- **Length and, 241–249**

Location of guardrail, 477
Location of subdrains, 311, 313, 319–339
Logarithms, T65-17, 503–504
Lynes, W. S.; tile drainage, 339

M

Machine
- excavation vs. hand, 182
- placing, 184

Maintenance
- costs, 193
- culverts vs. bridges, 238, 468
- guardrail, 479
- roadway, street, detour, 188, 189
- sewers, 282, 290
- subdrains, 338

Mal-alignment, 353
Manhole, 282, 285
Man-hour (see Installation cost studies)
Manning formula, 206, 351

Manning formula—Continued
coefficient *n*, 270
comparison with Kutter formula, 270
solution
diagrams, 274–277
table, T33-3, 278–279
square roots of decimals, T65-19, 506
Marston, Anson
culvert load research, 6
Martens, R. W.; sewer inspections, 163
Mason, Clyde; load research, 29
Materials, compressive and tensile strength, T65-22, 509
Material deterioration, 150–152, 161
Materials for structures, 1, 3, 7, 55, 466
Materials, weight of construction, T65-21, 508
McLeod, N. W.; airport load, 135
Median strips, 252, 408
Menefee, F. N.; transverse forces, 30
Metal bridge plank (see Bridge plank)
Metal, chemical analysis, 172
Metcalf and Eddy; sewerage, 271
Metric units (see Tables), 491, 493
Miami Conservancy District, Ohio
theory of backwater and critical flow, 214, 240
Michigan State College
corrugated plate research, 38–43
Michigan State Highway Dept.
corrugated plate research, 38–43
subgrade research, 318
Michigan, University of, 30, 51
Military Engineer, The, 345
Mine entries, shafts, escapeways, 399, 404
ventilation, 415
Mineral waters, 168
Minnesota, State Highway Dept.
Multi-Plate research, 27
subgrade research, 318
Minnesota, University of
subdrainage runoff, 312, 352
Miscellaneous Problems, 378–431
Missouri State Hy. Dept.
research on guardrail, 43
Modern Railroads magazine, 240
Moisture (see also Capillary, Gravitational, Hygroscopic, Water)
amount in soils, 295, 335
agricultural requirements, 333
kinds of, 307
Mollard, J. B.; aerial mapping, 310
Moment of inertia
Multi-Plate, 78
stand. corr. metal, 36
Mosquito elimination, 371
Movement (see Soil, Landslide)
Multiple opening vs. single, 238, 441
minimum permissible spacing, 442, 489
Multiple track drainage, 325
Municipal Subdrainage, 329–332
Multi-Plate
Arches
abutments, 102, 103
design for strength, 86–103

Multi-Plate, Arches—Continued
durability inspection, 157
foundation design, 93–103
gages recommended
H-20 live load, T9-13, 116
H-15 live load, T9-14, 116
H-10 live load, T9-15, 117
No live load, T9-16, 117
H-10 live load, sewer, T10-8, 123
H-20 live load, sewer, T10-9, 123
E-70 live load, railroad, T11-7, T11-9, 130, 131
E-50 live load, railroad, T11-8, 130
installation instructions, 441
lining with, 466
load tests, 26
reactions, load, 93–103
representative sizes, T8-14, 90–93
rise/span ratio, T8-14, 90–93
shape, 87, 94
waterway, T8-14, 86, 90–93
bolts, T8-9, T8-10, 79, 80
corrugations, 36
Design, 78–103
development, 69
physical properties, T8-7, 78
Pipe
deflection, T1-3, 18
design for strength, 81–82
durability inspection, 157
gages recommended
H-20 live load, unstrutted, T9-5, 109
H-20 live load, strutted, T9-6, 110
No live load, unstrutted, T9-7, 111
No live load, strutted, T9-8, 111
H-10 live load, trench cond., T10-4, 120
H-20 live load, trench cond., T10-5, 120
E-70, live load, unstrutted, T11-3, 126
E-70 live load, strutted, T11-4, 127
Airport loading, T13-7, 139
installation instructions, 441
weight, T8-10, 80
Pipe-arches
design for strength, 83–85
gages recommended
H-20 live load, T9-9, 112
H-15 live load, T9-10, 113
H-10 live load, T9-11, 114
No live load, T9-12, 115
H-10 live load, sewer, T10-6, 122
H-20 live load, sewer, T10-7, 122
E-70 live load, T11-5, 128
E-50 live load, T11-6, 129
Airport loading, T13-5, T13-6, 138
installation instructions, 441
live load tests, 26
weight, T8-12, 85
Plates (sections)
beam tests, 38, 41
description, 78–79

Multi-Plate, Plates (sections)—Continued
physical properties, 78
weights, T8-9, 79
Seams or Joints, 48–50
sewers, 120–123
structures, fabrica. details, 78–81
assembly costs, 187
trade name, 14
tunnels, 404
waterway, 90–93, 229, 237

N

Negative projecting conduit, 8, 10
Nestable corrugated metal pipe, 54, 405
Nesting of corr. metal pipe, 181
New York State Dept. of Public Wks., 317
Noonan, N. G.; corrosion, 177
North Carolina, State Hy. Dept., 18
North Carolina, University of
load research, 10–12, 62
Notch, capacity of weir, 365

O

Obsolescence, 166, 193, 239
Offset joint, research, 51
Ohio Public Works mag., 171
Ohio State Highway Dept., 239
Ohio State University
beam tests on c.m.p., 60
subgrade research, 310
Open channel (see Ditch)
Opening (see Size)
Open-trench installation, 405, 455
Outfalls, sewer, 288
Outlet
bridge drains, 343
culvert (see Free, Submerged)
drain pipe, 348
free, 218–221, 231, 365
sewer, 269
subdrain, 316, 335, 452
submerged, 232–233
Overcasts, mine, 399, 416
Overhead, costs, 190

P

Paaswell, Geo.
soil pressures, 31, 211
Painting, guardrail, 479
Panama Railroad, 9
Parallel system of drains, 336
Parking lot, 252, 397, 408
Parks, drainage of, 329
Parkway, New Jersey State, 318
Part Circle Culverts, 291–293
Passenger terminal
drainage, 328
Paved-Invert Pipe, 174, 369, 439
culverts, 132, 154
durability design, 174
inspection, 155
sewer, 121
strutting, 444
weight, 74–77
Percolation, surface and ground water, 322
Perforated Pipe, Corrugated Metal (see also Subdrainage)
advantages, 315
Agricultural Subdrainage, 333–339
Airport Subdrainage, 347, 348, 352
Bridge Drainage, 340–343
Highway Subdrainage, 317–322
Instructions for Installing, 452–454
Landslide Subdrainage, 355–358
Municipal Subdrainage, 329–332
Railway Subdrainage, 323–328
Perforations, position of, 313, 315–316, 343, 453
Perimeter, wetted, 206
Permeability (see also Impervious), 301
Peck, O. K., 14
Peck, R. B., 14, 31, 310
Pervious backfill (see also Subbase), 314, 318, 323, 325, 331, 338, 342, 354, 469
Physical properties
metal bridge plank, T62-1, 482
metal sheets, standard corrugated, 36
Multi-Plate plates, 78
Tunnel liner plates, 402, 428
Piers, Multi-Plate arch, 103
Piling, 356 (see also Sheeting)
Pile-driving, 392, 473
Pipe (see also Asbestos-Bonded, Cast iron, Concrete, Corrugated metal, Culverts, Multi-Plate, Perforated, Paved-Invert, Storm sewer, Vitrified, etc.)
-arches, riveted
dead load tests, 15
design for strength, 76–77
gages, T9-4, 108
installation instructions, 440
live load tests, 25, 26
fabrication details, T8–5, T8–6, 76, 77
weights, T8–6, 77
-arches, Multi-Plate, 26, 83–85
gages, 112–131
weights, T8–12, 85
drop, 366
jacking, 459
sewers, 265–289
spillway
for dam, 368
stream enclosures, 253, 265
subdrains, 313, 315
Plane figures, areas of, T65-11, 498
Plasticity of soils, 299, 300, 301, 303
Plate arrangement
liner plate arches, T48–4, 403
liner plate pipes, T48–1, T48–2, 400, 401
Plates (see Multi-Plate)
Playground drainage, 330

Poling plates, boards, 464
Porosity (see Permeability, Pervious backfill)
Post spacing, guardrail, 411–412, 477
Powers of numbers, 2/3rds, T65-18, 505
Precipitation (see Rainfall)
Prefabricated structures, 179, 470
Preparing bed, culvert, 184, 434
Pressure (see also Frost, Landslide, Load, Retaining wall, Strain gages)
- cells, earth, 12
- collapsing, 59
- equivalent fluid, 393
- frost, 31
- hydrostatic, 59–60
- internal, 32
- jacks, of, 459
- passive, 70
- transverse (lateral), 30, 341
- units, equivalent, T65-5, 494

Preventing Soil Erosion, 359–367
Prices
- bid, pipe, 187

Projecting conduits, 8–15
Public Roads (magazine), 10, 11, 21
Pumping for
- subdrainage, 326, 343
- surface water, 322, 371

Purdue University, Ind.; soils, 309, 356

Q

Quicksand, 473, 475, 489

R

Radial gates, 377, 485
Radius of gyration, 36, 78, 402
Railroad (see Industrial, Terminals, Wet cuts, Yards, etc.)
Railway Culvert Inspections, 159–161
Railway Eng. and Maintenance, 166, 238
Railway Subdrainage, 323–328
Railway Surface Drainage, 254–255
Railway Track and Structures, 257, 327
Rain, Rainfall
- airport design, 344
- annual, average in U. S., 199
- culvert runoff formulas, 226–229
- formula, 267
- frequency, 200
- **Hydrology, 195–205**
- intensities, 196
- maximum, world, U. S., 197, 198
- seasonal, T23-3, 199
- storm sewer design, 266

Ramser, C. E.; hydrology, 200
Rankine's formula, 211
Rating, durability, culvert
- material and structural, 150–152

Rational method
- storm sewer sizes, 266, 350
- strength design, 66

Reciprocals of numbers, T65-17, 503-504
Reclamation, Land, and Flood Control, 371–377
Reducer, fittings, 283
Reinforcement, steel, T65-24, 510
Relief culvert, 249
Relining, 97, 404, 465, 467
Relocation, culvert, 242
Removal, of old structure, 184
Repairs, sewer, 290
Replacement of bridges, 239, 468
Repose, Slope or angle of, 30, 211
Republic Steel Corp., 38
Research
- **Corr. Steel and Iron Sheets and Plates, 35–46**
- **Durability, 147–177**
- frost heaving, 309
- **guardrail, 43–45**
- **Hydrology and Hydraulic Capacity, 195–293**
- **Installation Costs, 179–193**
- Internal Pressures, 32–34
- **Loads and Earth Pressures, 5–31**
- **Pipe, Arches and Pipe-Arches, 55–63**
- Pressures in deep bins, 422
- **Seams and joints, riveted and bolted, 47–54**
- **Soil Studies, 295–310**
- **Tests on Corrugated Metal Products, 55–63**
- **Underground Conduits, Appendix A**

Retaining wall
- cost to install, 192
- drainage of, 378, 380, 454
- durability, 176
- **Design, 378–388**
- headwalls as, 259
- installation considerations, 388
- landslide remedy, 356
- metal, 367, 381
- purposes, 379
- types, 380

Revetment (see Riprap)
Rigid type of culvert or conduit (see also Concrete, Cast iron, Vitrified clay)
- bending moment, 57–59
- definition, 7, 68
- degree of, 11
- design, 69
- durability rating, 151
- encasement, 463

Riprap, 243, 245, 264, 360, 367
Rise/span ratio, 87, 90–93
Risers, 255, 349, 368
Riveted joint tests, 48
Riveting, 72, 372
Roadbed drainage, 250–255, 317–329
Roads & Streets (magazine), 21
Rock cuts, drainage, 321
Rock foundation, 437
Roller gates, 485
Roughness coefficient, 208, 222, 271
Runoff
- airport runways, 312, 349–352
- computations, 200, 313
- critical rate of, 195

Runoff—Continued
  Rainfall and, 195–205
  storm sewer, 266
  subsurface, 312–313, 352
  surface, 250–255
Runways, airport, 346
Rupture, modulus of, 38

S

Saddle-branch, sewer, 286
Safety
  aviation, 344
  factor of,
    capacity, 224, 225, 231, 233
    strength, 68, 70, 81
  pedestrian, 397
  traffic, 248, 252, 291, 317, 407
Salt water service, 163, 169
Salvage, 193
Sandbox strength test, 59
Sanitary sewers (see Sewers)
Sand bag headwalls, 264
Sand drains, vertical, 318, 319
Santa Fe Railway, 159, 326
Scheer, A. C.; bin pressures, 431
Schlick, W. J.; load research, 7
Schwab, G. O.; subdrainage research, 339
Scobey, Fred C.; hydraulics, 207, 273
Scour (see Erosion, Undermining)
Seams
  liner plate, research, 51–53
  bolted, research, 47–50
  riveted joint, strength, 48
    watertightness, 372
  soldered, 369
Section modulus, 36, 37, 78, 390, 402, 481
Sedimentation, 245, 359, 487
Seepage (see also Infiltration, Percolation)
  cut section, 320, 325
  detection, 306
  fill softening, 320
  interception, 308, 436
  landslide cause, 357
  longitudinal, 321
  prevention, 259, 486
  sidehill, 319
Selection (see also Design)
  corrugated metal, 69
  subdrains, 313
  types and materials, 65, 68
  type of sewer, 265
Septic tanks, 289
Serafin, C. J.; culvert research, 158
Service
  conditions (see Culvert and Sewers)
  life (see Durability)
Settlement (see also Landslide, Shrinkage, Tamping)
  embankment, 319, 446, 488
  foundation, 67
  research, 8, 18
  retaining wall, 471
Settlement—Continued
  soil, 6
  structures, 150, 151, 245
Sewage
  domestic, 171, 267, 268
  industrial, 171
  quantity, storm and sanitary, 265–268
  treatment plants, 267, 289
Sewers (see also Sewage)
  aerial, 144
  Appurtenances, 281–290
  durability inspections, 162–163
  Hydraulics of, 269–280
  loadings and gages, 118–123
  maintenance, 290
  Multi-Plate, 120–123
  outfalls, 288
  sanitary, 170, 280
  separate vs. combined, 171, 265
  service conditions, design for, 170, 171
  Size Determination, 265–268
  storm (see Storm sewer)
Shafer, George E, 21, 57, 70, 158
Shape of
  arches, 86, 87, 94
  conduits, culverts, 224-240
  tunnels, 399-401
Sharp airport engineering, 354
Shaw airport engineering, 354
Shear, failure of joints, 48
Sheeting, corrugated steel, 389–396
  culvert cutoff wall, 261
  ditch check, 363
  durability, 177
  erosion protection, 367
  physical properties, T47-3, 390
  soil-saving dam, 367
  installation instructions, 473–476
Sheet metal (see also corr. metal)
  specifications, 72–77, 173
Sheet piling (see Sheeting)
Sheffield guardrail, 43
Sheldon, A. J.; durability, 153
Sherman, Chas. W.; hydraulics, 271
Shoulders, 251, 252, 311
Sidehill seepage, 319
Side road culvert, 248
Side support, 70
Silencer, jet engine, 419
Silt (see Sediment)
Single vs. multiple opening, 238
Siphon, 32, 249
Size of waterway opening (see also Capacity)
  airport surface interceptors, 349–352
Size
  airport storm drains, 349–352
  bridges, 236
  corrugated metal pipe, T8-4, 74
  corrugated metal pipe-arches T8-6, 77
  Design of Culverts, 224–240
  ditch, 206–211
  drop-inlet culverts, 234
  levee culverts, 486
  Multi-Plate arches, T8-14, 90–93

Size—Continued
Multi-Plate pipe, T8-10, 80
Multi-Plate plates, T8-8, T8-9, 79
Multi-Plate pipe-arches, T8-11, T26-7, 84, 237
part circle culverts, 292–293
reduction by silting, 245
by threading, 467
sewers, 265–268, 272–280, 349–352
spillway notches, 365
subdrains, T37-1, 312, 316
water control gates, 376
Skew, 243, 247
Slack, S. B.; Ga. Hy. Dept., 148
Slater, C. S.; subdrainage, 339
Slide gates, 377, 483
Slope (see also Grade)
conversion, T65-10, 497
critical (hydraulic), 215, 222
culvert, 230, 244, 245
embankment, 251
erosion, 359, 367
repose, of, 30, 211
sewer, 272–280
subdrain, 316, 325, 338
watershed, 226, 351
Slow orders, 189
Sluiceway, 372
Smith, Rockwell; railroad, soils, 29, 305
Snow, properties of, T65-7, 495
Sod, sodding
erosion prevention, 243, 359
imperviousness factor, 201
landing field, 346
Soft fills, 320
Soil, 295–310
airport, 345
alkali, 156
analysis (see Soil Studies)
bearing value, 302, 323
capillarity, 301
characteristics, 295–297, 301–303
classification T36-2, T36-3, 296–300, 304
Conservation, 359–370
corrosion, 167–171
embankments and foundations, T36-5, 302
grain size, T36-1, 297
highway subgrades, T36-4, 300
identification procedures, 298
liquid limit, 300
moisture retaining capacity, 307–310
movements (see Landslides, Settlement, etc.)
plasticity, 300
sampling for jacking, 456
saving dam, 367–370
Studies, 295–310, 311
bibliography, 310
surveys, 345, 357, 456
texture, 296–300
Spacers, bin-wall, 385
Spacing
bents, for pipe, 145
multiple culverts, 486, 489

Spacing—Continued
struts, 444
subdrains, T41-2, T41-3, 337, 352
Span (see Multi-Plate arches and pipe-arches)
Spangler, M. G.; load research, 7, 8, 10, 18, 55–56, 70, 103
soil engineering, 196, 297
Special Drainage Problems, 340–377
Specifications
design and fabrication (strength), 70
for corr. metal drain. struct., T8-2, 71
Spelter, 81, 150, 161, 163, 173, 175
Spillway
ditch (checks), 365
open (flume or apron), 245
pipe, 245, 257, 342
soil-saving dam, 368, 370
Spindler, W. H.; durability, 158
Spokane, Portland & Seattle Ry., 239
Springs, 307
Squares of numbers, T65-17, 503–504
Square roots
decimal numbers, T65-19, 506
whole numbers, T65-17, 503–504
Stabilization,
cut slopes, 320, 325
Roadbed, 295, 302
Stadium drainage, 331
Stahl, B. M.; grain storage, 431
Station platform drainage, 326
Steelox panel, perforated, 419
Steel reinforcement, area, T65-24, 510
Stock pass, 398
Storage Bins, 420–431
Storm Sewers (see also Sewers)
airport, 346
capacity, 272–280
life expectancy, 167
runoff, 266–267
service conditions, 162–163, 170, 174
size, rational method, 266
submerged outlet, 269
Storms, intensity of, 196
Strain gage
Stream Enclosures and Sewers (see also Ditch enclosure), 253, 265, 345
Street drainage, 291–293
Street subdrainage, 329
Strength
beam, 38, 41, 44, 45, 61
bolted joints, 48–54
cantilever, 245, 335
column, T15-2, 144–145
corrugated steel sheets and plates, 35–46
design for
airport drains, 353
Design, pipe, arches, pipe-arches, 65–145
Fowler test, 59
guardrail joints, 54
increase by strutting, 82
inherent, 55, 70
liner plate joints, 51

Strength—Continued
materials, T65-22, 509
Multi-Plate arches, 26–27
Multi-Plate bolts, 49–50
Multi-Plate pipe, 38–43
Multi-Plate seams, 49–50
nestable pipe seams, 54
part circle culverts, 291
Pipe, Arches and Pipe-arches, 55–63
Research on Loads and Earth Pressures, 5–31
riveted seams, 48
Talbot test
corr. metal pipe, 59
rigid pipe, 57–59
torque, of bolts, 49
tunnel liner plates, 402
Stringers, bin-wall, 385
Structural deterioration, 150–152
Structural plate (vs. Multi-Plate), 14, 404
Struts for trench sheeting, 393
Strutting
costs, 188
effect of, 82, 443
gages required, 107–127
installation instructions, 443–445
Sub base under,
pavement, 304, 318, 320, 346
running track, 332
Subdrains
capacity of, 312
design of, 311–316
kinds of, 313, 338
spacing of, T41-2, T41-3, 337
strength, airport, 138
Subdrainage, 294–339
Agricultural, 333–339
airport, 352–354
bridge abutments, 343
definition, 311
design of system, 311–316
durability, 176
fill foundations, 436
Highway, 317–322
instructions, 452–454
pipe, 138, 313, 315, 316
Railway, 323–328
retaining walls, 471
Subgrade
research, 300–306
soils, T36-4, T36-5, 300, 302, 304
Submerged outlet, 232–233, 244, 269
Subsidence (see also Landslides, Settlement), 319, 320
Subsoil (see Soil)
Subsurface (see also Subdrainage)
runoff, 312–313, 352
Subsurface Drainage, 294–339, 357
Superloads (see Loads)
Supervision costs, 190
Surface loads (see Loads)
Surface water
airport, 344, 345
bridges, 342
culvert design, 224–249

Surface water—Continued
highway drainage, 250–253
open channel design, 206–211
railroad yards, 326
railway drainage, 254–255
removal, 224, 265, 357
street drainage, 291
Surge bins, 420
Surveys
aerial, drainage, 225
engineering, 344
soil, 305, 334, 357, 456
Swamps, 163, 169, 436

T

Tables (see subject in question)
Conversion, 491–497
General, 498–511
Talbot, A. N.
culvert formula, 226, 229, 236
rainfall formula, 267
strength tests, 57, 59
Tamping (see also Backfill)
effect of, 6, 81
equipment, 447
methods, 67
room for, 441
Tank, water, bottomless, 431
Temperature equivalents, T65-7, 495
Tennessee Highway Department durability investigations, 148
Tennis court drainage, 330
Tensile, high strength bolts, 49
Tension tests on bolted joints, 51–54
Terminals, railroad, 328
Terracing, 359, 367
Terzaghi, Karl
subgrade research, 31, 310, 355
Tests (see Research)
Texture (see Soil)
Theory of Critical Flow, 212–223
Theory of loads, 5, 7, 70, 421
Theory of statistics and probability, 196
Thickness, (see Gages)
Thornburn, T. H.; foundations, 310
Threading Failing structures, 467
Three-edge bearing, 57
Timber headwalls
Timbers
jacking, 459
strutting, 444
Time
effect on loads, 11, 14, 25
measure, units, T65-7, 495
of concentration, 198, 200, 350
Tooles, C. W.; bin pressures, 431
Tools, 188
Torque strength of bolts, 49
Track
drainage, railway, 254–255, 323–328
race, running, 332

Traffic interference (see also Detours, Slow orders), 188–189, 238, 455, 463
Train delays, 189
Transportation
  costs, 181–182
  gates and pipe, 486
Transverse forces, 30, 341
Transverse sections, bin-wall, 384
Trautwine, J. C.; freezing pressure, 31, 211
Trench
  bottom for subdrains, 313, 452
  condition of installation, 118–123
  sealed top, 314
  sheeting, 389, 474
Trenching costs, 182–184
Trestle replacement, 239, 450, 468
Tribble, J. F.; Ala. load research, 21
Trickling filters, 431
Trigonometric
  formulas, T65-13, 500
  functions, T65-12, 499
Truck, weights, 105
  transportation costs, 182
Tubing, perforated, 358
Tunneling, 357, 406
  instructions, 462–464
Tunnel liner plate
  gages, 140–143
  stabilizing fill, Erie RR, 327
Tunnels, service, etc., 397–406
Turnpikes (see also Expressways & Parkways)
  New Jersey, traffic, 105
  Oklahoma, design, 171
  Pennsylvania, culverts, 155
  West Virginia, 358
Two-thirds powers of numbers, T65-18, 505
Types (see Flexible, Rigid)

U

Underdrainage (see Subdrainage)
Undermining
  backslopes; side ditch, 359
  prevention, 258
  subdrain outlet, 335
Underpasses, cattle and pedestrian
  design, 397–406
  liner plate, elliptical, T14-4, T14-5, 143
Union Pacific Railroad, 17
United Steel Fabricators, Inc., 38, 45
Units, equivalent, 491–495
U. S. Air Force, 134
U. S. Army, 133
U. S. Bureau of Mines, 415
U. S. Bureau of Public Roads, 7, 38, 56, 71, 108, 148, 155, 224, 232, 296, 300, 304
U. S. Bureau of Reclamation, 177, 206, 210, 297, 444
U. S. Bureau of Soils, 296, 314
U. S. Bureau of Standards, 147, 150, 167, 171
U. S. Dept. of Agriculture, 200–205, 273
U. S. Engineers, Corps of, 9, 27, 71, 133, 186, 190, 297, 304, 349, 373
U. S. Geological Survey, 225, 228, 310, 334
U. S. Gvmt. Printing Offices, 257
U. S. House of Representatives, 171
U. S. Navy, 135
U. S. standard gages, T65-20, 507
U. S. Waterways Experi. Sta., 27–28, 314
U. S. Weather Bureau, 197–199
Utilidor, 5, 402

V

Valve (see Drainage gate)
Vawter, Jamison, 38
Vegetation, erosion prevention, 360
Velocity of flow
  critical, 212–223
  culverts, 224, 226–233
  head of approach, 214, 269
  permissible in canals, 207, 210
  relative, in circular conduits, T33-4, 280
  sewers, 278–280
Ventilation, mines, tunnels, etc., 415–419
Vertical sand drains, 318, 319
Vibration, 23, 135
Vitrified clay pipe
  coefficient of roughness, 271
  design, 69
  strength, 7
  subdrains, 271, 454
  weight, 183
Volume, equivalent units, T65-3, 492–493

W

Wales for steel sheeting, 393–396
Washout (see Undermining)
Water (see also Moisture)
  chemical characteristics, 168–171
  kinds, 307
  methods of tracing, 306
  pockets, 305, 324
  sources, 196, 307
Water control gates, 376
Water Resources Review (USGS), 228
Watershed
  area, 200, 225–229, 234, 236, 266, 313
  characteristics, 200, 265, 344
Water table (see also Ground water), 319, 321, 347
Watertight (see also Infiltration)
  bin structures, 431
  corrugated metal pipe, 33, 368, 372
  couplings, 75, 286, 287, 369, 439
  drainage gate, 374
  Hel-Cor pipe, 34
  sewers, 268, 270, 288
  sheeting, 389
  siphons, 32, 249
Waterway (see Size of opening)

Wear (see Erosion)
Weepholes, abutment, 343
Weight (see also Load)
- airplanes, 134
- bridge plank, 481
- construction materials, 181, 508
- Multi-Plate arches, T8-13, 88
- Multi-Plate sections, T8-9, 79
- Multi-Plate pipe, T8-10, 80
- Multi-Plate pipe-arches, T8-12, 85
- part circle culverts, 292
- pipe, various kinds, T22-1, 183
- pipe, galv. corr. metal, T8-3, T65-25, 73, 511
  - Asbestos-Bonded, 74
  - bituminous coated, 74
- pipe-arches, T8-6, 77
- sheeting, corrugated, 390
- standard gage sheets and plates, 73
- tunnel liner plates, 402
- units, equivalent, T65-4, 493–494

Weir, 365
Welborn, J. Y.; culvert research, 158
West Virginia State Rd. Comm., 356
West Virginia, University of, 154
Western Construction magazine, 459
Wet cut, 320, 325
Wetted perimeter, 206, 351, 511
White, H. L.; bridge deck research, 46
Width of trench, 183, 184
Widtsoe, J. A.; soil moisture table, 339
Wilson, W. M.; bolted structures, 54
Winfrey, Robley; load research, 29
Wisconsin, University of, 365
Wolford, D. S.; bridge deck research, 46
Woodward, S. M.
- flow research, 214, 231

Wrenches, impact, 49
Wright-Patterson Air Force Base, 134

Y

Yards, railroad, 326
Yarnell, D. L.; rainfall and flow research, 201